Earth Science:
Earth's Weather, Water, and Atmosphere

Earth Science:
Earth's Weather, Water, and Atmosphere

Volume 2

Editors

MARGARET BOORSTEIN, PH.D.
Long Island University

RICHARD RENNEBOOG, M.SC.

Salem Press
A Division of EBSCO Publishing
Ipswich, Massachusetts

Library of Congress Cataloging-in-Publication Data

Earth science. Earth's weather, water, and atmosphere / editors, Margaret Boorstein, Ph. D., Long Island University, Richard Renneboog, M. Sc.
        volumes cm
    Includes bibliographical references and index.
    ISBN 978-1-58765-989-8 (set) – ISBN 978-1-58765-985-0 (set 4 of 4) – ISBN 978-1-58765-986-7 (volume 1) – ISBN 978-1-58765-987-4 (volume 2) 1. Meteorology. 2. Hydrology. 3. Atmosphere. I. Boorstein, Margaret. II. Renneboog, Richard. III. Title: Earth's weather, water, and atmosphere.
    QC863.E27 2013
    551.5–dc23
                            2012027577

PRINTED IN THE UNTED STATES OF AMERICA

CONTENTS

COMMON UNITS OF MEASURE

Notes: Common prefixes for metric units—which may apply in more cases than shown below—include giga- (1 billion times the unit), mega- (one million times), kilo- (1,000 times), hecto- (100 times), deka- (10 times), deci- (0.1, or one tenth), centi- (0.01, or one hundredth), milli- (0.001, or one thousandth), and micro- (0.0001, or one millionth).

UNIT	QUANTITY	SYMBOL	EQUIVALENTS
Acre	Area	ac	43,560 square feet 4,840 square yards 0.405 hectare
Ampere	Electric current	A *or* amp	1.00016502722949 international ampere 0.1 biot *or* abampere
Angstrom	Length	Å	0.1 nanometer 0.0000001 millimeter 0.000000004 inch
Astronomical unit	Length	AU	92,955,807 miles 149,597,871 kilometers (mean Earth-sun distance)
Barn	Area	b	10^{-28} meters squared (approximate cross-sectional area of 1 uranium nucleus)
Barrel (dry, for most produce)	Volume/capacity	bbl	7,056 cubic inches; 105 dry quarts; 3.281 bushels, struck measure
Barrel (liquid)	Volume/capacity	bbl	31 to 42 gallons
British thermal unit	Energy	Btu	1055.05585262 joule
Bushel (U.S., heaped)	Volume/capacity	bsh *or* bu	2,747.715 cubic inches 1.278 bushels, struck measure
Bushel (U.S., struck measure)	Volume/capacity	bsh *or* bu	2,150.42 cubic inches 35.238 liters
Candela	Luminous intensity	cd	1.09 hefner candle
Celsius	Temperature	°C	1 degree centigrade
Centigram	Mass/weight	cg	0.15 grain
Centimeter	Length	cm	0.3937 inch
Centimeter, cubic	Volume/capacity	cm³	0.061 cubic inch
Centimeter, square	Area	cm²	0.155 square inch
Coulomb	Electric charge	C	1 ampere second

UNIT	QUANTITY	SYMBOL	EQUIVALENTS
Cup	Volume/capacity	C	250 milliliters 8 fluid ounces 0.5 liquid pint
Deciliter	Volume/capacity	dL	0.21 pint
Decimeter	Length	dm	3.937 inches
Decimeter, cubic	Volume/capacity	dm³	61.024 cubic inches
Decimeter, square	Area	dm²	15.5 square inches
Dekaliter	Volume/capacity	daL	2.642 gallons 1.135 pecks
Dekameter	Length	dam	32.808 feet
Dram	Mass/weight	dr or dr avdp	0.0625 ounce 27.344 grains 1.772 grams
Electron volt	Energy	eV	$1.5185847232839 \times 10^{-22}$ Btu $1.6021917 \times 10^{-19}$ joule
Fermi	Length	fm	1 femtometer 1.0×10^{-15} meter
Foot	Length	ft or '	12 inches 0.3048 meter 30.48 centimeters
Foot, cubic	Volume/capacity	ft³	0.028 cubic meter 0.0370 cubic yard 1,728 cubic inches
Foot, square	Area	ft²	929.030 square centimeters
Gallon (British Imperial)	Volume/capacity	gal	277.42 cubic inches 1.201 U.S. gallons 4.546 liters 160 British fluid ounces
Gallon (U.S.)	Volume/capacity	gal	231 cubic inches 3.785 liters 0.833 British gallon 128 U.S. fluid ounces
Giga-electron volt	Energy	GeV	$1.6021917 \times 10^{-10}$ joule
Gigahertz	Frequency	GHz	—
Gill	Volume/capacity	gi	7.219 cubic inches 4 fluid ounces 0.118 liter

Unit	Quantity	Symbol	Equivalents
Grain	Mass/weight	gr	0.037 dram 0.002083 ounce 0.0648 gram
Gram	Mass/weight	g	15.432 grains 0.035 avoirdupois ounce
Hectare	Area	ha	2.471 acres
Hectoliter	Volume/capacity	hL	26.418 gallons 2.838 bushels
Hertz	Frequency	Hz	$1.08782775707767 \times 10^{-10}$ cesium atom frequency
Hour	Time	h	60 minutes 3,600 seconds
Inch	Length	in *or* "	2.54 centimeters
Inch, cubic	Volume/capacity	in^3	0.554 fluid ounce 4.433 fluid drams 16.387 cubic centimeters
Inch, square	Area	in^2	6.4516 square centimeters
Joule	Energy	J	$6.2414503832469 \times 10^{18}$ electron volt
Joule per kelvin	Heat capacity	J/K	$7.24311216248908 \times 10^{22}$ Boltzmann constant
Joule per second	Power	J/s	1 watt
Kelvin	Temperature	K	-272.15 degrees Celsius
Kilo-electron volt	Energy	keV	$1.5185847232839 \times 10^{-19}$ joule
Kilogram	Mass/weight	kg	2.205 pounds
Kilogram per cubic meter	Mass/weight density	kg/m^3	$5.78036672001339 \times 10^{-4}$ ounces per cubic inch
Kilohertz	Frequency	kHz	—
Kiloliter	Volume/capacity	kL	—
Kilometer	Length	km	0.621 mile
Kilometer, square	Area	km^2	0.386 square mile 247.105 acres
Light-year (distance traveled by light in one Earth year)	Length/distance	lt-yr	5,878,499,814,275.88 miles 9.46×1012 kilometers
Liter	Volume/capacity	L	1.057 liquid quarts 0.908 dry quart 61.024 cubic inches

UNIT	QUANTITY	SYMBOL	EQUIVALENTS
Mega-electron volt	Energy	MeV	—
Megahertz	Frequency	MHz	—
Meter	Length	m	39.37 inches
Meter, cubic	Volume/capacity	m³	1.308 cubic yards
Meter per second	Velocity	m/s	2.24 miles per hour 3.60 kilometers per hour
Meter per second per second	Acceleration	m/s²	12,960.00 kilometers per hour per hour 8,052.97 miles per hour per hour
Meter, square	Area	m²	1.196 square yards 10.764 square feet
Metric. See unit name			
Microgram	Mass/weight	mcg *or* μg	0.000001 gram
Microliter	Volume/capacity	μL	0.00027 fluid ounce
Micrometer	Length	μm	0.001 millimeter 0.00003937 inch
Mile (nautical international)	Length	mi	1.852 kilometers 1.151 statute miles 0.999 U.S. nautical mile
Mile (statute or land)	Length	mi	5,280 feet 1.609 kilometers
Mile, square	Area	mi²	258.999 hectares
Milligram	Mass/weight	mg	0.015 grain
Milliliter	Volume/capacity	mL	0.271 fluid dram 16.231 minims 0.061 cubic inch
Millimeter	Length	mm	0.03937 inch
Millimeter, square	Area	mm²	0.002 square inch
Minute	Time	m	60 seconds
Mole	Amount of substance	mol	6.02×10^{23} atoms or molecules of a given substance
Nanometer	Length	nm	1,000,000 fermis 10 angstroms 0.001 micrometer 0.00000003937 inch

UNIT	QUANTITY	SYMBOL	EQUIVALENTS
Newton	Force	N	0.224808943099711 pound force 0.101971621297793 kilogram force 100,000 dynes
Newton-meter	Torque	N·m	0.7375621 foot-pound
Ounce (avoirdupois)	Mass/weight	oz	28.350 grams 437.5 grains 0.911 troy or apothecaries' ounce
Ounce (troy)	Mass/weight	oz	31.103 grams 480 grains 1.097 avoirdupois ounces
Ounce (U.S., fluid or liquid)	Mass/weight	oz	1.805 cubic inch 29.574 milliliters 1.041 British fluid ounces
Parsec	Length	pc	30,856,775,876,793 kilometers 19,173,511,615,163 miles
Peck	Volume/capacity	pk	8.810 liters
Pint (dry)	Volume/capacity	pt	33.600 cubic inches 0.551 liter
Pint (liquid)	Volume/capacity	pt	28.875 cubic inches 0.473 liter
Pound (avoirdupois)	Mass/weight	lb	7,000 grains 1.215 troy or apothecaries' pounds 453.59237 grams
Pound (troy)	Mass/weight	lb	5,760 grains 0.823 avoirdupois pound 373.242 grams
Quart (British)	Volume/capacity	qt	69.354 cubic inches 1.032 U.S. dry quarts 1.201 U.S. liquid quarts
Quart (U.S., dry)	Volume/capacity	qt	67.201 cubic inches 1.101 liters 0.969 British quart
Quart (U.S., liquid)	Volume/capacity	qt	57.75 cubic inches 0.946 liter 0.833 British quart
Rod	Length	rd	5.029 meters 5.50 yards

UNIT	QUANTITY	SYMBOL	EQUIVALENTS
Rod, square	Area	rd^2	25.293 square meters 30.25 square yards 0.00625 acre
Second	Time	s or sec	$\frac{1}{60}$ minute $\frac{1}{3,600}$ hour
Tablespoon	Volume/capacity	T or tb	3 teaspoons 4 fluid drams
Teaspoon	Volume/capacity	t or tsp	0.33 tablespoon 1.33 fluid drams
Ton (gross or long)	Mass/weight	t	2,240 pounds 1.12 net tons 1.016 metric tons
Ton (metric)	Mass/weight	t	1,000 kilograms 2,204.62 pounds 0.984 gross ton 1.102 net tons
Ton (net or short)	Mass/weight	t	2,000 pounds 0.893 gross ton 0.907 metric ton
Volt	Electric potential	V	1 joule per coulomb
Watt	Power	W	1 joule per second 0.001 kilowatt $2.84345136093995 \times 10^{-4}$ ton of refrigeration
Yard	Length	yd	0.9144 meter
Yard, cubic	Volume/capacity	yd^3	0.765 cubic meter
Yard, square	Area	yd^2	0.836 square meter

COMPLETE LIST OF CONTENTS

Volume 1

Volume 2

CATEGORY LIST OF CONTENTS

Earth Science:

Earth's Weather, Water, and Atmosphere

OBSERVATIONAL DATA OF THE ATMOSPHERE AND OCEANS

Two important areas of concern for Earth scientists are the oceans and atmosphere. Technologies have improved significantly in this arena, with sensors and other equipment integrated onboard satellites, aircraft, and ships and on buoys placed in key areas. These systems provide extensive observational data on such issues as air quality, pressure, ocean currents, salinity, and temperature changes. Although areas of the oceans and atmosphere remain difficult to gauge, the continued evolution of technologies and research approaches may soon enable effective analyses of these regions.

PRINCIPAL TERMS

- **algorithm:** a set of instructions used to perform a task
- **downburst:** a convective windstorm associated with strong thunderstorm systems
- **El Niño/La Niña:** cyclical increases and decreases, respectively, in Pacific Ocean water temperature that foster shifts in weather patterns worldwide
- **polar low:** a severe, mesocyclonic winter storm that occurs in higher ocean latitudes
- **salinity:** concentration of salt in a given area of the ocean
- **tsunami:** a series of long, high sea waves caused by seismic activity or other disturbances

BASIC PRINCIPLES

Earth's oceans and atmosphere are two key areas to which scientists are increasingly paying attention as they examine climate change. For most of the twentieth century, however, scientific technology used in these arenas was limited in the amount of data it could collect.

Many sensor systems, for example, could detect conditions at the ocean's surface but not in areas well beneath the surface. Similarly, meteorological sensors were for many years hampered by an inability to penetrate cloud cover when studying atmospheric phenomena. Since the latter half of the twentieth century, however, technologies have improved steadily, enabling researchers to examine a wide range of aspects related to trends in the oceans and atmosphere.

In addition to improvements to data-gathering systems found in ground observation facilities; aboard planes, ships, and buoys; and attached to weather balloons, satellite-based remote sensors have generated an even greater amount of data on much larger target areas. This technological evolution means that a greater amount of observational data can be collected, collated, and utilized to generate comprehensive models of the environment and of climate change. Such data also can help scientists to understand and even predict atmospheric and oceanic phenomena with greater precision than ever before.

COLLECTING AND ANALYZING DATA

In the pursuit of observational data, scientists utilize a wide range of technologies. Some of these systems (such as weather balloons) are sent directly into a layer of the atmosphere or are placed on a research ship. Others are placed on board satellites, enabling the observation of a much wider target range.

In the oceans, for example, a growing network of surface and subsurface buoys using sophisticated sensors is generating data. One such data area is sea-level tracking. Here, buoys can be used to track tidal changes, currents, and even high-water events such as tsunamis (a series of long, high sea waves that are caused by seismic activity or other disturbances). Buoys designed by the Science Applications International Corporation are among the types of state-of-the-art buoy systems commonly used, many of which can be configured for multiple tasks, such as detecting tsunamis or monitoring temperature or chemical changes associated with climate change.

The National Oceanic and Atmospheric Administration (NOAA) in the United States utilizes an extensive network of such buoy technologies. NOAA operates nearly three dozen buoys along the Atlantic and Pacific coastlines and in the Gulf of Mexico and the Great Lakes. This network gathers observational data on sea-level changes brought on by the tides and other phenomena, and it detects changes in water temperatures, currents, and salt content.

Meanwhile, meteorologists utilize airborne and satellite-based sensors to collect observational data on atmospheric conditions and related phenomena. Using such technologies as passive and active radars, scientists can detect high concentrations of gases and particles in a given target area. For example, international scientific organizations (such as the World Meteorological Organization) are using data compiled from these technologies to study the emission and distribution of greenhouse gases from their sources.

The growing ability of research technologies to compile larger and more comprehensive observational data sets in turn fosters the need for programs and systems that can compile the data and help generate models. In some cases, models of oceanic and atmospheric trends and events are generated using complex mathematical algorithms (sets of instructions used to perform a task), assigning values to certain data sets. Algorithms also are utilized to analyze irregularities within data sets; by isolating these inconsistencies (and, potentially, errors), researchers can develop observational data sets with greater simplicity and reliability.

In addition to using mathematical models, researchers examining oceanic and atmospheric observational data can call upon computer modeling systems. This software can compile large amounts of observational data, generating frameworks on local, regional, and global scales as they occur through time. These models can be created using multiple grids, allowing the user to analyze data collected within a specific region and to compare conditions in one grid with conditions in another.

STUDYING CLIMATE CHANGE

For decades, scientists from a wide range of fields (including oceanography and meteorology) have looked critically at the effects of climate change. Remote sensors and other technologies have been used to analyze changes in atmospheric and surface temperatures, precipitation patterns, and other environmental changes associated with global warming and climate shift. These technological systems can gather large volumes of observational data and use it to generate models that analyze climate changes.

Scientists, for example, are monitoring the rate of temperature changes and salinity (the concentration of salt in a given area of the ocean) to monitor the rate of climate change occurring in the oceans. Combining the observational data acquired from sensor networks from all over the world, researchers can create a composite of the changes in temperature and salinity associated with global climate change.

Observational data on the relationship between salinity and temperature also are proving useful in predicting the length and potential effects of El Niño and La Niña (cyclical increases and decreases, respectively, in water temperature that foster shifts in weather patterns worldwide). As scientists argue that El Niño and La Niña patterns may become prolonged because of climate change, observational data on such phenomena are becoming an important component of this aspect of climatological research.

The use of observational data on different types of severe weather events also can assist researchers who are attempting to track and predict future climate shifts. For example, one study analyzed strong winter storms in the higher latitudes of the oceans. Such storms are powerful and frequently cause damage to offshore oil rigs and disrupt shipping lanes. However, these polar lows, as they are called, are relatively small in size and have seen little scientific study as distinct phenomena. Still, scientists believe that, as the climate continues to shift, polar lows may increase both in terms of size and volume. Such a trend could mean further disruptions to international trade routes and the energy industry and could mean harm to populated areas.

Meteorologists are studying observational data from polar lows to model their development and behavior. It is hoped that such data can help them predict future polar lows and assist interested parties in adapting to the likely increase in polar low occurrences.

In addition to the copious amounts of data gathered by individual studies of oceanic and atmospheric phenomena are the combined research efforts of regional and global networks and organizations. For example, the World Climate Research Programme, an international network of governmental and nongovernmental organizations, operates the Climate Variability and Predictability program. This network enables participants to collaborate, share observational data, and use this information to generate models on a broad spectrum of research areas, such as sea temperatures, atmospheric circulation, and ocean currents.

PREDICTING SEVERE PHENOMENA

In addition to providing localized data on climate change, observational data of the oceans and atmosphere help in the prediction of severe events and phenomena. In the oceans, for example, the presence of buoy nets in areas susceptible to volcanic and seismic activity (and hurricanes) has helped scientists understand the conditions that can create tsunamis and other high-water events.

NOAA, in collaboration with other organizations around the world, has formed an extensive network of observational data-collecting buoys. The National Data Buoy Center, which provides real-time data on conditions at a single buoy, provides useful data on sea-level changes and on underwater pressure (a key indicator of a tsunami). These data can help scientists track so-called killer waves and dangerous surf. In turn, emergency authorities can notify coastal residents of potential danger.

Similarly, observational data gathered from ground-based, airborne, and satellite-borne sensors are being used to more accurately track the development and movement of severe atmospheric storms. In some cases, observational data can help scientists generate models that can cast a light on the nature of previously unpredictable atmospheric phenomena.

For example, meteorologists are learning more and more about tornadoes but have been somewhat hampered in the study of downbursts. Unlike a tornado, in which winds spin violently, a downburst is a convective windstorm, in which cool air may rush from the storm cloud downward toward the surface. Once the downburst reaches the ground it quickly spreads outward, sometimes at gusts of more than 160 kilometers (100 miles) per hour.

Predicting and gauging downburst activity has long been a challenge for researchers. In 2010, however, scientists developed a three-dimensional model of downbursts based on a tremendous amount of observational data gathered at storm sites. This computer model, which assigns numerical values to observational data, can help researchers simulate a wide range of storm events that may produce downbursts. While such research cannot prevent these dangerous storm phenomena, it can help residents

prepare for such storms, potentially reducing casualties and property damage.

Michael P. Auerbach

FURTHER READING

Feudale, Laura, and Jagadish Shukla. "Influence of Sea Surface Temperature on the European Heat Wave of 2003 Summer. Part I: An Observational Study." *Climate Dynamics* 36, nos. 9/10 (2011): 1691-1703. A review of observational data on ocean surface temperatures and their contributions to a dangerous heat wave in Europe in 2003.

Jury, Mark R. "An Intercomparison of Observational, Reanalysis, Satellite, and Coupled Model Data on Mean Rainfall in the Caribbean." *Journal of Hydrometeorology* 10, no. 2 (2009): 413-420. Discusses the use of a wide range of technologies to generate data on rainfall trends in the Caribbean in a twenty-one-year period. Different types of data and models were generated based on this data.

Melanotte-Rizzoli, P., ed. *Modern Approaches to Data Assimilation in Ocean Modeling.* New York: Elsevier Science, 1996. A compilation of articles on oceanographic data assimilation. Contributors focus on developing improved data assimilation techniques for ocean-oriented computer-model development.

Mozdzynski, George, ed. *Use of High Performance Computing in Meteorology.* Singapore: World Scientific, 2007. Features discussions on the use of comprehensive observational data in atmospheric and oceanographic computer modeling.

Steere, Richard C., ed. *Buoy Technology: An Aspect of Observational Data Acquisition on Oceanography and Meteorology.* Berkeley: University of California Press, 1967. This book, based on presentations at the 1964 Buoy Technology Symposium, features an analysis of engineering developments in buoy technologies and how its evolution generates improved observational data.

Steinacker, Reinhold, Dieter Mayer. and Andrea Steiner. "Data Quality Control Based on Self-Consistency." *Monthly Weather Review* 139, no. 12 (2011): 3974-3991. Reviews methods for addressing different types of errors associated with the acquisition of observational data in meteorological studies. Introduces quality control approaches in this field.

See also: Atmospheric Properties; Carbon-Oxygen Cycle; Climate; Climate Change Theories; Climate Modeling; Drought; Earth-Sun Relations; El Niño/

Southern Oscillations; Floods; Geochemical Cycles; Global Energy Transfer; Global Warming; Greenhouse Effect; Hurricanes; IPCC; Long-Term Weather Patterns; Monsoons; Ocean-Atmosphere Interactions; Ozone Depletion and Ozone Holes; Precipitation; Recent Climate Change Research; Remote Sensing of the Atmosphere; Remote Sensing of the Oceans; Satellite Meteorology; Sea Level; Seasons; Severe and Anomalous Weather in Recent Decades; Severe Storms; Surface Ocean Currents; Tropical Weather; Tsunamis.

OCEAN-ATMOSPHERE INTERACTIONS

The complex interactions between the oceans and the atmosphere are basic to the understanding of oceanography and meteorology. The liquid and gaseous envelopes surrounding Earth have powerful effects on weather and climate on a global scale.

PRINCIPAL TERMS

- **atmosphere:** the envelope of mixed gases containing liquid and solid particles that surrounds the planet
- **Coriolis effect:** the apparent force causing the deflection of any moving body on Earth to the west or east, depending on whether the latitude is north or south, respectively; an effect of Earth's rotation
- **El Niño:** an accumulation of relatively warm surface ocean waters along the west coast of tropical South America due to changes in the air pressure and wind patterns of the Southern Oscillation
- **gyres:** generally circular oceanic current systems that have formed by a combination of the global wind system and the Coriolis effect
- **Kuroshio:** the current, also known as the Japan Current, where cold continental air flows over warm ocean currents moving toward the poles
- **La Niña:** the phase of the Southern Oscillation that brings cold water to the South American coasts, which makes easterly trade winds stronger, the waters of the Pacific off South America colder, and ocean temperatures in the western equatorial Pacific warmer than normal

ATMOSPHERE AND OCEAN

The largest fraction of the heat energy the atmosphere receives toward maintaining its circulation is derived from the condensation of water vapor originating mainly from marine evaporation. Therefore, fundamental to the understanding of atmospheric behavior and oceanic behavior is an understanding of the processes occurring at the air-sea boundary. The interactions between the marine and atmospheric environments involve constant exchanges of moisture, heat, momentum, and gases.

The study of oceanic and atmospheric interactions involves both a huge gaseous body and a massive liquid body, neither of which is ever homogeneous in content. The makeup of the atmosphere varies continually, depending on the areas over which it flows. The content of the oceans also varies in density, temperature, salinity, rate of movement by regular currents, and surface movement under the influence of winds. As a consequence, this interaction is very complex and not entirely understood. Certain conditions that are regularly met, however, can act as a general guide to understanding ocean-atmosphere interactions.

Atmospheric circulations depend on heat rising from the ground surface. Because of the large area of Earth's surface that is covered by oceans, the main source of heat to the atmosphere is the sea surface. In the oceans, heat is supplied primarily from the sun, with some additional contribution from atmospheric sources. Heat-supply processes are important in the development of convection currents in the surface layer of the ocean, for the local exchange of energy with the atmosphere, and with slower, deep-water circulation currents. Heat exchange between the ocean and atmosphere has a pattern similar to evaporation. Wherever the surface of the ocean is warmer than the atmosphere, heat is transferred from the ocean to the air, usually as latent heat, and is moved to great heights by eddies and convection currents in the air.

The range of weather extremes is smaller over the ocean than over land because of the enormous heat-storage capacity of the ocean, which tends to stabilize atmospheric conditions and properties. The upper layer of the oceans (to a depth of approximately 70 meters) can store some thirty times more heat than the atmosphere. Ocean climates, therefore, are largely determined by the atmospheric circulation and latitude. Ocean climate and atmospheric circulation are both affected by the solar distribution over Earth's surface, which is a function of the latitude and the season of the year. Northern and southern latitudes receive proportionally less solar radiation than latitudes at the equator; in winter, polar latitudes receive practically no solar radiation. Because of the greater capacity of the oceans to store heat, for a given change in heat content, the temperature change in the atmosphere will be around thirty times greater than in the ocean. Therefore, the ocean will lose its heat content by radiation much more slowly than the air. Land, which is intermediate with regard to heat storage and heat loss, can be modified by the effect of heat storage and heat loss of the ocean.

PROCESSES AT THE AIR-SEA BOUNDARY

The atmosphere adjacent to the oceans is constantly interacting with the oceans. Air does not simply flow along the surface of the sea but has a frictional effect or wind stress, which causes lateral displacement of the surface water. Wind stresses on the surface of the sea produce ocean waves, storm surges, and shallow ocean currents. Pure wind-driven currents are the result of frictional wind-surface stresses and Earth's rotational motion. This rotational motion can be seen in the Coriolis effect, by which air currents and ocean currents are deflected from true linear motion to the left in the Northern Hemisphere and to the right in the Southern Hemisphere. Because the sea is continually in contact with the atmosphere, the gases that are present in the atmosphere are also found in seawater. The concentration of those gases depends on their solubilities and on the chemical reactions in which they become involved. Their concentrations are affected by temperature, which is determined by many factors, and by wind and wave actions.

The sea also has a large storage and regulating capacity with respect to processes involving carbon dioxide in the atmosphere and in the sea, including those processes relevant to photosynthesis. This whole group of reactions concerning carbon dioxide, generally referred to as the carbon cycle, is extremely complex. Carbon dioxide, a "greenhouse gas," has a high capacity for absorbing infrared energy or heat. Solar energy that is absorbed at the ground surface is radiated back into the atmosphere and is absorbed by carbon dioxide. The heated carbon dioxide molecules reradiate that infrared energy as they cool, returning at least 50 percent of the heat they have absorbed into the atmosphere and back to the surface. This "greenhouse effect" acts to raise the functional temperature of the air and maintain it well above what it would be in the absence of the effect.

The largest fraction of radiant energy absorbed by the oceans is used in evaporation. The maximum evaporation and heat exchange between the sea and the atmosphere occur where relatively cold continental air flows over warm ocean currents moving toward the poles. Examples of where this phenomenon is most evident include the Kuroshio (Japan

Current) and the Gulf Stream. The radiant energy that is absorbed and stored by the oceans at tropical latitudes may thus be moved and given off to the atmosphere elsewhere. This process is important to understand in terms of the Southern Oscillation and the effect of El Niño and La Niña.

Major wind systems are responsible for the formation and operation of the broadly symmetrical patterns of surface-water movement known as gyres, which rotate clockwise around the North Pacific and North Atlantic and counterclockwise around the South Pacific and South Atlantic oceans. Their tropical segments are the North and South Equatorial currents, which are driven westward by trade winds. The Equatorial Countercurrent, a compensating flow, travels west to east in the Pacific between the North and South Equatorial currents along a course that averages a few degrees north of the equator.

EL NIÑO AND LA NIÑA

Marked by warm water and high winds from the western Pacific, El Niño typically brings heavy winter rains to Peruvian deserts and warm weather to the West Coast of the United States. El Niño arises through interaction between the oceanic and atmospheric systems. During El Niño, the southeast trade winds over the equatorial Pacific collapse, allowing warm water from the western Pacific to flow eastward along the equator. This warm-water flow suppresses the normal upwelling of cold, nutrient-rich water and leads to the northward displacement of fish normally feeding in the nutrient-laden cold water.

El Niño is part of a gigantic meteorological system called the Southern Oscillation that links the ocean and atmosphere in the Pacific. This system normally functions as a kind of huge heat pump, distributing energy from the tropics at the equator to the higher latitudes through storms that develop over the warm western Pacific. Another part of the Southern Oscillation has been dubbed La Niña, which brings cold water to the central Pacific. La Niña exaggerates the normal conditions of the system. During this activity, easterly trade winds are stronger, the waters of the eastern Pacific off South America are colder, and ocean temperatures in the western equatorial Pacific are warmer. Atmospheric and oceanic conditions in the equatorial Pacific region can generate powerful effects on global weather. Therefore, the study of this interaction is essential.

Study of Ocean-Atmosphere Interactions

Because the study of the ocean-atmosphere interactions is concerned with the boundary between marine and air masses, it is of necessity an interdisciplinary type of study. The data used in such studies are gathered by oceanographers and meteorologists who have made this interaction the focus of their research. The same instruments are used that are employed in oceanographic and meteorologic research, drawing heavily upon the same type of data collected, but with a shift in emphasis. Because gathering data is expensive and utilizes costly specialized equipment, nearly all studies are conducted by government scientists or are sponsored by government grants.

Scientists who study ocean-atmosphere interactions are interested in seeing how these huge bodies of matter affect each other and how these effects influence the weather and climate in the rest of the world. They are also interested in the ability to predict weather and climate changes more accurately. Each element researched, such as salinity, is compared with some other element, such as temperature, to see what relationship may exist. Air temperature and air movement are compared with wave movement, changing ocean currents, and water temperature. Each of a vast number of data points is examined for possible interrelations and interactions. When relationships are found, the data are fed into a computer model for correlation with other data. Computer models have been effective to some extent in predicting the results of interactions between marine and atmospheric environments. Separate computer models are used with the output aimed at the interactions between these forces.

Scientists do not fully understand all the mechanisms that link certain phenomena of the ocean and atmosphere interactions, such as El Niño and La Niña. It is their hope that in studying and understanding the mechanisms involved, they may be able to make accurate long-range predictions of the amount and area of precipitation in specific regions.

Significance

The interaction between the oceans and the atmosphere can cause immense problems on a global scale. An example of this interaction and its consequences is seen in the phenomenon known as El Niño. Every three to five years, the surface waters of the central and eastern Pacific Ocean become unusually warm at the equator. Warm currents and torrential rains are brought to the normally dry desert area of central Peru, and nutrient supplies for marine life along the west coast of South America are disrupted. Hardship can occur as a result, including widespread flooding in Peru.

La Niña brings an effect opposite to that of El Niño; easterly trade winds are stronger, the waters of the eastern Pacific off South America are colder, and ocean temperatures in the western equatorial Pacific are warmer than normal. As a result, the deserts in Peru and Chile become drier than normal, and the Indian subcontinent is inundated by heavier-than-usual rainfall and flooding as changes in the Southern Oscillation combine with the East Asian monsoon. In Bangladesh in late 1988, heavy rains and flooding killed more than 1,000 people, destroyed the homes of 25 million people, inundated 5 million acres of rice land, and damaged 70,000 kilometers of roads. While the storms were attributed to the La Niña phenomenon, much of the flooding was the result of massive deforestation in the Himalaya and foothills, which allowed water to rush down from the barren, eroded hills onto Bangladesh near sea level.

George K. Attwood

Further Reading

Bigg, Grant. *The Oceans and Climate*. 2d ed. Cambridge, England: Cambridge University Press, 2003. Introduces and describes the numerous systems that function in the ocean-atmosphere interaction and act as a self-regulating mechanism.

Chassignet, Eric P. and Jacques Verron, eds. *Ocean Weather Forecasting: An Integrated View of Oceanography*. Dordrecht: Springer, 2006. Brings together expert summaries of ocean modeling and observing systems and data assimilation in their application to provide an integrated view of oceanography as a result of the Global Ocean Data Assimilation Experiment.

Clarke, Allan J. *An Introduction to the Dynamics of El Niño and the Southern Oscillation*. Burlington, Mass.: Academic Press, 2008. Presents the physics of ENSO, including currents, temperature, winds, and waves. Discusses ENSO forecasting models. Provides good coverage of the influence ENSO has on marine life, from plankton to green turtles. Includes references, a number of appendices, and indexing. Best suited for environmental scientists, meteorologists, and academics studying ENSO.

Curry, Judith A., and Peter Webster. *Thermodynamics of Atmospheres and Oceans.* San Diego, Calif.: Academic Press, 1999. Offers a look at the effects of the interaction between the oceans and atmosphere on weather patterns and climatic changes. Provides good insight into the role that atmospheric thermodynamics play in meteorology. Illustrations, maps, and index.

Hamilton, Kevin, and Wataru Ohfuchi, eds. *High Resolution Numerical Modeling of the Atmosphere and Ocean.* New York: Springer Science+Business Media, 2008. A specialist publication containing articles and documentation from the first international meeting focused on high-resolution atmosphere and ocean modeling. Numerous aspects of the ocean-atmosphere relationship are discussed.

Ittekko, Venugopalan, et al., eds. *Particle Flux in the Ocean.* New York: John Wiley & Sons, 1996. Contains descriptions of the chemical and geobiochemical cycles of the ocean, as well as the ocean currents and movement. Suitable for the high school reader and beyond. Illustrations, index, bibliography.

Kagan, Boris A. *Ocean-Atmosphere Interaction and Climate Modeling.* Cambridge, England: Cambridge University Press, 2006. Written for advanced students and professional researchers. Presents a comprehensive treatment of ocean-atmosphere interactions.

Majumdar, Shyamal K., et al., eds. *The Oceans: Physical-Chemical Dynamics and Human Impact.* Easton, Pa.: Pennsylvania Academy of Science, 1994. A compilation of essays that provides an overview of oceanography while focusing on the relationship between the atmosphere and oceans. Many of the sections deal with both the effects of this relationship on humans and the effects of humans on the ocean environment. Suitable for the college-level reader.

Marshal, John, and R. Alan Plumb. *Atmosphere, Ocean and Climate Dynamics: An Introductory Text.* Burlington, Mass.: Elsevier Academic Press, 2008. An excellent introduction to atmospheres and oceans. Discusses topics such as the greenhouse effect, convection and atmospheric structure, oceanic and atmospheric circulation, and climate change. Suited for advanced undergraduates and graduate students with some background in advanced mathematics.

Oceanography Course Team. *Ocean Circulation.* 2d ed. Oxford: Butterworth-Heinemann, 2001. Discusses surface currents and deep water currents, with a focus on the North Atlantic Gyre, Gulf Stream, and equatorial currents. Discusses the El Niño phenomenon as well as the great salinity anomaly. Provides a good introduction to oceanography.

Sarachik, Edward S., and Mark A Cane. *The El Niño-Southern Oscillation Phenomenon.* New York: Cambridge University Press, 2010. A comprehensive discussion of ENSO and other oceanic/atmospheric processes. Covers research measurements, models, and predictions of future occurrences. Includes many diagrams, appendices, a reference list, and index.

Schmitt, Raymond W. *The Ocean Freshwater Cycle.* College Station, Tex.: A&M University, 1994. Examines the importance of the interaction between the atmosphere and the oceans in the study of meteorology and climatology. Suitable for advanced high school readers. Color illustrations and bibliographical references.

Thurman, Harold V., and Alan P. Trujillo. *Introductory Oceanography.* 10th ed. Upper Saddle River, N.J.: Prentice Hall, 2003. Describes the Coriolis effect, the heat budget of the world's oceans, currents, and weather and climate. Includes glossary and index. Well illustrated.

Vallis, Geoffrey K. *Atmospheric and Oceanic Fluid Dynamics: Fundamentals and Large-Scale Circulation.* New York: Cambridge University Press, 2006. Begins with an overview of the physics of fluid dynamics to provide foundational material on stratification, vorticity, and oceanic and atmospheric models. Discusses topics such as turbulence, baroclinic instabilities, wave-mean flow interactions, and large-scale atmospheric and oceanic circulation. Best suited for graduate students studying meteorology or oceanography.

Wells, Neil C. *The Atmosphere and Ocean: A Physical Introduction.* 3d ed. New York: John Wiley &Sons, 2012. Describes the oceans and atmosphere as equally affected by Earth's rotation and incorporates the newest material from research and modeling studies to discuss ocean-atmosphere interactions. Written for second- and third-year meteorology and oceanography students.

See also: Atmospheric Properties; Barometric Pressure; Carbonate Compensation Depths; Climate Change Theories; Deep Ocean Currents; Gulf Stream; Hydrothermal Vents; Observational Data of the Atmosphere and Oceans; Ocean Pollution and Oil Spills; Oceans' Origin; Oceans' Structure; Ocean Tides; Ocean Waves; Remote Sensing of the Atmosphere; Remote Sensing of the Oceans; Sea Level; Seamounts; Seawater Composition; Surface Ocean Currents; Tsunamis; Turbidity Currents and Submarine Fans; World Ocean Circulation Experiment

OCEAN POLLUTION AND OIL SPILLS

Oil spills resulting from human error often affect marine and coastal areas. Past oil spills in different areas of the world demonstrate that environmental damage depends on the toxicity and the persistence of the oil, both of which vary widely depending on a variety of factors.

PRINCIPAL TERMS

- **boom:** a floating oil fence made of a weighted flexible sheet protruding vertically above and below the sea surface; used to contain or move floating oil during a spill, they are most effective during calm seas
- **environmental persistence:** the relative length of time that oil remains in the environment with the possibility of causing negative environmental effects
- **mechanical toxicity:** the process by which most organisms are impacted or killed by spilled oil, as ingesting or being coated by oil may lead to death by suffocation or exposure
- **mousse:** a gelatinous oil-water emulsion resembling chocolate pudding that is created when crude oil is spilled in churning seawater
- **skimmer:** a specialized oil-spill response vessel that picks up floating oil with an absorbent conveyor belt; skimmers are most effective during calm seas
- **toxicity:** a measure of the dose required to produce a negative health effect

WHY OIL SPILLS OCCUR

Oil is the lifeblood of modern lifestyles, especially in the most economically developed nations of the world, including North America. With only about 6 percent of the world's population, the United States consumes more than 25 percent of world's petroleum supply, much of which is imported from other nations. The percentage of imported oil that Americans use grew steadily after 1982, largely negating the lessons learned about cartel politics and energy conservation in the late 1970's. The amount of oil imported into the United States continued to grow even during periods when its merchandise trade deficit was in decline. Americans have also demonstrated that they are willing to go to war for oil. In the 1991 Gulf War with Iraq, the United States paid a huge cost to protect Kuwaiti oil fields and world oil markets in spite of the fact that very little of the oil produced in the Arabian Gulf is imported to the United States. Most of the nation's imported oil comes from Canada, Africa, Central and South America, and the Indo-Pacific region. Domestic production continues to be an important but dwindling source, with most coming from the north slope of Alaska via the Alaska Pipeline and Port Valdez in Prince William Sound.

Almost all imported and Alaskan oil is transported to U.S. refineries and consumers by ocean-going bulk shipping vessels, or tankers. Most oil spills result from marine transportation accidents, with human error often being the cause or at least playing a major role. Navigation errors, equipment malfunctions, bad judgment, and even the inability of all crew members to speak a common language have all been major contributing factors in the largest and most environmentally damaging oil spills. Spilled oil can decimate plant and animal populations by a combination of mechanical and chemical toxicity effects resulting from an organism's physiological reaction to the chemicals present in oil.

ENVIRONMENTAL DAMAGE

The most common sight during an oil spill is dark, gelatinous masses of "mousse," an oil and water emulsion that floats on top of the water, sticking to everything with which it comes into contact. Mousse usually causes the majority of the environmental damage during an oil spill by processes of mechanical toxicity, as it suffocates and smothers organisms that ingest it or are covered by it. Seabirds and furry marine mammals are highly susceptible to this process, succumbing to exposure, dehydration, or starvation.

Crude oil is a complex mixture of thousands of different chemicals called hydrocarbons, named after their molecular structures that consist solely of hydrogen and carbon atoms. Different hydrocarbons vary in their chemical properties, toxicity, and behavior during an oil spill. The major groups are classified by molecular geometry and weight. The simplest and lowest-molecular-weight molecules (aliphatics) are generally single-bonded, chain-shaped molecules, such as those that make up gasoline. They are the most volatile, and are acutely toxic. Such compounds tend to evaporate or burn easily during an oil spill and therefore do not persist in the environment for long periods. The aromatics, are ring-shaped molecules, such as benzene. They also tend to be highly volatile and are more reactive than the simple hydrocarbons, and so can cause biological impacts because of both acute and chronic toxicity. Aromatic hydrocarbon compounds and aliphatic hydrocarbons of higher molecular weight are more environmentally persistent than the simple aliphatics. Because many are carcinogenic, they can also cause different forms of biological damage, disease, and death even after a long time period and in low doses. The highest-molecular-weight oil compounds include polycyclic aromatic hydrocarbons having structures composed of ring shapes bonded together to form molecules, and very large aliphatic and aromatic hydrocarbons whose molecular structures consist of long chains of carbon-hydrogen units. These typically have the consistency of heavy lubricating oils, greases, waxes, and even the tar used in road paving. Although they are generally not very chemically reactive under environmental conditions and do not dissolve well in water, many are carcinogenic, and they tend to be very environmentally persistent.

For hundreds of millions of years before human beings evolved, oil "spilled" naturally into the world's oceans from natural oil seeps, which are fractures in the earth that tap deep, oil-bearing rocks. A variety of natural processes act to reduce the environmental impacts of this oil, and these same processes also take place during a human-caused oil spill. Oil is dispersed from the oil slick and into the larger environment by five basic processes. Evaporation of the low-molecular-weight hydrocarbon compounds removes much of the oil relatively quickly. Sunlight can degrade additional oil in a process called photodegradation if the oil is exposed for enough time. Because oil is an organic substance, additional oil is removed by natural biodegradation thanks to "oil-eating" microorganisms. Most of the rest of the oil either washes up onto a coastal area or breaks up into heavy "tar balls" rich in high-molecular-weight hydrocarbons that eventually sink.

Some oil spills put so much oil into the environment that these processes cannot respond quickly enough to prevent environmental damage. Other factors can also enhance environmental damage from oil spills. Some types of oil or refined petroleum products are more toxic than others. Oil spills in cold climates generally cause more damage because cold temperatures retard evaporation and the microbial metabolic rates necessary for rapid oil removal. Furthermore, sunlight is often of low intensity, which retards photodegradation. Wave conditions and tidal currents can affect how much oil washes up onto a coastal area and how rapidly it is moved elsewhere or removed. Finally, the amount of environmental damage from an oil spill is highly dependent on the type of coastal environment affected by the spill, as coastal environments vary in the density (or biomass) and varieties of wildlife. Coastlines also vary in the degree to which they are sheltered from natural oil-removal processes. In general, rocky headlands, wave-cut rock platforms, and reefs exposed to high wave activity suffer far less damage during an oil spill than do sheltered marshes, tidal flats, and mangrove forests. The damage on beaches is related to the grain size of the beach sediment. Fine-sand beaches are relatively flat and hard-packed, and oil does not soak into the sediment or persist for long. Oil will soak deeply into coarse sand, gravel, and shell beaches, causing more damage over a longer period.

Most of what has been learned about oil spill behavior, environmental damage, and oil spill cleanup techniques comes from studying past spills. In most cases, spill prevention is far cheaper and infinitely more effective than spill response, and cleanup efforts usually capture very little of the spilled oil.

GULF OF MEXICO OIL SPILLS

The Ixtoc I spill of June 3, 1979, was the result of an explosion, or "blowout," of an offshore oil well that was drilling into a subsurface oil reservoir. Although human error was definitely a factor, the cause of the blowout remains unresolved. It has been blamed on the use of drilling mud that was not dense enough to counteract the pressure of the oil and gas at depth, as well as on the improper installation of the blowout preventer, a fail-safe device used on drilling rigs to prevent just this type of disaster. The result was a continuous 290-day oil spill, during which an estimated 475,000 metric tons of crude oil (one metric ton equals approximately five barrels) was released into the environment. In addition to doing considerable environmental damage on the coast of Mexico, oil fouled much of the barrier island coast of Texas. However, most of the oil did not make it to shore, and the final accounting for this spill gives a good indication of the long-term fate of spilled oil in offshore areas: 1 percent burned at the spill site, 50 percent evaporated, 13 percent photodegraded or biodegraded, 7 percent washed up on the coast (6 percent in Mexico, 1 percent in Texas), 5 percent was mechanically removed by skimmers and booms, and 24 percent sank to the sea floor (assumed by mass balance).

A similar accident occurred in 2010 when the blowout preventer on BP's *Deepwater Horizon* well site failed, causing an explosion at the drilling platform. In the resulting spill, oil jetted continuously from the wellhead on the sea bottom for a prolonged period of time, as various efforts to recap the well failed. Massive amounts of crude oil expanded over a large portion of the water's surface and washed up along the coastline between Louisiana and Florida. The incident decimated the fisheries in the Gulf of Mexico, creating an extensive "dead zone" where natural water currents had localized much of the toxic spill materials and created areas that could no longer support plant or animal life. The disruption of the beaches in the area also had a great negative impact on the tourist industry upon which the region depends.

THE *Exxon Valdez*

The *Exxon Valdez* oil spill—which occurred in Prince William Sound, Alaska, on March 24, 1989—is a good example of how environmental damage follows human error and inadequate response. After departing Port Valdez with a full cargo, the *Exxon Valdez* oil tanker struck a well-charted submerged rock reef located 1.6 kilometers outside the shipping lane. The ship was under the command of an unlicensed third mate in calm seas and left the shipping lane with permission from the Coast Guard to avoid ice. However, it strayed too close to the reef before evasive action was attempted. The captain, who had a history of drunk-driving convictions, was in his cabin under the influence of alcohol during events leading to the accident. His blood alcohol level nine hours after the grounding was measured at 0.06 percent; the estimate at the time of the accident was 0.19 percent. Convicted of negligence and stripped of his commander's license, he was subsequently employed as an instructor to teach others to operate supertankers.

Leaking oil was observed immediately. Oil-spill response crews funded by Exxon and the Alyeska Pipeline Consortium, oil companies that used the Port Valdez terminal, were poorly prepared and reacted too slowly and with inadequate equipment. The first response arrived ten hours after the accident with insufficient booms and skimmers. Chemical dispersants applied to break up the oil slick were ineffective in the calm seas and caused the oil slick to thin and spread more rapidly. Four days later, the weather changed: 114-kilometer-per-hour winds mixed the oil with seawater, creating a frothy mousse. More than 65,000 metric tons of oil spilled out of the stricken vessel over the next several weeks. About 15,600 square kilometers of ocean and 1,300 kilometers of shoreline were affected. Federal estimates of wildlife mortality include 3,500 to 5,500 otters; 580,000 seabirds; and 300 deer poisoned by eating oiled kelp. Economic damages totaled more than $5 billion. The long-term effects on commercial marine organisms, larval organisms, and bottom-dwelling life are not known.

Exxon promised to clean nearly 500 kilometers of shoreline by September 1989, but cleaned only 2 kilometers during the first month after the spill. Exxon and its contractors used a variety of cleanup techniques, including placing booms and skimmers, sopping up oil with absorbent materials, scraping oil by hand from rocks, stimulating the growth of oil-eating bacteria cultures, and washing coastal areas with cold water, hot water, and steam. The use of hot water and steam was effective at cosmetically removing surface oil, but it did not remove oil that had soaked into the sediment; the technique subsequently killed most of the organisms that had escaped the oil. The oil washed from the beach was to be collected by booms and skimmers offshore, but this process was so inefficient that much of the oil migrated to tide pools that had not been affected by the spill directly. Ironically, only eighteen months after the spill, life had returned to oiled coasts that had received little or no cleanup, while beaches that had been cleaned with hot water were still relatively sterile and required several years to repopulate. Exxon announced that it would not return to clean more shoreline in 1990 but relented under threat of a court order from the Coast Guard to enforce federal cleanup requirements. During the summer of 1990, shoreline cleanup resumed, including application of fertilizer to stimulate growth of naturally occurring oil-eating bacteria, a technique that is not very efficient in the cold waters of southern Alaska.

The tale of the *Exxon Valdez* is not complete without mentioning that the Port Valdez Coast Guard did not have state-of-the-art radar equipment for monitoring ship movement in this heavily used and environmentally sensitive area. In the early 1980's, federal and state funds for monitoring the Port Valdez oil companies' compliance with oil-spill preparedness legislation had been cut by more than 50 percent. The original environmental impact statement for oil-handling activity in Prince William Sound included an agreement that defines cleanup responsibility for oil spills. Exxon, as the company responsible for the spill, was to pay the first $14 million of cleanup costs, with $86 million in additional cleanup funds from the Alyeska contingency fund. Thus, the maximum financial responsibility to oil companies from a spill was $100 million unless the spill was judged to be caused by negligence. Cleanup activities ceased eighteen months after the spill with total expenditure of $2.2 billion—most of this at taxpayer expense. In 1994, a federal court unanimously awarded $5.3 billion in punitive and compensatory damages, the largest-ever jury award, to some 35,000 people impacted by the spill. By June 1999, Exxon had yet to pay a single dollar as the case continued through the legal process. Finally, it is interesting to note that Exxon's estimate of cleanup costs in late 1989 were $500 million, and it carried $400 million of oil spill liability insurance. Exxon saved $22 million by not building the *Exxon Valdez* with a double hull; its 1988 annual profits were $5,300 million.

According to National Oceanic and Atmospheric Administration (NOAA) estimates, less than 1 percent of *Exxon Valdez*'s oil burned at the site, 20 percent evaporated, 8 percent was mechanically removed, and nearly 72 percent was deposited on the sea floor. According to Exxon's estimates, 7 percent of the oil burned at the site, 32 percent evaporated, 9 percent photodegraded or biodegraded, 15 percent was mechanically removed, and 37 percent was assumed deposited on the sea floor.

THE GULF WAR OIL SPILL

In January 1991, the Gulf War oil spill, the largest oil spill in history at that time, occurred when the Iraqi military opened valves and pumps at Sea Island

Terminal, a tanker loading dock located 16 kilometers off the coast of Kuwait. This facility had a production capacity of 100,000 barrels per day, about three *Exxon Valdez* loads each week. The Iraqis also opened plugs on five Kuwaiti tankers, spilling an additional 60,000 barrels. The estimate for the entire spill is 6 million barrels, or roughly 30 times the volume of the *Exxon Valdez*. About 650 square kilometers of coast was heavily contaminated.

Three days after starting the spill, the Iraqis ignited the oil leaking from the terminal. This was the best thing to happen from an environmental perspective. During most spills, more oil is removed by natural evaporation than by any cleanup technique; igniting the oil merely speeds up this process. Burning can be an important mechanism for removing oil from the sea and avoiding environmental damage, and tests have shown purposeful ignition in open water away from the coast to be an excellent oil-slick fighting strategy. However, this must be done within the first few hours of the spill. In order to maintain the fire, the slick must be more than 1 millimeter thick and must contain relatively little emulsified water. To maintain thickness, the slick is best surrounded with fireproof booms. However, at the time of the Gulf War oil spill, almost all the fireproof boom in the world was in Prince William Sound. Saudi Arabia also used dispersants on portions of the slick, but this effort was too late to be effective before a thick mousse had formed.

The prime objectives of causing the spill were to hamper an amphibious military landing by oiling the beaches and to disrupt desalinization of drinking water at Khafji and Jubail, the two primary sources of potable water for Saudi Arabia. The Saudis used booms to protect the plant intakes with great success. The retreating Iraqis also ignited more than seven hundred of about one thousand inland wells, resulting in an additional 6 million barrels per day burned. This volume eventually made the marine spill insignificant, and the burning created 3 percent of total global carbon emissions during the time period of the event.

The Arabian Gulf is an unusual body of water. It is very shallow (average 33 meters) and is nearly enclosed as a marine basin. Because it is also microtidal (the tidal range is less than 0.6 meter), it flushes out slowly (once every two hundred years, compared with once every few days for Prince William Sound). It is also important to remember that this is not a pristine marine environment. Natural oil seeps are very common, there is a general lack of environmental standards and poor cooperation among Persian Gulf nations, and virtually no oil spill preparations or equipment were present in this part of the world. Earlier spills had occurred in the region, but they typically were associated with ongoing wars; the hostile environment made it difficult to utilize spill abatement specialists and equipment. For example, during the Iran-Iraq War, Iraq attacked an Iranian offshore platform (Nowruz) in 1982, spilling more than 2 million barrels of oil, a volume nearly half as large as the Gulf War spill. Losses of marine mammals and birds were great.

During the Gulf War oil spill, about 180 kilometers of Saudi Arabian coastline was oiled (65 kilometers was severely damaged), and oil reached south as far as the United Arab Emirates and Bahrain. Much of the southern Kuwaiti coast, made up of sea-grass beds, marsh, and mangroves, was severely damaged, and about 25 percent of the Saudi shrimp industry was lost. Although some twenty thousand wading birds were killed, no deaths of dolphins or dugongs were reported. However, these animals suffered greatly during the Iran-Iraq War. Estimates of the time required for ecological renewal of the Persian Gulf following the Gulf War spill (one to four years) were relatively short for two reasons: The high water temperature results in high microbial activity and biodegradation of the oil, and much of the oil was burned.

James L. Sadd

FURTHER READING

Alaska Wilderness League. *Preventing the Next Valdez Ten Years After Exxon's Spill New Disasters Threaten Alaska's Environment.* Washington, D.C.: Alaska Wilderness League, 1999. Published by the Alaska Wilderness League in conjunction with the Sierra Club. Reports on the status of the environment in Prince William Sound ten years after the *Exxon Valdez* oil spill.

Curley, Robert. *New Thinking About Pollution.* New York: Britannica Educational Publishing, 2011. Examines the root causes and effects of pollution of land, air, and water with regard to local and global responses, and to the various technological developments that are brought into the ongoing battle against environmental pollution.

Etkin, Dagmar Schmidt. *Financial Costs of Oil Spills in the United States.* Arlington, Mass.: Cutter Information, 1998. Discusses the economic aspects of water pollution, particularly oil spills, in the United States. Includes information on liability for oil pollution damages. Bibliography, illustrations.

_____. *Marine Spills Worldwide.* Arlington, Mass.: Cutter Information, 1999. Includes statistics concerning oil spills, the offshore oil industry, and oil pollution in the sea worldwide between 1960 and 1999. Illustrations and charts.

Fall, J. A., et al. *Long-Term Consequences of the Exxon Valdez Oil Spill for Coastal Communities of Southcentral Alaska.* Alaska Department of Fish and Game, Division of Subsistence, Anchorage, Alaska. Technical Report 163 (2001).

Graham, Bob, et al. *Deep Water: The Gulf Oil Disaster and the Future of Offshore Drilling.* National Commission on the BP Deepwater Horizon Oil Spill and Offshore Drilling, 2011. A government report addressing the disaster in the Gulf of Mexico, the events leading up to it, and repercussions to follow. Focuses on future prevention of such disasters. Provides great detail from key players, scientists, and local residents.

Hall, M. J. *Crisis on the Coast.* Portland, Ore.: USCG Marine Safety Office, 1999. Published by the U.S. Coast Guard Safety Office. Focuses on the grounding of the *New Carissa* oil tanker off the coast of Coos Bay, Oregon, in 1999.

Hilgenkamp, Kathryn. *Environmental Health: Ecological Perspectives.* Sudbury, Mass.: Jones and Bartlett Publishers, 2005. Written as a textbook for both undergraduate- and graduate-level studies. Discusses oil spills in particular in the broader context of environmental issues.

Kaye, Catheryn Berger, and Philippe Cousteau. *Going Blue.* Minneapolis, Minn.: Free Spirit Publishing, 2009. Relevant to high school students. Discusses conservation issues related to oceans, lakes, rivers, and other bodies of water. Discusses topics such as pollution, watershed management, coral bleaching, and ocean acidification. Also provides a guideline for action with multiple chapters discussing how teenagers can get involved in water conservation. Lists many resources to help the reader find more information or get started on projects.

Letcher, Trevor, and Daniel Vallero, eds. *Waste: A Handbook for Management.* Burlington, Mass.: Academic Press/Elsevier, 2011. Provides some level of uniformity across the many diverse aspects of waste by examining the manner in which waste is defined in different occupations, professions, and disciplines. Covers oceanic pollution issues.

McKinney, Michael L., Robert M. Schoch, and Logan Yonavjak. *Environmental Science: Systems and Solutions.* 4th ed. Sudbury, Mass.: Jones and Bartlett Publishers, 2007. Uses a systems approach to examine a number of contentious environmental concerns in order to present the interconnectedness and interdependence of the natural environment and human society.

Novotny, Vladimir. *Water Quality: Diffuse Pollution and Watershed Management.* 2d ed. Hoboken, N.J.: John Wiley & Sons, 2003. Describes many topics related to nonpoint source pollution. Discusses causes of water pollution, water quality statistics, the water cycle, erosion, and soil pollution. Provides good descriptions of management practices and mitigation. Also discusses environmental assessment and modeling.

Randolph, John. *Environmental Land Use Planning and Management.* Washington, D.C.: Island Press, 2004. Describes basic principles and strategies of land-use planning and management. More specific chapters discuss various land features, types, and environmental issues, such as soils, wetlands, forests, groundwater, biodiversity, and runoff pollution. Provides case studies and specific examples.

Smith, Roland. *The Sea Otter Rescue: The Aftermath of an Oil Spill.* New York: Puffin Books, 1999. Intended for juveniles. Recounts the rescue of sea otters following the 1989 *Exxon Valdez* oil spill in Prince William Sound off the coast of Alaska.

U.S. Department of the Interior, Minerals Management Service (USDI MMS). *Alaska Outer Continental Shelf Beaufort Sea Planning Area Oil and Gas Lease Sales 186, 195, and 202; Final Environmental Impact Statement.* Anchorage: OCS EIS/EA, MMS, 2003. Provides information on the continental shelf environment along the north coast of Alaska. Includes an overview of the Outer Continental Shelf Land Act. Addresses possible impacts due to very large oil spills.

See also: Atmosphere's Global Circulation; Atmosphere's Structure and Thermodynamics; Carbonate Compensation Depths; Clouds; Deep Ocean Currents; Gulf of Mexico Oil Spill; Gulf Stream; Hurricanes; Hydrothermal Vents; Monsoons; Observational Data of the Atmosphere and Oceans; Ocean-Atmosphere Interactions; Oceans' Origin; Oceans' Structure; Ocean Tides; Ocean Waves; Ozone Depletion and Ozone Holes; Remote Sensing of the Oceans; Sea Level; Seamounts; Seawater Composition; Severe Storms; Surface Ocean Currents; Tsunamis; Turbidity Currents and Submarine Fans; Weather Forecasting; Wind; World Ocean Circulation Experiment

OCEANS' ORIGIN

Oceanic waters were derived from the outgassing of hydrated minerals bound up during Earth's formation. Subsequent evolution of the waters primarily involved ions dissolving in the fluid medium by interactions with the continental and oceanic bottom sediments to give the basic salinity of Earth's oceans.

PRINCIPAL TERMS

- **carbonaceous chondrites:** a class of meteoritic bodies found to contain large amounts of carbon in conjunction with other elements; used to date the solar system and provide chemical composition assessments of the original solar nebula
- **geochemical sinks:** the processes by which elements and compounds are removed from the crust and oceans to be recycled in active chemical cycles
- **outgassing:** the process by which volatile materials trapped within rock formations are released into the atmosphere and the environment
- **primordial solar nebula:** the original collection of dust and gases that constituted the basic cloud from which the solar system formed
- **smokers:** undersea vents on the active rift areas that emit large amounts of superheated water and dissolved minerals from within the crust
- **solar wind:** the stream of highly charged particles emitted into space from the surface of the sun
- **volatiles:** chemical elements and compounds that become gaseous at fairly low temperatures
- **water of hydration:** water that is bound to the crystal structure of minerals without being part of their actual molecular structure

EARTH'S OCEANS

Of all the planets in the solar system, Earth stands out as a watery world, distinguished from the others by great quantities of liquid water. Encompassing more than 1.35 billion cubic kilometers, Earth's seas contain enough salt to cover all of Europe to a depth of 5 kilometers. The salt content of the oceans is composed primarily of sodium chloride, some 86 percent of the ions by weight, in association with other ions of magnesium, calcium, potassium, sulfate, and carbonate groups, providing a salinity of 35,000 parts per million, with pH 8 for the hydrogen-ion concentration (slightly alkaline in nature). Of all the water on Earth, 97 percent of it is salty, the remainder being proportioned among ice (77 percent of total freshwater) and continental and atmospheric waters. The ice itself, principally in the Arctic-Greenland area (1.72 million square kilometers, 3,200 meters thick) and the Antarctic area (12 million square kilometers, 4,000 meters thick), provides effects ranging from climatic control to habitats for living organisms and sources of new seawater that, in the past, have caused sea levels to rise more than 100 meters.

Consideration of the oceans' origin is twofold: the primordial origin of the water itself and the origin and rate of addition of the salt ions present in the past and contemporary waters. The data sources for consideration include the chemistry of water, the amounts and types of runoff delivered by rivers into the sea, and the composition of volcanic gases, geysers, and other vents opening to the surface. In addition, most researchers find the oceans and atmosphere to be linked in origin, providing even more data for analysis.

Numerous sources for the world's water have been proposed, although a definitive resolution has not been achieved. Possible sources include the primordial solar nebula, the solar wind acting over time, bodies colliding with Earth, impact degassing, and outgassing from the planetary interior. A complete consideration of the origin of Earth's oceans necessarily involves the investigation of factors controlling water on Earth, particularly the rates, amounts, and types of outgassing, modes of planetary formation, possible chemical reactions providing water, loss rates of gases to space, and, finally, internal feedback mechanisms such as changes in Earth's albedo (reflective power), temperature, alteration of mass, and other factors not clearly understood.

SOLAR WIND, COLLIDING BODIES, AND IMPACT DEGASSING

The solar wind as a primary source of terrestrial water can be eliminated for several reasons. Its basic constituents, charged protons, can formulate water in the atmosphere by reactions with oxygen, but all evidence indicates that there was no free oxygen in the primordial atmosphere. The geologic record shows the presence of liquid water at least 4 billion years ago that was substantially devoid of free oxygen. Astrophysical evidence suggests that the solar flux of energy, associated with the solar wind, was such that, early in Earth's history, water on Earth should have been frozen, not liquid, if that was the primary source. The presence of liquid water through at least 80 percent of Earth's history, however, has been established.

Colliding bodies would include two primary sources: meteorites and comets. The occurrence of cometary bodies striking Earth has yet to be documented. However, the basic chemical makeup of comets consisting of various ions, metals, organic molecules, and dust grains in a mass of water ice, could theoretically have supplied enough water to account for the amount of water present on the planet, providing that large numbers of cometary objects struck the early Earth during the first half-billion years of its history. No evidence for such happenings is available at present, although a theory of Earth still being bombarded incessantly by small comets composed primarily of water ice has been fiercely debated.

Meteoritic impact, particularly during the earlier stages after final planetary accretion, would also have added water to the crust via two mechanisms. Through the study of carbonaceous chondrites (the oldest and most primitive meteorites), abundant volatiles, such as water, are found to be bound chemically to minerals such as serpentine. Additional waters, trapped in crustal and mantle rocks, would have been released during impact, particularly from large meteoritic rocks. It has been calculated that such impact degassing could have released 10^{22} kilograms of volatiles, quite close to the currently estimated value of 4×10^{21} kilograms for Earth as a whole. Remnants of such ancient astroblemes are lacking, however, because of subsequent erosion, filling in by molten magma, or shifting of the continental masses over 4 billion years.

OUTGASSING

The most widely accepted origin for the oceans and atmosphere combines the features of the primordial solar nebula and slow outgassing from within the solidifying Earth. Original water would have been combined, under gravitational collapse, with silicates and metallic materials during the planetary accretion process, with the hydration of minerals assisted by the heating of Earth due to infalling bodies and radioactive elemental decay. Such "wet silicates" appear to hold large quantities of bound water for indefinite periods of time. The primordial Earth is believed to have formed by cold accretion, and would have trapped the water molecules. If it had been too hot during the accretion, all the minerals would have been dehydrated, and if too cold, no water would have been released. A delicate balance of temperature must therefore have been achieved. Further, the volatiles forming the atmosphere must have outgassed first, because water must be insulated from solar radiation in order to form a liquid phase.

A secondary problem examines how swiftly the fluids would have outgassed, whether all at once, as individual events, or in a continuous fashion. Most data suggest the continuous mode of emission, with the greatest reliance on data from still-active sources—mainly volcanoes, undersea vents, and associated structures. Fumaroles, at temperatures of 500 to 600 degrees Celsius, emit copious quantities of water, sulfur gases, and other molecules. These bodies grade gradually into hot spots and geysers, areas where water is moved upward through the crust from great depths. Magmatic melts rising in volcanoes release water and other gases directly to the surface.

In Hawaii, for example, the Halemaumau Pit, the volcano Kilauea's most active vent, emits—in terms of material—68 percent water, 13 percent carbon dioxide, and 8 percent nitrogen, with the rest mostly sulfurous gases. Similar types of values are found in ridge-axis black and white smokers, where hydrothermal accretions result in spectacular deposits of minerals falling out of solution from the emerging hot waters. Detailed studies show water trapped in the structures of altered minerals within the basaltic crustal rock of the oceanic plates, with 5 percent of the rocks, by weight, in the upper 2 to 3 kilometers being water and hydroxide ions. Free water is known to be extremely buoyant, rising in the crust along shallow dipping faults. Bound water, subducted to great depths, would be expected to cook, moving upward as the rock density lessens, then acting as a further catalyst for melting the surrounding rocks.

In Earth's earliest stages, the primordial atmosphere probably escaped from Earth's gravitational pull because of overheating. In the second phase, gases released from molten rocks, with a surface temperature of 300 degrees Celsius, provided 70 percent water and large quantities of carbon dioxide and nitrogen. In stage three, the atmosphere and oceans gradually changed, with gases and liquid water ejected from volcanoes resulting in more and more water deposited as liquid as the temperature fell. Oxygen was added to the atmosphere through thermal dissociation of water molecules, photochemical breakdown of high-altitude water, or photosynthetic alteration of carbon dioxide to oxygen in plants.

OCEAN SALT

The saltiness of the oceans can be accounted for by the inordinately large dielectric constant of water, a property that essentially ensures that it does not remain chemically pure. Geologic evidence shows the general composition to be similar over time, the stability of water content attributable to the continuous seawater-sediment interface. Geophysicist John Verhoogen determined that only 0.7 percent of the present ocean has been added since the Paleozoic era, primarily from lava materials. The salty quality is a product of acidic gases from volcanoes (forming hydrochloric, sulfuric, and carbonic acids) that act to leach out the common silicate rocks. Paleontological evidence indicates that the change in ions must have been extremely slow, as demonstrated by the narrow tolerance of organisms then alive, such as corals, echinoderms, brachiopods, and radiolarians. Ion concentrations in present-day river waters differ drastically from the ocean's values, however, indicating a different atmospheric environment in the past. Geochemists Robert M. Garrels and Fred T. Mackenzie have divided the oceans into three historical periods. In the earliest, water and volcanic acidic emissions actively attacked the crustal rock, leaching out ions and leaving residues of alumina and silicates. During the next period, from 3.5 to 1.5 billion years ago, slow continuous chemical action continued to attack sedimentary rocks, adding silica and ferrous ions. During the third period, from 1.5 billion years ago to the present, ions have accumulated to the point of modern concentrations, such that the composition is in apparent equilibrium with a mixture of calcite, potassium-feldspars, illite-montmorillonite clays, and chlorite.

Because it is known that, in an equilibrium state, the output of ions is equal to the input of ions, a new problem, that of geochemical "sinks," has been identified. Calcium carbonate (limestone) is removed from solution by living organisms to form skeletons, as is silica for opaline skeletons. Metals are dropped from seawater as newly formed mineral clays, oxides, sulfides, and zeolites, and as alteration products at the hot-water basaltic ridges. Sulfur is removed as heavy-metal sulfides precipitating in anaerobic environments, while salts are moved in pore waters trapped in sediments. Residence times for many of the ions have been determined. For example, sodium cycles in 210 million years, magnesium in 22 million years, calcium in 1 million years, and silicon in 40,000 years. With such effective removal systems, it is truly a measure of the geochemical resistance of Earth's ocean waters to change that has allowed their composition to achieve stability over 4 billion years.

STUDY OF THE OCEAN

Numerous avenues of approach have been used to investigate the ocean and its ions, including geological, chemical, and physical means. Geology has supplied basic data on the types and makeup of rocks from the earliest solidified materials to present depositional formations. Using a petrographic microscope to view thin sections of rock under polarized light enables the identification of minerals and provides quantitative measurements of the water attached to the minerals themselves. Paleontological studies of fossil organisms and paleosols indicate the range of ions in the sea at diverse geologic periods, both by the ions themselves left in the deposited soils and rocks and through studies of the ion tolerance ranges for similar, twentieth-century organisms. Such studies, along with sedimentology investigations of the rates and types of river depositions, dissolved ion concentrations, and runoff rates for falling rain, provide determinants for comparing present-day ion concentrations with those of the past for continentally derived materials.

Chemical analysis reveals the various ions present in seawater and rocks via two principal methods. Use of the mass spectrometer identifies the types and quantities of ions present by use of a magnetic field to accelerate the charged ions along a curved path with a radius that is strictly determined by the weight and charge of the ions. Collection at the end of the path provides a pure sample of the different ions present. For solid samples, electron beam probe studies provide analysis from an area only one micron in diameter. The electrons, fired at the sample, cause characteristic X rays to arise from the point. The energy of each type of X ray is characteristic of a specific element or compound. By use of various optics to focus the X rays, identification of even minute variations in concentration is possible.

Solubility studies provide residence times as a means of geochemical analysis for cyclical research. Similar laboratory projects, testing the ability of water to dissolve and hold ions in solution, argue for a primordial atmosphere that was essentially neutral, or mildly reducing in nature. Such reduction characteristics are based on the study of planetary composition for Earth and for other solar planets as supplemented by the various "lander missions" to Venus and Mars, and by modern astrophysical satellite observations. Chemical analysis from such missions in interplanetary space has also determined compositions for meteoritic gases, cometary tails and nuclei, and the mixing ratios for noble gases, all important for determining the origin of the solar system. The latter study, involving analysis of radioactive isotopes such as helium-3 (^{3}He), an isotope of helium that is formed in the mantle, has prompted geophysicists to consider the mantle as a major source and sink for elements in various geochemical cycles.

Laboratory analysis reaches two other areas. Petrographic studies of returned lunar rocks suggest that the moon is essentially devoid of water, lacking even hydroxyl ions, at least on the surface. This discovery initially helps eliminate the solar wind and meteoritic impact as major factors in the initial formation of oceans. However, the recent identification of bound subsurface water on the moon is cause for reconsideration of that conclusion. Furthermore, high-temperature/high-pressure metallurgical and chemical studies indicate molten granite, at temperatures of 900 degrees Celsius and under 1,000 atmospheres of pressure, will hold 6 percent water by weight, while basalt holds 4 percent. Based on geochemical calculations of the amounts of magma in the planet and lavas extruded over the first billion years, all the oceans' waters can be accounted for, particularly if parts of the fluid, as steam under pressure, are a result of oxidation of deep-seated hydrogen deposits trapped within or combined with mantle rocks. This supposition is thus considered an excellent likelihood from evidence gathered on radioactive decay in Earth's interior.

Arthur L. Alt

FURTHER READING

Brancazio, Peter J., ed. *The Origin and Evolution of Atmospheres and Oceans.* New York: John Wiley & Sons, 1964. Collects papers dealing with the chemical problems relevant to the early formation of the fluid parts of Earth. Traces all the basic arguments and clearly explains the criteria for water formation and its relationship to minerals and rocks. Some heavy reading, charts, extra references.

Chamberlain, Joseph W. *Theory of Planetary Atmospheres: An Introduction to Their Physics and Chemistry.* 2d ed. San Diego, Calif.: Academic Press, 1987. Provides a detailed analysis of the characteristics of diverse atmospheres in the solar system, including water contents. By comparisons of chemical compositions and meteorological observations, criteria are established for examining the possible origins for atmospheric gases and oceans. Some mathematics, heavy reading, numerous charts, and comprehensive references.

Frakes, L. A. *Climates Throughout Geologic Time.* New York: Elsevier, 1980. Offers a well-written explanation of how the interaction of the atmosphere and oceans has caused the climate of Earth to change over the history of the planet. Beginning with the possible origin of ocean and atmosphere, changes are traced as revealed through the geological and paleontological records. Numerous graphs and charts and extensive references.

Hamblin, Kenneth W., and Eric H. Christiansen. *Earth's Dynamic Systems.* 10th ed. Upper Saddle River, N.J.: Prentice Hall, 2003. Offers an integrated view of Earth's interior not common in books of this type. Includes superb illustrations, diagrams, and charts. Provides a glossary and laboratory guide. Suitable for high school readers.

Henderson-Sellers, A. *The Origin and Evolution of Planetary Atmospheres.* Bristol, England: Adam Hilger, 1983. Details the theories of the origins of Earth and how the oceans and other planetary atmospheres came into existence from the creation of the solar system. Considers water as a direct result of outgassing of planetary interiors, as are the effects from lack of water molecules. Harder reading, but an advanced layperson should find it comprehensible. Includes an extensive bibliography.

Holland, Heinrich D. *The Chemical Evolution of the Atmosphere and Oceans.* Princeton, N.J.: Princeton University Press, 1984. Provides a very detailed reference guide to the basic chemical elements present in the oceans and atmosphere. Examines the wide variety of reactions occurring in each area. Emphasizes ocean-atmosphere interactions and their common origin from materials outgassed from within Earth. Describes the action of their chemicals on the terrestrial areas in detail. Contains references and numerous charts of data but is difficult reading.

Imberger, Jeorg, ed. *Physical Processes in Lakes and Oceans*. Washington, D.C.: American Geophysical Union, 1998. Details the origins, processes, and phases of oceans, lakes, and water resources, as well as the ecology and environments surrounding them. Illustrations and maps.

Ittekko, Venugopalan, et al., eds. *Particle Flux in the Ocean*. New York: John Wiley & Sons, 1996. Contains descriptions of the chemical and geobiochemical cycles of the ocean, as well as the ocean currents and movement. Suitable for the high school reader and beyond. Illustrations, index, bibliography.

Kandel, Robert. *Water from Heaven: The Story of Water From the Big Bang to the Rise of Civilization and Beyond*. New York: Columbia University Press, 2003. Describes the origins and evolution of water in its three basic forms on Earth to provide an overview that is at once entertaining and thought-provoking, using recent data from several scientific fields. Suitable for all readers.

McElhinny, M. W., ed. *The Earth: Its Origin, Structure, and Evolution*. New York: Academic Press, 1979. Deals with all the basic elements of Earth science. Covers the origin of oceans, atmosphere, land, and life-forms starting with the theory of planetary formation. Provides excellent descriptions of the changes occurring on the planet throughout geologic time. Well written. Contains good pictures and extra references.

Plummer, Charles C., Diane H. Carlson, and Lisa Hammersley. *Physical Geology*. 13th ed. Columbus, Ohio: McGraw-Hill, 2009. Offers a general introduction to physical geology and oceanography. Intended for use at the college-freshman level. Contains many tables, illustrations, and photographs, as well as a glossary and an index.

Ponnamperuma, C., ed. *Cosmochemistry and the Origins of Life*. Dordrecht: Reidel, 1982. A collection of works dealing with the distribution of elements in the universe, particularly those necessary for life. Provides information on the formation of the planetary system, showing how the chemicals combined at various temperatures to make the planets as different as they are. Discusses origins of oceans, atmospheres, and life; detailed reading with many charts and an extensive bibliography.

Redfern, Ron. *Origins: The Evolution of Continents, Oceans and Life*. Norman, Okla.: University of Oklahoma Press, 2001. Discusses the history and origins of Earth's features. Divided into sections of time, the chapters cover polar wander, the formation of the Atlantic Ocean, opening of the Nordic seaway, glacial retreat, and development of societies along waterways.

Schwartz, M. *Encyclopedia of Coastal Science*. Dordrecht: Springer, 2005. Contains many articles specific to ocean and beach dynamics. Discusses coastal habitat management topics, hydrology, geology, and topography. Articles may run multiple pages and have diagrams. Each article has bibliographical information and cross referencing.

Seibold, E., and W. Berger. *The Sea Floor*. 3d ed New York: Springer-Verlag, 2010. Covers the chemistry, geology, and biology of the bottom of the world's oceans. Emphasizes the idea that the oceans are a result of outgassing. Well written, with a very interesting section on white and black smokers and their relation to the origin of waters and life. Contains excellent illustrations, along with additional references.

Wegener, Alfred. *The Origin of Continents and Oceans*. Mineola, N.Y.: Dover Publications, 1966. Represents a classic text in the field of geology. Covers the genesis of plate tectonics and continental drift. Provides a historical foundation of these concepts upon which many current topics in geology are built, although outdated.

See also: Beaches and Coastal Processes; Carbonate Compensation Depths; Deep Ocean Currents; Gulf Stream; Hurricanes; Hydrothermal Vents; Lakes; Monsoons; Ocean-Atmosphere Interactions; Ocean Pollution and Oil Spills; Oceans' Structure; Ocean Tides; Ocean Waves; Sand; Sea Level; Seamounts; Seawater Composition; Sediment Transport and Deposition; Severe Storms; Surface Ocean Currents; Tsunamis; Turbidity Currents and Submarine Fans; Weathering and Erosion; Wind; World Ocean Circulation Experiment

OCEANS' STRUCTURE

The ocean has a complex structure, both at its surface and in the vertical dimension descending to the ocean floor. This internal structure results in layering with respect to temperature, salinity, density, and the way in which the ocean responds to the passage of light and sound waves.

PRINCIPAL TERMS

- **convective overturn:** the renewal of the bottom waters caused by the sinking of surface waters that have become denser, usually because of changes in temperature or salinity
- **doldrums:** the equatorial zone where winds are calm and variable and there is heavy thunderstorm rainfall
- **halocline:** a zone within a body of water, characterized by a rapid rate of change in salinity
- **horse latitudes:** the belts of latitude approximately 30 degrees north and 30 degrees south of the equator, where the winds are very light and the weather is hot and dry
- **pycnocline:** a zone within a body of water, characterized by a rapid rate of change in density
- **salinity:** the quantity of dissolved salts in seawater, usually expressed as parts per thousand
- **saltwater wedge:** a wedge-shaped intrusion of seawater from the ocean into the bottom of a river; the thin end of the wedge points upstream
- **thermocline:** a zone within a body of water, characterized by a rapid change in temperature

TEMPERATURE LAYERING

One highly significant aspect of ocean structure is the layering of water based on temperature and salinity differences. In order to understand the reasons for the thermal layering of the ocean, one must bear in mind that the primary source of heating for the ocean is sunlight. About 60 percent of this entering radiation is absorbed within the first meter of seawater, and about 80 percent is absorbed within the first 10 meters. As a result, the warmest waters in the ocean are found at its surface.

That does not mean, however, that surface temperatures in the ocean are the same everywhere. Because more heat is received at the equator than at the poles, ocean surface temperatures are closely related to latitude. As a result, they are distributed in bands of equal temperature extending east and west, parallel to the equator. Temperatures are highest along the equator because of the near-vertical angles at which the sun's rays are received here. As latitude increases toward the poles, ocean temperatures gradually cool as a result of the decreasing angle of incidence of the incoming solar radiation.

Measurements of ocean surface temperature range from a high of 33 degrees Celsius in the Persian Gulf, a partly landlocked, shallow sea in a desert climate, to a low of −2 degrees Celsius in close proximity to ice in polar regions. There, the presence of salt in the water lowers the water's freezing point below the normal 0 degree Celsius level. Because salinity of this cold water is so high, it sinks to the ocean floor and travels along it for substantial distances. Ocean surface temperatures may also vary with time of year, with warmer waters moving northward into the Northern Hemisphere in the summertime and southward into the Southern Hemisphere in the wintertime. These differences are most noticeable in midlatitude waters. In equatorial regions, water and air temperatures change little seasonally, and in polar regions, water tends to be cold all year long because of the presence of ice.

Vertically downward from the equator, toward the ocean floor, water temperatures become colder. This results from the facts that solar heating affects the surface waters only and that cold water is denser than warm water. When waters at the surface of the ocean in the polar regions are chilled by extremely low winter temperatures, they become denser than the underlying waters and sink to the bottom. They then move slowly toward the equator along the sea floor, lowering the temperature of the entire ocean. As a result, deep ocean waters have much lower temperatures than might be expected by examination of the surface waters alone. Although the average ocean surface temperature is 17.5 degrees Celsius, the average temperature of the entire ocean is a frigid 3.5 degrees.

Oceanographers recognize the following layers within the ocean, based on its temperature stratification: First, there is an upper, wind-mixed layer, consisting of warm surface water up to 500 meters thick.

This layer may not be present in polar regions. Next is an intermediate layer, below the surface layer, where the temperature decreases rapidly with depth; this transitional layer can be 500 to 1,000 meters thick and is known as the main thermocline. Finally, there is a cold, deep layer extending to the ocean floor. In polar regions, this layer may reach the surface, and its water is relatively homogeneous, with temperature slowly decreasing with depth.

Because the upper surface layer is influenced by atmospheric conditions, such as weather and climate, it may contain weak thermoclines as a result of the daily cycle of heating and cooling or because of seasonal variations. These are temporary, however, and may be destroyed by severe storm activity. Nevertheless, the majority of ocean water lies below the main thermocline and is uniformly cold, the only exception being hot springs on the ocean floor that introduce water at temperatures of 300 degrees Celsius or higher. Plumes of warmer water emanating from these hot springs have been detected within the ocean.

SALINITY

A second phenomenon responsible for layering within the ocean is variation in the water's salinity. For the ocean as a whole, the salinity is 35 parts per thousand. Considerable variation in the salinity of the surface waters from place to place results from processes that either add or subtract salt or water. For example, salinities of 40 parts per thousand or higher are found in nearly landlocked seas located in desert climates, such as the Red Sea or the Persian Gulf, because high rates of evaporation remove the water but leave the salt behind. High salinity values are also found at the surface of the open ocean at the same latitudes where there are deserts on land (the so-called horse latitudes). There, salinities of 36 to 37 parts per thousand are common.

At the equator, however, much lower salinity values are encountered, despite the high temperatures and nearly vertical rays of the sun. The reason is that the equatorial zone lies in the so-called doldrums, a region of heavy rainfall. The ocean's surface waters are therefore diluted, which keeps the salinity relatively low. Similarly low salinities are also found in coastal areas, where rivers bring in large quantities of freshwater, and in higher latitudes, where rainfall is abundant because of numerous storms.

Despite the variation in salinity in the ocean's surface water, the deep waters are well mixed, with nearly uniform salinities ranging from 34.6 to 34.9 parts per thousand. Consequently, in some parts of the ocean, surface layers of low-salinity water overlie the uniformly saline deep waters and, in other parts of the ocean, surface layers of high-salinity water overlie the uniformly saline deep layer. Between these layers are zones of rapidly changing salinity known as haloclines. An important exception to this picture is a few deep pools of dense brine—such as are found at the bottom of the Red Sea, for example—where salinities of 270 parts per thousand have been recorded.

Haloclines are very common in coastal areas. Off the mouth of the Amazon River, for example, a plume of low-salinity river water extends out to sea as far as 320 kilometers, separated from the normally saline water below by a prominent halocline. In many tidal rivers and estuaries, a layer of heavier seawater will extend many kilometers inland beneath the freshwater discharge as a conspicuous saltwater wedge.

DENSITY STRATIFICATION

A prominent density stratification within the ocean results from the variation in ocean temperatures and salinity just described. As noted, two factors make water heavier: increased salinity, which adds more dissolved mineral matter, and decreased temperature, which results in the water molecules being more closely packed together. Therefore, the least-dense surface waters are found in the equatorial and tropical regions, where ocean temperatures are at their highest. Toward the higher latitudes, the density of surface ocean waters increases because of the falling temperatures. In these areas, low-density surface water is found only where large quantities of freshwater are introduced, by river runoff, by high amounts of precipitation, or by melting ice.

Vertical density changes are even more pronounced. As water temperatures decrease with depth, water densities increase accordingly. This increase in density, however, is not uniform throughout the ocean. At the poles, the surface waters are almost as cold as the coldest bottom waters, so there is only a slight increase in density as the ocean floor is approached. By contrast, the warm surface waters in the equatorial and tropical regions are underlain by markedly colder water. As a result, a warm upper layer of low-density water is underlain by an intermediate layer in which the density increases rapidly with depth. (This middle layer is known as the pycnocline.) Below it is a deep zone of nearly uniform high-density water.

Convective overturning takes place when this normal density stratification is upset. In a stable density-stratified system, the less dense surface water floats on top of the heavier, deeper water. Occasionally, however, unstable conditions will arise in which heavier water forms above lighter water. Then, convective overturning takes place as the mass of heavier water sinks to its appropriate place in the density-stratified water column. This overturning may occur gradually or quite abruptly. In lakes and ponds, it occurs annually in regions where winter temperatures are cold enough. In the ocean, convective overturning is primarily associated with the polar regions, where extremely low winter temperatures result in the sinking of vast quantities of cold water. In addition, convective overturning has been observed in the Mediterranean during the wintertime, when chilled surface waters sink to replenish deeper water.

LIGHT PENETRATION AND SOUND WAVES

Oceanographers also recognize stratification in the ocean based on the depths to which light penetrates, and they divide the ocean into two zones. The upper zone, which is known as the photic zone, consists of the near-surface waters that have sufficient sunlight for photosynthetic growth. Below this zone is the aphotic zone, where there is insufficient light for photosynthetic growth. The lower limit of the photic zone is generally taken as the depth at which only 1 percent of the surface intensity of sunlight still penetrates. In the extremely clear waters of the open ocean, this depth may be 200 meters or more.

Stratification in the ocean based on the behavior of sound waves has also been observed. Because sound waves travel nearly five times faster under water than in the air, their transmission in the ocean has been extensively studied, beginning with the development of sonar, the echo sounder. So-called scattering layers have been recognized as regions that reflect sound, usually because of the presence of living organisms that migrate vertically, as layers within the water column, depending on light intensity. The sofar (sound fixing and ranging) channels are density layers within the ocean where sound waves can become trapped and can travel for thousands of kilometers with extremely small energy losses. These channels have the potential to be used for long-distance communications. Shadow zones are also caused by density layers within the ocean. These layers trap the sound waves and prevent them from reaching the surface. One advantage of shadow zones is that submarines can travel in them undetected.

STUDY OF THE OCEAN

The measurement of water temperatures at the ocean's surface is quite simple. A thermometer placed in a bucket of water that has been scooped out of the ocean at the bow of a boat will suffice, provided the necessary precautions have been taken to prevent temperature changes caused by conduction and evaporation. For oceanwide or global studies, satellites provide near-simultaneous readings of ocean surface temperatures within an accuracy of 1 degree Celsius. These satellites utilize infrared and other sensors, which are capable of measuring the amount of heat radiation emitted by the ocean's surface to within 0.2 degree.

Measuring the temperature of the deeper subsurface waters posed a problem, however, because a standard thermometer lowered over the side of a ship will "forget" a deep reading on its way back to the surface. As a result, the so-called reversing thermometer was developed in 1874. This thermometer has an S-bend in its glass tube. When the thermometer is inverted at the desired depth, the mercury column breaks at the S-bend, thus recording the temperature at that depth. Today, electronic instruments record subsurface water temperatures continuously. These devices can be either dropped from a plane or ship or moored to the ocean floor.

The measurement of the salinity of seawater is not as easy as one might think. An obvious way to determine water salinity would be to determine the amount of dried salts remaining after a weighed sample of seawater has been evaporated, but in actual practice, that is a messy and time-consuming procedure, hardly suitable for use on a rolling ship. A variety of other techniques have been used over the years, based on such water characteristics as buoyancy, density, or chloride content. By far the most popular relies on seawater's electrical conductivity. In this method, an electrical current is passed through the seawater sample; the higher the salt content of the water, the lower the electrical resistance of the solution and the faster this current is observed to pass. Using this method, oceanographers have been able to determine the salinity of seawater samples to the nearest 0.003 part per thousand. This is an important advantage, in view of the fact that the salinity differences between deep seawater masses are very minute.

Measurement of the densities of surface water samples can easily be accomplished by determining the water sample's buoyancy or weight, but the real difficulty comes with attempts to determine a subsurface water sample's density. If this water sample is brought to the surface, its temperature, and therefore its density, will change. Although sophisticated techniques are available for the determination of density at depth, in actual practice the density is not measured at all; instead, it is computed from the sample's known temperature, salinity, and depth. The density of the water is almost wholly dependent on these three factors.

Various methods are available for measuring the depth of light penetration in seawater. A crude estimate can be made using the Secchi disk, which was first introduced in 1865. This circular, white disk is slowly lowered into the water, and the depth at which the disk disappears from sight is noted visually. More sophisticated measurements can be made using photoelectric meters. Another good indicator of the maximum depth of light penetration in the sea is the lowest level at which photosynthetic growth can take place. For sound studies within the ocean, various methods are used to create the initial sound, including the use of explosives in seismic profiling. The returning echo is detected by means of a receiver known as a hydrophone.

Donald W. Lovejoy

Further Reading

Broecker, Wally. *The Great Ocean Conveyor.* Princeton, N.J.: Princeton University Press, 2010. Discusses ocean currents, focusing specifically on the great conveyor belt. Written by the great ocean conveyor's researcher. Explains the conception of this theory and the resulting impact on oceanography. Written in a manner easy to follow with some background in science, yet still relevant to graduate students and scientists.

Charlier, R. H., and C. W. Finkl. *Ocean Energy: Tide and Tidal Power.* Berlin: Springer-Verlag, 2009. Discusses fundamentals of oceanic energy harvesting. Describes historical and current technologies, with examples drawn from around the world. Also discusses social, economic, and environmental impacts. Contains dense, verbose, and technical writing and is therefore best suited for graduate students and researching oceanographers or engineers with some prior knowledge of ocean dynamics.

Emelyanov, Emelyan M. *The Barrier Zones in the Ocean.* Berlin: Springer-Verlag, 2005. Suitable as a textbook for advanced oceanography and ocean geochemistry courses, and for research reference. Discusses the properties of forty different ocean barrier zones with regard to salinity, hydrodynamics, temperature, and light, as well as processes that affect sedimentation in the open ocean and in bodies of water such as the Baltic and Mediterranean Seas.

Fairbridge, Rhodes W., ed. *The Encyclopedia of Oceanography.* New York: Reinhold, 1966. An outstanding oceanography source book for students or professionals. Contains sections on the temperature structure of the ocean, salinity, density, underwater light properties, and underwater sound channels. Suitable for college-level readers who have some technical background. A well-illustrated and carefully cross-referenced volume.

Gross, M. Grant. *Oceanography: A View of the Earth.* 7th ed. Englewood Cliffs, N.J.: Prentice Hall, 1996. A well-written and well-illustrated oceanography text. Provides a thorough treatment of the topic. Includes many useful diagrams and charts, as well as color plates showing temperature distribution in the ocean based on satellite imagery. Suitable for college-level readers or the interested layperson.

Imberger, Jeorg, ed. *Physical Processes in Lakes and Oceans.* Washington, D.C.: American Geophysical Union, 1998. An extensive volume that details the origins, processes, and phases of oceans, lakes, and water resources, as well as the ecology and environments surrounding them. Illustrations and maps.

Ingmanson, Dale E., and William J. Wallace. *Oceanography: An Introduction.* 5th ed. Belmont, Calif.: Wadsworth, 1995. Offers useful information on ocean-surface salinities and gives typical salinity profiles for the ocean. Discusses temperature, density, light, and sound. Well illustrated throughout. Suitable for college-level readers.

McLellan, H. J. *Elements of Physical Oceanography*. Elmsford, N.Y.: Pergamon Press, 1977. A thorough treatment of temperature, salinity, and density distribution within the ocean and the methods used for their measurement. Gives data for selected locations with helpful tables and charts. Includes photographs that help to explain the workings of the reversing thermometer and the bathythermograph.

Redfern, Ron. *Origins: The Evolution of Continents, Oceans and Life*. Norman, Okla.: University of Oklahoma Press, 2001. Discusses the history and origins of Earth's features. Divided into sections of time, the chapters cover polar wander, the development of the Atlantic Ocean, the opening of the Nordic seaway, glacial retreat, and the development of societies along waterways.

Schwartz, M. *Encyclopedia of Coastal Science*. Dordrecht: Springer, 2005. Contains many articles specific to ocean and beach dynamics. Discusses coastal habitat management topics, hydrology, geology, and topography. Articles may run multiple pages and have diagrams. Each article has bibliographical information and cross referencing.

Segar, Douglas. *Introduction to Ocean Sciences*. 2d ed. New York: W. W. Norton & Co., 2007. Comprehensive coverage of all aspects of the oceans, their chemical makeup, and circulation. Readable and well illustrated. Suitable for high school students and above.

Seibold, Eugen, and Wolfgang H. Berger. *The Sea Floor: An Introduction to Marine Geology*. 3d ed. New York: Springer-Verlag, 2010. Offers an introduction to many topics in marine geology that covers geological structures from the continental shelf to deep-ocean trenches. Discusses processes such as seafloor spreading, the sediment cycle, currents, and pelagic rain.

Soloviev, Alexander, and Roger Lukas. *The Near-Surface Layer of the Ocean: Structure, Dynamics and Applications*. Dordrecht: Springer, 2006. Uses the results of major air-sea interaction experiments to present the physics and thermodynamics of this oceanic system, providing a detailed treatment of the surface microlayer, upper-ocean turbulence, thermohaline and coherent structures, and the high-speed wind regime.

Talley, Lynne D., et al. *Descriptive Physical Oceanography: An Introduction*. 6th ed. San Diego: Academic Press, 2011. Designed to introduce oceanography majors to the field of physical oceanography. Has useful sections on the temperature, salinity, density, light, and sound structure of the ocean. Includes a discussion of the various instruments and methods used for measuring these properties.

Teramoto, Toshihiko. *Deep Ocean Circulation: Physical and Chemical Aspects*. New York: Elsevier, 1993. A college-level text that provides a detailed look at ocean circulation and currents. Provides information on the chemical processes that occur in the deep ocean. Illustrations, maps, and bibliographical references.

Van Dover, Cindy Lee. *The Ecology of Deep-Sea Hydrothermal Vents*. Princeton, N.J.: Princeton University Press, 2000. Discusses geology, chemistry, and biology of hydrothermal vents. Examines the microbial and microbial ecosystems as well as their symbiotic relationships. Places great emphasis on the ecology of hydrothermal communities. Accessible to graduate students, but could easily be used in an advanced undergraduate course.

See also: Atmosphere's Structure and Thermodynamics; Carbonate Compensation Depths; Deep Ocean Currents; Geochemical Cycles; Gulf Stream; Hydrologic Cycle; Hydrothermal Vents; Observational Data of the Atmosphere and Oceans; Ocean-Atmosphere Interactions; Oceans' Origin; Ocean Pollution and Oil Spills; Oceans' Origin; Ocean Tides; Ocean Waves; Precipitation; Remote Sensing of the Oceans; Sea Level; Seamounts; Seawater Composition; Surface Ocean Currents; Tsunamis; Turbidity Currents and Submarine Fans; World Ocean Circulation Experiment

OCEAN TIDES

Tides are the displacements of particles on Earth caused by the differential attraction of the moon and the sun. There are atmospheric tides, land or crustal tides, and ocean tides. Of these, ocean tides are the most apparent because the ocean, as a fluid, is more easily stretched out of shape by the gravitational pull of the moon.

PRINCIPAL TERMS

- **basins:** container-like places on the ocean floor, usually elliptical, circular, or oval in shape, varying in depth and size
- **bore:** a sudden rise in water level in a river channel manifested as an incoming wave of tidal waters
- **diurnal tide:** having only one high tide and one low tide each lunar day; tides on some parts of the Gulf of Mexico are diurnal
- **mixed tide:** having the characteristics of diurnal and semidiurnal tidal oscillations; these tides are found on the Pacific coast of the United States
- **neap tide:** a tide with the minimum range, or when the level of the high tide is at its lowest
- **range:** the difference between the high-tide water level and the low-tide water level
- **semidiurnal:** having two high tides and two low tides each lunar day
- **spring tide:** a tide with the maximum range, occurring when lunar and solar tides reinforce each other a few days after the full and new moons

CAUSES OF TIDES

Each particle in the ocean moves in response to the force of gravitational attraction exerted on it by both the sun and the moon. Although the sun is some 27 million times the size of the moon, the moon is the primary factor in the tidal movement of ocean waters. In fact, the moon's power is more than double the periodic tidal-stretching force exerted by the sun because it is much closer to Earth. This is described by Newton's universal law of gravity, which states that the gravitational force between two bodies is directly proportional to their masses, but inversely proportional to the square of the distance between their centers of mass. Thus, the proximity of the moon counts for more than the distant mass of the sun in solar and lunar relations with Earth.

In order to explain how tides are caused, tidal scientists use the concept of a theoretical "equilibrium tide." This concept is based on an ideal in which the ocean waters are always in static equilibrium and in which no continents obstruct the flow of water on Earth's surface. When the moon is directly above a particular location, its force of attraction causes the mass of water to bulge up directly under the moon and also on the opposite side of Earth. Meanwhile, in the opposite quadrants of the globe, two low-water troughs result from the movement of the water away from these areas. Thus, Earth rotates beneath tidal bulges and troughs, which results in high and low tides.

Tides generally follow the lunar day, which is twenty-four hours and fifty minutes, or the time it takes the moon to complete one full orbit of Earth. Some complex tidal cycles, however, result from the combined influences of the sun and moon. If there were no moon, the sun's influence alone would cause tides to occur at the same time each day. However, because the plane of the moon's orbit around Earth is in a different plane from that of Earth's orbit around the sun, combinations of full diurnal and semidiurnal tides result. In most areas, semidiurnal tides are the rule, with high and low tides occurring twice each lunar day, averaging twelve hours and twenty-five minutes apart. Diurnal tides occur when only one high tide and one low tide take place in one lunar day. They are found in parts of the China Sea and the Gulf of Mexico. Mixed tides result from a combination of both diurnal and semidiurnal tidal oscillations. Such tides are found along the Pacific coast of North America and in parts of Australia.

OTHER TIDE VARIABILITY FACTORS

Other factors that contribute to the variability of ocean tides are the phases of the moon, the position of the sun and moon relative to Earth, and the latitude and topography of the tide's location on Earth. When the sun, moon, and Earth are aligned (in "conjunction" or "opposition"), then the combined gravitational effects of these bodies will exert additional gravitational pull on Earth, resulting in increased tidal amplitude. This phenomenon, when lunar and solar tides reinforce each other, is called the spring tide and occurs around the full and new moons. In between the spring tides, a neap tide takes place when the sun, moon, and Earth are positioned at the apexes of a triangle. At this time, during the first and third quarters of the moon's phase, solar high tides are superimposed on lunar low tides, so resulting tides are the lowest in the month. In the open ocean, spring tides may be more than 1 meter high, while neap tides may be less than 1 meter. Tidal amplitude will also vary, depending on latitude and the declination of the moon.

Despite the complexity of the many variables that determine tidal behavior, tidal scientists can now predict the time and height of a tide anywhere, on any past or future date, given the one condition that they have sufficient information on how the local topography of the site modifies the tide. Local geographical conditions such as the width of a bay's mouth, the uneven slope of the bottom, and the depth of the body of water are the types of features that determine the range, amplitude, and time of the local tide. It is observed that the island of Nantucket, off the coast of the U.S. state of Massachusetts, experiences a difference of no more than 0.3 meter between high and low water, while only a few hundred kilometers away, the Bay of Fundy, in the Canadian province of Nova Scotia, has the highest tides in the world, with a rise of 15 meters during spring tides. To account for such phenomena, scientists have developed a model of tidal oscillation, in which the ocean structure is divided up among a great many basins of water, each with its own depth, length, and resulting period of oscillation. The boundaries of each basin are determined by the surrounding land forms, both above and below the ocean, and the influences of gravitational attraction in each are always changing, as are the currents that flow in. Ordinarily, when water rocks up and down in a basin, the water at the rim is most active, while the least amount of motion occurs in the center of the basin around a tideless node. Thus the physical dimensions of these basins determine the period of oscillation of the waters throughout the basin.

OPPOSING TIDAL BULGES

When the pull of the moon creates a high tide on the side of Earth closest to it, a high tide occurs simultaneously on the opposite side of the planet. Logically, one would not expect this to be the case. To understand this, it is necessary to know

that the moon and Earth revolve not only around each other but also around a common center of gravity located 1,600 kilometers below the surface of Earth. As the Earth and moon revolve, the centrifugal force stretches the oceans outward against Earth's gravity. At its center, Earth is not still but is moving in a circle that is a small fraction of the size of the moon's orbit. This invisible revolution of Earth around the moon produces a centrifugal force throughout Earth, which varies as the moon revolves and pulls Earth's surface out of shape. It is the resulting "prolate," or lemon-shaped, elongations of Earth that are observed as the tides. The tides nearest the moon are caused by gravitational attraction. On the side of Earth farthest from the moon, however, the centrifugal force is greater than the pull of the moon. To compound the complexity of the situation, the moon's gravitational force is also pulling the ocean floor of that area away from the waters there. Thus high tides are produced on both sides of Earth in line with the moon.

Because tides are actually long waves, an observer on the moon might expect to see the two tidal bulges move around Earth at a speed consistent with the pace of the moon. Instead, tidal waves move out of step with the moon. Keeping pace with the moon would be possible under two conditions: if the oceans of the world were 22 kilometers deep (they average a bit more than 3 kilometers deep) and if there were no continents obstructing the movement of tidal waves. Thus, the speed of the movement of the tides is only 1,100 to 1,300 kilometers per hour, and the tides do not keep up with the moon as it travels westward around the terrestrial globe.

EARTH'S ANGULAR MOMENTUM

The angular momentum of Earth is slowed by ocean tides. Because the momentum of the Earth-moon system is conserved, the slowing of Earth results in a speeding up of the moon's rotation around Earth. For unknown geophysical reasons, several abrupt increases in the length of Earth's day, some approaching 1 millisecond, have been observed over the past several decades. Ocean tides are not responsible for these abrupt changes but rather for small, steady increases over millennia. However, the U.S. National Bureau of Standards must sometimes add a "leap second" to the Earth year to take into account the observed slowing of Earth. Assuming that the position of Earth's orbital distance with respect to the sun has not changed, the number of days in a year has changed from about 400 during the Devonian period to about 365 at the current time. Thus, the current length of a day is now quite a bit longer than it was during the Devonian, about 400 million years ago. Over this same time period, the moon's angular momentum is estimated to have increased by about 1.6 percent. As Earth's rotation slows and the moon revolves around Earth more quickly, the moon moves farther away from Earth. Accordingly, the moon has moved about 1.6 kilometers away from Earth in the last 100,000 years.

STUDY OF OCEAN TIDES

Tides are not simple to predict. Qualitative prediction of the tides has been going on in harbors around the world for centuries, but quantitative prediction began in the nineteenth century, when people first designed tide-predicting machines to help forecast the tides. The first such machine was invented in 1872 by Lord Kelvin, who is often referred to as the first electrical engineer. Kelvin's machine was capable of drawing a line picture of the curve of the tide, and for this achievement he was knighted. Soon after this breakthrough, an employee of the United States Coast and Geodetic Survey invented a tide-predicting machine that showed the times and heights of the tides. The survey later designed a simpler machine that combines the capabilities of both previous inventions: It gives the curve of the tides as well as the times and the heights of the tides. Unfortunately, these machines are not completely reliable because other factors, such as heavy storms, winds, or accumulation of sand as a result of wave action, can have dramatic impact on the water levels. Tide tables can only give the approximate high and low tides.

Today, tide-predicting machines have been replaced by faster digital computers. Tidal analysis still involves many complex computations, and predictions can be made only for places where a long series of observations are available. For each given spot on Earth, and for given time intervals, observations must be made that provide the value of the gravitational acceleration, the deflection of the vertical, and the measurements for the elevation of the water level. With this set of numbers in hand, the matter of prediction becomes one of extrapolating from the past into the future. Thus, around the coasts of

the world, in inlets, in tidal rivers, and on islands, the water levels caused by tidal forces are carefully recorded. These measurements are analyzed locally. Once these measurements of the water level at a given place are taken within specified time intervals, the phases and amplitudes of the tide can be determined by a number of mathematical methods. Then, knowing the phases and amplitudes, scientists can reproduce the measurements according to a harmonic series. This harmonic method is a fairly reliable means of tidal prediction for deep-water ports, but in shallow-water areas, nonharmonic methods may need to be used. Finally, a determination of harmonic constants is made by national authorities, and the resulting data are sent to the International Hydrographic Bureau in Monaco. As a result, hydrographic offices in countries around the globe publish tide tables forecasting the high- and low-water times and water heights for the world's ports.

The problem of the measurement of tidal displacements in the open ocean has yet to be solved. This situation results from the fact that tidal sea-level records pertain primarily to coastal locations, and there are few or no measurements from the open ocean.

SIGNIFICANCE

Knowledge of ocean tides serves crucial purposes in the fields of navigation, coastal engineering, and tidal power generation. In addition, it holds a key position in relation to geophysics, marine geodesy, and astronomy.

Tides are of vital importance in navigation. Although the tides have become more predictable, and hence tamer, they still both help and hinder all mariners. The *Coast Pilots and Sailing Directions* for different parts of the world reveals the menacing possibilities which tides in various places are known to cause. Tidal currents often move violently when opposed by winds or confined in narrow channels. People have been swept off boats by an onslaught of giant waves when sailing in a flood tide through narrow straits. At certain stages of the tide, the waters can have dangerous eddies, whirlpools, or bores. A bore is created when a large portion of the flood tide enters a channel at once as one wave. Wherever they occur, they control the schedule of all shipping, as well as the rhythm of harbor life in the area. Even where there are no bores, the largest oceangoing liner must wait for slack water before entering a harbor where rushing tidal currents can fling it against piers. Since it is to the ship's advantage to sail in the direction of the tidal current flow, knowledge of tides is invaluable. All navigators approaching a coast rely on tide tables to supplement the information on depths in their nautical charts.

Coastal-engineering work is dependent on knowledge of the tides for such undertakings as the management of tidal estuaries, construction of harbors, and damming of tidal rivers. Another practical aspect of tide information concerns the handling of problems that arise from the pollution of coastal waters and the ocean.

Tidal power generation is a new field that has gained increasing attention because of the shortage of available energy sources. Humans have long dreamed of harnessing the tidal forces for their energy needs. In 1966, the first tidal power station ever built was completed in the La Rance estuary in France. Construction of the project took place just after the Suez crisis, when France felt uncertain about the future of its oil supply. The half-mile Rance Dam was built to harness energy from the very large tides of the area—with a mean range of nearly 8.5 meters and rising to more than 13 meters at equinoctial spring tides. This power installation transmits electricity to Paris and the surrounding area, producing more than 580 billion watt-hours of energy a year but costing slightly more than the cost of operation of hydroelectric plants. In 1968, the Soviet Union finished construction on a 400-kilowatt tidal plant north of Murmansk, at a site where the maximum tide is less than 4 meters in height. In 2004, China announced plans for a tidal plant that would be the world's largest, sited where a famous bore occurs on the mouth of the Yalu River. In the United States, at Passamaquoddy Bay in Maine, a major tidal power plant project was abandoned because of the expense of maintaining the pipes and machinery in saltwater, and of transmitting the electricity generated to the nearest big users.

Additional areas of practical concern involving tides include the correlation of tides with earthquakes, volcanic eruptions, and geyser activity. Some scientists believe that the pressures exerted by water moving with the tides can trigger earthquakes.

Nan White

FURTHER READING

Boyle, Godfrey, ed. *Renewable Energy*. 2d ed. New York: Oxford University Press, 2004. Provides a complete overview of renewable energy resources. Discusses solar energy, bioenergy, geothermal energy, hydroelectric energy, tidal power, wind energy, and wave energy, as well as the basic physics principles, technology, and environmental impact. Contains references and a further reading list. An excellent starting point, although the advanced technical details of these power supplies are limited.

Christopherson, Robert W., and Mary-Louise Byrne. *Geosystems: An Introduction to Physical Geography*. Toronto: Pearson Prentice Hall, 2006. Begins with the basic principles of Earth-sun interactions to deliver an in-depth overview of Earth as a whole made up of individual systems, of which the oceans and their behavior is a major part.

Freuchen, Peter. *Peter Freuchen's Book of the Seven Seas*. Guilford, Conn.: The Lyons Press, 2003. A well-written general-interest book that gives a very clear explanation of the tides. Includes scientific explanations for laypersons of all ages, as well as folklore and history as the author imagined it. An entertaining book full of photographs.

Garrison, Tom S. *Essentials of Oceanography*. 6th ed. Belmont, Calif.: Brooks/Cole Cengage Learning, 2012. An undergraduate textbook designed for nonscience students in an introductory oceanography course that presents an entertaining overview of the ocean environment.

_____. *Oceanography: An Invitation to Marine Science*. Belmont, Calif.: Brooks/Cole, Cengage Learning, 2010. Discusses the circulation of the oceans, including deep water and surface currents. Also discusses various aspects of waves and the physics of tides. Abundant diagrams aid readers from the layperson to advanced undergraduates.

Gregory, R. L., ed. *Tidal Power and Estuary Management*. Dorchester, England: Henry Ling, 1978. A collection of papers presented at the Symposium on Tidal Energy and Estuary Management, held under the auspices of the Colston Research Society at the University of Bristol in 1978. Written by eminent authorities in the field of estuary management, many of them associated with tidal power production. Presents a holistic picture of the research and thinking in two of the fields most intensively concerned with the tides. Includes the viewpoints of engineers, botanists, zoologists, mathematicians, and economists to make interesting reading.

Hamblin, Kenneth W., and Eric H. Christiansen. *Earth's Dynamic Systems.* 10th ed. Upper Saddle River, N.J.: Prentice Hall, 2003. A geology textbook that offers an integrated view of Earth's interior not common in books of this type. Includes excellent illustrations, diagrams, and charts, as well as a glossary and laboratory guide. Suitable for high school readers.

Komar, Paul D. *Beach Process and Sedimentation.* Upper Saddle River, N.J.: Prentice Hall, 1998. Provides extensive treatment of waves, longshore currents, and sand transport on beaches. Presents and elaborates upon equations and mathematical relationships. College-level material. Intended for those interested in the specifics of coastal processes.

Koppel, Tom. *Ebb and Flow: Tides and Life on Our Once and Future Planet.* Ontario: Dundern Press, 2007. Presents a discussion of how tides influence the interaction between the ocean and humans. Blends detailed descriptions of the development of tidal theory, tidal influence of coastline characteristics, and current knowledge of tides into a single theme. Easily accessible to the general public and of interest to any ocean-lover.

McCully, James Greig. *Beyond the Moon: A Conversational, Common Sense Guide to Understanding the Tides.* Hackensack, N.J.: World Scientific Publishing, 2006. Written in a manner that can easily be understood by the layperson. Covers the physics concepts behind tidal motions. Gradually guides the reader through the topics to reach a strong understanding by the end.

Melchoir, Paul. *The Tides of the Planet Earth.* Elmsford, N.Y.: Pergamon Press, 1978. Written by one of the foremost authorities on tides. Suited for college-level readers who are not intimidated by technical language and who understand some mathematics or are willing to skip through it. Extensive bibliography covers all papers to 1978 published on the subject of tides and related topics. The introduction gives a brief summary of the relation of tidal research to the fields of astronomy, geodesy, geophysics, oceanography, hydrology, and tectonics, as well as a brief history of discoveries made about tides.

Schwartz, M. *Encyclopedia of Coastal Science.* Dordrecht: Springer, 2005. Contains many articles specific to ocean and beach dynamics. Also discusses coastal habitat management topics, hydrology, geology, and topography. Articles may run multiple pages and have diagrams. Each article has bibliographical information and cross referencing.

Talley, Lynne D., George L. Pickard, William J. Emery, and James H. Swift. *Descriptive Physical Oceanography: An Introduction.* 6th ed. London: Elsevier, 2011. An introductory college-level textbook for students who will specialize in the field of oceanography.

Wilhelm, Helmut, Walter Zuern, Hans-Georg Wenzel, et al., eds. *Tidal Phenomena.* Berlin: Springer, 1997. A collection of lectures from leaders in the fields of earth sciences and oceanography. Examines Earth's tides and atmospheric circulation. Complete with illustrations and bibliographical references. Can be understood by someone without a strong knowledge of the earth sciences.

Wylie, Francis E. *Tides and the Pull of the Moon.* Brattleboro, Vt.: Stephen Greene Press, 1979. Presents a lucid account of lunar and tidal phenomena and their influences on daily life. Includes information from science, history, and marine lore. Contains extensive bibliographical notes at the end of each chapter to guide readers to excellent sources on each topic covered. A complete introduction for anyone interested in the subject.

See also: Beaches and Coastal Processes; Carbonate Compensation Depths; Deep Ocean Currents; Gulf Stream; Hurricanes; Hydrothermal Vents; Ocean-Atmosphere Interactions; Ocean Pollution and Oil Spills; Oceans' Origin; Oceans' Structure; Ocean Waves; Sea Level; Seamounts; Seawater Composition; Surface Ocean Currents; Tsunamis; Turbidity Currents and Submarine Fans; World Ocean Circulation Experiment

OCEAN WAVES

Waves continually shape and reshape beaches, and wave energy can be harnessed to generate power. Waves generated by the force of wind pose great dangers to life and human-made structures, and waves generated by seismic activity have killed thousands of people.

PRINCIPAL TERMS

- **deep-water wave:** a wave traveling in water with a depth greater than one-half of its wave length
- **fetch:** the area or length of the sea surface over which waves are generated by wind having a constant direction and speed
- **storm surge:** a general rise above normal water level resulting from a hurricane or other severe coastal storm
- **swell:** ocean waves that have traveled out of their wind-generating area
- **tsunami:** a long-period sea wave produced by a displacement of crustal material due to submarine earthquake, volcanic eruption, or landslide
- **wave height:** the vertical distance between a wave crest and the adjacent wave trough
- **wave length:** the horizontal distance between two successive wave crests or wave troughs
- **wave orbit:** the path followed by a water particle affected by wave motion; in deep water, the orbit is nearly circular
- **wave period:** the time (usually measured in seconds) required for two adjacent wave crests to pass a point
- **wave refraction:** the process by which a wave crest is bent as it moves toward shore

CAUSES OF WAVES

The waves that agitate a lake or ocean are rhythmic, vertical disturbances of the water's surface. Their appearance may vary from a confused seascape of individual hillocks of water, each with a rounded or peaked top, to long, orderly swell waves with parallel, rounded crests. Waves involve a transfer of energy from place to place on the ocean's surface. An earthquake that jolts the California coast one evening may generate a tsunami that races across the Pacific and destroys a pier in Japan the next morning. The water itself, however, does not move; it is the wave form, or the energy impulse, that travels. The water stays where it is but oscillates as the wave form goes past.

Waves can originate in many ways. Tsunamis are shock waves resulting from a sudden displacement of water by a submarine earthquake, landslide, or volcanic eruption. Shock waves are also generated when a pebble is tossed into a pond or a moving ship creates a wake. A second type of wave is the type produced by the gravitational pull of the sun and the moon, the tides that raise and lower the ocean's surface. Tidal waves are the largest ocean waves of all, stretching halfway around the world as they travel along the equator at speeds of up to 1,600 kilometers per hour.

The great majority of waves originate through the action of the wind. Ordinary waves on the ocean or a lake form in this way. If there is no wind, the water surface is calm and smooth. If a slight breeze arises, the water surface instantly becomes roughened by patches of tiny capillary waves, the smallest waves of all. As the wind continues to blow steadily and in the same direction, ripples will appear because the surface roughness created by the capillary waves provides a vertical surface for the wind to push against. Soon the crests of adjacent ripples are pushed together to create larger and larger crests. This process continues as the intensity of the wind increases, with small waves steadily giving way to larger and larger ones.

Three factors determine the size of the waves ultimately produced: the wind speed; the duration, or the length of time that the wind blows in a constant direction; and the fetch, or the extent of open water over which the wind blows. A 37-kilometer-per-hour wind blowing for ten hours along a fetch of 120 kilometers will generate waves 3 meters high, but a 92-kilometer-per-hour wind blowing for three days along a 2,400-kilometer fetch will generate waves 30 meters high. Fortunately, such waves are very rare.

One way to understand the motion of water particles within a wave is to analyze the direction of water movement at various places in the wave. One can do so by sitting in a boat beyond the breakers. As the forward slope of a wave crest approaches, a lifting motion is experienced, followed by a forward push as the crest passes beneath the boat. This forward push is seen when waves break at the beach and their crests

Waves at the Coastline

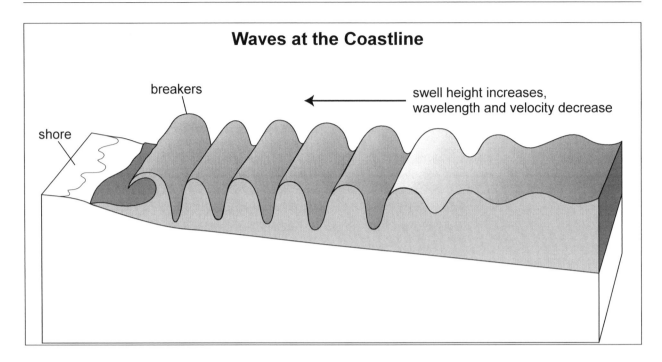

breakers

shore

swell height increases,
wavelength and velocity decrease

are thrown forward in a violent rush of water. Once the crest has passed, the boat is on the back slope of the wave, and now a downward motion is experienced. Next comes a backward motion, as the trough passes beneath the boat. This backward motion is also in a beach's breaker zone; after the crest has crashed forward on the beach, there follows a strong outward surge of water. This outward surge represents the backward water motion in the wave's trough. When all the preceding observations are combined, it can be seen that when a wave passes, the water particles move first up, then forward, then down, and finally back. This circular path is known as the wave orbit.

OTHER WAVE TYPES

The term "heavy sea" is often encountered in descriptions of the ocean. A heavy sea results from the prolonged action of strong winds over the open ocean. The waves are large, peaked, and confused, totally lacking in orderly arrangement by size. Frequently, there is much spray in the air as a result of the tops being blown off the waves. A heavy sea is what one would expect to encounter in a hurricane or a violent storm. The term "swell," in contrast, refers to waves that have moved out of the wind-generating area. As these waves approach the beach,

they appear as long rows of smoothly rounded wave crests, evenly spaced at wide intervals and of uniform height. These swells have been produced by a distant storm at sea and have then moved out of the wind-generating area. As they travel outward, their original irregularities are diminished. Very little energy is lost, however, because a wave traveling at the ocean's surface encounters very little friction.

Groups of larger swell waves will be interspersed with groups of smaller ones. Oceanographers believe that such variation is caused by two or more wave patterns traveling together across the ocean's surface. When the crest of one wave pattern is superimposed on the crests of the other wave pattern, larger swell waves will result. This is known as "constructive interference." When the trough of one pattern is superimposed on the crests of the other pattern, the swell waves will be smaller. This is known as "destructive interference."

Oceanographers also recognize two major categories of wind-generated waves: deep-water and shallow-water waves. Deep-water waves travel in water with depths greater than one-half of the wave length, and wind waves in the open ocean are generally in this category. Shallow-water waves, in contrast, travel in water so shallow that their wave orbits are affected by friction with the bottom. The shallower the water becomes, the more slowly the wave moves forward. This reduction in speed as waves approach the shoreline results in a process known as wave refraction, in which apparently straight wave crests approaching a shoreline from an angle are seen to be bent when viewed from above.

Close to the beach is the surf zone. There, the forward speed of waves is progressively slowed as the water depth decreases, and their crests become bunched more closely together. The shape of the crests changes from nearly flat to broadly arched, and there is a conspicuous increase in the height of the wave. In addition, the water in the crest of the wave begins moving faster than the water in the trough because of the friction created by the bottom, and this friction soon causes the crest to collapse in a torrent of water. The wave has "broken." Oceanographers recognize two types of breaker. The first is a plunging breaker, in which the wave crest curls smoothly forward and over, enclosing a tubular pocket of air below. The other type is known as a spilling breaker, in which foaming water spills down the forward slope of the crest as the breaker advances. This type of breaker has no air-filled tube.

The final zone, found between the breakers and the beach, is a narrow strip characterized by the rhythmic alteration of water rushing shoreward on the beach and water sliding back out to sea. The inward rush of water is known as the swash; it is a miniature wall of foaming water filled with air bubbles. The backward flow is a thin, glistening film of water termed the backwash.

TSUNAMIS AND STORM SURGES

Two additional wave types require special mention. The first is a giant ocean wave known as a tsunami, which can be caused by submarine earthquakes, volcanic eruptions, or a landslide dumping massive amounts of debris into a body of water. In the open ocean, tsunamis behave just as any other ocean wave. They have crests and troughs that vary in height by 1 meter or so while the wave is still at sea. The tsunami wave length is enormously long, however, averaging perhaps 240 kilometers between crests. Tsunamis also have astonishingly high speeds, sometimes 650 kilometers per hour or more. A tsunami does not come ashore as a plunging breaker; rather, the crest rushes in as a surge of foaming water whose motion is more indicative of a sudden rise in water level than of a typical wave.

The second special wave type is known as a storm surge. Storm surges are drastic rises in sea level accompanying hurricanes or other severe coastal storms. Several factors combine to create such a surge. One factor is the reduced atmospheric pressure that occurs in the eye of a hurricane. This reduction may allow the ocean's surface to rise 1 meter or more. If, in addition, the sun and moon are aligned in such a way as to produce unusually high tides, the storm surge may rise 1 meter higher. A third contributing factor is the presence of strong onshore winds. In a major hurricane, these winds will push an accumulating mass of water toward the coast by preventing it from washing completely back into the sea as it normally would, increasing the impact of the storm surge. Finally, the nature of the offshore bottom plays a role. Shallow offshore bottoms permit wind to get a better "grip" on the water, raising its level higher. As a result, a hurricane that creates a 4-meter storm surge along Florida's east coast, with its deep offshore waters, would be able to raise a 10-meter storm surge on Florida's west coast, where the bottom is flat and shallow for a distance of 160 kilometers offshore.

STUDY OF OCEAN WAVES

Until the early 1940's, the principal method for studying waves was to observe the sea's surface and to record the length, height, speed, and period of individual waves. Based on an analysis of wave period, it was determined that the various types of ocean wave could be arranged in an increasing spectrum of size. Capillary waves were found to be the smallest ocean waves, with periods of less than 0.1 second. Ripples came next, with periods of 0.1 to 1 second. Ordinary wind waves followed, with periods ranging from 1 second to 1.4 minutes. Larger still were tsunamis, with periods averaging 17 minutes, and finally the tides, with periods of 12 or 24 hours.

One basic wave-measuring instrument is the tide gauge, which is used to study tsunamis. The tide gauge is usually mounted on a pier in the quiet waters of a harbor, where it will not be exposed to damaging surf. It consists of a float inside a vertical, hollow pipe. The float is free to rise and fall with the water level, and a continuous record is made of the float's movement. The pipe is sealed at the bottom in such a way that only the long-period waves associated with a tsunami can force the float to rise. In this way, the tide gauge can record the preliminary waves of a tsunami and serve as a warning of the larger waves that follow. After the destruction of Hilo, Hawaii, by a tsunami on April 1, 1946, a seismic sea wave warning system was set up for the Pacific Ocean utilizing seismograph records and the type of tide gauge just described. Present-day tsunami warning systems linked to seismic observatories are able to provide warning of tsunami activity up to several hours in advance, depending on the location of the causal event.

Other instruments measure the impact of storm waves against pilings, piers, and deep-water structures. The measurements obtained from these instruments have enabled engineers to design structures that can better withstand the impact of storm waves. Before the 1950's, lighthouses and breakwaters were the structures most vulnerable to wave attack, but since that time, large oil drilling and production platforms have been built in the open ocean many kilometers from shore. During severe storms, a number of these platforms have been capsized by the impact or damage caused by oncoming waves, resulting in tragic losses of life.

In laboratory experiments, ocean waves can be simulated in wave tanks. These range from tabletop models with glass sides that look like aquariums to outdoor tanks that can hold large boats and generate breakers several meters in height. The mathematical treatment of waves is facilitated by the regularity of their pattern, and computers are able to predict wave heights and other wave characteristics with a high degree of accuracy.

Stimulated by the energy crisis in the late 1970's, intensive consideration has been given to the possibility of harnessing wave energy to generate power. Many systems have been designed and tested, and some have been constructed and now produce millions of watt-hours of energy each year. The fundamental principle on which most wave generators work is that the motion of a passing wave exerts force that is similar to the rise and fall of a piston. This can then be mechanically harnessed and used to drive a generating system.

Significance

Beaches owe their origin to wave action. The waves carry in the sand from which the beach is formed over time, and then smooth it daily, erasing imprints with their in-and-out motion. New sand is also formed as stones and rocks are made to grind against each other, chipping and eroding them slowly into sand grains. Storm waves, however, are capable of doing a great deal of damage in a much shorter span of time. The height of such waves in the open ocean can be dramatic; the USS *Ramapo* measured waves 34 meters high in 1933, for example. When waves this height reach shore, the destruction can be enormous due to the energy and momentum of the moving mass of water. Concrete blocks weighing 65 tons or more have been torn loose from breakwaters by such waves. Sandy coastlines are also susceptible to attack. A longshore current develops when the waves encroach upon the shoreline at an angle, and this current can transport vast quantities of sand along a coast. Where this transported sand is trapped by an obstacle, such as a harbor jetty, excessive deposition will take place, perhaps requiring expensive dredging. At other points along the coastline, beach erosion may occur, also causing problems.

One of the most feared wave types is the tsunami, which is most frequently encountered on the shores of the Pacific due to the seismic activity associated with the so-called "Ring of Fire" of the Pacific Rim, but can occur in any body of water. Although tsunamis are almost imperceptible in the open ocean, their nature changes dramatically when they reach shore. Video records of incoming tsunamis amply demonstrate the immense, destructive force that such waves bring to bear against ships, buildings, and people. There are records of tsunamis rushing up mountain sides to elevations of 30 meters and more. The tsunami generated by the explosion of Krakatau, for example, is known to have transported an ocean-going vessel several kilometers inland, depositing it in the jungle far up a mountainside. An added danger is that tsunamis have a series of crests that arrive approximately twenty minutes apart, and often the third or fourth to arrive is the largest.

Storm surges are another dangerous wave type. They are commonly encountered along the Atlantic and Gulf coasts of the United States and have been known to carry oceangoing ships 1 kilometer or more inland. Six thousand people lost their lives in one such storm surge in Galveston, Texas, in 1900, and hundreds of thousands have drowned in a single storm surge on the shores of India's Bay of Bengal. Expensive storm surge barriers now guard Providence, Rhode Island; London; and the Netherlands.

Two other wave types that may present hazards for humans are rogue waves and seiches. Rogue waves are huge, solitary waves occasionally encountered in the ocean. They are particularly associated with the southward-flowing Agulhas current off South Africa and have been credited with sinking or severely damaging several large cargo ships. Seiche waves are oscillations in an enclosed water body such as a lake or bay. One such seiche, created by a hurricane, overflowed the dike surrounding Florida's Lake Okeechobee in 1928 and drowned two thousand people.

Donald W. Lovejoy

FURTHER READING

Bascom, Willard. *Waves and Beaches: The Dynamics of the Ocean Surface.* Rev. ed. New York: Anchor Books, 1980. Presents a thorough treatment of the nature of waves and beaches and the principles that govern them. Offers a good introduction for the nonscientist and an excellent source for the professional oceanographer. Contains many helpful diagrams and tables and numerous black-and-white photographs. Suitable for college-level readers.

Bird, Eric C. *Coastline Changes: A Global Review.* New York: John Wiley & Sons, 1985. Based on the results of a project conducted by the International Geographical Union's Working Group on the Dynamics of Coastline Erosion. Presents a detailed picture of the effects of wave erosion on the coastlines of 127 countries. Illustrated with numerous photographs and maps. Suitable for college-level readers.

Charlier, R. H., and C. W. Finkl. *Ocean Energy: Tide and Tidal Power.* Berlin: Springer-Verlag, 2009. Discusses fundamentals of oceanic energy harvesting. Describes historical and current technologies, with examples drawn from around the world. Also discusses social, economic, and environmental impacts. Contains dense, verbose, and technical writing and is therefore best suited for graduate students and researching oceanographers or engineers with some prior knowledge of ocean dynamics.

Clarke, Allan J. *An Introduction to the Dynamics of El Niño and the Southern Oscillation.* Burlington, Mass.: Academic Press, 2008. Presents the physics of ENSO, including currents, temperature, winds, and waves. Discusses ENSO forecasting models.

Provides good coverage of the influence ENSO has on marine life, from plankton to green turtles. Each chapter has references, and there are a number of appendices and indexing. Best suited for environmental scientists, meteorologists, and similar academics studying ENSO.

Cruz, Joan. *Ocean Wave Energy: Current Status and Future Perspectives.* Berlin: Springer-Verlag, 2010. Presents information on the theory of wave energy conversion, wave energy and dynamics, and numerical and experimental modeling of wave energy conversions. Case studies are provided and references are included for each topic.

Garrison, Tom S. *Oceanography: An Invitation to Marine Science.* Belmont, Calif.: Brooks/Cole, Cengage Learning, 2010. Discusses the circulation of the oceans, including deep water and surface currents. Describes various aspects of waves. Also discusses physics of tides. Abundant diagrams aid readers from the layperson to advanced undergraduates.

Gross, M. Grant. *Oceanography: A View of the Earth.* 7th ed. Englewood Cliffs, N.J.: Prentice Hall, 1996. A well-written and well-illustrated text. Provides a comprehensive overview of all aspects of ocean waves, with diagrams, tables, and photographs. The appendix contains a table of conversion factors and an excellent glossary. Suitable for general audiences.

Haykin, Simon S., and Sadasivan Puthusserypady. *Chaotic Dynamics of Sea Clutter.* New York: John Wiley, 1999. A technical book that offers the reader mathematical models designed to simulate the conditions necessary for wave generation. There is much attention given to the equipment to monitor ocean movement, including radar and remote sensing systems.

Holthujsen, Leo H. *Waves in Oceanic and Coastal Waters.* New York: Cambridge University Press. Slightly above introductory level. Contains a chapter on observation techniques such as remote-sensing, altimetry, and wave buoys. Thoroughly discusses the physics of water waves and linear wave theory.

Joseph, Antony. *Tsunamis: Detection, Monitoring and Early Warning Technologies.* Burlington, Mass.: Academic Press/Elsevier, 2011. Discusses international and regional tsunami warning systems through comparative assessments of detection, monitoring and real-time reporting technologies in this professional reference book.

Komar, Paul D. *Beach Process and Sedimentation.* Upper Saddle River, N.J.: Prentice Hall, 1998. Offers extensive treatment of waves, longshore currents, and sand transport on beaches. Presents and elaborates upon equations and mathematical relationships. College-level material. Intended for those interested in the specifics of coastal processes.

Myles, Douglas. *The Great Waves.* New York: McGraw-Hill, 1985. Designed for the lay reader and scientist alike. Gives background information pertaining to the origin of tsunamis and describes major destructive tsunamis throughout world history. Includes eyewitness accounts whenever available. There are no photographs, but the endpapers reproduce a fine etching of the tsunami accompanying the Lisbon earthquake of 1775. Suitable for high school readers.

Schwartz, M. *Encyclopedia of Coastal Science.* Dordrecht: Springer, 2005. Contains many articles specific to ocean and beach dynamics. Discusses coastal habitat management topics, hydrology, geology, and topography. Articles may run multiple pages and have diagrams. Each article has bibliographical information and cross referencing.

Talley, Lynne D., George L. Pickard, William J. Emery, and James H. Swift. *Descriptive Physical Oceanography: An Introduction.* 6th ed. London: Elsevier, 2011. An introductory college-level textbook for students who will specialize in the field of oceanography.

Trujillo, Alan P. and Harold V. Thurman. *Essentials of Oceanography.* New York: Prentice Hall, 2010. Written for nonscience students using a systems approach to highlight various oceanographic phenomena and their relationship to other systems.

Young, Ian R. *Wind Generated Ocean Waves.* New York: Elsevier, 1999. Looks at the environmental factors involved in producing waves and the role waves play in coastal processes. Suitable for the high school reader or above. Illustrations, index, and bibliographical references.

See also: Beaches and Coastal Processes; Carbonate Compensation Depths; Dams and Flood Control; Deep Ocean Currents; Gulf Stream; Hydrothermal Vents; Ocean-Atmosphere Interactions; Ocean Pollution and Oil Spills; Oceans' Origin; Oceans' Structure; Ocean Tides; Sea Level; Seamounts; Seawater Composition; Surface Ocean Currents; Tsunamis; Turbidity Currents and Submarine Fans; World Ocean Circulation Experiment

OZONE DEPLETION AND OZONE HOLES

One of the natural gases in the atmosphere, ozone absorbs ultraviolet radiation from the sun. Chlorofluorocarbons, once used as primary refrigerants, aerosol propellants, and in the making of certain plastics, react in the atmosphere and release chlorine atoms, which then react with and destroy molecules of ozone. Scientists are concerned that depletion of stratospheric ozone will allow incoming ultraviolet radiation from the sun to reach the surface, resulting in severe damage to all living organisms if ozone depletion continues. The term "ozone hole" refers to the seasonal decrease in stratospheric ozone concentration occurring over Antarctica. Ozone-hole formation is evidence that human activities can significantly alter the composition of the atmosphere.

PRINCIPAL TERMS

- **catalyst:** a substance that increases the rate of a chemical reaction without itself being altered in the process
- **chlorofluorocarbon (CFC):** a group of chemical compounds containing carbon, fluorine, and chlorine, used in air conditioners, refrigerators, fire extinguishers, spray cans, and other applications
- **Dobson spectrophotometer:** a ground-based instrument for measuring the total column abundance of ozone at a particular geographic location
- **food chain:** the arrangement of the organisms of an ecological community according to the order of predation in which each consumes the next, usually lower, member as a food source
- **ozone layer:** a region in the lower stratosphere, centered about 25 kilometers above the surface of Earth, which contains the highest concentration of ozone found in the atmosphere
- **ozone:** the molecular form of oxygen containing three atoms of oxygen per molecule as O_3, as compared to elemental oxygen having the molecular formula O_2
- **phytoplankton:** free-floating microscopic aquatic plants that use sunlight to convert carbon dioxide and water into food for themselves and for other organisms in the food chain
- **polar stratospheric clouds:** clouds of ice crystals formed at extremely low temperatures in the polar stratosphere
- **polar vortex:** a closed atmospheric circulation pattern around the South Pole that exists during the winter and early spring; atmospheric mixing between the polar vortex and regions outside the vortex is slow
- **stratosphere:** the region of the atmosphere between 10 and 50 kilometers above the surface of Earth

- **total column abundance of ozone:** the total number of molecules of ozone above a 1-centimeter-square area of Earth's surface
- **Total Ozone Mapping Spectrometer (TOMS):** a space-based instrument for measuring the total column abundance of ozone globally
- **ultraviolet solar radiation:** electromagnetic radiation having wavelengths between 4 and 400 nanometers

CONCENTRATION OF OZONE IN ATMOSPHERE

Ozone, although only a minor component of the atmosphere, plays a vital role in the survival of life on Earth. Ozone molecules absorb incoming high-energy ultraviolet (UV) light from the sun. Absorption of ultraviolet light in the stratospheric ozone layer, a region that contains the maximum concentration of atmospheric ozone, though only about 12 parts per million, prevents most UV light from reaching the surface of the planet. If none of the sun's ultraviolet radiation were blocked by the ozone layer, it would be difficult for most forms of life, including humans, to survive on land.

The concentration of ozone in the atmosphere is highly variable, changing with altitude, geographic location, time of day, time of year, and prevailing local atmospheric conditions. Long-term fluctuations in ozone concentration are also seen, some of which are related to the solar sunspot cycle. While long-term average ozone concentrations are relatively stable, short-term fluctuations of as much as 10 percent in total column abundance of ozone as a result of the natural variability in ozone concentration are often observed.

Beginning in the early 1970's, a new and unexpected decrease in stratospheric ozone concentration was first observed. The decrease was localized near Antarctica, and appears in early spring (which begins in September in the Southern Hemisphere). The initial decrease in ozone was small, but by 1980, decreases in total column abundance of ozone of as much as 30 percent were being recorded, well outside the range of variation expected as a result of random fluctuations. This seasonal depletion of stratospheric ozone above Antarctica, which by 1990 had reached 50 percent of the total column abundance of ozone, was soon given the label "ozone hole."

ROLE OF CFCS

While it was initially unclear whether the formation of the Antarctic ozone hole stemmed from natural causes or from anthropogenic effects on the environment, extensive field studies combined with the results of laboratory experiments and computer modeling of the atmosphere quickly led to a consistent and detailed explanation for ozone-hole formation. The formation of the ozone hole has two principal causes: chemical reactions that occur generally throughout the stratosphere, and special conditions that exist in the Antarctic region.

Under normal conditions, the concentration of ozone in the stratosphere is determined by an equilibrium balance between reactions that remove ozone and those that produce ozone. The removal reactions are mainly catalytic chain reactions, in which trace atmospheric chemical species destroy ozone molecules without themselves being consumed. In such processes, it is possible for one chain component to remove many ozone molecules before being itself removed. A single chlorine atom, for example, is estimated to remove as many as 100,000 ozone molecules through chemical chain reactions before it is itself removed by forming a nonreactive species. The trace species involved in ozone removal include hydrogen oxides and nitrogen oxides, formed primarily by naturally occurring processes, and chlorine and bromine atoms and their corresponding oxides.

A major source of chlorine in the stratosphere is the decomposition of a class of compounds called chlorofluorocarbons (CFCs). Such compounds are used as refrigerants in refrigeration and air conditioning applications, and were commonly used as aerosol propellants and solvents, freely released into the atmosphere. Their use and handling is now strictly regulated. Chlorofluorocarbons are extremely stable in the lower atmosphere, with lifetimes of several decades, due to their extreme lack of chemical reactivity. The main fate of chlorofluorocarbons in the atmosphere, however, is slow migration into the stratosphere, where they absorb ultraviolet light and

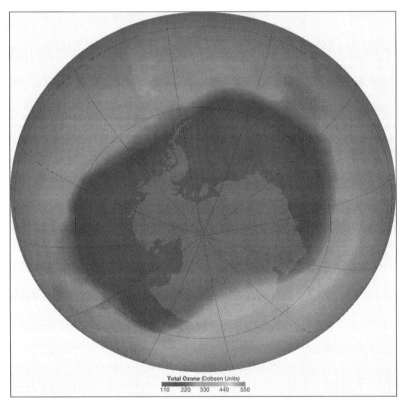

Total Ozone (Dobson Units)
110   220   330   440   550

This image provided by NASA was compiled by the Ozone Monitoring Instrument on NASA's Aura satellite from September 21-30, 2006. The average area of the ozone hole was the largest ever observed, at 10.6 million square miles according to government scientists. In this image, from September 24, the Antarctic ozone hole was equal to the record single-day largest area of 11.4 million square miles, reached on September 9, 2000. The so-called hole is a region where there is severe depletion of the layer of ozone—a form of oxygen—in the upper atmosphere that protects life on Earth by blocking the sun's ultraviolet rays. The blue and purple colors are where there is the least ozone, and the greens, yellows, and reds are where there is more ozone. (NASA Ozone Watch) fragment to release chlorine atoms. The chlorine atoms produced from the breakdown of chlorofluorocarbons in the stratosphere provide an additional catalytic process by which stratospheric ozone is destroyed. A similar set of reactions involving a class of bromine-containing compounds called halons, used in some types of fire extinguishers, leads to additional ozone destruction by similar photochemical processes. By 1986, the average global loss of stratospheric ozone caused by the release of chlorofluorocarbons, halons, and related compounds into the environment was estimated to be 2 percent.

ANTARCTIC CONDITIONS

While the decomposition and subsequent reaction of chlorofluorocarbons, halons, and other synthetic compounds can explain the slow general decline in ozone concentration observed in the stratosphere, additional processes are needed to account for the more massive seasonal ozone depletion observed above Antarctica. These processes involve a set of special conditions that in combination are unique to the stratosphere above Antarctica.

During daylight hours, a portion of the chlorine present in the stratosphere is tied up in the form of reservoir species—compounds such as hydrogen chloride and chlorine nitrate that do not react with ozone. This slows the rate of removal of ozone by chlorine. Processes that directly or indirectly involve absorption of sunlight transform reservoir species and release ozone-destroying chlorine atoms. During the Antarctic winter, when sunlight is entirely absent, stratospheric chlorine is rapidly converted into reservoir species.

In the absence of additional chemical processes, the onset of spring in Antarctica and the return of sunlight convert a portion of the reservoir compounds into reactive chlorine species and reestablish the balance between ozone-producing and ozone-destroying processes. However, the extremely low temperatures occurring in the stratosphere above Antarctica during the winter months lead to the formation of polar stratospheric clouds, which, because of the extremely low concentration of water vapor in the stratosphere, do not form during other seasons or outside the polar regions of the globe. The ice crystals that compose the clouds act as catalysts that convert reservoir species into diatomic chlorine and other gaseous chlorine compounds that, in the presence of sunlight, re-form ozone-destroying species. At the same time, nitrogen oxides in the collection of reservoir species are converted into nitric acid, which remains attached to the ice crystals. As these ice crystals are slowly removed from the stratosphere by gravity, the potential for conversion of active forms of chlorine into reservoir species is greatly reduced. Because of this, when spring arrives, large amounts of ozone-destroying chlorine species are produced by the action of sunlight, and only a small fraction of this reactive chlorine is converted into reservoir species. The increased rate of ozone removal caused by the abundance of reactive chlorine present in the stratosphere leads to ozone depletion and formation of the ozone hole.

An additional process important in formation of the ozone hole is the unique air-circulation pattern in the stratosphere above Antarctica. During the winter and early spring, a vortex of winds circulates about the South Pole. This polar vortex minimizes movement of ozone and reservoir-forming compounds from other regions of the stratosphere. As this polar vortex breaks up in midspring, ozone concentrations in the Antarctic stratosphere return to normal levels, and the ozone hole gradually disappears.

ATMOSPHERIC OZONE STUDY AND INTERPRETATION

Researchers utilize a great diversity of devices and techniques in the study and interpretation of atmospheric ozone. One popular technique is the use of simulation models. A good model is one that simulates the interrelationships and interactions of the various parts of the known system. The weakness of models is that, often, not enough is known to give an accurate picture of the total system or to make accurate predictions. Most modeling is done on computers. Scientists estimate how fast chemicals such as CFCs and nitrous oxide will be produced in the future and build a computer model of the way these chemicals react with ozone and with one another. From this model, it is possible to estimate future ozone levels at different altitudes and at different future dates.

Similar processes appear to be at work in the Arctic stratosphere, leading to ozone depletion, as in the Antarctic. However, the National Oceanic and Atmospheric Administration (NOAA) Aeronomy Laboratory in Boulder, Colorado, reported a discrepancy between observed ozone depletion and predicted levels, based on models that account accurately for Antarctic ozone depletion. This report suggests that some other mechanism is at work in the Arctic. Thus, while good models can be very useful in studying new data, observed discrepancies highlight the need for better system models and modeling algorithms. There are two models favored by most scientists in this area. Some scientists put forth a chemical model that says the depletion is caused by chemical events promoted by the presence of chlorofluorocarbons created by industrial processes. Acceptance of this model was promoted by the discovery of fluorine in the stratosphere. Fluorine does not naturally occur there, but it is related to and can be formed photochemically from CFCs. The other model assumes that the ozone hole was formed by dynamic air movement and mixing. This model best fits data gathered by ozone-sensing balloons that sample altitudes up to 30 kilometers and then radio the data back to Earth. Ozone depletion is confined to the atmosphere at altitudes between 12 and 20 kilometers. While the total ozone depletion is 35 percent, different strata have shown various amounts of depletion from 70 to 90 percent. Surprisingly, about half the ozone was gone in twenty-five days. This finding does not fit the chemical model very well.

Besides ozone-sensing balloons, satellite survey data provide more direct measurements obtained over longer periods of observation time. The National Aeronautics and Space Administration (NASA) obtains measurements with its Nimbus 7 satellite. Ozone measurements made by this satellite helped to develop flight plans for the specialized aircraft NASA also deploys in ozone studies. NASA's ER-2 aircraft is a modified U-2 reconnaissance plane that carries instruments up to 20 kilometers in altitude for seven-hour flights to 80 degrees north latitude. A DC-8, operating during the same period, is able to survey the polar vortex, owing to its greater range. In addition, scientists utilize many meteorological techniques and instruments, including chemical analysis of gases by means of infrared spectroscopy, mass spectroscopy and gas spectroscopy combined, gas chromatography, and oceanographic analysis of planktonic life in the southern Atlantic, Pacific, and Indian oceans. As new research methods and techniques become available, they are also applied to this essential study.

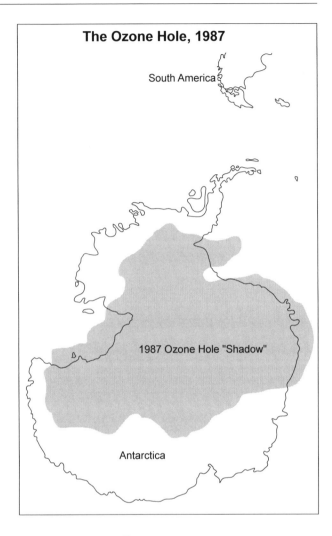

The Ozone Hole, 1987

South America

1987 Ozone Hole "Shadow"

Antarctica

PUBLIC HEALTH CONCERNS

Stratospheric ozone provides global protection from the lethal effects of ultraviolet radiation from the sun. This ability to absorb ultraviolet radiation protects all life-forms on Earth's surface from excessive ultraviolet radiation, which destroys plant and animal cells. Currently, between 10 and 30 percent of the sun's ultraviolet B (UV-B) radiation reaches the ground surface. If ozone levels were to drop by 10 percent, the amount of UV-B radiation reaching Earth would increase by 20 percent.

Present-day UV-B levels are responsible for the fading of paints and the yellowing of window glazing and for car finishes becoming chalky. These kinds of degradation will accelerate as the ozone layer is depleted. There could also be increased smog, urban air pollution, and a worsening of the problem of acid rain in cities. In humans, UV-B causes sunburn, snow blindness, skin cancer, and cataracts, and promotes aging and wrinkling of the skin. Skin cancer is the most common form of cancer, with more than 400,000 new cases reported every year in the United States alone. The National Academy of Sciences has estimated that each 1 percent decline in ozone would increase the incidence of skin cancer by 2 percent. Therefore, a 3 percent depletion in ozone would be expected to produce some 24,000 more cases of skin cancer in the United States every year.

Ecological Concerns

Many other forms of life, from bacteria to forests and food crops, are adversely affected by excessive radiation. Ultraviolet radiation affects plant growth by slowing photosynthesis and by delaying germination in many plants, including trees and food crops. Scientists have a great concern for the organisms that live in the ocean and the effect ozone depletion may have on them. Phytoplankton, zooplankton, and krill (a shrimplike crustacean) could be greatly depleted if there were a drastic increase in ultraviolet A and B. The result would be a tremendous drop in the population of these free-floating organisms, which are extremely important because they are the foundation species of the global food chain. Phytoplankton use the energy of sunlight to convert inorganic compounds into organic plant matter. This process provides food for the next step in the food chain, the herbivorous zooplankton and krill. They, in turn, become the food for the next higher level of animals in the food chain. Initial studies of this food chain in the Antarctic suggest that elevated levels of ultraviolet radiation impair photosynthetic activity. Recent studies show that a fifteen-day exposure to UV-B levels 20 percent higher than normal can kill off all anchovy larvae down to a depth of 10 meters. There is also concern that ozone depletion may alter the food chain and even cause changes in the organisms' genetic makeup. An increase in the ultraviolet radiation is likely to lower fish catches and upset marine ecology, which has already suffered damage from human-made pollution. On a worldwide basis, fish presently provide 18 percent of all the animal protein consumed.

International Response

The United Nations Environmental Program (UNEP) is working with governments, international organizations, and industry to develop a framework within which the international community can make decisions to minimize atmospheric changes and the effects they could have on Earth. In 1977, UNEP convened a meeting of experts to draft the World Plan of Action on the Ozone Layer. The plan called for a program of research on the ozone layer and on what would happen if the layer were compromised. In addition, UNEP created a group of experts and government representatives who framed the Convention for the Protection of the Ozone Layer. This convention was adopted in Vienna in March, 1985, by twenty-one nations and the European Economic Community and has subsequently been signed by many more nations. The convention pledges that the nations that sign are to protect human health and the environment from the effects of ozone depletion. Action has already been taken under the Convention to protect the ozone layer. Several countries have restricted the use of CFCs or the amounts produced. The United States banned the use of CFCs in all nonessential applications in 1978. Some countries, such as Belgium and the Nordic countries, have in effect banned CFC production altogether. The group has also worked with governments on a Protocol to the Convention that required signatory nations to limit their production of CFCs. It is the hope and aim of these nations that such international cooperation will lead to a better global environment.

George K. Attwood and Jeffrey A. Joens

Further Reading

Bast, Joseph L., Peter J. Hill, and Richard C. Rue. *Eco-Sanity: A Common Sense Guide to Environmentalism.* Lanham, Md.: Madison Books, 1994. Presents a highly critical view of claims that human activities have the potential to degrade the global environment significantly. Selective in the information presented. Represents an interesting minority opinion on issues of global change. Briefly discusses ozone depletion and the ozone hole.

Cagin, Seth, and Philip Dray. *Between Earth and Sky: How CFCs Changed Our World and Endangered the Ozone Layer.* New York: Pantheon Books, 1993. Presents a history of chlorofluorocarbons beginning with the discovery of CFCs in 1928 and going on to discuss the increasing use of CFCs during the following decades, the establishment of the link between CFCs and stratospheric ozone depletion, and the subsequent restrictions placed on the use and manufacture of CFCs. Chapters 16 through 21 focus on the ozone hole.

Firor, John. *The Changing Atmosphere: A Global Challenge.* New Haven, Conn.: Yale University Press, 1990. Offers an interesting and readable introduction to atmospheric science and global change. Presents complex scientific research in a clear and balanced manner. Discusses both scientific issues and the corresponding political challenges.

Graedel, T. E., and Paul J. Crutzen. *Atmospheric Change: An Earth System Perspective.* New York: W. H. Freeman, 1993. Presents an introduction to atmospheric science by two well-known workers in the field, one of whom shared the 1995 Nobel Prize in Chemistry for his work in atmospheric chemistry. Portions require an understanding of college-level mathematics and chemistry, but most can be understood without such a background. Includes a large number of figures and tables of particular interest.

Hoffmann, Matthew J. *Ozone Depletion and Climate Change: Constructing a Global Response.* Albany: State University of New York Press, 2005. Uses formal analytical methods, in-depth case studies, and agent-based computer simulations to examine the sociopolitical approaches of various nations around the world to the ozone depletion problem.

Lang, Kenneth. *Sun, Earth and Sky.* 2d ed. New York: Springer, 2006. Discusses the sun, its energy, solar radiation, and magnetism. The final two chapters cover the relationship between the sun and earth. Covers geomagnetic storms, aurora, the greenhouse effect, and the ozone layer. Also contains a glossary, quotation references, a further reading list, websites, and both author and subject indexing.

Marshal, John, and R. Alan Plumb. *Atmosphere, Ocean and Climate Dynamics: An Introductory Text.* Burlington, Mass.: Elsevier Academic Press, 2008. Provides an excellent introduction to atmospheres and oceans. Discusses topics such as the greenhouse effect, convection and atmospheric structure, oceanic and atmospheric circulation, and climate change. Suited for advanced undergraduates and graduate students with some background in advanced mathematics.

Parker, Larry, and Wayne A. Morrissey. *Stratospheric Ozone Depletion.* Hauppauge, N.Y.: Nova Science Publishers, 2003. Discusses the history of the response to the realization that halogenated compounds being released into the atmosphere have been destroying the stratospheric ozone layer. Presents and discusses the potential and real effects of the loss of protection from solar ultraviolet radiation as the basis for the 1987 Montreal Protocol on Substances That Deplete the Ozone Layer.

Roan, Susan. *Ozone Crisis: The Fifteen-Year Evolution of a Sudden Global Emergency.* New York: John Wiley & Sons, 1989. A detailed account of the scientific and political events associated with the discovery of the connection between chlorofluorocarbons and stratospheric ozone depletion. Provides evidence linking the ozone hole to increasing atmospheric concentrations of CFCs, and the regulation of CFCs that followed.

Rowland, F. Sherwood. "Stratospheric Ozone Depletion." *Annual Review of Physical Chemistry* 42 (1991): 731. May be difficult to find, but well worth the effort. Written by the cowinner of the 1995 Nobel Prize in Chemistry for his work on ozone depletion. Proivdes a thorough but highly readable review of stratospheric ozone chemistry and the role of chlorofluorocarbons and related compounds in ozone depletion. Some background in chemistry is useful for full understanding of the material, but the essential points of the article can be understood by the layperson.

Shell, E. R. "Weather Versus Chemicals." *The Atlantic* 259 (May, 1987): 27-31. Discusses in fairly simple terms the complex problems of the ozone hole and the widely recognized role of chlorofluorocarbons in this global issue. Offers thorough discussion of environmental issues on a popular reading level.

Somerville, Richard C. J. *The Forgiving Air: Understanding Environmental Change.* 2d ed. Boston: American Meteorological Society, 2008. Presents a thorough investigation of the relationship between human activities and changes in the atmosphere and global climate. Written by a scientist involved in atmospheric research, but aimed at a nonscientific audience. Chapter 2 offers a discussion of the ozone hole.

Sportisse, Bruno. *Fundamentals in Air Pollution: From Processes to Modelling.* New York: Springer, 2009. Discusses issues arising from air pollution such as emissions, the greenhouse effect, acid rain, urban heat islands, and the ozone hole. Topics are well organized and clearly explained, making this text accessible to the layperson, although it was written for the undergraduate.

Wallace, John M., and Peter V. Hobbs. *Atmospheric Science*. 2d ed. Burlington, Mass.: Academic Press, 2006. Represents a complete study of the atmosphere that covers fundamental physics and chemistry topics as well as specific topics in atmospheric science such as radiative transfer, weather forecasting, and global warming. Contains significant detail and technical writing, but is still accessible to the undergraduate studying meteorology or thermodynamics.

See also: Acid Rain and Acid Deposition; Air Pollution; *AR4 Synthesis Report*; Atmosphere's Evolution; Atmosphere's Global Circulation; Atmosphere's Structure and Thermodynamics; Atmospheric Properties; Auroras; Barometric Pressure; Climate; Climate Change Theories; Cosmic Rays and Background Radiation; Earth-Sun Relations; Geochemical Cycles; Global Warming; Greenhouse Effect; Ice Ages and Glaciations; Icebergs and Antarctica; Long-Term Weather Patterns; Radon Gas; Rainforests and the Atmosphere; Recent Climate Change Research; Remote Sensing of the Atmosphere

P

PACIFIC OCEAN

The world's largest ocean, the Pacific has an overall area of 182 million square kilometers. It is twice the size of the next largest ocean, the Atlantic. The Pacific Ocean covers approximately one-third of Earth's surface and is larger than Earth's entire landmass area.

PRINCIPAL TERMS

- **continental drift:** the gradual movement of continental landmasses within Earth's crust, driven by magmatic convection in the underlying mantle layer
- **continental shelf:** part of a continental landmass, usually gently sloping, that extends beneath the ocean from the water's edge to the continental slope
- **continental slope:** the defining edge of a continental shelf where it drops off sharply toward the ocean's floor
- **delta:** a triangular area with its longest side abutting the sea where a river deposits silt, sand, and clay as it flows into an ocean, lake, or other body of water
- **equator:** an imaginary line, equidistant from the North and South Poles, around the middle of the planet where day and night are of equal length
- **guyot:** an undersea mountain, or seamount, that has formed by volcanic activity, from which the peak has been eroded through wave action
- **lagoon:** a body of saltwater separated from the ocean by a bank of sand
- **tectonic plate:** a segment of Earth's crust that is put into movement by magmatic convection in the underlying mantle layer
- **tidal range:** the difference in water depth between high and low tides
- **trench:** an extraordinarily deep region of the sea floor where two tectonic plates meet and the one making up the deep sea floor is subducted beneath the less dense, and therefore lighter, continental mass of the adjacent tectonic plate

LOCATION OF THE PACIFIC OCEAN

The Pacific Ocean, with a mean depth of 4,255 meters and a maximum depth of 10,970 meters, extends from its southern extreme at Antarctica some 15,550 kilometers north to the Bering Strait, which separates North America from Asia. Its east-west area extends almost 19,440 kilometers from the western coast of Colombia in South America to Asia's Malay Peninsula.

The Pacific and Arctic Oceans meet at the Bering Strait in the north. In the far south at Drake Passage, south of Cape Horn, the Atlantic and Pacific Oceans come together. Exactly where the Pacific meets the Indian Ocean is more difficult to define because the two bodies of water intermingle along a string of islands that extends to the east from Sumatra through Java to Timor and across the Timor Sea to Australia's Cape Londonderry. South of Australia, the Pacific runs across the Bass Strait to the Indian Ocean and continues from Tasmania to Antarctica.

The eastern Pacific generally follows the Cordilleran mountain system, which runs the entire length of North and South America from the Bering Strait to Drake Passage and includes both the Rocky Mountains and the Andes. The east coast of the Pacific is, comparatively, quite regular except for the Gulf of California and the fjord regions in its northern and southern extremes. The continental shelf of the eastern Pacific is narrow, and the continental slope at times quite steep, as is characteristic of subduction zones.

The Pacific's western extreme in Asia is, by contrast, quite irregular. As on the eastern coast of the Pacific, the western coast is bordered by mountain systems that run roughly parallel to the coast. The western Pacific has many dependent seas, notable among them the Bering Sea, the East China Sea, the Sea of Japan, the Sea of Okotsk, the South China Sea, and the Yellow Sea. The eastern extremes of these seas are characterized by peninsulas jutting out toward the south, by island arcs, or by both.

The Pacific coast. (PhotoDisc)

Unlike the Atlantic, much of whose water flows into it from the rivers that feed it, only about one-seventh of the Pacific's water comes from direct river flow. Most of its water comes from the dependent seas that are nourished by such East Asian rivers as the Amur, the Xi, the Mekong, the Yangtze, and the Yellow Rivers.

ORIGINS AND DIVISIONS

The Pacific Ocean is the present-day remnant of the world ocean called Panthalassa and has been evolving to its present state for some 200 million years, since the single landmass called Pangaea began to split apart through tectonic action. Through continental drift that has occurred over the intervening millions of years, the landmass divided into the several smaller fragments that are the present-day continents. As the spaces between the continental segments became larger, they filled with the water that surrounded them and, through eons, formed the various oceans and seas that encompass the surface of the planet.

The Pacific Ocean is so large that it is difficult to discuss it as a single ocean. Various parts of it are substantially different from other parts. For purposes of discussion, the Pacific is usually thought of as comprising three distinct regions.

The western region begins in Alaska's western Aleutian Trench, extends through the Kuril and Japanese Trenches, runs south to the Tonga and Kermadec Trenches, then continues on to an area northeast of New Zealand's North Island. This region is characterized by large strings of islands, the largest constituting Japan, New Guinea, New Zealand, and the Philippines. Some of these strings, notably Japan, New Guinea, and New Zealand, were, through time, sheered off from the continent by tectonic movements. The entire western Pacific is also dotted with volcanic islands, which are the peaks of high underwater mountains. These were formed as molten rock from successive volcanic eruptions cooled and solidified.

The ocean floor of the central area of the Pacific is the largest underwater expanse on Earth. It is the most geologically stable area on the Pacific floor. It contains sprawling underwater plains, most at a depth of about 4,500 meters, that are essentially flat, although they contain some irregularities and some geological formations, called guyots, that resemble the mesas found in above-water plains.

The eastern part of the Pacific, which abuts the United States' west coast, has a narrow continental shelf and a steep continental slope so that close to shore there are deep areas, such as the Monterey Canyon, which is more than 3 kilometers below the water's surface. The two most significant trenches in this part of ocean are the Middle America Trench in the North Pacific and the Peru-Chile Trench in the South Pacific.

Volcanic activity has historically been more pronounced along the western edge of the Pacific than along its eastern edge, although the East Pacific Rise, a chain of underwater mountains that runs from Southern California almost to the tip of South America, is also quite volcanically active. In the central and western Pacific, however, there is a profusion of islands that are the tops of underwater volcanic mountains.

PACIFIC CURRENTS

The Pacific, like the Atlantic, has two large systems of currents called gyres. The Northern Gyre moves in a westerly direction from near the equator and carries warm surface water into the Kuroshio Current and gives Japan moderately warm temperatures. The Kuroshio Current then moves northeast away from the Kamchatka Current, which brings cold water from the area around the Bering Strait. Part of it divides, moving north into the North Pacific Drift. The other part heads southeast.

Off the west coast of North America, part of the North American Drift moves north and becomes the Alaska Current. It brings to the Alaskan coastline waters warm enough to keep its shoreline and harbors from freezing in winter. Another part of the North American Drift veers south and forms the California Current, whose waters are cooled as they flow south to join the North Equatorial Current, which again flows west, completing its clockwise motion.

The South Equatorial Current also moves west toward Australia and New Guinea, but it then veers south to begin its counterclockwise course. The East Australian Current skirts Australia's east coast and

passes between Australia and New Zealand, south of which it feeds into the West Wind Drift, which moves east toward the coast of South America. Just north of South America's tip, it feeds into the Peru or Humboldt Current, which runs north along South America until it connects with the South Equatorial Current, which moves west to complete the South Pacific Gyre.

In both the northern and southern areas of the Pacific, winds from the west move the water in an easterly direction. Closer to the equator, however, trade winds move the water toward the west. This balance permitted early sailors to head east by riding the westerly winds and to return to the east by riding the trade winds. There are virtually no winds on the equator itself. Sailors can founder there, in the so-called doldrums, for days with none of the propulsive forces that nature provides both north and south of the Earth's dividing line.

The currents of the Pacific are important both for transportation and for bringing warm and cold waters to parts of the ocean, thereby giving them and the land adjoining them more moderate temperatures than might be expected at their latitudes. Occasionally, nature runs afoul of this balance as the southern trade winds diminish and fail to push the cool Peru Current north. Instead, the Peru Current is replaced by the Pacific Equatorial Countercurrent. The Peruvians first dubbed this phenomenon El Niño, which means "the Christ child," because it usually comes at the Christmas season. In some years, El Niño is followed by its opposite sibling La Niña, resulting in two successive years of hardship. As waters reach unaccustomed temperatures, much sea life fails to appear where it would otherwise be, bringing catastrophe to people dependent upon fish and seaweed for their diets or for income.

FORMATION OF PACIFIC ISLANDS

The Pacific Ocean has more islands than any other ocean. In the west, most of these islands are volcanic, although some, such as Japan, New Guinea, and New Zealand, were formed when the corresponding chunks of land became separated from the continental landmass in prehistoric times through tectonic action. The volcanic islands in the western Pacific often rise just barely above sea level. Any change in the ocean's level or tidal range can inundate them. Global warming threatens to melt ice in the polar regions, which will in turn cause sea levels to rise and, in some cases, cause islands to disappear. Indeed, some small, politically independent island nations face total inundation. It is estimated that by the year 2050, the oceans of the world might rise as much as 50 centimeters, which could wipe out currently habitable regions occupied by millions of people in the South Pacific.

Another major structure in the South Pacific is the atoll, a tropical island on which a massive coral reef, often ringlike, generally rests on a volcanic base. Kwajalein is the largest atoll in the world, with a circumference of nearly 324 kilometers. Other coral formations, such as ridges or reefs composed of coral, can grow to enormous lengths, such as the Great Barrier Reef east of Australia. Coral formations are composed of living organisms that require light and a stable environment in order to survive. They are, therefore, always close to the surface of the ocean and often protrude above the surface as tidal sea levels change. Most of them teem with aquatic life. In some cases, when they form around low-lying islands, the island disappears as the ocean surrounding it rises. The coral formation, however, often remains, filled with entrapped sand and rising above the water's surface as an atoll.

Such island chains as the Hawaiian, Pitcairn-Tuamotu, and Tubai Islands are the result of great plumes of extraordinarily hot magma that have risen through the Earth's mantle over millions of years and erupted through fissures in the oceanic plate above. The resulting formation that occurs when the molten rock cools is an island composed largely of basaltic rock. Over great time spans, the island is slowly carried away to the northwest as the Pacific Ocean tectonic plate continues its normal motion, clearing the way for another such island to be formed above the plume at the same relative location in the oceanic plate. Hundreds of islands, lined up almost like pearls in a necklace, have resulted from this ongoing volcanic activity, though many have not survived to breach the ocean surface due to erosion by waves and currents in the ocean water.

PACIFIC RIM

The areas around the Pacific have many volcanic mountains, large ranges of which line the coasts and still larger ranges of which are submerged. The highest mountains on Earth are the Himalayas, with

Mount Everest towering to 8,795 meters; many of the mountains submerged in the Pacific, however, are higher. From the ocean's floor at the Mariana Trench, undersea mountains, or seamounts, rise more than 10,600 meters as they approach the ocean's surface.

Many of the mountains on the Pacific Rim arose as, over time, the oceanic crust is subducted beneath the continental crust. Intense heat is generated by friction in the subduction zone beneath a continental mass, while the pressure exerted by the inexorable motion of the crustal plates causes fractures to form in the overlying rock, permitting magma to erupt through the continental crust as volcanoes. This process occurs all around the so-called Ring of Fire, from the North Island of New Zealand, through the Philippines, Malaysia, Japan and Siberia, to the Aleutian Islands and on down the west coast of North and South America to Peru and Chile.

The coast along the Pacific Rim is narrow, giving way to the mountain ranges that run close to the shoreline. An exception to this is in eastern China where the Yellow and the Yangtze Rivers have, for many centuries, carried silt toward the ocean, creating fertile coastal plains.

Geological activity beneath the Pacific results in thousands of small earthquakes every year along the Pacific Rim as oceanic plates move relative to each other. These earthquakes, most of which are too insignificant to be felt by humans, result in little or no damage. They relieve pressure that builds up between tectonic plates as they collide. When such pressure builds up without relief over a period of many years, however, a major earthquake, usually causing considerable property damage and loss of life, may occur. Severe earthquakes in the sea floor may generate extraordinarily large waves called tsunamis. Tsunamis, known to have achieved heights of more than 30 meters, can engulf large stretches of shoreline, as happened in Alaska in 1964. The worst tsunamis are usually caused by sudden displacements of crustal material in the subduction process, in turn causing a massive displacement of seawater that translates to the surface as an energy wave. Such waves travel through the ocean at speeds of up to 800 km per hour, and can cross the entire Pacific Ocean in a matter of hours. The tsunami that devastated the coast of Japan in 2011, producing worldwide economic consequences, was produced by a subduction zone earthquake.

FOOD RESOURCES

The feeding hierarchy that exists among the creatures of the sea is usually referred to as a food chain. One can envision this hierarchy as a triangle, at whose broad base are phytoplankton, microscopic plant organisms that require sunlight for their survival and are plentiful near the surfaces of oceans. Zooplankton, microscopic animal organisms, feed on the phytoplankton. They, in turn, constitute the diet of numerous species of small fish called anchoveta. These fish in turn are food for such larger fish as tuna and dolphin, as well as such birds as cormorants and pelicans, which dive into the water to catch fish. Animal waste, decaying plants, and dead fish and birds sink to the ocean floor, where scavengers consume them. Bacteria at those levels cause such droppings to decay, in the process releasing nutrients into the seawater that provide the phytoplankton with nourishment, thereby completing the food chain.

The food chain triangle becomes smaller as it approaches the top. Small fish survive by eating plankton. Larger fish eat the smaller fish, then sharks and whales eat the larger fish. A food chain that begins with millions of plankton may end up producing hundreds of thousands of anchoveta; thousands of cod, hake, and mackerel; and one-half dozen sharks for every whale that is part of this intricate hierarchy.

Although fish are the major food source harvested from the world's oceans, the Pacific also yields a great deal of kelp and seaweed, which, particularly in Asian countries, constitute a significant part of human diets. Seaweed is often harvested and laid in strips beside the ocean, where the sun dries it, thereby preserving it and making it easy to transport and to store. Even though they are not consumed as readily in the eastern parts of the Pacific Rim as in Asia, kelp and other sea plants are used in many food and pharmaceutical preparations. They have valuable pharmacological properties that are in great demand by drug manufacturers throughout the world.

MINERAL RESOURCES

The mineral wealth beneath the Pacific Ocean has barely been tapped. Among the minerals available near the shore are chromite, gold, iron, monazite, phosphorus, tin, titanium, and zircon. The greatest exploitation of the ocean's treasure trove has been by the petroleum industry. Offshore drilling takes place worldwide for the recovery of crude oil and natural gas. In addition, large quantities of sand and gravel are harvested every year for use in construction and manufacturing.

The deep sea has remained a mysterious place. The historic descent in 1960 of the bathyscaphe *Trieste* into the Mariana Trench, the deepest area of ocean anywhere in the world, unlocked many mysteries. Subsequent exploration of the deepest areas of the ocean has challenged many long-held beliefs and revolutionized deep-sea research. It was long thought impossible for life to exist under the enormous pressure of the ocean below 760 meters, but the *Trieste* discovered life at the very bottom of the Mariana Trench, much to the surprise of oceanographers. In early 2012, James Cameron undertook a solo dive mission to the floor of the Mariana Trench in a specially-built one-man submarine, returning with a priceless video record of that environment.

The deep ocean is richest in its deposits of cobalt, copper, manganese, and nickel. These deposits remain largely unharvested because of the difficulty of getting to them, but such problems will undoubtedly be overcome as deep-sea mining technology is developed.

R. Baird Shuman

FURTHER READING

Allen, Gerald R., and D. Ross Robertson. *Fishes of the Tropical Eastern Pacific.* Honolulu, Hawaii: University of Hawaii Press, 1994. One of the best books on the marine life of the eastern Pacific Ocean.

American Museum of Natural History. *Ocean.* New York: Dorling Kindersley Limited, 2006. An all-encompassing text on oceans that discusses geology, tides and waves, circulation and climate, physical characteristics of the ocean, and more. Covers marine biology and ocean chemistry, along with discussion of icebergs and polar ocean circulation. With so many topics covered, each section provides merely an overview. An excellent starting point for anyone learning about oceans and marine ecology. Includes numerous images on each page, an extensive index, a glossary, and references.

Benson, Keith Rodney, and Philip F. Rhebock. *Oceanographic History: The Pacific and Beyond.* Seattle, Wash.: University of Washington Press, 2002. An interdisciplinary book that discusses many aspects of the history of oceanography, particularly in regard to the Pacific Ocean.

Broad, William J. *The Universe Below: Discovering the Secrets of the Deep Sea.* New York: Simon and Schuster, 1997. Fascinating and cogent information about the very deep parts of the ocean. A well-written discourse that presents compelling information about the Monterey Canyon, which is close to the mainland of central California in the eastern Pacific. Illustrates the pressing need for accelerated exploration of the deep sea, noting that scientists know more about outer space than about the deepest oceans.

Clarke, Allan J. *An Introduction to the Dynamics of El Niño and the Southern Oscillation.* London: Academic Press/Elsevier, 2008. Geared toward atmospheric and environmental scientists working with or studying the El Niño/Southern Oscillation phenomenon. Presents a step-by-step explanation of the mechanics of that system. Assumes knowledge of fluid dynamics.

Glavin, Terry. *The Last Great Sea.* Vancouver: Greystone Books, 2000. Discusses the natural history and human history of the Pacific Ocean. Addresses ecological phenomena, marine biology, and the Pacific Ocean processes, though some chapters address colonization and war. Discusses algae blooms, El Niño, and species diversity.

Henderson, Bonnie. *Strand: An Odyssey of Pacific Ocean Debris.* Corvallis, Oreg.: Oregon State University Press, 2008. Written in the popular style. Addresses many of the current environmental issues facing our oceans. Focuses on debris and contaminants of the Pacific Ocean. Discusses North Pacific Circulation, oil spills, the plight of minke whales, and the Eastern Garbage Patch. Ties science into the stories of each item found along the Oregon coast.

Kowahata, Hodaka, and Yoshio Awaya. *Global Climate Change and Response of the Carbon Cycle in the Equatorial Pacific and Indian Oceans and Adjacent Landmasses.* Amsterdam: Elsevier, 2006. Showcases the global influence of the Pacific Ocean and climate phenomena associated with it. Collects a great deal of information about the global climate in one place for the advanced reader.

Nunn, Patrick D. *Climate, Environment and Society in the Pacific During the Last Millenium.* Amsterdam: Elsevier, 2007. Covers the period from A.D. 750 to the present day in order to present a historical examination of the relationship between climate and the development of human societies in the Pacific Ocean.

Ogawa, Yujiro, Ryo Anma, and Yildirim Dilek. *Accretionary Prisms and Convergent Margin Tectonics in the Northwest Pacific Basin.* New York: Springer Science+Business Media, 2011. Discusses new techniques in plate tectonic studies. One volume in the series Modern Approach in Solid Earth Sciences. Covers accretionary prisms, tectonics, and Pacific Ocean events.

Severin, Tim. *The China Voyage: Across the Pacific by Bamboo Raft.* Reading, Mass.: Addison-Wesley, 1994. Intended for anyone interested in the migrations of ancient inhabitants of the South Pacific. Tells of the author's long voyage across the Pacific in a primitive craft similar to the ones used by the ancient Polynesians and Melanesians during their migrations.

Taylor, Brian, and James Natland, eds. *Active Margins and Marginal Basins of the Western Pacific.* Washington, D.C.: American Geophysical Union, 1995. Focuses on geological activity in the western Pacific and its implications. Provides an excellent background for those interested in the volcanic activity of the area, though contributions are specialized.

See also: Aral Sea; Arctic Ocean; Atlantic Ocean; Black Sea; Caspian Sea; Gulf of California; Gulf of Mexico; Hudson Bay; Indian Ocean; Mediterranean Sea; North Sea; Ocean Pollution and Oil Spills; Persian Gulf; Red Sea

PERSIAN GULF

The Persian Gulf, located in the southwest part of Asia, is an extension of the Indian Ocean. The surrounding region is characterized by an arid climate, oil-rich desert land, and lightly populated areas. The Desert Storm operation that ended the Gulf War in 1991 had a dramatic effect on the ecology and environment of the territory.

PRINCIPAL TERMS

- **limestone:** a common sedimentary rock containing the mineral calcite that originated from fossil shells of marine plants and animals or by precipitation directly from seawater
- **petroleum:** a natural mixture of hydrocarbon compounds produced by conversion of organic matter under conditions of high heat and pressure in the absence of oxygen
- **salinity:** a measure of the degree of salt content in seawater

GEOGRAPHICAL LOCATION

The Persian Gulf is the marginal part of the Indian Ocean that lies in the southwest part of Asia between the Arabian peninsula and southeast Iran. The gulf has an area of almost 250,000 square kilometers. Its length is almost 1,000 kilometers, and its width varies from a maximum of 330 kilometers to a minimum of 55 kilometers at the Strait of Hormuz. It is a relatively shallow sea with an average depth of about 25 meters.

The Persian Gulf is bordered on the north and northeast by Iran; on the northwest by Iraq and Kuwait; on the west and southwest by Bahrain, Qatar, and Saudi Arabia; and on the south and southeast by the United Arab Emirates. The gulf is referred to as the Arabian Gulf in all Arab states. The term Persian Gulf is often used to refer not only to the Persian Gulf itself but also to its outlets, the Strait of Hormuz and the Gulf of Oman, which open into the Arabian Sea. The Gulf of Oman is an extension of the Arabian Sea lying between southeastern Iran and Oman. It is connected with the Persian Gulf via the Strait of Hormuz, and its most important cities are Jask in Iran and Muscat in Oman.

Several islands lie on the Iranian side of the gulf. Other small islands belong to the United Arab Emirates, Kuwait, and Saudi Arabia, with Bahrain and Abu Dhabi being the largest islands off the Saudi Arabian coast.

The only major rivers that flow into the Persian Gulf are the Tigris and Euphrates. The Tigris River has its source in eastern Turkey and flows southward for about 1,800 kilometers. Just south of the Iraqi city of Al Mawsil (Mosul), it is joined by two smaller rivers, the Zab al Kabir and the Zab al Sagir. The combined river then flows southeast past Baghdad, the Iraqi capital, and joins the Euphrates to form a single waterway, Shatt-al-Arab. About 200 kilometers farther south, the waterway enters the Persian Gulf. The Euphrates River also has its sources in eastern Turkey and travels a much longer path before it meets the Tigris.

Other than these two major rivers, there are only a few small streams that discharge into the Persian Gulf, mostly on the Iranian coast south of Bushehr. No freshwater flows into the gulf on its southwest side. Frequently occurring dust storms instead bring large quantities of fine dust into the sea via the predominant northwest winds from the desert areas of the surrounding lands. As a result, the lands of the Persian Gulf adjacent to the Iranian coast, as well as the land around the Tigris-Euphrates Delta, are covered with fine green-gray soil that is rich in calcium carbonate.

The Zagros Mountains stretch along the Iranian coastline east of the Euphrates and Tigris Rivers. Mountains as high as 1,200 meters rise abruptly in parts of the coastline of the United Arab Emirates, whose coastal plain blends southward into the hot and dry Rub' Al-Khali Desert. Desert lands also occupy the greatest part of Kuwait with occasional oases such as the Al-Jahrah. The lightly populated Hasa Plain lies on the coastline of the eastern coast of the Arabian peninsula, with occasional hills also found to rise above the shore. Elsewhere the coastal plain is covered with beaches and intertidal flats.

Geological studies of the past have suggested that during the Triassic period (200 million years ago), the Tethys Sea extended as far east as Turkestan and the Aral Sea area. This placed the area now occupied by the Persian Gulf between the Tethys Sea and the Indian Ocean in a supercontinent known as Gondwanaland. Faulting, earthquakes, continental drift, and the river flow slowly created what is now the land around the Persian Gulf.

HISTORY

The huge valley created by the Euphrates and the Tigris has often been equated with the biblical Garden of Eden. Certainly, the people living in that area had a most significant civilization several thousands of years ago. The many civilizations that developed in the area over time—the Chaldeans, the Assyrians, the Babylonians, the Medes, the Persians, and, later, the Arabs in cities such as Ur, Babylon, and Uruk—were among the leaders in farming, housing, animal domestication, and building construction.

The Persians eventually became the dominant force until 330 C.E., when they were defeated by the Greek armies led by Alexander the Great. The area residents later struggled under the Romans, the Byzantines, the Arabs, and the Turks. The British and the Portuguese fought over the Persian Gulf during the seventeenth century, with the British eventually winning it after aligning with the Persian forces and destroying key fortresses at Qishm and Hormuz. The Persian Gulf's importance increased dramatically during the twentieth century, with the British using their military bases to combat the Ottoman Empire in Mesopotamia during World War I. During World War II, the Persian Gulf served as a supply route by the Allies to the Soviet Union through Iran.

The importance of the Persian Gulf further increased after the end of World War II with the growing dependence of the world on oil. Since the Strait of Hormuz is narrow, a naval blockade is relatively easy and has led to several incidents of political friction between Iran and the neighboring Arab states, especially on the issue of ownership of several small islands in the Persian Gulf. A long, enduring war between Iran and Iraq started in 1980 and ended eight years later after the loss of about 1 million lives. In 1990, Iraqi president Saddam Hussein ordered the invasion of Kuwait and Iraqi forces then occupied it for about one year. They retreated only after several other nations aligned themselves with Kuwait and resoundingly defeated the Iraqi aggression. The region remained relatively stable for another decade, until Western forces again entered the area to remove the Hussein regime, ostensibly as a counter-terrorism measure.

OIL RESERVES

The Persian Gulf has traditionally been known as the single largest source of petroleum in the world. The Alberta Tar Sands, in Canada, as well as the

Bakker Formation in central North America and other recent discoveries in the Gulf of Mexico, however, are now believed to hold more extractable petroleum than all of the Persian Gulf states. All Persian Gulf states combined at one time held more than 50 percent of the world's known oil reserves, which gives evidence to the existence of the so-called Arabian Platform under and around the Persian Gulf. Most Persian Gulf oil is extracted from a limestone or dolomite reservoir, unlike the rest of the world's fields where oil is extracted from sandstone structures. Approximately one-half of the fields are on-shore, while the remainder are either partly or totally offshore in the Persian Gulf. Generally, the Persian Gulf fields have a large anticlinal or dome structure with little faulting and structural complications that are usually encountered in most of the fields in the rest of the world. This leads to a larger oil content, as well as an easier and less costly extraction. This is the main reason why the total number of wells in the Persian Gulf area is no more than 4,300 with an average production of 3,500 barrels per day per well.

Saudi Arabia has two of the largest (Ghawar and Sanfaniya) oil fields in the world. The Ghawar field is approximately 240 kilometers long and 16 kilometers wide. Kuwait's largest oil field is the Burgan field, which is relatively shallow and was discovered in 1938. The largest oil fields in Iran (Ahwaz, Marun, Gach Saran, and Agha Jari) were also discovered late (between 1928 and 1963) and have not been extensively depleted.

Oil and gas pipelines have been built to provide oil to other countries. The Trans-Arabian Pipeline, which was built after World War II, is more than 1,600 kilometers long and carries oil from Saudi Arabia to the Lebanese city of Sidon. Two other major crude oil pipelines start from the Iraqi city of Kirkuk. One is 1,000 kilometers long and sends oil to Dortyol and Yumurtalik in Turkey, and the other is 800 kilometers long and ends in the Lebanese city of Tripoli.

CLIMATE

The Persian Gulf is considered to be the hottest part of Asia, with land temperatures reaching 49 degrees Celsius. Temperatures are normally high, although winters may be rather cool, especially in the northwestern regions. Despite an extremely high degree of humidity, the sparse rainfall occurs mainly as sharp, heavy downpours between November and

April, and is heavier in the northeast. Kuwait, for example, has as much as 10 centimeters of rain each year. The region has few clouds, and thunderstorms and fog are rare throughout the year. However, dust storms, sand storms, and haze occur frequently, especially in the summer. Because of the lack of freshwater sources, water is valuable and may be either imported or treated in desalination plants.

The pattern of sea-surface temperatures changes significantly with the seasons. In February, the Intertropical Convergence Zone is near 10 degrees south and the heat equator is also in the Southern Hemisphere. As a result, most of the area between the equator and 20 degrees south has temperatures as low as 27 degrees Celsius. The water temperature is even cooler, down to almost 20 degrees Celsius in the northern parts of the Persian Gulf.

The different climatic conditions over various parts of the Indian Ocean cause the formation of characteristic surface water masses. During the southwestern monsoon, water flows inward toward the Strait of Hormuz, while from January to April, there is a slight outward flow. The Arabian Sea water has a great degree of salinity for three reasons. First, there are very few rivers that discharge their waters into it. Second, the arid climate allows more water evaporation than precipitation to take place. Third, water of even higher salinity originally formed in the Red Sea, and the Persian Gulf leaves these basins and spreads as a layer of high salinity that lies below the surface. The Persian Gulf water was proved to spread at a depth of almost 300 meters, while the Red Sea water spread as deep as 1,000 meters. This subsurface water was traced as far south as the island of Madagascar in southeastern Africa and as far east as Sumatra in Indonesia. Because of all these factors, the Arabian Sea has a rather moderate seasonal temperature variation, which is classified as subtropical.

OPERATION DESERT STORM

In 1991, Iraqi soldiers, retreating from the allied forces of Operation Desert Storm, set fire to 732 Kuwaiti oil wells. Operation Desert Storm's bombing campaign also accidentally created some fires but spared the desalination plants to the south of Saudi Arabia, as well as the coastal industries. The effort required by firefighting companies to stop the flow of oil from the wells and to extinguish the blazes was

enormous. The environment was made hazardous by choking soot, airborne gases, incredibly high heat, and a vast blanket of smoke. This was the largest oil spill in history, estimated to be about forty times greater than the amount of oil that leaked from the *Exxon Valdez* in the 1980's.

The expensive task ended much earlier than expected, primarily because of the advanced technology and the persistent efforts of the hired private companies. Modern techniques of remote sensing were applied and provided critical information that determined the location of wells, as well as fire and plume movement. Ground stations helped monitor the air quality and particulate matter, while modeling techniques were used to study the dispersion characteristics of pollutants and the deposition of soot. Unfortunately, the postwar cleanup efforts were undermanned and underfunded, and a lot of spilled oil was eventually buried under the shifting sand. Moreover, the effect of contaminated air must have been considerable, but few critical health data were accumulated partly because of the insistence of the Kuwaiti government on curbing the reports of the dangers associated with the hazards of breathing contaminated air.

SIGNIFICANCE

Until the discovery of oil in the late nineteenth and early twentieth centuries, the Persian Gulf area was important mainly for fishing, pearling, sailcloth making, camel breeding, and growing date crops, as well as for mining red ocher from the islands of the south. Most of these traditional industries declined dramatically after the economy of the region began to be determined by oil. The first major discovery of Iranian oil in 1908 triggered the rivalry among many European nations for control of the Persian Gulf. Britain eventually succeeded in controlling the fields until the late 1930's, when American companies discovered oil reserves in Kuwait and Saudi Arabia and won the dominance of the world market. Oil has also served as a primary cause of many of the region's internal conflicts and uprisings, such as the Iranian Revolution, the Iraqi invasion of Kuwait, the Desert Storm operation, and subsequent arms races among the Persian Gulf countries. The strategic importance of the Persian Gulf will therefore be great as long as oil, which is fundamental for transportation, industrial polymers, heating, food distribution, and construction, is available there. However, the threat of embargoes in the 1970's created the need to look for alternative energy sources. Modern scientific technology has provided nuclear energy, solar heating, and electric cars that are not oil dependent.

The pollution in the Persian Gulf is different from that seen in other seas such as the Mediterranean, where tourism is much more significant and where the waste produced is often hard to dispose of properly. Oil spills and the poor air quality attributed to the oil-extracting industry and the haziness of the climate are important contributors to pollution in the Persian Gulf. The Kuwaiti oil fires produced by the retreating Iraqi forces of Saddam Hussein at the end of the 1991 created an environment whose long-range impact on health is yet to be seen.

Since the Euphrates and Tigris are the only major rivers that discharge into the Persian Gulf and since earthquakes are not as prominent as in other Middle Eastern regions, such as northern Iran and Turkey, the Persian Gulf's geographical area is not expected to change dramatically. However, should the greenhouse effect and global warming occur, melting of the Arctic and Antarctic icecaps may bring about a considerable change in the salinity of the Arabian Sea and the Persian Gulf, as well as a change in the formation of the surface water masses.

Soraya Ghayourmanesh

FURTHER READING

Abuzinada, Abdulaziz H., et al., eds. *Protecting the Gulf's Marine Ecosystems from Pollution.* Basel, Switzerland: Birkhäuser Verlag, 2008. The industrialization and development of the Persian Gulf Region have generated an increase in environmental impact and sustainability research in the area. A compilation of articles that discuss environmental effects of oil spills in the Persian Gulf. Articles also discuss the importance of freshwater influx on the marine environment, marsh restoration techniques, and the gulf's biogeophysical characteristics.

Adib-Moghaddam, Arshin. *The International Politics of the Persian Gulf: A Cultural Genealogy.* New York: Routledge, 2006. Despite being Islamic states, the nations surrounding the Persian Gulf are politically very different; presents a critical study of the sociopolitical nature of the area and explores the effects of recent historical events.

Al-Azab, M., W. El-Shorbagy, and S. Al-Ghais, eds. *Oil Pollution and Its Environmental Impact in the Arabian Gulf Region.* San Diego: Elsevier, 2005. Volume 3 of the Developments in Earth & Environmental Science series. Discusses the major issues of oil pollution in the Persian Gulf, as well as prevention and treatment, monitoring, and modeling of oil pollution. A chapter also presents research on the environmental effects of oil pollution.

Brauer, Jurgen. *War and Nature: The Environmental Consequences of War in a Globalized World.* Lanham, Md.: AltaMira/Rowman and Littlefield, 2009. Any significant war, anywhere in the world, has catastrophic environmental effects; presents a comprehensive review of environmental case studies of wars following World War II, particularly the 1991 Gulf War.

Etheridge, Laura S., ed. *Persian Gulf States: Kuwait, Qatar, Bahrain, Oman and the United Arab Emirates.* New York: Britannica Educational Publishing, 2011. A well-written book that explores the organization, culture and history of each of the title Persian Gulf states.

Hawley, T. M. *Against the Fires of Hell: The Environmental Disaster of the Gulf War.* New York: Harcourt, Brace and Jovanovich, 1992. A careful assessment of the environmental damage created during the Operation Desert Storm, both globally and locally. Describes the cleanup efforts after the army coalition was dissolved, as well as the attempts of the firefighters to extinguish the fires while preventing the oil from flowing off the Kuwaiti wells. Also analyzes the impact of that disaster by gathering critical health data.

Husain, Tahir. *Kuwaiti Oil Fires: Regional Environmental Perspectives.* New York: Elsevier Science, 1995. A very readable text that analyzes the effect that the oil-well fires set by the Iraqi army had on the environment. Different chapters discuss topics such as the success of the technology used to extinguish the fires, the smoke plume characterization, the monitoring of the gaseous products and other particulates, and outlines for future emergency response. Also includes several impressive photographs.

Kämpf, J., and M. Sadrinasab. "The Circulation of the Persian Gulf: A Numerical Study." *Ocean Science Discussions* 2 (2005): 129-164. A technical article discussing research on the circulation of the Persian

Gulf that examined water mass properties and circulation, and seasonal differences in circulation. The introduction contains detailed information on the physical characteristics of the Persian Gulf. Best suited for researchers and academics.

McKinnon, Michael. *Arabia: Sand, Sea, Sky*. BBC/Parkwest, 1992. Examines the dramatic changes that have shaped Arabia and its wildlife in the last several thousands of years, as well as the profound and rapid environmental transformations and their impact on the future of the Persian Gulf's ecology, people, and wildlife.

Sadiq, Muhammad, and John C. McCain. *Gulf War Aftermath: An Environmental Tragedy*. Dordrecht: Kluwer Academic Publishers, 1993. Discusses the impact that the 1991 Desert Storm operation had on the environment. Individual chapters analyze the effect that the military operations and oil fires had on air quality, land resources, human health, and the marine environment.

SOMER. *Regional Report of the State of the Marine Environment*. Safat, Kuwait: Regional Organization for the Protection of the Marine Environment, 2003. Provides detailed information on marine pollution and the coastal ecology in and along the Persian Gulf. Includes a bibliography.

Sosson, M., et al., eds. S*edimentary Basin Tectonics from the Black Sea and Caucasus to the Arabian Platform*. Special Publication 340. London: Geological Society of London, 2010. A compilation of articles discussing the geology, geomorphology, natural history, and seismology of the Black Sea region. Each of these technical papers includes an abstract and references. Useful to graduate students and researchers.

Soucek, Svatopluk. *The Persian Gulf: Its Past and Present*. Costa Mesa, Calif.: Mazda Publishers, 2008. Examines the unique geographic position of the Persian Gulf that allowed it to exert such pronounced influence over human affairs in the distant past and on into the present day.

See also: Aral Sea; Arctic Ocean; Atlantic Ocean; Black Sea; Caspian Sea; Deep Ocean Currents; Global Warming; Gulf of California; Gulf of Mexico; Hudson Bay; Indian Ocean; Mediterranean Sea; North Sea; Ocean Tides; Pacific Ocean; Red Sea; Reefs; Tsunamis

PRECIPITATION

Precipitation consists of particles of liquid or frozen water that fall from clouds toward the ground surface. Thus, precipitation links the atmosphere with the other reservoirs of the global hydrologic cycle, replenishing oceanic and terrestrial reservoirs. In addition, precipitation is the ultimate source of freshwater for irrigation, industrial consumption, and supplies of drinking water.

PRINCIPAL TERMS

- **acid precipitation:** rain or snow that is more acidic than normal, usually because of the presence of sulfuric and nitric acid
- **Bergeron process:** precipitation formation in cold clouds whereby ice crystals grow at the expense of supercooled water droplets
- **cold cloud:** a visible suspension of tiny ice crystals, supercooled water droplets, or both at temperatures below the normal freezing point of water
- **collision-coalescence process:** precipitation formation in warm clouds whereby larger droplets grow through the merging of smaller droplets
- **rain gauge:** an instrument for measuring rainfall, usually consisting of a cylindrical container open to the sky
- **supercooled water droplets:** droplets of liquid water at temperatures below the normal freezing point of water
- **warm cloud:** a visible suspension of tiny water droplets at temperatures above freezing

CLOUD PARTICLES

Precipitation consists of liquid or frozen particles of water that fall from clouds and normally reach the ground surface. Under certain conditions, however, a type of precipitation known as virga forms and falls normally, but evaporates before reaching the ground. The most familiar types of precipitation are rain and snow. Perhaps surprisingly, most clouds, even those associated with large storm systems, do not produce precipitation. A typical cloud particle is about one-millionth the size of a raindrop. Special circumstances are required for the extremely small water droplets or ice crystals that compose a cloud to grow into raindrops or snowflakes.

Cloud particle diameters are typically in the range of 2 to 50 micrometers, with one micrometer being one-millionth of a meter. They are so small that they remain suspended within the atmosphere unless they vaporize or somehow undergo considerable growth. Upward-directed air currents, or updrafts, are usually strong enough to prevent cloud particles from leaving the base of a cloud. Even if cloud droplets or ice crystals descend from a cloud, their fall rates are so slow that they quickly vaporize in the relatively dry air under the cloud. In order to precipitate, therefore, cloud particles must grow sufficiently massive that they counter updrafts and survive thousands of meters of descent to the ground surface. Cloud physicists have identified two processes whereby cloud particles grow large enough to precipitate: the Bergeron process and the collision-coalescence process.

THE BERGERON AND COLLISION-COALESCENCE PROCESSES

Most precipitation originates via the Bergeron process, named for the Scandinavian meteorologist Tor Bergeron, who, in about 1930, first described the process. It occurs within cold clouds at a temperature below freezing (0 degrees Celsius). Cold clouds are composed of ice crystals or supercooled water droplets or a mixture of the two. Supercooled water droplets are tiny drops that remain liquid at temperatures below their normal freezing point. Bergeron discovered that precipitation is most likely to fall from cold clouds composed of a mixture in which supercooled water droplets at least initially greatly outnumber ice crystals. In such a circumstance, ice crystals grow rapidly while supercooled water droplets vaporize. As ice crystals grow, their fall rates within the cloud increase. They collide and merge with smaller ice crystals and supercooled water droplets in their paths and thereby grow still larger. Eventually, the ice crystals become so heavy that they fall out of the cloud base. If the air temperature is below freezing during most of the descent, the crystals reach the surface as snowflakes. If, however, the air below the cloud is above freezing, the snowflakes melt and fall as raindrops.

Growth of ice crystals at the expense of supercooled water droplets in the Bergeron process is linked to the difference in the rate of escape of water molecules from an ice crystal versus a water droplet. Water molecules are considerably more active in the liquid phase than in the solid phase. Hence, water molecules escape from water droplets more readily than they do from ice crystals. Within a cold cloud, air that is saturated for water droplets is actually supersaturated for ice crystals. Consequently, water molecules diffuse from the water droplets and deposit on the ice crystals. That is, the water droplets vaporize and release water molecules to the air as the ice crystals grow by accruing those water molecules from the air.

The collision-coalescence process occurs in warm clouds (clouds at temperatures above 0 degrees Celsius). Such clouds are composed entirely of liquid water droplets. Precipitation may develop if the range of cloud droplet sizes is broad. Larger cloud droplets have greater fall velocities than do smaller droplets, as they are less affected by upwelling air currents. As a result, larger droplets collide and coalesce with smaller droplets in their paths. Collision and coalescence are repeated a multitude of times until the droplets become so large and heavy that they fall from the base of the cloud as raindrops. Since the force of upwelling air currents varies, the forming droplets may be pushed back up to higher altitudes time and time again, becoming larger each time as their fall path through the cloud is extended.

Once a raindrop or snowflake leaves a cloud, it enters drier air, a hostile environment in which some of the precipitation vaporizes. In general, the longer the journey to the ground surface and the drier the air beneath the cloud, the greater the amount of rain or snow that returns to the atmosphere as vapor. It is understandable, then, why highlands receive more precipitation than do lowlands, which are hundreds to thousands of meters farther from the base of the clouds.

TYPES OF PRECIPITATION

Precipitation occurs in a variety of liquid and frozen forms. Besides the familiar rain and snow, precipitation also occurs as drizzle, freezing rain, ice pellets, and hail. Drizzle consists of small water drops less than 0.5 millimeter in diameter that drift very slowly downward to the ground. The relatively small size of drizzle drops stems from their origin in low stratus clouds or fog. Such clouds are so shallow that droplets originating within them have a limited opportunity to grow by coalescence.

Rain falls most often from thick nimbostratus and cumulonimbus (thunderstorm) clouds. The bulk of rain originates as snowflakes or hailstones, which melt on the way down as they enter air that is warmer than 0 degrees Celsius. Because rain originates in thicker clouds, raindrops travel farther than does drizzle, and they undergo more growth by coalescence. Most commonly, raindrop diameters range from 0.5 to 5 millimeters; beyond this range, drops are unstable and break apart into smaller drops. Freezing rain (or freezing drizzle) develops when rain falls from a relatively mild air layer onto the ground-level objects that are at temperatures below freezing. The drops become supercooled, then freeze immediately on contact with subfreezing surfaces. Freezing rain forms a layer of ice that sometimes grows thick and heavy enough to bring down tree limbs, power lines, and grid towers; disrupt traffic; and make walking or transportation hazardous.

Snow is an assemblage of ice crystals in the form of flakes. Although it is said that no two snowflakes are identical, all snowflakes have hexagonal (six-sided) symmetry. Snowflake form varies with air temperature and water vapor concentration and may consist of flat plates, stars, columns, or needles. Snowflake size also depends in part on the availability of water vapor during the crystal growth process. At very low temperatures, the water vapor concentration is low so that snowflakes are relatively small. Snowflake size also depends on collision efficiency as the flakes drift toward the ground. At temperatures near freezing, snowflakes are wet and readily adhere to each other after colliding, so flake diameters may eventually exceed 5 centimeters. Snow grains and snow pellets are closely related to snowflakes. Snow grains originate in much the same way as drizzle, except that they are frozen. Their diameters are generally less than 1 millimeter. Snow pellets are soft conical or spherical white particles of ice with diameters of 1 to 5 millimeters. They are formed when supercooled cloud droplets collide and freeze together, and they may accompany a fall of snow.

Ice pellets, often called sleet, are frozen raindrops. They develop in much the same way as does freezing rain except that the surface layer of subfreezing air is so deep that raindrops freeze before striking the ground. Sleet can be distinguished readily from freezing rain because sleet bounces when striking a hard surface, whereas freezing rain does not.

Hail consists of rounded or irregular pellets of ice, often characterized by an internal structure of concentric layers resembling the interior of an onion. Hail develops within severe thunderstorms as vigorous updrafts propel ice pellets upward into the higher reaches of the cloud. It is not unusual for clouds in severe thunderstorms reach altitudes of more than 10 kilometers. Along the way, ice pellets grow via coalescence with supercooled water droplets and eventually become too heavy to be supported by updrafts. The ice pellets then descend through the cloud, exit the cloud base, and enter air that is typically above freezing. As ice pellets begin to melt, those that are large enough may survive the journey to the ground as hailstones. Most hail consists of harmless granules of ice less than 1 centimeter in diameter, but violent thunderstorms may spawn destructive hailstones the size of golf balls or larger. Hail is usually a spring and summer phenomenon that can be particularly devastating to crops as it shreds leaves and flowers, breaks fruit loose from the branches, and can even render damages to agricultural equipment.

Changes in Precipitation Chemistry

Over the past few decades, considerable concern has been directed at the environmental impact of changes in the chemistry of precipitation. Water vapor in the atmosphere is molecularly pure water. The global hydrologic cycle purifies water through what is essentially the process of distillation, and the droplets of liquid water that form from the vapor are also composed of molecularly pure water, which has a Ph value of 7. But as raindrops and snowflakes fall from clouds to the ground, they dissolve and interact with pollutants in the air. In this way, the chemistry of precipitation is altered. Rain is normally slightly acidic because it dissolves atmospheric carbon dioxide, producing a very weak solution of carbonic acid having a pH only slightly less than 7. Where air is polluted with oxides of sulfur and oxides of nitrogen, however, these gases interact with moisture in the atmosphere to produce droplets of sulfuric acid and nitric acid solutions. These acidic droplets greatly increase the acidity of precipitation. Precipitation that falls through such polluted air may become orders of magnitude more acidic than normal, and was once measured in Scotland, in 1974, as having a pH of only 2.4, more than ten thousand times more acidic than normal, unpolluted rainfall.

Field studies have confirmed a trend toward increasingly acidic rains and snows over the eastern one-third of the United States. Much of this upswing in acidity can be attributed to acid rain precursors emitted during fuel combustion. Coal-burning for electric power generation is the principal source of sulfur oxides, while high-temperature industrial processes and motor vehicle engines produce nitrogen oxides. Where acid rains fall on soils or bedrock that cannot neutralize the acidity, lakes and streams become more acidic. Excessively acidic lake or stream water disrupts the reproductive cycles of fish and has numerous other negative environmental effects. Acid rains leach metals (such as aluminum) from the soil, washing them into lakes and streams, where they may harm fish and aquatic plants.

Study of Precipitation

Precipitation is collected and measured with essentially the same device that has been used since the fifteenth century: a container open to the sky. The standard U.S. National Weather Service rain gauge consists of a cone-shaped funnel that directs rainwater into a long, narrow cylinder that sits inside a larger cylinder. The narrow cylinder magnifies the scale of accumulating rainwater so that rainfall can be resolved into increments of 0.01 inch. (Rainfall of less than 0.005 inch is recorded as a "trace.") Rainwater that accumulates in the inner cylinder is measured against a graduated scale. Rainfall is measured at some fixed time once every twenty-four hours, and the gauge is then emptied.

With regard to snow, scientists are interested in measuring snowfall during each twenty-four-hour period between observations, as well as the meltwater equivalent of that snowfall, and the depth of snow on the ground at each observation time. New snowfall is usually collected on a simple board that is placed on top of the old snow cover. When new snow falls, the depth is measured to the board; the board is then swept clean and moved to a new location. The meltwater equivalent of new snowfall can be determined by melting the snow collected in a rain gauge (from which the funnel has been removed). Snow depth is usually measured with a special yardstick or meterstick. In mountainous terrain where snowfall is substantial, it may be necessary to use a coring device to determine snow depth (and meltwater equivalent). Snow depth is determined at several representative locations and then averaged.

The average density of fresh-fallen snow is 0.1 gram per cubic centimeter. As a general rule, 10 centimeters of fresh snow melts down to 1 centimeter of rainwater. This ratio varies considerably depending on the temperature at which the snow falls. "Wet" snow falling at surface air temperatures at or above 0 degrees Celsius has a much greater water content than does "dry" snow falling at surface air temperatures well below freezing. The ratio of snowfall to meltwater may vary from 3:1 for very wet snow to 30:1 for dry, fluffy snow.

Monitoring the timing and rate of rainfall is often desirable, especially in areas prone to flooding. Hence, some rain gauges provide a cumulative record of rainfall. In a weighing-bucket rain gauge, the weight of accumulating rainwater (determined by a spring balance) is calibrated as water depth. Cumulative rainfall is recorded continuously by a device that either marks a chart on a clock-driven drum or sends an electrical pulse to a computer or magnetic tape. During subfreezing weather, antifreeze in the collection bucket melts snow as it falls into the gauge so that a cumulative meltwater record is produced.

Both rainfall and snowfall are notoriously variable from one place to another, especially when produced by showers or thunderstorms. The emplacement of a precipitation gauge is particularly important in order to ensure accurate and representative readings. A level site must be selected that is sheltered from strong winds and is well away from buildings and vegetation that might shield the instrument. In general, obstacles should be no closer than about four times their height.

SIGNIFICANCE

Without precipitation, Earth would have no freshwater and thus no life. When water vaporizes from oceans, lakes, and other reservoirs on the ground surface, all dissolved and suspended substances are left behind. Hence, water is purified (distilled) as it cycles into the atmosphere and eventually returns to the surface as freshwater precipitation. In this way, the global hydrologic cycle supplies the planet with an essentially fixed quantity of freshwater.

As the human population continues its rapid growth, however, demands on the globe's fixed supply of freshwater are also increasing. In some areas, such as the semiarid American Southwest, water demand

for agriculture and municipalities has spurred attempts to enhance precipitation locally through cloud seeding. Usually, cold clouds that contain too few ice crystals are seeded by aircraft with either silver iodide crystals (a substance with molecular properties similar to ice) or dry-ice pellets (solid carbon dioxide at a temperature of –78 degrees Celsius) in an effort to stimulate the Bergeron precipitation process.

Cloud seeding, although founded on an understanding of how precipitation forms, is not always successful and at best may enhance precipitation by perhaps 20 percent. The question remains as to whether the rain or snow that follows cloud seeding would have fallen anyway. Even if successful, cloud seeding may merely bring about a geographical redistribution of precipitation so that an increase in precipitation in one area is accompanied by a compensating reduction in a neighboring area. Cloud seeding that benefits agriculture in eastern Colorado, for example, might also deprive farmers of rain in the downwind states of Kansas and Nebraska. The uncertainties of cloud seeding underscore the need for conservation of the planet's freshwater resource. Conservation should entail not only strategies directed at wise use of freshwater but also measures to manage water quality. Abatement of water pollution not only reduces hazards to human health and aquatic systems but also increases the available supply of freshwater.

Joseph M. Moran

FURTHER READING

Ahrens, C. Donald. *Meteorology Today:An Introduction to Weather, Climate and the Environment*. 8th ed. Belmont, Calif.: Thomson Brooks-Cole, 2007. One of the most widely used and authoritative introductory textbooks for the study of meteorology and climatology. Explains complex concepts are in a clear, precise manner and supports them with numerous images and diagrams.

Christopherson, Robert W., and Mary-Louise Byrne. *Geosystems. An Introduction to Physical Geography*. Toronto, Ontario Pearson Education Canada, 2006. A highly readable and extremely well-illustrated book in which precipitation, in its many forms, is represented as an essential basic property of world geography. An introductory college-level text suitable for all readers.

Desbois, Michel, and Françoise Désalmand, eds. *Global Precipitations and Climate Change*. New York:

Springer-Verlag, 1994. A look at meteorology, paleoclimatology, precipitation, and the methodology used in determining the factors involved with climatic changes. Certain essays look specifically at the atmospheric changes that create precipitation. Illustrations, bibliography, and index.

Martin, John Wilson. *Precipitation Hardening.* 2d ed. Boston: Butterworth-Heinemann, 1998. Looks at the atmospheric factors necessary to evoke precipitation, particularly snow, sleet, and hail. A good introduction to the study of precipitation for the nonscientist.

Moran, Joseph M., and Michael D. Morgan. *Meteorology: The Atmosphere and the Science of Weather.* 5th ed. Upper Saddle River, N.J.: Prentice Hall, 1996. A well-illustrated survey of atmospheric science. Includes chapters on the hydrologic cycle, cloud development, and precipitation processes.

Oliver, John E., ed. *The Encyclopedia of Climatology.* Dordrecht: Springer, 2004. A comprehensive treatise on the basics of climatology. Includes a detailed discussion of the global and seasonal distribution of precipitation.

Pruppacher, Hans R., and James D. Klett, eds. *Microphysics of Clouds and Precipitation.* 2d ed. New York: Springer, 2010. A lengthy volume, part of the Atmospheric and Oceanography Sciences Library series, that gives the reader an overview of precipitation by examining the structure of clouds, the chemical makeup and surface properties of water, cloud chemistry and electricity, and the formation, growth, and diffusion of water drops and snow crystals. Suitable for the nonscientist.

Randall, David. *Atmosphere, Clouds and Climate.* Princeton, N.J.: Princeton University Press, 2012. The three components of the title are the essential ingredients for all forms of precipitation; provides a comprehensive discussion of the dynamics of the atmosphere with regard to precipitation.

Schaefer, Vincent J., and John A. Day. *A Field Guide to the Atmosphere.* Boston: Houghton Mifflin, 1998. An exceptionally well-illustrated survey of cloud and precipitation processes. Includes suggested simple experiments and demonstrations.

Schneider, Bonnie. *Extreme Weather: A Guide to Surviving Flash Floods, Tornadoes, Hurricanes, Heat Waves, Snowstorms, Tsunamis and Other Natural Disasters.* Basingstoke: Palgrave Macmillan, 2012. Presents vivid explanations of how, when, and why major natural disasters occur. Discusses floods, hurricanes, thunderstorms, mudslides, wildfires, tsunamis, and earthquakes. Presents a guide of how to prepare for and what to do during an extreme weather event, along with background information on weather patterns and natural disasters.

Schneider, Stephen Henry, and Michael D. Mastrandrea. *Encyclopedia of Climate and Weather.* 2d ed. New York: Oxford University Press, 2011. Provides over 300 succinct articles discussing basic and advances topics in weather, climate, and meteorology. Articles contain cross-referencing and a bibliography of related resources. A glossary and list of abbreviations is also provided.

Smith, Jerry E. *Weather Warfare: The Military's Plan to Draft Mother Nature.* Kempton, Ill.: Adventures Unlimited Press, 2006. Covers processes that cause weather events and natural disasters, and our ability to influence these processes. Discusses cloud seeding, electromagnetic wave production, weather modification legislation, contrails, and stratospheric engineering. Written for the general population. Lacking in "hard science," but presents a wide range of topics that provoke further research.

Snow, J. T., and S. B. Harley. "Basic Meteorological Observations for Schools: Rainfall." *Bulletin of the American Meteorological Society* 69 (1988): 497-507. Discusses rainfall measurement and evaluates inexpensive rain gauges suitable for classroom use.

Straka, Jerry M. *Cloud and Precipitation Microphysics: Principles and Parameterizations.* New York: Cambridge University Press, 2009. Covers cloud formation principles, vaporization and saturation dynamics, and analysis of vapor collection in the process of cloud formation. Contains highly technical writing well suited for graduate students, researchers, and professional meteorologists. Also discusses various forms of precipitation. References and indexing are substantial.

Strangeways, Ian. *Precipitation: Theory, Measurement and Distribution.* New York: Cambridge University Press, 2007. A succinct presentation of basic theories of precipitation. A section of this text discusses various measuring techniques. Also discusses analysis and future methodology. Written in a nontechnical style that is easy to follow. Accessible to high school students and the layreader.

Vasquez, Tim. *Weather Analysis and Forecasting Handbook.* Garland, Tex.: Weather Graphics Technologies,

2011. Discusses technology, techniques, and physics principles used in modern weather forecasting, as well as thermal structure and dynamics of weather systems. Also covers model use in weather forecasting and weather system visualization. Easily accessible and still technical; useful to anyone studying weather forecasting and meteorology.

See also: Aquifers; Artificial Recharge; Atmosphere's Evolution; Atmospheric Properties; Barometric Pressure; Clouds; Cyclones and Anticyclones; Dams and Flood Control; Floods; Freshwater and Groundwater Contamination Around the World; Groundwater Movement; Groundwater Pollution and Remediation; Hurricanes; Hydrologic Cycle; Ice Ages and Glaciations; Long-Term Weather Patterns; Monsoons; Oceans' Origin; Salinity and Desalination; Saltwater Intrusion; Surface Water; Tropical Weather; Water Quality; Waterfalls; Watersheds; Water Table; Water Wells; Weathering and Erosion

R

RADON GAS

The chemical element radon (Rn) is a radioactive gas and the heaviest of the noble gases. It is produced by the radioactive decay of radium, which is itself a natural decay product of the uranium found in various types of rocks. Trace amounts of radon seep from rocks and soil into the atmosphere and can become a health hazard when trapped in sufficient concentrations in enclosed spaces such as basements.

PRINCIPAL TERMS

- **half-life:** the time required for one-half of the nuclei in a sample of a radioactive isotope to spontaneously decay through the process of nuclear fission
- **isotopes:** atoms of an element containing the identical number of protons but different numbers of neutrons in their nuclei
- **ligand:** an atom, ion or molecule that combines with a central metal atom or ion, without being chemically bonded to it, to form a stable molecular complex
- **noble gas:** any of the elements helium, neon, argon, krypton, xenon, and radon; they are often called inert gases since they are normally chemically inert
- **picocurie (pCi):** a unit of radioactivity corresponding to one-trillionth of that from 1 gram of radium (0.037 disintegration per second or 2.22 disintegrations per minute)
- **radioactivity:** the spontaneous emission from unstable atomic nuclei of high-energy sub-nuclear particles and electromagnetic radiation; radioactive emissions typically include helium nuclei (alpha particles), electrons (beta particles), and electromagnetic waves (gamma and X rays)

DISCOVERY AND PROPERTIES OF RADON GAS

The French physicist Antoine Henri Becquerel discovered radioactivity in 1896 when he accidentally detected spontaneous and continuous radiation emitted by uranium. One of his students, Polish scientist Marie Curie, found that thorium was also radioactive and that the energy of radioactivity was about 1 million times greater than the energy of chemical reactions. In 1898, Marie and her husband Pierre Curie discovered the radioactive elements polonium and radium by separating various components of the uranium ore pitchblende. Within a few years, radioactivity was found to consist of three components in increasing order of their ability to penetrate matter: helium nuclei (alpha particles), electrons (beta particles), and electromagnetic radiation (gamma and X rays).

In 1900, the German chemist Friedrich E. Dorn detected a radioactive gas given off in the decay of radium along with helium. This gas was originally called "radium emanation" but was later officially named radon. It was found to have a half-life of 3.82 days. Even before Dorn's discovery, British physicists R. B. Owens and Ernest Rutherford had observed in 1899 that some of the radioactivity of thorium compounds could be blown away in the form of a gas that they called thoron, which was found to have a 51.5-second half-life. In 1904, Friedrich Giesel and André-Louis Debierne independently discovered another radioactive gas produced from actinium that they termed "actinon," which was found to have a 3.92-second half-life. After the development of the isotope concept by Rutherford and Frederick Soddy in 1912, it was eventually found that "thoron" and "actinon" were in fact isotopes of radon, with atomic masses 220 for thoron (radon-220, ^{220}Rn), 219 for actinon (radon-219, ^{219}Rn), and 222 for radon (radon-222, ^{222}Rn). Radon is now known to have at least seventeen artificial radioactive isotopes in addition to its three natural isotopes.

Radon is an odorless, tasteless, colorless gas nearly eight times heavier than air and more than one hundred times heavier than hydrogen. It has an atomic number of 86 (having 86 protons in its atomic nucleus), and its isotopes have atomic mass numbers (protons plus neutrons) ranging from 204 to 224, all of which are radioactive. It has the stable "noble gas" electronic configuration of eight electrons in its outer shell, accounting for its usual chemical inactivity, although it is not completely inert. In fact, the most massive of the noble gases, xenon and radon, can be induced to form chemical compounds with the appropriate ligand materials. In 1962, the compound radon difluoride was produced in the laboratory and is apparently more stable than other noble-gas compounds.

Radon is rare in nature because its isotopes all have short half-lives and because its source, radium, is such a scarce element. Radon-222 is the longest lived of the radon isotopes and is an alpha-decay product of radium-226, which itself results from the decay of uranium-238 (^{238}U) along with about one dozen other radioactive isotopes. Traces of radon are found in the atmosphere near the ground because of seepage from soil and rocks, most of which contain a small amount of uranium that produces the minute amounts of radium that continually decay into radon.

Health Effects of Radon Gas

Because it is inert and has a relatively short half-life, radon in itself poses little danger. However, in the process of radioactive decay, it produces several daughters that are normally solids rather than gases, some of which emit alpha particles that can be especially dangerous to the delicate tissues of the lungs. Radon-222 poses the greatest danger because it has the longest half-life and occurs most commonly in nature, making up about 40 percent of background radiation. It is a daughter product of the decay of uranium-238, which makes up 99.3 percent of natural uranium and has a half-life of 4.5 billion years so that it is a virtually unending source of radioactivity in the earth. Other radon isotopes pose less danger because of their short half-lives and less common occurrence, with the possible exception of thoron in some local areas where it occurs at higher than normal concentrations.

The decay products of radon-222 are solids, two of which emit high-energy alpha particles. These two radon daughters are polonium-218, with a half-life of 3.05 minutes, and polonium-214, with a half-life of 164 microseconds. Because they form with an electric charge, these isotopes readily attach to airborne particles. When the polonium is inhaled, it lodges in the lung and can cause damage to the lining of the lung by alpha radiation. Most of the damage is done in the bronchial tubes, which contain the precursor (stem) cells that are particularly sensitive to the cancer-causing effects of alpha radiation. The primary data relating to lung cancer deaths caused by radon exposure come from studies of underground uranium miners. These studies indicate that from 3 to 8 percent of the miners developed lung cancer above and beyond those cancers attributed to smoking and other causes.

In the 1970's, concern began to be expressed about radon contamination of indoor air, especially for homes constructed on or with waste rock or tailings associated with the mining and processing of uranium and phosphate ores with significant concentrations of radium-226. This led Congress to pass the Uranium Mill Tailings Act in 1978. Wider concern emerged in 1984 when a nuclear power engineer named Stanley Watras set off monitors at his job, as they detected radioactivity that was subsequently traced to exposure to high radon concentration in his home in Boyertown, Pennsylvania. Further studies indicated that radon levels in houses far removed from uranium tailings or phosphate ores were often as high as or higher than houses near such sites, especially in poorly sealed basements.

By the late 1980's, it was recognized that radon gas seeping into the foundations, basements, or piping of poorly ventilated buildings is a potentially serious health hazard. Radon levels are highest in well-insulated homes built over geological formations that contain uranium mineral deposits. Even though these levels might be significantly lower than those in underground mines, it was feared that long-term exposure to even moderate amounts of radon might greatly increase the risk of developing lung cancer. Radon is now thought to be the largest source of natural radiation exposure and the single most important cause of lung cancer among nonsmokers in the United States. Studies indicate that indoor radon exposure increases considerably in the presence of cigarette smoke, both primary and secondary (passive smoke), since radon daughters apparently bind more effectively with smoke particles in the air.

Concentrations of Radon Gas

In the United States, the concentrations of radon and its decay products are usually expressed in picocuries per liter (pCi/L). A picocurie is one-trillionth

(10^{-12}) of a curie, and 1 curie equals 37 billion becquerels (Bq, or disintegrations per second). In the International System of Units, radon concentrations are expressed as becquerels per cubic meter, so that 1 picocurie per liter equals 37 becquerels per cubic meter. Average radon concentrations in outdoor air at ground level are about 0.20 picocurie per liter and range from less than 0.1 picocurie per liter to about 30 picocuries per liter. Radon dissolved in groundwater ranges from about 100 to nearly 3 million picocuries per liter. Indoor air averages about 1.5 picocuries per liter, but local conditions can result in levels several orders of magnitude higher than these, especially in some single-family dwellings. The National Academy of Science (NAS) estimates that at least fifteen thousand fatal lung cancers per year are caused by indoor radon, and another estimate suggests an additional five thousand fatalities from increased radon exposure caused by passive smoke inhalation.

Various standards for indoor radon have been established by extrapolating down from levels as high as 30,000 picocuries per liter in uranium mines associated with lung cancer. The Environmental Protection Agency (EPA) has set a radon guideline of 4 picocuries per liter for remedial action in buildings, which it estimates could produce between one and five lung cancer deaths for every one hundred individuals. The EPA projects up to seventy-seven fatalities out of one hundred people exposed to levels of 200 picocuries per liter. These estimates assume seventy years in the dwelling with about 75 percent of time spent indoors. The International Council on Radiation Protection (ICRP) has set an indoor radon level of 8 picocuries per liter as unsafe, which is about seventeen atoms per minute of radon decaying in every liter of air. The EPA estimates that a level of 10 picocuries per liter has a lung cancer risk similar to smoking one pack of cigarettes per day. Since the 1970's, a radiation safety limit of about 100 picocuries per liter has been set for uranium mining.

The indoor contamination problem in the Boyertown area of southeastern Pennsylvania was found to have radon levels as high as 2,600 picocuries per liter. Boyertown lies on a geological formation called the Reading Prong, which extends east from Reading through three counties of Pennsylvania and into parts of New Jersey, New York, and New England, with bedrock minerals containing elevated levels of uranium and thorium. These conditions led to the monitoring of eighteen thousand homes by the EPA in conjunction with the Pennsylvania Department of Health and local utilities, which found radon levels in excess of the EPA's 4 picocurie per liter guideline for remedial action in 59 percent of the homes. In a nationwide EPA residential survey, average radon levels ranged from 0.1 picocurie per liter in Hawaii to 8.8 picocuries per liter in Iowa. Researchers estimate that 2 percent of U.S. homes have radon levels in excess of the ICRP guideline of 8 picocuries per liter.

DETECTION AND REDUCTION OF INDOOR RADON GAS

Indoor radon levels are difficult to measure because of such factors as air movement, the effects of cigarette smoke, water tables, barometric pressure, and seasonal conditions, with higher readings in the summer than in the winter. Both active and passive testing devices can be used to test homes. Active devices include continuous radon monitors used by trained testers over several days. Passive radon kits, which are available at hardware stores, include charcoal canisters and alpha-track detectors. Sealed charcoal-filled canisters are exposed for two or three days and then sent to EPA-approved laboratories for analysis of the level of gamma radiation that they have captured, which is related to the radon level. Alpha-track detectors contain plastic strips that must be suspended for two or three months before being sent for analysis based on counting microscopic alpha tracks.

Radon levels in residential structures can be reduced by various techniques. Site selection is important in avoiding the high radon contamination associated with highly permeable (porous) soils. These can be identified from soil maps prepared by the Soil Conservation Service. High-radium-content surface materials can be covered with soil that has low permeability and radium content. A 3.3-meter fill depth can reduce radon emanation rates by about 80 percent.

The choice of substructure is also important in radon reduction, with well-ventilated crawl spaces providing much lower radon levels than basements. Radon control in basements is aided by using good-quality concrete on top of an impermeable plastic barrier and a complete system of drainage tile around the perimeter. Radon can be reduced in existing basements by sealing floor and wall cracks, capping sumps, and venting the air from under the basement floor.

SIGNIFICANCE

Radon has both positive and negative implications, although there are some claims that the risks from radon have been overstated. Radon-222 is used in the treatment of some cancers. It can be collected by passing air through an aqueous solution of a radium-226 salt or a porous solid containing a radium-226 salt and then pumping off the accumulated radon every few days. It is then purified and compressed in small tubes, which can be inserted into the diseased tissue. The gas produces penetrating gamma radiation from the bismuth-214 decay product of radon and can be used for both radiotherapy and radiography.

Radon is also a useful tracer for groundwater and atmospheric mixing. It is used in studies of groundwater interaction with streams and rivers. A high radon concentration in groundwater that makes its way into a stream or river is a sensitive indicator of such local inputs. Since atmospheric radon concentrations decrease exponentially with altitude and are lower over water than land, radon can serve as an effective tracer in measuring atmospheric mixing.

Critics of the EPA's 4 picocuries per liter radon guideline have raised questions about extrapolating from statistical data on lung-cancer deaths among miners with radon exposures as high as 30,000 picocuries per liter. Studies have indicated no unusual incidence of lung-cancer deaths for U.S. uranium miners when exposures are below 12,000 picocuries per liter. A massive study (published in *Science* magazine on August 22, 1980) of two groups in China, one living in a high-radiation area and the other in a low-radiation area, showed no significant cancer-rate difference between the two groups. A 1996 study by the Finnish Center for Radiation and Nuclear Safety found no increased risk for residents exposed to as much as 2.5 times the EPA's guideline. Perhaps the nearly half-billion dollars spent by Americans testing for radon and renovating their homes has been an overreaction to the natural background radiation humans have lived with for thousands of years.

Joseph L. Spradley

FURTHER READING

Bolch, Ben W., and Harold Lyons. *Apocalypse Not: Science Economics and Environmentalism.* Washington, D.C.: Cato Institute, 1993. Attempts to debunk many of the arguments used by environmentalists. Chapter 5 on "A Multibillion-Dollar Radon Scare" is a good summary and evaluation of the radon problem.

Brookins, Douglas G. *The Indoor Radon Problem.* New York: Columbia University Press, 1990. A comprehensive book on radon and its health effects, detection, and reduction. Contains a good glossary and many tables, graphs, and references.

Cole, Leonard A. *The Element of Risk: The Politics of Radon.* Washington, D.C.: AAAS Press, 1993. An interesting discussion of the politics of the radon problem, with information on many of the officials and scientists involved in shaping policy.

Fang, Hsai-Yang. *Introduction to Environmental Geotechnology.* New York: CRC Press, 1997. Chapter 10 on "Radiation Effects on Water, Soil and Rock" in this college-level text on environmental geology has many tables, graphs, and diagrams on radon and reduction methods.

Gates, Alexander E., and Linda C. S. Gundersen, eds. *Geologic Controls on Radon.* Boulder, Colo.: Geological Society of America, 1992. A collection of papers on the geology of radon that is somewhat specialized, but the introductory paper on "Geology of Radon in the United States" has good information that is accessible to the nonspecialist.

Godish, Thad. *Indoor Air Pollution Control.* Chelsea, Mich.: Lewis, 1989. Chapter 1 contains information on the problem of radon, and Chapter 2 discusses the control of radon. Includes useful tables, diagrams, and references.

Gray, Theodore. *The Elements: A Visual Exploration of Every Known Atom in the Universe.* New York: Black Dog & Leventhal Publishers, 2009. An easily accessible overview of the periodic table. Written for the general public. Provides a useful introduction of each element to high school students and the layperson. Useful to those studying non-chemistry disciplines as well. Full of excellent images and complete with indexing.

Pluschke, Peter. *Indoor Air Pollution.* Berlin: Springer-Verlag, 2004. A compilation of articles covering chemical and biological indoor air pollutants. The articles are well organized to provide the reader with a clear understanding of topics, each building on the previous article. Discusses sources of pollution, detection methods, and measurements, and processes of adsorption and desorption. Best suited for researcher scientists and university students.

Sportisse, Bruno. *Fundamentals in Air Pollution: From Processes to Modelling.* New York: Springer, 2009. Discusses issues arising from air pollution such as emissions, the greenhouse effect, acid rain, urban heat islands, and the ozone hole. Topics are well organized and clearly explained, making this text accessible to the layperson, although it was written for the undergraduate.

Turekian, K. K., and H. D. Holland, eds. *Treatise on Geochemistry.* San Diego, Calif.: Elsevier, 2004. A 10-volume set that draws from the top scientists in the field to compile information on current geochemistry. Chapters are written in a similar manner to journal articles, yet they are presented so as to draw correlations and integrate subjects across volumes. Each volume contains its own index.

World Health Organization. *WHO Handbook on Indoor Radon: A Public Health Perspective.* Geneva, Switzerland: WHO Press, 2009. Produced by the WHO International Radon Project, which began in 2005. Epidemiological evidence relates exposure to residential radon gas and the general incidence of lung cancer. Overall readability and tone used in order to present radon exposure from the point of view of a public health issue.

See also: Acid Rain and Acid Deposition; Air Pollution; Atmosphere's Evolution; Atmosphere's Global Circulation; Atmosphere's Structure and Thermodynamics; Auroras; Cosmic Rays and Background Radiation; Earth-Sun Relations; Geochemical Cycles; Global Warming; Greenhouse Effect; Nuclear Winter; Ozone Depletion and Ozone Holes; Rainforests and the Atmosphere

RAINFORESTS AND THE ATMOSPHERE

Rainforests, which are found around the world at tropical latitudes, play a critical role in processing carbon dioxide. They also store carbon and aid in cloud formation. Rainforests are rapidly disappearing because of human interference.

PRINCIPAL TERMS

- **anoxic:** lacking oxygen
- **ATP:** Adenosine triphosphate is a chemical that is the primary carrier of energy in all organisms
- **biochar:** charcoal used for soil enrichment or carbon sequestration
- **carbon-oxygen cycle:** cycle in which carbon dioxide, living organisms, and the atmosphere are related by the cycling of carbon in the atmosphere and in organisms through photosynthesis and respiration
- **carbon sequestration:** long-term storage of carbon in a stable state to remove carbon from cycling in the environment
- **greenhouse effect:** the process by which some gases trap heat on Earth, rather than allowing it to be reflected back to space
- **photosynthesis:** process by which plants convert carbon dioxide and water into sugar and oxygen
- **slash-and-burn agriculture:** a paradigm of subsistence agriculture commonly practiced in the developing world
- **subsistence agriculture:** the practice of growing to meet the needs of a self-sufficient farmer rather than the market
- **tropical climate:** a climate characterized by high annual temperature
- **water cycle:** the process by which water cycles through the environment

THE RAINFOREST AND THE ATMOSPHERE

Rainforests are an integral part of the environment. Although they do not produce vast amounts of oxygen, as previously thought, they effectively sequester a great deal of carbon dioxide in biomass. They also aid in cycling the carbon dioxide from the atmosphere, though they release as much as they store. As deforestation has increased since the early twentieth century, scientists have worked to understand the relationship between the rainforests and the atmosphere and their global effects.

RAINFORESTS

Rainforests are characterized by high rainfall. While most rainforests are in the tropics, they also exist in temperate zones, limited to narrow belts that get much rain or snow and are typically near mountains (which tend to have moist seaward slopes because of the rain shadow effect). The California redwood forests and the mountains of Manchuria and Japan are examples of temperate rainforests.

Most other rainforests fall in a band around the tropics and mark the tropical rainforests, hot spots of biodiversity. Rainforests are characterized by poor soil quality, as rapid decay prevents soil buildup. Trees have root networks near the surface to catch the nutrients from the top layer of decomposing plants and animals. There are, however, exceptions. A few rainforests, typically young ones on volcanic land, have rich soils. Examples of such rainforest include those on volcanic islands, such as Sumatra or Jakarta, and those in the volcanic regions of Africa and Central America. Tropical rainforests in general can be found in the tropics around the world where it is wet enough, including Southeast Asia, Borneo and New Guinea, the Amazon, Central America, Central Africa, and many islands in that range, such as Madagascar and Hawaii.

AMAZON

The Amazon rainforest is in the Amazon Basin, mostly in Brazil but also in parts of Colombia, Bolivia, Peru, and other countries. For many persons the iconic rainforest, the Amazon is the largest in the world and comprises the greatest biodiversity on the planet.

It is thought that a large population once inhabited the forest, as indicated by terra preta, a black soil not natural to the Amazon Basin and rich in nutrients. It is believed the soil was created by farmers who buried charcoal and biochar in the soil to enrich it. Terra preta actually has been shown to regenerate itself, and is so highly sustainable when used carefully. This system of soil-enrichment collapsed when Spanish and Portuguese colonists introduced diseases that caused the demise of local societies.

Today, the Amazon is being deforested at an alarming rate, with a loss of nearly 12,000 square kilometers (7,500 square miles) in 2008. Much of the land is being used as cattle pasture because the soil quality is too poor to farm. Many projections expect 40 percent deforestation by about 2030.

CENTRAL AFRICA

The Central African rainforest is the second largest in the world and is home to many species, including bonobos and gorillas. Much of this rainforest is drier than other rainforests. It, too, is being deforested at an alarming rate. Much of the West African forest is gone, and at present rates of deforestation, it could be gone entirely by as early as 2020. The densest and most intact portion is in the Congo Basin. Countries with land in the Congo Basin have created a nature preserve that may help to stop deforestation.

SOUTHEAST ASIA

The rainforests of Southeast Asia cover land from Bangladesh to New Guinea, though New Guinea is technically part of the Australian continent and is home to organisms more closely related to those in Australia than to those in Southeast Asia. The rainforests of Indonesia and particularly Borneo are the oldest on this planet; they compose the second highest biodiversity on Earth.

All of these forests are being deforested, however, and all are nearly totally gone, especially in Java. New Guinea's rainforests, however, are mostly intact because of the inaccessibility of that country's interior.

DEFORESTATION

Rainforest loss, occurring globally, is estimated to account for 20 percent of greenhouse gas emissions. Removal of such forest causes massive extinctions, as species lose their habitats. Additionally, deforestation causes mass erosion, which can sweep organic matter out to sea, where it can fuel algal blooms (which create greenhouse gases). Forests also can serve to filter the atmosphere and remove some pollutants, so their destruction eliminates that buffer.

According to the United Nations, agriculture accounts for most rainforest clearing, with 48 percent caused by subsistence agriculture and another 32 percent by commercial agriculture. Typically, subsistence agriculture takes the form of slash and burn. In slash and burn, the existing forest is cut down and the detritus is set ablaze. This temporarily enriches the soil, though much of the nutrients are lost as carbon dioxide. The land is then worked until it is depleted of nutrients, at which point the farmer moves on. Ideally, the land is left for the growth of new forest, and the farmer returns; however, when the surrounding population grows rapidly, as it often does now, reforestation fails. Additionally, extensive deforestation prevents reforestation of the exhausted land. As populations increase, the time the land can be allowed to lay fallow decreases. This means declining productivity, which makes the land more vulnerable to effects such as erosion, which causes problems elsewhere. While traditional (going back to the Neolithic revolution ten thousand years ago, when farming was invented), slash and burn is not a sustainable system in times such as these, with large population growth. Further environmental damage exacerbates the situation.

Slash and burn differs from slash and char, which uses biochar to enrich the soil by being buried along with other organic matter. It generates less loss and can be used to create terra preta. As a result, slash and char is being presented as a more sustainable alternative.

HISTORY

Rainforests have existed almost since large land plants evolved in the Late Devonian period, around 380 million years ago. The Carboniferous period (359 to 299 million years ago) is known for the coal that formed from its rainforests. Since this time, rainforests have been a constant feature of the planet, with their range varying with the planet's climate.

During the Eocene period, about 50 million years ago, rainforests grew as far north as Northern Europe and covered Antarctica. Today's rainforests are thought to be parts of those of the Mesozoic era Gondwana. The current Borneo rainforest is thought to be 130 million years old and the Amazon, 60 million years old. No matter the era, ancient rainforests provided an environment similar to the one of today and harbored great biodiversity.

PHOTOSYNTHESIS AND RESPIRATION

The rainforest is a center of turnover in the carbon-oxygen cycle because of the high density of biomass. The large number of plants leads to high levels of photosynthesis.

427

Photosynthesis is the process by which plants make oxygen and sugar from carbon and water. It occurs in two primary stages. The first stage is the light-dependent reaction, which involves the separation of hydrogen ions from water and the preparation of chemicals, such as ATP (adenosine triphosphate), for the second stage and also produces oxygen. Photosynthesis is an endothermic reaction, meaning that photosynthesis requires energy, so efficiency of light absorption is critical. Scientists believe that plants may use quantum phenomena such as electron tunneling to increase efficiency.

The second stage of photosynthesis is the Calvin or dark cycle. This stage does not involve captured photons, but uses the ATP from stage one to bind carbon dioxide to make sugars. Several variations have evolved through time, and the C4 variant is particularly efficient under proper conditions. Plants that use this mechanism include sedge, millet, corn, and sugar cane. Scientists are considering creating bioengineered plants that use this variant to help mitigate climate change.

The other process at work in rainforests is respiration. Respiration is the means by which organisms extract energy from organic compounds. There are three forms of respiration, two of which—aerobic and anaerobic—will be discussed here.

Aerobic respiration is the form used by animals and plants. It requires oxygen. The other form is anaerobic respiration, which uses no oxygen and is used mainly by bacteria, such as bacteria involved in decomposition. Aerobic respiration is more efficient than anaerobic respiration and is developed in response to the oxygenation of the atmosphere. Aerobic respiration involves a chemical process called the Krebs or citric acid cycle to release the binding energy in the form of ATP. This accompanies the oxygenation of the carbon as carbon dioxide, which is released as a waste product. Plants are able to use this to photosynthesize. However, some bacteria use the older process of anaerobic respiration, which does not produce as much ATP but works in anoxic environments, such as those inside a decomposing animal. Typical waste products, which include hydrogen sulfide, ammonia, and methane, are greenhouse gases. Both of these forms occur in the rainforests, where animals and plants employ aerobic respiration and where organic material decomposes after death.

CARBON SEQUESTRATION

It was once thought that rainforests produced an excess of oxygen, but recent data suggest that before human influence on the rainforests, the net oxygen output of rainforests was low, if not zero. Rainforests have some of the highest concentrations of photosynthetic life, but the high biomass and turnover rate of material, and the many animals that inhabit the rainforests, effectively release carbon equal to the oxygen output and use the oxygen in the process. This process is ideal for trees, which use the carbon to make more oxygen. As a result, the rainforest is naturally more or less carbon neutral. What, then, is the significance of the rainforest to the atmosphere?

The primary impact of the rainforest is its storage of vast amounts of carbon. Carbon sequestration is the storage of carbon, typically as a result of human activity. Due to carbon sequestration, stored carbon has been removed from and is less likely to harm the environment. Many proposals for carbon sequestration involve processes such as carbon-soaking chemical reactions, or pumping excess carbon dioxide into coal seams, old oil wells, or other similarly inaccessible locations. Other approaches, collectively called biosequestration, use living systems to capture and store carbon dioxide. Some, such as biochar systems, seal carbon by reducing the carbon to a stable state and burying it. Other methods are designed to store it in a living ecosystem through reforestation or better-managed forests. Lumber industries around the world, in countries such as Canada and Finland, are planting trees to replace those cut down. Additionally, China has launched several massive reforestation projects, though it will be a very long time before it counterbalances forest losses and emissions.

Because a rainforest sequesters carbon in trees and organisms, when a rainforest is destroyed, not only is it no longer producing oxygen, all the stored carbon is released, increasing atmospheric carbon. Additionally, recent evidence suggests that even old groups of trees still absorb carbon dioxide. In fact, it is thought that rainforests absorb one-fifth of the carbon dioxide output. This means they serve as a buffer against greenhouse gas increase. It is important to note that they are not producing oxygen, but simply removing the carbon dioxide from the atmosphere. Their capacity to do this, however, is not unlimited. Thus it is imperative to stop emitting carbon dioxide beyond the environment's carrying capacity.

RAINFORESTS AND THE WATER CYCLE

In addition to their carbon-oxygen role, rainforests play a role in the water cycle, which also plays a significant role in the atmosphere. The water cycle is the process by which water is cycled through the environment. Water evaporates from various bodies, such as lakes, rivers, and oceans. It then condenses into clouds and rains. The rain water is caught and used by plants and animals or runs down the land into rivers and back to the ocean.

Plants need water for photosynthesis and rainforests have a large effect on the atmospheric water content in a set of phenomena called evapotranspiration. Evapotranspiration is made of two phenomena, evaporation and transpiration. Transpiration is the process by which plants lose water to the atmosphere. In fact, 90 percent of the water that enters a plant's roots is lost in this manner. As a result, plants can contribute greatly to the humidity of a region, and thus to rainfall and cloud production patterns. When forest is lost and the climate is drier, it causes additional water to be lost by trees, which stresses them further, resulting in a negative feedback loop. It is because of evapotranspiration that the climate of deforested rainforest regions often grows drier.

PROTECTING THE RAINFORESTS

As a result of the enormous impact the rainforests have on the atmosphere, protecting them is of the utmost importance. There is currently much study being done to determine the best way to do this, not only in the field of biology, but also by economists and political scientists. This is because the factors influencing rainforest loss are often economic in nature. As a result, the best means of protection for them seems to be international efforts, since many rainforests are international, the countries that have them are often developing, and the rainforests are the common heritage of the whole species. Shifts in agricultural practice and reforestation seem the best method for the defense of this vital bioregion.

Gina Hagler

FURTHER READING

Adams, J. M. *Vegetation-Climate Interaction: How Vegetation Makes the Global Environment.* New York: Springer, 2007. A general guide to the ways in which plant life produces climate. Places the rainforest's effects on climate in a larger systemic context.

Beehler, Bruce M. P. *Lost Worlds: Adventures in the Tropical Rainforest.* New Haven, Conn.: Yale University Press, 2008. The large numbers of pictures and narrative structure make this work accessible to younger readers. A valuable resource on the world's rainforests for all readers.

Malhi, Y., and O. Phillips. *Tropical Forests and Global Atmospheric Change.* New York: Oxford University Press, 2005. Details the interaction between rainforests and atmospheric change using the Amazon rainforest as a model. Scholarly in scope but accessible to all readers.

Mann, Charles C. *1491: New Revelations of the Americas Before Columbus.* New York: Knopf, 2005. Recommended for its section on the Amazon rainforest. Fascinating and highly recommended for all readers.

Oldfield, Sara. *Rainforest.* Cambridge, Mass.: MIT Press, 2002. Covers the biology of rainforests. Includes sections for rainforests around the world. Recommended for all readers. Includes many photographs.

Sponsel, Leslie E., Thomas N. Headland, and Robert C. Bailey. *Tropical Deforestation: The Human Dimension.* New York: Columbia University Press, 1996. Details the human factors driving tropical deforestation. Covers all the tropical regions of the world.

See also: Acid Rain and Acid Deposition; Air Pollution; Amazon River Basin; Atmosphere's Structure and Thermodynamics; Atmospheric Properties; Carbon-Oxygen Cycle; Clouds; Global Warming; Greenhouse Effect; Hydrologic Cycle; Nitrogen Cycle; Ozone Depletion and Ozone Holes; Precipitation; Surface Water; Tropical Weather; Watersheds; Water and Ice; Water Table

RECENT CLIMATE CHANGE RESEARCH

Scientists are studying the effects of greenhouse gases emitted through industrialization and transportation—namely vehicles. Greenhouse gases are believed to be causing an increase in global temperatures and triggering climate change. The technologies and research methods employed toward this end are steadily improving. Climatologists can now analyze prehistoric evidence of periods in which climate change occurred, can analyze current trends, and can create models that can predict future conditions.

PRINCIPAL TERMS

- **aerosol:** a gaseous suspension of fine liquid and solid particles
- **geographic information system:** a network of satellite mapping technologies that can capture detailed images of the land surface
- **ice core:** long, cylindrical sample of ice bored from glaciers that provides evidence of ancient climate conditions
- **paleoclimatology:** study of climate conditions in Earth's ancient and prehistoric past
- **sedimentary rock:** rock that has broken from igneous, metamorphic, or other sedimentary rocks to form new deposits

PALEOCLIMATOLOGY

One way climatologists and other scientists analyze climate change on Earth is to compare current conditions with conditions that existed during ancient and prehistoric eras. For example, in 1835, prominent scientist Louis Agassiz, after having listened to a number of theories offered by his peers that the world's glaciers were likely retreating, developed a hypothesis that there was once an Ice Age, during which the massive glaciers that cover the North Pole actually covered most of North America and Europe.

As Agassiz's theory gained popularity in the nineteenth century, another scientist, Svante Arrhenius, offered another groundbreaking idea. In 1895, Arrhenius theorized that the Ice Age was caused by a drop in carbon dioxide levels in the atmosphere, which in turn triggered a dramatic drop in global temperatures. Arrhenius also offered a warning that few people took seriously until almost one century later: that the emissions caused by industrialization could eventually trigger another shift in climate.

The theories offered by Agassiz and Arrhenius are examples of paleoclimatology. In this scientific field, researchers analyze evidence of past events of climate change. This evidence is found in a number of areas. For example, paleoclimatologists may examine the rings inside trees, which can reveal periods of prolonged drought. Other studies entail the analysis of layers of sedimentary rock (rock that broke from igneous, metamorphic, or other sedimentary rocks to form new deposits). Scientists also study sediment at the bottom of the ocean or beneath lakes and swamps. Such sediment can provide clues about the climates in which they were formed millions of years ago. They also can reveal much about the origins of the sediment and, therefore, how far it was carried by ancient glaciers or volcanoes.

One of the most useful types of paleoclimatological evidence is the ice core. Ice core samples are long, cylindrical samples that are removed from glaciers by boring downward from a certain area. The core samples that are removed contain gas bubbles, pollen, sediment, and other compounds and elements from hundreds, thousands, and even millions of years ago. Ice core samples help scientists obtain a simple, vertical time line of different periods of climate change in Earth's ancient history.

COMPARATIVE STUDIES

To analyze the climate changes in Earth's history (and to analyze more recent changes), scientists conduct comparative studies. In some cases, comparative studies might entail the analysis of climate conditions in a single region through millennia.

Climatologists may examine sedimentary basins for evidence of climate temperatures during a particular era and compare the findings with recent and current conditions. This type of study can help scientists develop models that catalog climatological changes in time and help predict conditions.

Other types of studies involve the comparative analysis of paleoclimatological evidence from several areas around the globe. One such study entailed the compilation of data in the subpolar northern Atlantic regions and the warmer Pacific waters. Using computer models, scientists constructed a profile of the temperature changes that occurred during one of the warmer periods in Earth's history: the middle

Pliocene epoch (about 3.5 million years ago). Based on this evidence, paleoclimatologists and other scientists have generated forecast models for climate changes.

A third type of comparative climate change study entails the analysis of similar systems in different parts of the world. Scientists might focus on rainforests in South America and Southeast Asia, collecting data that can provide an illustration of the sensitivities of such forested areas to dramatic and gradual temperature changes. Similarly, climatologists have conducted comparative studies of the sensitivity of rivers and coastal areas with periods of significant temperature shifts.

METHODS OF STUDYING CLIMATE CHANGE

Scientists utilize a number of technologies to study climate change. These technologies have evolved steadily, particularly in the late twentieth century and early twenty-first century. Among these technologies are remote sensors, which are systems that target a region from a distance.

Remote sensors are used to detect temperature and thermal pockets near the surface or in the water, to detect dense particle clouds in the atmosphere, and to detect other environmental conditions. Some examples of remote sensors are active and passive radars, thermal imagers, and spectral scanners. Many later developments in remote sensing have enabled technologies to penetrate cloud cover, study the ocean floor, and scan targets at all times of day and in most weather conditions.

In addition to providing clearer images of a target and gaining access to previously daunting targets, advanced remote sensors are providing larger and larger amounts of data. Scientists compiling the voluminous data are aided by the ongoing evolution of computer modeling systems. This evolution in computer modeling is particularly evident in the amount of data that can be gathered, compiled, assessed, and incorporated into computer models. Computer modeling can in turn provide detailed conceptualizations of past examples of climate change and can predict regional and global climate change trends.

SATELLITE-BASED CLIMATE STUDIES

A significant development in the field of climate change study is the use of satellite-based sensors. Unlike aerial, ground-based, and shipboard remote sensors, satellite-based radars, thermal scanners, and infrared and other sensors can perform scans of considerably larger target areas.

Satellite-based sensors have been in operation since the 1960's, but in recent decades, satellite systems have undergone significant upgrades. The latest in satellite sensors can detect and quantify carbon monoxide levels, atmospheric temperature shifts, water vaporization rates, and other detailed climatological areas.

For example, studying the aerosols (gaseous suspensions of fine liquid and solid particles) in the atmosphere is an important aspect of climate change research. Satellites can be highly useful in this regard because they can scan broad areas of the atmosphere at multiple angles. However, some sensors have had difficulty in scanning aerosol depth. In 2007, scientists developed a corrective measure. By creating a new algorithm to calculate aerosol depth and by then applying it to remote sensors that are designed to scan a wide range of land areas, scientists have scanned aerosol depths with greater precision than before.

Another major innovation for the study of climate change is the geographic information system (GIS), a network of satellites developed to generate detailed maps of the ground surface. However, as the study of climate change has grown as a scientific discipline, more scientists are turning to GIS to map such trends as coastal erosion and the retreat of vegetation.

CLIMATE CHANGE NETWORKS

Developments in climate change research include the formation of climate change networks. These groups comprise scientists, advanced students, government officials, business leaders, and others who are interested in playing a role in understanding and preventing (where possible) climate change.

Climate change networks commonly employ the use of the Internet, allowing participants to share global data, take part in seminars and webinars, and collaborate on research projects. The U.S. Forest Service, for example, runs the Climate Change Resource Center (CCRC). The CCRC, part of a larger network of U.S. and global climate-change research groups, also produces a wide range of scholarly papers on such subjects as vegetation distribution, air pollution, and innovations in sensor technologies.

Climate change networks also are found at major universities and at nonprofit organizations. The University of New Hampshire's Climate Change Research Center, for example, offers undergraduate and graduate students a number of grant programs for climate change studies. The nonprofit Electric Power Research Institute conducts research on climate policy costs, energy market viability, and other topics. This group also has an information-sharing forum for its members.

Climate change networks represent the continuing evolution of climate change research, as they integrate the latest in technology and research practices into the global information system. These innovations help researchers, government decision makers, business leaders, and private citizens alike understand in greater detail (and with greater speed) any changes in the environment and how those changes contribute to regional and global climate change.

Michael P. Auerbach

FURTHER READING

Aghedo, A. M., et al. "The Impact of Orbital Sampling, Monthly Averaging, and Vertical Resolution on Climate Chemistry Model Evaluation with Satellite Observations." *Atmospheric Chemistry and Physics* 11, no. 13 (2011): 6493-6514. Describes the combined use of satellite-based sensors and computer climate-change models for a series of assessments performed by the Intergovernmental Panel on Climate Change in 2011.

Dassenakis, Manos, et al. "Remote Sensing in Coastal Water Monitoring: Applications in the Eastern Mediterranean Sea (IUPAC Technical Report)." *Pure and Applied Chemistry 84*, no. 2 (2012): 335-375. Discusses the wide range of applications of satellite-based remote sensing to the study of climate change in coastal areas. Demonstrates how such systems can help scientists study large areas.

Organization for Economic Cooperation and Development. *Space Technologies and Climate Change: Implications for Water Management, Marine Resources, and Maritime Transport.* Paris: Author, 2008. An overview of the various types of technologies used in the study of climate change as it pertains to water resource management. Focuses on space-based systems.

Seidel, Klaus, and Jaroslav Martinec. *Remote Sensing in Snow Hydrology: Runoff Modelling, Effect of Climate Change.* New York: Springer, 2010. Describes the use of remote sensors to gauge snow- and ice-melting trends and how the resulting melt runoffs affect the nearby and global environments. The book reviews one hundred regions worldwide.

Ward, Peter D. *Under a Green Sky: Global Warming, the Mass Extinctions of the Past, and What They Can Tell Us About Our Future.* New York: Harper Perennial, 2008. A discussion of the Permian extinction, which occurred more than 252 million years ago and killed nearly 97 percent of all living organisms on Earth. Theorizes that a dramatic rise in global temperatures, triggered by an increase in carbon dioxide in the atmosphere, was likely the biggest contributor to this mass extinction.

Zhong, B., S. Liang, and B. Holben. "Validating a New Algorithm for Estimating Aerosol Optical Depths Over Land from MODIS Imagery." *International Journal of Remote Sensing* 28, no. 18 (2007): 4207-4214. Describes new algorithms for the estimation of aerosol depth in the atmosphere using remote sensors. Aerosols provide vital clues about elements that lead to climate change.

See also: *AR4 Synthesis Report*; Atmosphere's Evolution; Atmospheric Properties; Carbon-Oxygen Cycle; Climate; Climate Change Theories; Climate Modeling; Deep-Sea Sedimentation; Earth-Sun Relations; Geochemical Cycles; Global Energy Transfer; Global Warming; Greenhouse Effect; Ice Ages and Glaciation; Impacts, Adaptation, and Variability; IPCC; Long-Term Weather Patterns; Observational Data of the Atmosphere and Oceans; Ocean-Atmosphere Interactions; Ozone Depletion and Ozone Holes; Precipitation; Remote Sensing of the Atmosphere; Remote Sensing of the Oceans; Satellite Meteorology; Severe and Anomalous Weather in Recent Decades; Volcanoes: Climatic Effects; Weather Forecasting

RED SEA

The Red Sea is one of the most dynamic and interesting geological features on Earth. Its location and continuing geological activity make it important in the geological history and development of both Africa and Asia, and an important source of information about geological processes and their impacts.

PRINCIPAL TERMS

- **asthenosphere:** the layer of the mantle immediately beneath the lithosphere; the asthenosphere exists in an almost "plastic" state and therefore behaves like a very thick liquid
- **continental shelf:** the gentle slope that extends from the coast into the ocean, generally to a depth of about 500 meters at the continental slope
- **graben:** a down-thrown block of rock between two steeply angled normal faults
- **hydrothermal vent:** an undersea location where superheated liquid and gases are released because of volcanic activity
- **Pangaea:** the supercontinent that geologists hypothesize existed about 280 million years ago, when all the landmasses of the world were one
- **rift:** a graben on a very large scale that results in a massive depression in the ground surface with steep sides; the most famous is the Great Rift Valley, which extends from Turkey in Asia to Mozambique in Africa
- **salinity:** the amount of dissolved salts present in seawater, usually expressed in parts per thousand
- **seismic activity:** movements occurring within the crust that often cause various other geological phenomena to occur

GENERAL DESCRIPTION AND LOCATION

The Red Sea is one of several important seas associated with the Indian Ocean. It is almost totally landlocked by the Sinai Peninsula and Egypt to the north and the narrow (32 kilometers) strait of Bab el-Mandeb, which divides Yemen from the kingdom of Djibouti, to the south. The southern end connects with the Gulf of Aden, which, in turn, connects to the Arabian Sea and thence to the Indian Ocean. The Suez Canal, completed in 1869 after a ten-year effort, directly links the waters of the Red Sea with the Mediterranean Sea through the innovative use of three natural lakes and a set of canals.

The northern end of the Red Sea splits into two small gulfs, the relatively shallow Gulf of Suez as

the western branch and the much deeper Gulf of Aqaba as the eastern branch. Eight nations (Egypt, North Sudan, Eritrea, Djibouti, Yemen, Saudi Arabia, Jordan, and Israel) border one or more sides of the Red Sea, which is recognized as the major divide between the continents of Africa and Asia. A number of islands (many of them actually exposed coral reefs) lie within its waters, particularly in the southern end. Somalia borders the Gulf of Aden, south of the mouth of the Red Sea at Bab el-Mandeb.

A body of water with a brilliant blue-green hue, the Red Sea likely takes its name from the occasional blooms of the red algae *Trichodesmium erythraeum*, which, upon death, give the waters a reddish-brown tint. Other explanations that have been proposed include the reflection of the sun-burnished cliffs in its waters or the reddish skin color of peoples living near it. Records of ancient Egypt, Palestine, and Mesopotamia provide references indicating that the sea was termed "red" by the earliest civilizations within the region, although at that time it referred to an area extending all the way to the northwest coast of India (today's Indian Ocean).

GEOLOGY

The Red Sea, technically a graben, is part of the African rift valley system or Great Rift Valley, a major geological depression and fault zone on the surface. This is the point where the African and Arabian tectonic plates have been slowly tearing apart (rifting) under the influence of a strong magmatic convection currents in the underlying mantle. Over the course of time, this will eventually split the African continent into two separate landmasses, forming a new sea between them in the process. This large rift valley extends south from the Sinai Peninsula 3,500 kilometers to Tanzania and about 450 kilometers north through the Dead Sea-Jordan Rift Valley. The Red Sea valley itself cuts through a mass of Precambrian igneous (basalt) and metamorphic rocks known as the Arabian-Nubian Massif, the upper portions of which form the rugged mountains, technically known as steep fault scarps, that ring the sea. On top of the Precambrian rock strata sit layers of Paleozoic marine sediments laid down some 544 to 245 million years ago, as well as Mesozoic and Cenozoic sediments as much as 57 million years old.

The 30-million-year-old Red Sea was created when the Arabian Peninsula began to break away from Africa and started to move north in two distinct phases. The northern part of the Red Sea was created over a process of about 10 million years. Subsequent geological movement that commenced about 3 to 4 million years ago created the much deeper Gulf of Aqaba and the southern half of the Red Sea. The movement, which continues to the present time, adds about 15 millimeters per year to the width of the Red Sea and supports unique forms of marine life among the hydrothermal vents at the deepest parts of the sea where extensive volcanism and seismic activity occurs. There are a number of active undersea volcanoes at the southern end just south of the Dahlak Archipelago, as well as a recently extinct volcano on the island of Jabal at-Ta'ir.

There are five major types of mineral resources present in the Red Sea region. Oil and natural gas deposits (more than 120 fields or discovery wells) have been found and extensively tapped near the junction of the Gulf of Suez and the main body of the Red Sea.

Evaporites such as halite, sylvite, gypsum, and dolomite are mined along the Sinai Peninsula, although not in proportion to what is available. Sulfur deposits have been extensively mined since the beginning of the twentieth century, while the phosphate deposits are of such a low grade that present extraction techniques make them economically unattractive resources. There are extensive and valuable heavy metal deposits in the deep portions of the Red Sea along the Atlantis II Deep area, but these deposits are not yet commercially mined. Because they are found in the form of fluid oozes rather than solid rocks, it is believed that they may be able to be pumped up to the surface, although attempts to do so in more than a casual manner have so far proved elusive.

PHYSICAL FEATURES AND CLIMATE

The Red Sea extends some 2,000 kilometers from north to south and is about 350 kilometers across at its widest point near the southern end. Its maximum depth is about 3,000 meters, although there is an extensive continental shelf around the periphery of the entire sea that is no more than a few hundred meters deep.

The Red Sea contains some of the world's hottest waters, with an average temperature of 25 degrees Celsius (77 degrees Fahrenheit), and some of the saltiest at forty parts per thousand. Little precipitation occurs in the entire area, although there is some evidence of greater precipitation having occurred during some periods in the past. A remarkable circulatory system maintains the water level in the face of very high evaporation rates of more than 2 meters per year along its length and breadth. The denser, saltier water of the north sinks and flows south along the lower depths, while winds drive less dense and less salty waters (about thirty-six parts per thousand) above it northward from the shallow southern end of the strait of Bab el-Mandeb. This results in a complete replacement of the sea's water about every twenty years. Underneath this exchange of saltwater, very deep in the central trough, brine with an

The Sinai Peninsula juts into the Red Sea in this satellite image. The Mediterranean Sea lies to the north, extending to the curved horizon. (PhotoDisc)

average temperature of almost 60 degrees Celsius and a salinity of 257 parts per thousand rises from underground sources. This upward movement adds to the general circulation within the Red Sea and measurably increases its overall salinity.

Fierce windstorms can arise suddenly on the Red Sea, especially coming off the desert sands to the northwest, which are referred to as the Egyptian winds. Daily air temperature ranges from 8 to 28 degrees Celsius during the fall, winter, and spring, with scorching highs of up to 40 degrees Celsius in the summer season (July and August) accompanied by intense relative humidity.

SCIENTIFIC AND ECONOMIC IMPORTANCE

The Red Sea provides scientists with a glimpse of geologic processes that likely occurred in the early stages of the formation of the Atlantic and Pacific Ocean basins during the breakup of Pangaea some 250 millions of years ago. The continuing movement of the Arabian plate northward adds to the width of the Red Sea each year in a small but measurable way and provides a living laboratory to observe ongoing volcanic and seismic activity associated with the evolution of crustal margins, along with the action of hydrothermal vents. The Red Sea's complex water chemistry and geology have been the focus of many scientific expeditions in the modern era, including those conducted in such submersibles as the Swedish *Albatross* (1948) and the American *Glomar Challenger* (1972), the latter of which drilled and removed core samples from some of the sea's deepest locations.

The undersea vents and the extreme saltiness of the Red Sea support a unique and varied marine life, including spectacular coral reefs, notably the Protector Reef near Port Sudan, Ras Muhammad at the southern tip of the Sinai (one of the top ten diving spots in the world), and the Deadalus Reef parallel with Aswan, Egypt. Vibrantly colored exotic fish and an abundance of rare and endangered species of marine life found nowhere else in the world attract visitors from all over the globe. More than one thousand species of invertebrates, one thousand species of fish, and more than two hundred coral types have been identified within its teeming waters. Its natural beauty has been a lure for divers since ancient times, a popular subject of nature films, and a playground for underwater photography enthusiasts.

The Red Sea has been important since ancient times as a commercial and cultural waterway that provides access to and from Africa, Arabia, and the Indian subcontinent. This is despite the danger posed by its many reefs that lie just below the surface and the need to keep the southern channel open at Bab el-Mandeb Strait by blasting and dredging on a regular basis. The Egyptians, from the time of Ramses II and Seti I, used shallow canals to connect the Red Sea to branches of the Nile River delta and permit the easy passage of goods via sea rather than by an arduous land route through blistering desert sands. The Greek, Roman and early Muslim empires continued this practice until the end of the eighth century C.E. Today the modern Suez Canal has assured the Red Sea an important place in world commerce, although hostilities among Arab nations, Israel, and African nations have sometimes led to complete closure of this important sea artery during the twentieth century. Major seaports in the Red Sea include Suez and El Suweis in Egypt, Jiddah in Saudi Arabia, Elat in Israel, Al Aqabah in Jordan, Massawa in Eritrea, and Bur Sudan and Suakin in Sudan. Fishing, a major regional industry at more than 8,000 metric tons per year, is supported by the extensive reefs that plunge thousands of meters to the ocean floor.

Dennis W. Cheek

FURTHER READING

Ambraseys, N. N., C. P. Melville, and R. D. Adams. *The Seismicity of Egypt, Arabia and the Red Sea: A Historical Review.* Cambridge, England: Cambridge University Press, 2005. Provides a detailed catalog of the earthquakes that have struck the region from the earliest times to the present day, using both historical sources and instrumental data.

Coleman, Robert G. *Geologic Evolution of the Red Sea.* New York: Oxford University Press, 1993. A geological treatment of the Red Sea that describes in considerable detail, using both words and maps, the geological history of the Red Sea. Technical in nature.

Edwards, Alasdair J., and Stephen M. Head. *Red Sea.* New York: Oxford University Press, 1987. A publication for the general public emphasizing the unique geological features and marine life of the Red Sea. The foreword, written by the Duke of Edinburgh, urges that the world concentrate its efforts on preserving this unique environment for future generations.

Ehteshami, Anoushiravan, and Emma C. Murphy. *The International Politics of the Red Sea.* London: Taylor & Francis, 2011. Argues that the Red Sea region is becoming an international sub-region in its own right. Discusses the various economic, military and political forces that function there.

Mojetta, Angelo. *The Red Sea: Underwater Paradise.* New York: Sterling/White Star, 2005. Intended to be a trustworthy biological guide to the flora and fauna of the Red Sea and proof of the thousand-plus species of sea creatures that dwell therein.

Taylor, Leighton R. *The Red Sea.* Woodbridge, Conn.: Blackbirch, 1998. A presentation for adolescent readers that succinctly summarizes the state of knowledge about the geology and biology associated with this unique body of water. Color illustrations, maps, glossary, and an index aid reader comprehension.

Tregenza, L. A., and Joseph John Hobbs. *The Red Sea Mountains of Egypt and Egyptian Years.* Cairo: American University in Cairo Press, 2004. Recounts the original text of works by L. A. Tregenza from 1955 and 1958, in which he recorded his observations during three walking treks throughout the region.

Zahran, M. A. *Climate-Vegetation: Afro-Asian Mediterranean and Red Sea Coastal Lands.* New York: Springer, 2010. Examines coastal habitats of the Mediterranean and the Red Sea. Discusses the interaction between climate and vegetation. The final chapter discusses sustainable development of coastal deserts. Very informative, without being too technical. Subject matter is quite specific; most useful to graduates or researchers studying climate-vegetation interactions or Afro-Asian Mediterranean and Red Sea coastal ecology.

See also: Aral Sea; Arctic Ocean; Atlantic Ocean; Black Sea; Caspian Sea; Deep Ocean Currents; Gulf of California; Gulf of Mexico; Hudson Bay; Indian Ocean; Mediterranean Sea; North Sea; Ocean Tides; Pacific Ocean; Persian Gulf; Saltwater Intrusion; Surface Ocean Currents; Volcanoes: Climatic Effects

REFS

Reefs are among the oldest known communities, existing at least 2 billion years ago. They exert considerable control on the surrounding physical environment, influencing turbulence levels and patterns of sedimentation. Ancient reefs are often important hydrocarbon reservoirs.

PRINCIPAL TERMS

- **calcareous algae:** green algae that secrete needles or plates of aragonite as an internal skeleton; very important contributors to reef sediment
- **carbonate rocks:** sedimentary rocks such as limestone, composed of calcium carbonate minerals
- **coralline algae:** red algae that secrete crusts or branching skeletons of high-magnesium calcite; important sediment contributors and binders on reefs
- **rugose corals:** a Paleozoic coral group also known as "tetracorals," sometimes colonial, but more often solitary and horn-shaped
- **scleractinian corals:** modern corals or "hexacorals," different from their more ancient counterparts in details of the skeleton and the presence of a symbiosis with unicellular algae in most shallow-water species
- **stromatolites:** layered columnar or flattened structures in sedimentary rocks, produced by the binding of sediment by blue-green algal (cyanobacterial) mats
- **stromatoporoids:** spongelike organisms that produced layered, mound-shaped, calcareous skeletons and were important reef builders during the Paleozoic era
- **tabulate "corals":** colonial organisms with calcareous skeletons that were important Paleozoic reef builders; considered to be more closely related to sponges than to corals

"TRUE" REEFS VERSUS REEFLIKE STRUCTURES

Reefs or reeflike structures are among the oldest known communities, extending more than 2 billion years into Earth's history. These earliest reefs were vastly different in their biotic composition and physical structure from modern reefs, which are among the most diverse of biotic communities and display amazingly high rates of biotic productivity (carbon fixation) and calcium carbonate deposition, despite their existence in a virtual nutrient "desert." Reefs are among the few communities to rival the power of humankind as a shaper of the planet. The Great Barrier Reef of Australia, for example, forms a structure some 2,000 kilometers in length and up to 150 kilometers in width.

It is necessary to distinguish between "true," or structural, reefs and reeflike structures or banks. Reefs are carbonate structures that possess an internal framework. The framework traps sediment and provides resistance to wave action. Thus, reefs can exist in very shallow water and may grow to the surface of the oceans. Banks are also biogenically produced but lack an internal framework. Thus, banks are often restricted to low-energy, deep-water settings. "Bioherm" refers to moundlike carbonate buildups, either reefs or banks, and "biostrome" to low, lens-shaped buildups.

REEF CLASSIFICATION

Modern reefs are classified into several geomorphic types: atoll, barrier, fringing, and patch. Many of these may be further subdivided into reef crest or flat, back-reef or lagoon, and fore-reef zones. Atoll reefs are circular structures with a central lagoon, thought to form on subsiding volcanic islands. Barrier reefs are elongate structures that parallel coastlines and possess a significant lagoon between the exposed reef crest and shore. These often occur on the edges of shelves that are uplifted by faulting. Fringing reefs are elongate structures paralleling and extending seaward from the coastline that lack a lagoon between shore and exposed reef crest. Patch reefs are typically small, moundlike structures, occurring isolated on shelves or in lagoons. The majority of fossil reefs would be classified as patch reefs, although many examples of extensive, linear, shelf-edge trends are also known from the geologic record.

Reefs form one of the most distinctive and easily recognized sedimentary facies (or environments). In addition to possessing a characteristic fauna consisting of corals, various algae, and stromatoporoids, they are distinguished by a massive (nonlayered) core that has abrupt contacts with adjacent facies. Associated facies include flat-lying lagoon and steeply inclined fore-reef talus, the latter often consisting of large angular blocks derived from the core. The reef core is typically a thick unit relative to adjacent deposits. The core also consists of relatively pure calcium carbonate with little contained terrigenous material.

REEF ENVIRONMENTS

Modern reefs are restricted to certain environments. They occur abundantly only between 23 degrees north and south latitudes and tend to be restricted to the western side of ocean basins, which lack upwelling of cold bottom waters. This restriction is based on temperature, as reefs do not flourish where temperatures frequently fall below 18 degrees Celsius. Reef growth is largely restricted to depths less than 60 meters, as there is insufficient penetration of sunlight below this depth for symbiont-bearing corals to flourish. Reefs also require clear waters lacking suspended terrigenous materials, as these interfere with the feeding activity of many reef organisms and also reduce the penetration of sunlight. Finally, most reef organisms require salinities that are in the normal oceanic range. It appears that many fossil reefs were similarly limited in their environmental requirements.

Some of the most striking features of modern reefs include their pronounced zonation, great diversity, and high productivity and growth rates. Reefs demonstrate a strong bathymetric (depth-related) zonation. This zonation is largely mediated through depth-related changes in turbulence intensity and in the quantity and spectral characteristics (reds are absorbed first, blues last) of available light. Shallow (1- to 5-meter) fore-reef environments are characterized by strong turbulence and high light intensity and possess low-diversity assemblages of wave-resistant corals, such as the elk-horn coral, *Acropora palmata*, and crustose red algae.

With increasing depth (10-20 meters), turbulence levels decrease and coral species diversity increases, with the occurrence of mound and delicate branching colonies. At greater depths (30-60 meters), corals assume a flattened, platelike form in an attempt to maximize surface area for exposure to ambient light. Sponges and many green algae are also very important over this range. Finally, corals possessing zooxanthellae, which live in the coral tissues and provide food for the coral host, are rare or absent below 60 meters because of insufficient light. Surprisingly, green and red calcareous algae extend to much greater depths (100-200 meters), despite the very low light intensity (much less than 1 percent of surface irradiance). Sponges are also important members of these deep reef communities.

REEF COMMUNITIES

Coral reefs are among the most diverse communities on Earth; however, there is no consensus on the mechanisms behind the maintenance of this great diversity. At one time, it was believed that reefs existed in a low-disturbance, highly stable environment, which allowed very fine subdivision of food and habitat resources and thus permitted the coexistence of a great number of different species. Upon closer inspection, however, many reef organisms appear to overlap greatly in food and habitat requirements. Also, it has become increasingly apparent that disturbance, in the form of disease, extreme temperatures, and hurricanes, is no stranger to reef communities.

Coral reefs exhibit very high rates of productivity (carbon fixation), which is a result of extremely tight recycling of existing nutrients. This is necessary, as coral reefs

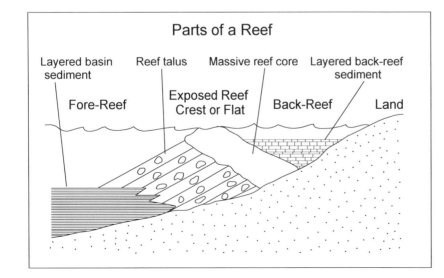

Parts of a Reef

Layered basin sediment   Reef talus   Massive reef core   Layered back-reef sediment

Fore-Reef   Exposed Reef Crest or Flat   Back-Reef   Land exist in virtual nutrient "deserts." Modern corals exhibit high skeletal growth rates, up to 10 centimeters per year for some branching species. Such high rates of skeletal production are intimately related to the symbiosis existing between the hermatypic or reef-building scleractinian corals (also gorgonians and many sponges) and unicellular algae or zooxanthellae. Corals that, for some reason, have lost their zooxanthellae or that are kept in dark rooms exhibit greatly reduced rates of skeleton production.

In addition to high individual growth rates for component taxa, the carbonate mass of the reefs may grow at a rate of some 2 meters per 1,000 years, a rate that is much higher than that of most other sedimentary deposits. This reflects the high productivity or growth rates of the component organisms and the efficient trapping of derived sediment by the reef frame. Although the framework organisms, most notably corals, are perhaps the most striking components of the reef system, the framework represents only 10-20 percent of most fossil reef masses. The remainder of the reef mass consists of sedimentary fill derived from the reef community through a combination of biosynthesis (secretion) and bioerosion (breaking down) of calcium carbonate. An example of the relative contributions of reef organisms to sediment can be found in Jamaica, where shallow-water, back-reef sediment consists of 41 percent coral, 24 percent green calcareous algae, 13 percent red calcareous algae, 6 percent foraminifera, 4 percent mollusks, and 12 percent other grains. The most important bioeroders are boring sponges, bivalves, and various "worms," which excavate living spaces within reef rock or skeletons, and parrot fish and sea urchins, which remove calcium carbonate as they feed upon surface films of algae.

TYPES OF REEF COMMUNITIES

A diversity of organisms has produced reef and reeflike structures throughout Earth's history. Several distinct reef community types have been noted, as well as four major "collapses" of reef communities. The oldest reefs or reeflike structures existed more than 2 billion years ago during the Precambrian eon. These consisted of low-diversity communities dominated by soft, blue-green algae, which trapped sediment to produce layered, often columnar structures known as stromatolites, similar if not identical to those being formed today. During the Early Cambrian period, blue-green algae were joined by calcareous, conical, spongelike organisms known as archaeocyathids, which persisted until the end of the Middle Cambrian. Following the extinction of the archaeocyathids, reefs again consisted only of blue-green algae until the advent of more modern reef communities in the Middle Ordovician period. These reefs consisted of corals (predominantly tabulate and, to a much lesser extent, rugose corals), red calcareous algae, bryozoans (moss animals), and the spongelike stromatoporoids. This community type persisted through the Devonian period, at which time a global collapse of reef communities occurred. The succeeding Carboniferous period largely lacked reefs, although algal and crinoidal (sea lily) mounds were common. Reefs again occurred in the Permian period, consisting mainly of red and green calcareous algae, stromatolites, bryozoans, and chambered calcareous sponges known as sphinctozoans, which resembled strings of beads. These reefs were very different from those of the earlier Paleozoic era; in particular, the tabulates and stromatoporoids no longer played an important role. The famous El Capitan reef complex of West Texas formed during this interval. The Paleozoic era ended with a sweeping extinction event that involved not only reef inhabitants but also other marine organisms.

After the Paleozoic extinctions, reefs were largely absent during the early part of the Mesozoic era. The advent of modern-type reefs consisting of scleractinian corals and red and green algae occurred in the Late Triassic period. Stromatoporoids once again occurred abundantly on reefs during this interval; however, the role of the previously ubiquitous blue-green algal stromatolites in reefs declined. Late Cretaceous reefs were often dominated by conical, rudistid bivalves that developed the ability to form frameworks and may have possessed symbiotic relationships with algae, as do many modern corals. Rudists, however, became extinct during the sweeping extinctions that occurred at the end of the Cretaceous period. The reefs that were reestablished in the Cenozoic era lacked stromatoporoids and rudists and consisted of scleractinian corals and red and green calcareous algae. This reef type has persisted, with fluctuations, until the present.

STUDY OF MODERN REEFS

Modern reefs are typically studied by divers, which enables observation and sampling to a depth of approximately 50 meters. Deeper environments have been made accessible through the availability of manned submersibles and unmanned, remotely operated vehicles that carry mechanical samplers as well as still and video cameras. The biological compositions of reef communities are determined by census (counting) methods commonly employed by plant ecologists. Studies of symbioses, such as that between corals and their zooxanthellae, employ radioactive tracers to determine the transfer of products between symbiont and host. Growth rates are measured by staining the calcareous skeletons of living organisms with a dye, such as Alizarin red, and then later collecting and sectioning the specimen and measuring the amount of skeleton added since the time of staining. Another method for determining growth is to X-ray a thin slice of skeleton and then measure and count the yearly growth bands that are revealed on the radiograph. Variations in growth banding reflect, among other factors, fluctuations in ocean temperature.

Reef sediments, which will potentially be transformed into reef limestones, are examined through sieving, X-ray diffraction, and epoxy impregnation and thin-sectioning. Sieving enables the determination of sediment texture, the relationships of grain sizes and abundance (which will reflect environmental energy and the production), and erosion of grains through biotic processes. X-ray diffraction produces a pattern that is determined by the internal crystalline structure of the sediment grains. As each mineral possesses a unique structure, the mineralogical identity of the sediment may be determined. Thin sections of embedded sediment or lithified rock are examined with petrographic microscopes, which reveal the characteristic microstructures of the individual grains. Thus, even highly abraded fragments of coral or algae may be identified and their contributions to the reef sediment determined.

STUDY OF FOSSIL REEFS

Because of their typically massive nature, fossil reefs are usually studied by thin-sectioning of lithified rock samples collected either from surface exposures or well cores. Reef limestones that have not undergone extensive alteration may be dated through carbon-14 dating, if relatively young, or through uranium-series radiometric dating methods.

NATURAL LABORATORIES AND ECONOMIC RESOURCES

Modern reefs serve as natural laboratories, enabling the geoscientist to witness and study phenomena, such as carbonate sediment production, bioerosion, and early cementation, that have been responsible for forming major carbonate rock bodies in the past. The study of cores extracted from centuries-old coral colonies shows promise for deciphering past climates and perhaps predicting future trends. This is made possible by the fact that the coral skeleton records variations in growth that are related to ocean temperature fluctuations. The highly diverse modern reefs also serve as ecological laboratories for testing models on the control of community structure. For example, the relative importance of stability versus disturbance and recruitment versus predation in determining community structure is being studied within the reef setting.

Modern reefs are economically significant resources, particularly for many developing nations in the tropics. Reefs and the associated lagoonal seagrass beds serve as important nurseries and habitats for many fish and invertebrates. The standing crop of fish immediately over reefs is much higher than that of adjacent open shelf areas. Reef organisms may one day provide an important source of pharmaceutical compounds, such as prostaglandins, which may be extracted from gorgonians (octocorals). In addition, research has focused upon the antifouling properties exhibited by certain reef encrusters. Reefs also provide recreational opportunities for snorkelers and for scuba divers, a fact that many developing countries are utilizing to promote their tourist industries. Finally, reefs serve to protect shorelines from wave erosion.

Because of the highly restrictive environmental tolerances of reef organisms, the occurrence of reefs in ancient strata enables fairly confident estimation of paleolatitude, temperature, depth, salinity, and water clarity. In addition, depth- or turbulence-related variation in growth form (mounds in very shallow water, branches at intermediate depths, and plates at greater depths) enables even more precise estimation of paleobathymetry or turbulence levels. Finally, buried ancient reefs are often important reservoir rock structures containing hydrocarbons and thus represent an important economic resources.

W. David Liddell

FURTHER READING

Darwin, Charles. *The Structure and Distribution of Coral Reefs.* Berkeley, Calif.: University of California Press, 1962. Originally published in 1851. Replete with observations on coral reefs from around the world. In addition, the theories presented on the formation of reef types such as atolls have withstood the test of time.

Davidson, Osha Gray. *The Enchanted Braid: Coming to Terms with Nature on the Coral Reef.* New York: Wiley, 1998. A beautifully illustrated introduction to the ecosystems of coral reefs. Sections deal with coral reef biology, ecology, and endangered reef ecosystems. Suitable for nonscientists. Color illustrations and maps.

Dubinsky, Zvy, and Noga Stambler, eds. *Coral Reefs: An Ecosystem in Transition.* Dordrecht: Springer, 2011. Gathers together information from hundreds of research papers on coral biology and coral reef research to discuss novel theories and challenge established paradigms in coral reef management and conservation.

Goreau, Thomas F., et al. "Corals and Coral Reefs." *Scientific American* 241 (August, 1979): 16, 124-136. A good overview of the ecology of modern coral reefs. The discussion of coral physiology and the symbiotic relationship with zooxanthellae is particularly valuable.

Harris, Peter T., and Elaine K. Baker, eds. *Seafloor Geomorphology as Benthic Habitat.* New York: Elsevier, 2011. Discusses benthic ecology, habitat mapping, biodiversity and community structure of seamounts, seabeds, reefs, fjords, and hydrothermal vents. Examines case studies and discusses methodologies of seafloor studies.

Hopley, David. *Encyclopedia of Modern Coral Reefs: Structure, Form and Process.* Dordrecht: Springer, 2011. Discusses the geology, geography, and ecology of Quaternary coral reefs, based on the most recent research by leading authorities from several countries.

Hovland, Martin. *Deep-Water Coral Reefs: Unique Biodiversity Hot-Spots.* Chichester, England: Praxis, 2008. Comprehensively discusses the concept that deep-water coral reefs provide examples of form, structure, and processes that might indicate the nature of ancient coral and carbonate reefs. Documents deep-water coral reefs around the world.

Kaplan, Eugene H. *A Field Guide to Coral Reefs of the Caribbean and Florida, Including Bermuda and the Bahamas.* Boston: Houghton Mifflin, 1988. Provides descriptions and illustrations (many in color) of common reef organisms, as well as an excellent overview of modern reef community structure, zonation, and environments.

Newell, Norman D. "The Evolution of Reefs." *Scientific American* 226 (June, 1972): 12, 54-65. Provides an overview of the composition of reef communities throughout Earth's history, including the various collapses and rejuvenations.

Rohwer, Forest, Merry Youle, and Derek Vosten. *Coral Reefs in the Microbial Seas.* Plaid Press, 2010. Provides a unique look at coral reefs by focusing on the microbial ecology and biology. Discusses coral formation, coral bleaching, overfishing, and other detriments. Mentions nutrient cycling. Includes some diagrams to supplement the text. Although the content is nonfictional science, the writing is in the style of a narrative of the author's exploration.

Sheppard, Charles R. C., Simon K. Davy, and Graham M. Pilling. *The Biology of Coral Reefs.* New York: Oxford University Press, 2009. Discusses the abiotic and biotic factors in the coral reef environment. Examines reef biodiversity and food chains. Presents chapters on human interactions with coral reefs.

Spalding, Mark D., Edmund P. Green, and Corinna Ravilious. *World Atlas of Coral Reefs.* Berkeley, Calif.: University of California Press, 2001. Discusses the biodiversity, ecology, and construction of coral reefs in a manner accessible to high-school students and undergraduates. Includes excellent photographs and images.

Stoddart, D. R. "Ecology and Morphology of Recent Coral Reefs." *Biological Reviews* 44 (1969): 433-498. Provides a review of the global distribution of coral reefs with emphasis on their ecology and geomorphology.

Vacher, Leonard, and Terrence M. Quinn. *Geology and Hydrogeology of Carbonate Islands.* New York: Elsevier, 2004. Looks at the geology, hydrology, geochemistry, and evolution of reefs and carbonate masses. Suitable for the careful high school-level reader. Illustrations, maps, index, and bibliography.

Wolanski, Eric. *Oceanographic Processes of Coral Reefs: Physical and Biological Links in the Great Barrier Reef.* Boca Raton, Fla.: CRC Press, 2001. Focuses primarily on coral reefs of Australia, Indonesia,

Thailand, and the Philippines. Covers a comprehensive range of subjects relevant to the long-term health of coral reefs around the world.

Wood, Rachel. *Reef Evolution*. New York: Oxford University Press, 1999. A detailed account that follows the geophysical and geochemical phases of reefs. Pays special attention to reef ecology and the animal communities that make up these environments. Appropriate for the nonscientist.

Illustrations, maps, index, and bibliographical references.

See also: Alluvial Systems; Beaches and Coastal Processes; Bleaching of Coral Reefs; Deep-Sea Sedimentation; Deltas; Desert Pavement; Drainage Basins; Floodplains; Lakes; Radiocarbon Dating; River Bed Forms; River Flow; Sand; Sediment Transport and Deposition; Weathering and Erosion

REMOTE SENSING OF THE ATMOSPHERE

Scientists utilize a variety of remote sensory technologies, including passive imaging systems, radar, and lidar (light direction and ranging), to study gases and aerosols in the five layers of Earth's atmosphere. Remote sensors analyze and forecast meteorological phenomena and conditions. The field of remote sensing has particular relevance in light of efforts to assess and reverse global warming caused by human-made greenhouse emissions. Remote sensory technologies are ground-based, airborne, and space-based.

PRINCIPAL TERMS

- **active sensor:** type of remote sensor that emits radiation at a target to study its composition and condition
- **lidar:** type of remote sensor that operates similarly to radar but uses lasers instead of radio waves
- **lower atmosphere:** region of the atmosphere comprising the troposphere and the tropopause, reaching an altitude as high as 19 kilometers, or 12 miles
- **middle atmosphere:** region of the atmosphere comprising the mesosphere, mesopause, stratosphere, and stratopause
- **passive sensor:** type of remote sensor that detects naturally emitted energy, such as reflected sunlight, from target sources
- **pulse Doppler:** type of radar system that emits waves of electromagnetic energy at an atmospheric target; provides a detailed profile of motion, precipitation, and other conditions and objects
- **thermosphere:** region of the atmosphere marked by thin gases and ultraviolet radiation; also known as the upper atmosphere

THE ATMOSPHERE

One of the keys to life on Earth is the planet's atmosphere, a multilayered field that spans thousands of miles from the ground surface. The atmosphere is the origin of weather patterns and the location in which surface temperatures are regulated. Although the atmosphere comprises three primary gases—oxygen, nitrogen, and argon—it also contains aerosols (mists), particles, and many other gases.

Five basic layers make up the atmosphere. Each of these layers has distinct thermal patterns, rates of motion, chemical compositions, and density. The first of these layers is the troposphere, which begins at the planet's surface and extends skyward between 6.5 kilometers, or 4 miles (at the poles), and 20 km, or 12.5 mi (at the equator), to the tropopause (a transitional boundary between the troposphere and the above layer). These two regions make up the lower atmosphere. Earth's weather patterns occur in this layer.

The second layer is the stratosphere, extending from the tropopause to about 50 km (31 mi) above the ground surface. In the stratosphere, heat (which is produced by the development of ozone) increases with height. This phenomenon is contrary to what occurs in the troposphere, wherein heat decreases with increased height. Although little water vapor is present in the stratosphere, about 19 percent of the gases of Earth's atmosphere are found in the troposphere. Separating the stratosphere from the level above it is another transitional boundary, the stratopause.

The third level is the mesosphere, extending from the stratopause outward about 90 km (56 mi) above the surface. The gases in this layer are thinner, and temperatures (caused by ultraviolet radiation from the sun) decrease with an increase in height. It is in the mesosphere where most space debris, such as meteors, burn up. The section separating the mesosphere from the layer above is called the mesopause. Combined, the mesopause, mesosphere, stratopause, and stratosphere are called the middle atmosphere.

The fourth level, located about 600 km (375 mi) above the earth, is the thermosphere. In this layer (which makes up the upper atmosphere), gases are thin and increasingly heated with height, a condition created by high-energy ultraviolet and X-ray solar radiation. Finally, the fifth level, the exosphere, which is located about 1,000 km (620 mi) above the surface, is the region in which satellites orbit the planet.

TYPES OF REMOTE SENSOR SYSTEMS

One type of remote sensory technology is ground-based technologies and systems, usually housed in observatories or in mobile units (such as ships and weather balloons). Scientists use ground-based remote sensors to analyze precipitation patterns, turbulence, temperature, and other atmospheric conditions and trends.

Aircraft-borne remote sensors, another type of remote sensory technology, often prove highly effective. For example, scientists may fly high-altitude aircraft into clouds to take readings and photograph images that are not available to sensors on the ground. One such study occurred in 2000, when a high-altitude aircraft operated by the National Aeronautics and Space Administration was flown into cloud fields over Oklahoma. Using a system known as a multiangle imaging spectroradiometer, researchers generated simulations of weather patterns at high altitudes.

In later decades, the evolution of satellite technologies has added another dimension to scientists' study of the atmosphere. Satellites now play an integral role in the examination of the many atmospheric layers, providing greater range and depth to atmospheric science. For example, the European scientific satellite *MetOp* includes in its cache of onboard equipment a thermal, infrared, spectral-imaging system. This technology enables scientists to develop a comprehensive and detailed profile of the changes in atmospheric composition caused by pollution.

Scientists also use remote sensing equipment to forecast changes in atmospheric conditions. Weather forecasting continues to evolve, enabling meteorologists and other scientists to analyze complex weather patterns and, based on the data compiled, to predict atmospheric phenomena. Doppler radar, lidar (light direction and ranging), thermal imaging, and other active and passive remote sensors are employed for this purpose, developing models that predict how weather systems (such as storms and even fog) form, how they will be constituted, and the tracks they will follow.

RADAR AND LIDAR

One of the best-known of these ground-based remote sensors is radar, which directs radio waves at a target and interprets the returning waves. Scientists use radar to study weather systems, including wind speeds, precipitation, and other elements. Radar has evolved considerably since the 1980's to include systems that can produce highly detailed images of atmospheric conditions and events.

One such radar system is pulse Doppler radar, which focuses electromagnetic radiation at a target at various frequencies. Arrays of Doppler radars can provide a comprehensive profile of a given target, generating three-dimensional models and enabling researchers to more accurately predict phenomena.

Another increasingly popular application in the study of the atmosphere is a variation of radar that uses lasers rather than radio waves and electromagnetic radiation. Lidar, as it is known, focuses laser beams primarily at lower-level atmospheric targets (such as weather systems) and gathers data on precipitation, particulates, clouds, and other features. Lidar can in many cases provide data on specific targets with greater detail than can traditional radar.

REMOTE SENSING, ABSORPTION, AND SCATTERING

Many different types of remote sensors rely on spectral images of targets as illuminated by the sun. Depending largely on the size and composition of the target in question (and on the wavelength at which the light is radiated), light is either absorbed or scattered by the target.

Oxygen and nitrogen molecules in the atmosphere, for example, scatter solar radiation along a short wavelength of light only. This selective scattering ability is known as Rayleigh scattering. The colors that are emitted through this scattering process are blue and violet, which is why the sky appears blue on clear days. However, through Mie scattering, some molecules are large enough to scatter virtually any light wavelength equally. Cloud droplets, for example, are large enough to demonstrate Mie scattering properties: With every wavelength of solar radiation scattered, clouds appear white (a combination of all colors on the spectrum).

Scattering has evolved into an important research method for scientists studying the atmosphere. As mentioned, many different types of molecules, particulates, gases, and clouds are found in this broad region, and each type of molecule is composed in such a way that it absorbs some light and scatters others. Lidar has proved to be an effective tool in this arena.

Using ground-based lidar, scientists emit a series of beams into a cloud or target area in the atmosphere. The backscattering (Rayleigh or Mie) that occurs enables researchers to profile the composition of the cloud. Some airborne remote sensors employ lidar, pointing the beam downward into a specific area. Satellites, which can profile a much larger area by virtue of their location, also sometimes include lidar.

An example of the successful study of scattering as it pertains to specific phenomena is a 2011 survey conducted near Bozeman, Montana. Scientists attempting to assess the composition and origin of a layer of aerosol in the overhanging atmosphere used lidar (in addition to other remote sensor systems designed to detect scattered light signatures) to generate backscatter. Based on the data retrieved from a variety of angles, scientists determined that the aerosol cloud was made up of smoke from forest fires that were burning in California more than 1,600 km (1,000 mi) to the southwest.

ACTIVE AND PASSIVE REMOTE SENSORS

The atmosphere is a highly complex environment, containing many different types of particles, aerosols, and gases. Scientists using remote sensors to study multifarious atmospheric conditions must therefore utilize different types of technology.

One of these technologies is passive in nature. Passive sensory systems focus on targets that reflect natural energy or that emit their own energy. Often, passive sensors are effective during the day, when sunlight is reflected off target molecules and other objects. However, remote sensors that detect infrared signatures (such as thermal energy that is emitted naturally from a source) are also used during the day or night.

Active sensors, however, emit radiation at a target to analyze that target. Such radiation includes microwaves, light waves, or radio waves. Active sensors are useful for a number of reasons. First, when analyzing a target that does not emit an energy signature, active sensors are equally as effective in daylight as they are during periods without illuminating sunlight. Second, these sensors can be adjusted to detect energy emissions other than solar radiation (energy that is released at different wavelengths). Third, by adjusting the wavelengths of the emissions focused on a target, scientists can study the target's different properties from multiple angles.

Many active and passive remote sensors focus on microwave emissions. Microwaves exist along wavelengths of between 1 centimeter (0.4 inch) and 1 meter (3 feet). Because of these relatively long wavelengths, microwaves do not scatter as sunlight does. Additionally, many microwaves (either emitted by an active sensor system or captured by a passive one) that are radiated at longer wavelengths penetrate thick clouds, haze, and even steady rainfall. In other words, microwave-oriented passive and active sensors can be utilized in most types of weather. Because of

this flexibility, meteorologists and other atmospheric scientists utilize such sensors not only to study phenomena but also to create models for weather prediction.

COMPUTER MODELING

An important complement to remote sensing is computer modeling. Such models are highly useful for their ability to compile large amounts of data from studies that encompass broad target areas or complex systems. This application is particularly useful when scientists conduct large-scale observations, such as global studies on air pollution and national weather forecasting.

One example of the successful application of computer modeling to remote sensing is found in ongoing research on transpiration (the process by which water is evaporated and carried into the air). Since the early 1990's scientists have used a number of ground-based, airborne, and satellite-based remote sensory systems to detect temperature, humidity, surface radiation, and other atmospheric elements. These studies are global, connecting the conditions of many different target areas to create a composite of transpiration systems.

Such studies require the consolidation of enormous amounts of remote sensor data and, based on the arrangement of such data, the creation of a number of computer models to better understand trends and to more accurately predict future conditions. One such project, the International Satellite Cloud Climatology Project, utilizes three different computer models that compile remote sensor data from around the world and generate models on such areas as surface energy and future transpiration rates.

FUTURE IMPLICATIONS

Remote sensors continue to evolve as a technology. They are creating greater image clarity and providing more comprehensive data on atmospheric targets and trends.

Satellite-based systems are enhancing the use of remote sensors in the study of specific areas. These systems also provide data on atmospheric trends and systems on a much broader (even global) scale. Coupled with the ability of scientists to view and share remote sensor data through the Internet (often in real time), this technology is likely to continue its contributions to meteorology and earth science.

This evolution is important, particularly in light of demands to better predict severe weather and to accurately monitor greenhouse gas emissions. An apparent increase in severe weather (such as the 2011 outbreak of tornadoes across the United States) has prompted scientists to explore the factors that contribute to severe storms. Remote sensors that can detect wind velocities, transpiration, and other key elements are vital.

Furthermore, heightened public attention to the effects of human-made greenhouse gas emissions (such as industrial pollution and automobile exhaust) continues to create the need to examine the types and volumes of particulates in the atmosphere. In this arena too, state-of-the-art remote sensors are making such studies possible.

Michael P. Auerbach

FURTHER READING

Clerbaux, Cathy, Solene Turquety, and Pierre Coheur. "Infrared Remote Sensing of Atmospheric Composition and Air Quality: Toward Operational Applications." *Comptes Rendus Geoscience* 342, nos. 4/5 (2010): 349-356. Discusses the uses of remote sensors for studying pollution's effects on the atmosphere. Reviews satellite-based technologies such as thermal infrared sensors to study the troposphere on a global scale.

Guzzi, Rodolfo, ed. *Exploring the Atmosphere by Remote Sensing Techniques.* New York: Springer, 2010. In this collection of lectures, the editor presents various remote sensing practices used in the study of gases, aerosols, and clouds in the atmosphere.

Hoff, Raymond, et al. "Applications of the Three-Dimensional Air Quality System to Western US Air Quality: IDEA, Smog Blog, Smog Stories, AirQuest, and the Remote Sensing Information Gateway." *Journal of the Air and Waste Management Association* 59, no. 8 (2009): 980-989. Describes an extensive network of remote sensors, based on ground and onboard satellites used to monitor aerosols released into the atmosphere in the United States. The system, which creates three-dimensional images of the atmosphere, is a joint partnership of local, state, and federal governments and private citizens.

Kokhanovsky, Alexander A., ed. *Light Scattering and Remote Sensing of Atmosphere and Surface.* Vol. 6 in *Light Scattering Reviews.* New York: Springer, 2011. A compilation of papers on remote sensing as it relates to light scattering and the images created by precipitation as influenced by light scattering phenomena.

Marzano, Frank S., and Guido Visconti, eds. *Remote Sensing of Atmosphere and Ocean from Space: Models, Instruments, and Techniques.* New York: Springer, 2011. A collection of lectures that focus on spaceborne remote-sensing techniques, including microwave, infrared, and passive sensors and weather forecasting practices.

"Radiometric Normalization of Sensor Scan Angle Effects in Optical Remote Sensing Imagery." *International Journal of Remote Sensing* 28, no. 19 (2007): 4453-4469. Describes some of the optical effects, caused by the content of the atmosphere, which can be scanned using satellite-based and airborne remote sensors.

See also: Atmospheric Properties; Climate; Climate Change Theories; Climate Modeling; Earth-Sun Relations; Geochemical Cycles; Global Energy Transfer; Global Warming; Greenhouse Effect; IPCC; Long-Term Weather Patterns; Ocean-Atmosphere Interactions; Ozone Depletion and Ozone Holes; Precipitation; Recent Climate Change Research; Remote Sensing of the Oceans; Satellite Meteorology; Seasons; Surface Ocean Currents

REMOTE SENSING OF THE OCEANS

Remote sensory systems are essential pieces of technology in oceanic studies. Because the oceans are whole systems, satellite-based remote sensors are rapidly becoming the tool of choice (although airborne sensors and shipboard systems also are used). Remote sensors are effective in detecting temperature changes, currents, sea levels, and even topography. Such technologies continue to evolve, providing clearer and more detailed images (and greater volumes of data). In light of concerns about global climate change and about environmental protection, wide-ranging remote sensors are integral for oceanic research.

PRINCIPAL TERMS

- **active sensor:** type of remote sensor that emits radiation at a target to study its composition and condition
- **gravest empirical mode:** concept in which the relationship between oceanic subsurface density and surface elevation is examined
- **lidar:** type of remote sensor that operates similarly to radar but uses lasers instead of radio waves
- **Northern Ocean:** Arctic portion of Earth's oceanic system
- **passive sensor:** type of remote sensor that detects naturally emitted energy, such as reflected sunlight, from target sources
- **scatterometer:** active radar that emits high-frequency microwave pulses at a target
- **Southern Ocean:** Antarctic portion of Earth's oceanic system
- **synthetic aperture radar:** type of radar that emits a high volume of radio waves at a target as it passes overhead, creating a multidimensional image of the target

STUDYING THE OCEANS

Oceans cover about 65.7 percent of Earth, spanning about 334 square kilometers (129 million square miles), with a volume of 1,370 million cubic km (329 million cubic mi). About 97 percent of Earth's water is found in oceans, which reach an average depth of about 3.8 km (2.4 mi).

Oceans play a critical role in many natural processes, including generating precipitation and weather patterns, transferring sediment, supporting countless marine ecosystems, and delivering essential chemical elements and compounds (such as carbon and methane).

Scientists have long studied the ocean. In the twenty-first century, as evidence of global climate change continues to surface, scientists are paying increased attention to changes in the extensive series of processes and systems under the ocean surface. In this arena, scientists are focusing on key indicators of shifts in oceanic systems and processes. Among these indicators are coastline erosion, temperature changes, changes in ocean currents, and the presence of organic materials (such as ice and algae blooms). Researchers also are carefully monitoring the discharge of human-made compounds, such as oil and waste materials, into the oceans.

In addition to researching isolated geographic areas, scientists are increasingly focusing on the system of oceans as a whole. Such pursuits require the application of satellite-based and airborne research technologies, which can compile data and images of broad oceanic regions.

REMOTE SENSORS AND THE OCEANS

Remote sensors are systems that, from a distance, collect data and imagery of a given object or phenomenon. In the study of oceans, such sensors are usually placed aboard aircraft or satellites. Remote sensors may detect thermal conditions, wave height, current speeds, water vaporization, and debris movements (including the movements of icebergs and sediment).

There exists a wide range of remote sensor technologies, most of which rely on the object in question emitting some form of detectable energy (such as microwaves or solar radiation). For example, radar emits radio waves at its target, reading the wave feedbacks. Lidar uses concentrated beams of light (lasers) to assess a target.

Remote sensors usually fall into one of two general categories: passive and active. Passive sensors target a specific area and seek naturally occurring energy emissions, such as the scattering of sunlight. To function, most passive sensors therefore rely on daylight hours. Active sensors emit a form of radiation of their own, targeting a geographic area on the ocean. When the light, microwave, or other form of emission is absorbed or reflected, the sensor reacquires the data.

DATA AND IMAGE TYPES

Remote sensors may be used to glean information about the spread of pollutants and erosion. For example, scientists use such technologies to study a key indicator of ocean pollution and erosion: the coastal plume, which appears along many coasts.

In a coastal plume, denser water pushes lighter, unpolluted water upward and, along with it, plankton and other materials. To detect coastal plumes, scientists frequently use thermal radiometers, which use infrared to capture the heat signatures of the dense substances caught in the plume.

Another highly useful tool for scientists studying the oceanic system is a scatterometer. Scatterometers are active radar systems that usually are mounted on a satellite. The device transmits high-frequency microwave pulses at the ocean surface. The pulses that bounce back to the satellite are then measured. The different return waves provide information about the winds at the ocean surface, creating a detailed composite of wave sizes and other aspects of the ocean's surface. Knowledge of these surface winds, combined with data from other instrumentation (such as the aforementioned thermal radiometers, radar, lidar, and other sensor systems), helps scientists understand the speed at which coastal plumes, algae blooms, and oceanic storm fronts move and provide information on surface water temperatures and wave sizes.

Microwave sensors also have a number of other highly useful applications to oceanic studies, as every object on the surface emits some type of microwave energy (although that energy is usually at a low level of radiation). Sea ice is one type of surface object that emits a detectable microwave signature that can be scanned from orbit, even through cloud cover and at any time of day. Passive microwave sensors (which were introduced in the early 1970's and have since evolved considerably) are found on many different satellites and are used to track sea ice, revealing clues about surface temperatures, wind conditions, and currents. Passive microwave sensors cannot assess the temperature of a piece of ice. Still, they can be used to detect the physical and chemical properties of a block of sea ice, including its crystalline structure.

SYNTHETIC APERTURE RADAR

Another useful remote sensor in this arena is synthetic aperture radar (SAR). Like other radar systems, SAR emits radio waves at a target, reading the echo to create an image of the target.

However, SAR, which is usually attached to an aircraft or a satellite, continuously sends such waves at the target as it moves overhead. The constant echoes create a more comprehensive, multidimensional image of the target. SARs are useful in the study of coastal plumes, as they generate images of the plumes themselves and track their growth and movements.

SAR systems are useful in gathering comprehensive data about oceanic conditions. Wind velocities and wave height are essential factors for scientists seeking to monitor changes in ocean currents, sedimentation transfer, and evaporation. Many SAR systems can even penetrate the ocean surface and provide detailed images of the topography of the ocean floor. Such detailed information can help scientists generate computer models and more accurately predict changes.

INNOVATIVE REMOTE SENSORS

In addition to using well-established remote sensors, scientists are exploring the use of innovative sensor technologies. When added to a series of other sensors, these sensors provide even greater clarity to the oceanic target at hand.

For example, polarimetric passive radiometers can detect electromagnetic waves emanating from the source target. Used in concert with radiometers and other remote sensors, polarimetric passive radiometers can help scientists gain readings on ocean salinity (the volume of salt in ocean water), adding a new dimension to the study of oceanic conditions.

Earth's oceans are dynamic and are changing in a wide range of areas almost constantly. Knowing this, scientists must consider certain environmental conditions when studying oceanic phenomena and characteristics. For example, in the study of circulation (that is, the water's flow patterns), scientists must account for rising and falling water levels. Ideally, such studies are conducted when the ocean is at its lowest tidal level so that elements such as high waves can be avoided (such conditions can disguise or muddle examinations).

An innovative tool in the calculation of oceanic elevation is the interferometric radar altimeter. This type of remote sensor observes two sets of waves from the target (such as the energy between high waves). An examination of this wave interference provides data on ocean's elevation and provides greater resolution to scientific measurements.

Remote sensors have proved effective at analyzing shallow-depth and surface conditions. A vexing pursuit, however, in the study of oceans (particularly in Arctic and Antarctic regions) is deep currents. Remote sensors have had problems penetrating the dense underwater environment, creating only low-resolution images that are largely unusable.

Scientists have applied another innovative remote sensory approach to this problem. In many areas of the Northern and Southern oceans, subsurface density can be used to provide clues about deep currents. In one study, researchers analyzed the relationship between subsurface density and surface elevation (a theoretical concept known as the gravest empirical mode [GEM]). The study's authors argued that these sizable areas of density can be used to calculate salinity and temperatures (two key elements that play a role in ocean currents). Because of these findings, researchers may begin to use satellite-based and aircraft-mounted remote sensors known as altimeters (which measure elevation) to isolate these columns of dense surface and subsurface water. From the data collected through this GEM-altimeter approach, researchers may find another useful tool in studying the oceans' dynamic systems.

Furthermore, scientists are considering new techniques in the study of sea ice through the use of microwave sensors. As stated earlier, passive microwave sensors do not detect the temperature of a piece of ice. However, some researchers have proposed utilizing the weather to assist in this capacity. This approach entails analysis of an ice block's microwave emissions and its brightness (as created by local weather conditions). Using a two-step mathematical algorithm, scientists are generating a catalog of global sea ice that may be used to track temperature changes on the ocean's surface.

IMPLICATIONS AND FUTURE PROSPECTS

In many ways the evolution of remote sensors has helped scientists better understand some of the most challenging aspects of the oceanic system. Researchers have long used contact sensors (such as those mounted on buoys or dragged behind moving ships) to study ocean elevations, wave height, floor topography, and temperature changes.

Remote sensors used today add many more dimensions to these studies. Satellite-based radars, altimeters, and radiometers, for example, generate data on these conditions but on a much larger scale and with much greater resolution.

Adding to the benefits of remote sensors in the study of the oceans is that the ever-evolving technologies can be used in locations in which previous systems would acquire unreliable data only; also, remote sensors can now be used to speed up thorough studies that used to take much longer. The remote and harsh environments of the Arctic and Antarctica (the Northern and Southern ocean regions) provide excellent examples of this fact.

Today, remote sensors can detect thermal changes, the formation of icebergs, density shifts, currents, and other important phenomena from orbit. Such developments in research of the Northern and Southern oceans are critical, as scientists who are concerned with global climate change tend to focus on ocean elevation and debris in and around these geographic areas.

Additionally, the remote sensors found particularly on satellites are easily accessed by participating scientists around the world. There exists a wide range of internationally managed satellites with onboard remote sensors that are trained on Earth's oceans. Among these satellites are SeaWiFS, SeaWinds, MODIS, and MERIS, which are part of a joint program of the National Aeronautics and Space Administration and the National Oceanic and Atmospheric Administration (NOAA). Government agencies such as NOAA and university-based researchers and graduate students can access such networks with relative ease.

Through such easy access and global communications networks, these scientists can share data and develop large-scale international studies. With the continued evolution of SAR, scatterometers, altimeters, and other remote sensors (and with the application of such innovative remote-sensing techniques as GEM), scientists will likely continue to generate voluminous and detailed data and images of Earth's oceanic system.

Michael P. Auerbach

FURTHER READING

Alberotanza, Luigi. "Active and Passive Remote Sensors as a New Technology for Coastal and Lagoon Monitoring." *Aquatic Conservation* 11, no. 4 (2001): 267-272. Discusses the importance of studying coastal and lagoon conditions within the scientific pursuit of oceanic conservation. Also discusses the use of several passive and active remote-sensor systems in this arena.

Martin, Seelye. *An Introduction to Ocean Remote Sensing.* New York: Cambridge University Press, 2004. Discusses the use of satellite-based remote sensors for the retrieval of biologic and physical data from the oceans. Presents programs that will likely be introduced as far ahead as 2019.

Mityagina, M. I., O. Y. Larova, and S. S. Karimova. "Multi-sensor Survey of Seasonal Variability in Coastal Eddy and Internal Wave Signatures in the North-Eastern Black Sea." *International Journal of Remote Sensing* 31, nos. 17/18 (2010): 4779-4990. Describes a multisystem approach to the application of remote sensors in the study of coastal areas and waves in the Black Sea. Among the systems employed in this study are synthetic aperture radar, radiometers, infrared sensors, and other active and passive radar systems.

Rees, W. G. *Physical Principles of Remote Sensing.* 2d ed. New York: Cambridge University Press, 2001. Provides general information about the principles of remote sensing technology and their application to earth sciences (including oceanic studies). The primary type of sensors described are those mounted on satellites.

Robinson, Ian S. *Discovering the Ocean from Space: The Unique Applications of Satellite Oceanography.* New York: Springer, 2010. Discusses the development of satellite-based remote sensor systems for oceanic studies. Provides a timeline of other major oceanic remote-sensor studies that starts in 1991 (the year the European Space Agency first launched such a program).

Sikora, Todd D., et al. "A Synthetic Aperture Radar-Based Climatology of Open-Cell Convection Over the Northeast Pacific Ocean." *Journal of Applied Meteorology and Climatology* 50, no. 3 (2011): 594-603. Describes the use of synthetic aperture radar (SAR) in the study of convection (the process by which warmer, less dense fluid rises and more dense, cooler fluid descends) in the northeastern regions of the Pacific. SAR assisted in an eight-year study of wind speeds and temperature changes associated with convection.

See also: Arctic Ocean; Atlantic Ocean; Atmospheric and Oceanic Oscillations; Atmospheric Properties; Climate; Climate Change Theories; Climate Modeling; Deep Ocean Currents; Deep-Sea Sedimentation; Deltas; Earth-Sun Relations; Geochemical Cycles; Global Energy Transfer; Global Warming; Gulf Stream; Hydrologic Cycle; Indian Ocean; Long-Term Weather Patterns; Mediterranean Sea; North Sea; Observational Data of the Atmosphere and Oceans; Ocean-Atmosphere Interactions; Ocean Pollution and Oil Spills; Oceans' Origin; Oceans' Structure; Ocean Tides; Ocean Waves; Pacific Ocean; Precipitation; Remote Sensing of the Atmosphere; Salinity and Desalination; Saltwater Intrusion; Sand; Satellite Meteorology; Sea Level; Seamounts; Seawater Composition; Sediment Transport and Deposition; Surface Ocean Currents; Surface Water; Turbidity Currents and Submarine Fans; Wind; World Ocean Circulation Experiment

RIVER BED FORMS

Bed forms, produced by flows of water or air in natural environments and in artificial channels, are a distinctive aspect of the transport of granular sediment. They have a strong effect on the magnitude of bottom friction felt by the flow. Because of their great variety as a function of flow conditions, bed forms are valuable in interpreting depositional conditions of ancient sedimentary deposits.

PRINCIPAL TERMS

- **aeolian deposits:** material transported by wind
- **angle of repose:** the natural angle formed between the horizontal plane and the side of a freestanding pile of sediment particles under the force of gravity in a fluid medium
- **antidune:** an undulatory upstream-moving bed form produced in free-surface flow of water over a sand bed in a certain range of high flow speeds and shallow flow depths
- **bed configuration:** the overall geometry of a sediment bed molded by sediment transport in a flowing fluid
- **bed form:** an individual geometrical element of a bed configuration
- **combined flow:** a flow of fluid with components of both unidirectional and oscillatory flow superposed on one another to produce a more complex pattern of fluid motion
- **current ripple:** a small bed form, oriented predominantly transverse to the direction of flow, produced at low to moderate flow speeds in unidirectional water flows
- **dune:** a large bed form, oriented predominantly transverse to the direction of flow, produced at moderate to high flow speeds
- **flume:** a laboratory open channel in which water is passed over a sediment bed to study the nature of the sediment movement
- **oscillation ripple:** a small to large bed form, oriented predominantly transverse to the direction of flow, produced at low to moderate flow speeds in oscillatory water flows
- **oscillatory flow:** a flow of fluid with a regular back-and-forth pattern of motion
- **plane bed:** a bed configuration without rugged bed forms produced in both unidirectional and oscillatory flows at high flow speeds
- **unidirectional flow:** a flow of fluid oriented everywhere and at all times in the same direction

CHARACTERISTICS

A striking feature of the transport of loose granular sediment over a bed of the same material by a turbulent flow of fluid such as air or water is that in a wide range of conditions of flow and sediment size, the bed is molded into topographic features, called bed forms, on a scale ranging from hundreds to millions of times larger than the grains themselves. Examples of such bed forms are sand ripples at the seashore or on a dry riverbed, sand dunes in the desert, and (less apparent to the casual observer) large underwater sand dunes in rivers and in the shallow ocean. The overall geometry of a sediment bed molded by a flow of fluid is called the bed configuration. Bed forms are individual elements of this configuration. The term "bed form" includes both the overall geometry and the individual elements of that geometry.

The enormous range of bed-form-producing flows, together with the complex dynamics of the response of the bed, makes for striking variety in the scale and geometry of bed forms. Scales typically span a range of five orders of magnitude, from a few centimeters to more than 1,000 meters in spacing. Bed forms may appear as long ridges or circumscribed mounds, and their crests may be rounded or sharp. Most bed forms are irregular in detail, but elongated bed forms tend to show a more or less strong element of regularity in their overall arrangement, some even being perfectly regular and straight-crested. Elongated bed forms tend to be oriented transversely to the direction of flow, although flow-parallel forms are produced under certain conditions, and forms with no strongly preferred orientation are produced in some flows. Most bed forms are approximately wave-shaped and are often likened to waves, but they are waves only in a geometrical sense, not in a functional sense.

The most common bed forms are in sands (sediments having a mean particle size between about 0.1 millimeter and 2 millimeters), but bed forms are produced in silts (sediments having a mean particle size between about 4 micrometers and 0.1 millimeter) and gravels (sediment having a mean particle size greater than 2 millimeters) as well. Bed forms produced by flows of air or water over mineral sediments in natural flow environments are of greatest interest to geologists. A far wider range of bed forms can be produced by flows of fluids with other densities and viscosities over sediments that are more or less dense than the common mineral sediments, which have densities mostly in the range 2.5 to 3.0 grams per cubic centimeter.

TYPES OF FLUID FLOW

Bed forms are made by unidirectional flows of air or water, as in rivers and tidal currents and under sand-moving winds, and by oscillatory flows, as on the shallow sea floor beneath wind-generated surface waves, which cause the water at the bottom to move back and forth with a period the same as that of the waves and with horizontal excursion distances of a few centimeters to a few meters. Bed forms are also made by what are called combined flows, which are superpositions of unidirectional and oscillatory flows. Such combined-flow bed forms are not as well understood as those made by unidirectional and oscillatory flows, but they are common in the shallow ocean. Bed forms made under wind are called subaerial or aeolian bed forms, and bed forms made under water are called subaqueous bed forms.

It might seem that the natural mode of sediment transport would be over a planar bed surface. In certain ranges of flow, a planar transport surface is indeed the stable bed configuration, but technically, such a plane bed is a bed configuration with no bed forms. In reality, plane-bed transport is the stable configuration only under a very limited set of conditions, whereas rugged bed forms cover the transport surface over a wide range of conditions in both oscillatory and unidirectional flows. Why such bed forms develop at all on transport surfaces is poorly understood. In certain ranges of flow, the planar transport surface is unstable in the sense that small bed irregularities of the kind that can be built at random by the plane-bed sediment transport become amplified to grow eventually into bed forms rather than being smoothed out again. The physics behind this instability is chaotic and complex, and is still not clearly understood. An essential element of this complexity is that there is a strong interaction or feedback between the bed configuration and the flow. The flow

molds the bed configuration, but the bed configuration in turn affects the nature of the flow.

In unidirectional flow, current ripples are formed in fine sands as soon as the current is strong enough to move the particles, and they persist to moderate currents of about 0.5 meter per second. In a vertical cross section parallel to the flow, these current ripples are triangular in shape, with downstream slopes about equal to the angle of repose of sand under water (about 30 degrees) and with gentler upstream slopes. In top or horizontal view, they are oriented mostly transverse to the direction of flow and are irregular in detail. Their spacings range from 10 to 20 centimeters, and their heights are a few centimeters. This characteristic size changes little with flow strength or sediment size. With increasing unidirectional-flow speed, ripples give way to dunes, which are geometrically fairly similar to ripples but are of much larger scale, ranging from meters to thousands of meters in spacing and tens of centimeters to tens of meters in height, depending in a complex and poorly understood way on conditions of flow as well as sediment size. With further increase in flow speed to about 1 meter per second, dunes are replaced by a plane-bed configuration. The sequence of bed configurations with increasing unidirectional flow speed over coarse sands is different from that over fine sands: Transport is over a plane bed at flow strengths just above the threshold for sediment movement, and then dunes develop with further increase in flow strength. In sediments coarser than about 0.6 millimeter, current ripples are not formed in any range of flow speeds.

Current ripples and dunes move upstream or downstream at a speed far lower than the flow speed. This movement proceeds by erosion of sediment on the upstream side of the bed form and deposition on the downstream side. When an individual ripple or dune can be watched carefully for a time, it is seen to change its size, shape, and speed irregularly, eventually to disappear by being absorbed into a neighboring bed form. Offsetting this loss of bed forms is the production of new ones by a kind of subdivision of one larger form into two smaller ones. In flows of water with a free upper surface, like rivers and tidal currents, undulatory bed forms called antidunes make their appearance at high flow speeds and shallow flow depths. Antidunes, so named because they tend to move slowly upstream by erosion of sediment on the downstream sides and deposition on the upstream sides, come about by a complex effect of standing surface waves (waves that move upstream about as fast as the flow is moving downstream) on the sediment bed.

In oscillatory flow, regular straight-crested bed forms called oscillation ripples, with sharp crests and broadly rounded troughs, are formed as soon as the sediment begins to be moved. At their smallest, their spacing is a few centimeters, but they grow in size to more than 1 meter in spacing as the period and amplitude of the oscillatory motion increase. In fine sands, these larger ripples become irregular and mound-shaped, but observations are not yet adequate for a detailed description. When the maximum flow speed during a single oscillation reaches about 1 meter per second, the bed forms are washed out to a plane-bed mode of transport. Combined flows produce a whole range of ripples intermediate between current ripples and oscillation ripples.

If the flow changes with time, as is the rule rather than the exception in natural flows, the bed configuration adjusts in response. Usually the bed configuration lags behind the change in the flow, with the result that the bed configuration is more or less out of equilibrium. Dunes formed by reversing flow in a tidal channel are a good example of such disequilibrium; commonly the weaker of the two flows (whether ebb or flood) modifies the shape of the dunes but does not reverse the asymmetry. Bed forms on a riverbed during passage of a flood also tend to lag behind changes in the flow.

STUDY OF BED FORMS

Bed forms can be observed and studied in natural flow environments and in laboratory tanks and channels. Each of these approaches has its advantages and disadvantages. In nature, observations on bed configurations are limited by various practical and technical difficulties. In laboratory tanks and channels, the bed forms can be studied much more easily, but for the most part water depths are unnaturally shallow.

A laboratory open channel in which a flow of water is passed over a sediment bed is called a flume. Flumes range from a few meters to more than 100 meters long, from about 10 centimeters to a few meters wide, and from several centimeters to about 1 meter deep. The water is usually recirculated from the downstream end to the upstream end to form a kind of endless river. The sediment may also be recirculated, or it may be fed at the upstream end and caught in a trap at the downstream end. In a flume, it is fairly easy to measure the profile of the bed configuration with a mechanical pointer gauge or with a sonic depth sounder, and the bed forms can be studied visually and photographed through the sidewalls and also from the top when the absence of surface turbulence permits. Time-lapse motion pictures of bed-form movement are also instructive. Oscillatory-flow bed forms can be studied either in long open tanks, in which water waves are passed over a sand bed to produce oscillatory flow at the bed, or in closed horizontal ducts, in which water is pushed back and forth in a regular oscillation between tanks at the ends of the duct.

In some natural flow environments, such as rivers and tidal currents, the geometry of the bed forms can be studied when they are exposed at low water. Observations of the bed forms when they are being molded by the flow, however, are more difficult. If the flow is not too strong, divers can make direct observations. Profiling of the bed geometry along lines or even across wide areas is usually possible by means of various sonar techniques, whereby the travel times of sound pulses reflected from the bed are converted to water depths. If the water is clear enough, bottom photographs of small areas can be taken. Current velocities can be measured with current meters anchored on the bed. Movement of large bed forms is difficult to measure because bed-form speeds are slow and usually no fixed reference points are available.

The status of observations on bed configurations leaves much to be desired. Even in laboratory channels and tanks, where the major outlines are by now fairly well known, there is much room for further work for two reasons: The narrowness of the flow tends to distort the three-dimensional aspects of the bed geometry, and little work has been done on bed forms in combined flows. There is a need for more observations on the geometry and movement of bed forms in natural flows as a function of flow strength, as well as on the effect of disequilibrium.

SIGNIFICANCE

Bed forms are ubiquitous in natural flow environments. They are most apparent to the casual eye in fields of sand dunes in deserts and in certain coastal environments where the wind molds available loose sand into dunes. They are widely present but less obvious in rivers and the shallow ocean. Apart from their intrinsic scientific interest as a widespread natural phenomenon, bed forms are of importance in both engineering and geology for various reasons. Large underwater bed forms many meters high in rivers and marine currents can be obstacles to navigation, and their movement can be a threat to submarine structures. Also, the inexorable movement of desert dunes or coastal dunes can bury roads and buildings. In other engineering applications, technology imitates nature and various processes to be carried out rely on the flow of a particle-bearing fluid medium, as is the case in fluidized bed processes. A comprehensive understanding of the behavior of the particle load within the fluid is essential to enhancing and ensuring the efficiency of those processes.

The rugged topography of ripple and dune bed forms leads to a pattern of flow over each bed form in which the pressure on the upstream surface is relatively high and the pressure on the downstream surface is relatively low, much like an unstreamlined motor vehicle on the highway or a house in a strong wind. This pressure difference adds greatly to the force the flow exerts on the bed and, conversely, to the force the bed exerts on the moving flow. Hydraulic engineers have expended much effort on studying the effect that this resistance force has on the depth a river assumes when it is given a particular rate of flow to carry. A river with a planar bed can pass a given flow rate at a shallower depth and greater velocity than can a river with a bed roughened by large dunes, which exert a large resistance force on the flow and make the velocity smaller and the depth greater.

Geologists have given attention to bed forms partly because of their effect on the geometry of the stratification that develops as a sediment bed is deposited while bed forms are active on the sediment surface. It is often possible to tell the kind of bed form that was present just by examining the stratification in a sedimentary rock like a sandstone. If the flow conditions responsible for making that kind of bed form are already known, from laboratory experiments or from observations in modern natural flow environments, the depositional conditions of that sedimentary rock (which may be geologically very ancient)

can be interpreted. Such interpretations are one of the tools used in mapping the geometry of subsurface petroleum reservoirs in sedimentary rocks.

John Brelsford Southard

FURTHER READING

Allen, J. R. L. *Principles of Physical Sedimentology.* Caldwell, N.J.: Blackburn Press, 2001. A lucidly written introduction to the movement and deposition of sediment for sedimentology students at the college level and beyond. The chapter on bed forms is moderately mathematical, but there is some good descriptive material and illustrations of bed forms. The treatment of bed forms is concise but fairly comprehensive.

Chorley, Richard J., Stanley A. Schumm, and David E. Sugden. *Geomorphology.* New York: Methuen, 1985. A somewhat older textbook of geomorphology, though well-referenced work. Provides a comprehensive treatment of river and other bed forms in the overall context of the subject. Includes numerous line drawings as well as working charts and graphs.

Collier, Michael. *Over the Rivers: An Aerial View of Geology.* New York: Mikaya Press, 2008. Discusses the dynamic landscape of the rivers. Explains the processes that shape the landscape and its influence on humans. Written in the popular style. Easily accessible to the general public. Filled with bits of information and extraordinary photographs. Presents multiple examples drawn from the Mississippi River.

Collinson, J. D., Nigel Mountney, and D. B. Thompson. *Sedimentary Structures.* 3d ed. Edinburgh: Dunedin Academic Press, 2006. Written for beginning college-level students in sedimentology. Presents a nonmathematical treatment of bed forms in the context of their sedimentological significance. Three chapters are devoted to bed forms and the sedimentary structures they produce. Numerous illustrations of the various kinds of bed forms.

Darby, Stephen, and David Sear. *River Restoration: Managing the Uncertainty in Restoring Physical Habitat.* Hoboken, N.J.: John Wiley & Sons, 2008. Begins with theoretical and philosophical issues with habitat restoration in order to provide a strong foundation for decision making. Addresses logistics, planning, mathematical modeling, and construction stages of restoration in later chapters. Rounds out with post-construction monitoring and long-term evaluations to provide a full picture of the habitat restoration process. Highly useful for anyone involved in the planning and implementing of habitat restoration.

Freitag, Bob, et al. *Floodplain Management: A New Approach for a New Era.* Washington, D.C.: Island Press, 2009. Each chapter presents a different case study that focuses on a new topic in flood control. Strategies of floodplain management revolve around the natural processes and dynamics of rivers. Discusses multiple approaches, as varying as the locations in which they are used. A technical text best suited for engineers and hydrologists taking part in floodplain management.

Klingeman, Peter C., et al., eds. *Gravel-Bed Rivers in the Environment.* Highlands Ranch, Colo.: Water Resources Publications, 1995. A somewhat technical book that describes the sediment transport and ecology of rivers and riverbeds, as well as their interaction with surrounding environments. Intended for the college-level reader. Illustrations, maps, index, bibliography.

Leeder, M. R. *Sedimentology and Sedimentary Basins: From Turbulance to Tectonics.* 2d ed. Hoboken, N.J.: Blackwell, 2011. An introductory college-level text on sedimentology, with a well-illustrated and mostly nonmathematical chapter on bed forms. Suitable for high school readers who are willing to do some preparatory reading in the earlier parts of the book.

Middleton, G. V., and J. B. Southard. *Mechanics in the Earth and Environmental Sciences.* New York: Cambridge University Press, 1994. Offers a long and mostly nonmathematical chapter on bed forms for sedimentologists, with material on both the observational characteristics and the basic hydrodynamics of bed forms. Emphasis on underwater bed forms. No photographs.

Newson, Malcolm. *Land, Water and Development: Sustainable and Adaptive Management of Rivers.* 3d ed. London: Routledge, 2008. Presents land-water interactions. Discusses recent research, study tools and methods, and technical issues, such as soil erosion and damming. Suited for undergraduate students and professionals. Covers concepts in managing land and water resources in the developed world.

Reineck, H. E., and I. B. Singh. *Depositional Sedimentary* Environments. 2d ed. Berlin: Springer-Verlag, 1992. An almost entirely nonmathematical book, designed as a monograph on modern depositional environments for sedimentologists and marine geologists, that has several long, nonmathematical, and extensively referenced sections on bed forms in a great variety of flow environments. Suitable for high school readers. Unusually well illustrated.

Vanoni, V. A., ed. *Sedimentation Engineering.* 2d ed. New York: American Society of Civil Engineers, 2006. An engineering reference manual, aimed at students and practicing engineers, that deals with the fundamentals of sediment-transport mechanics from an applied standpoint. Parts of two chapters deal with bed forms, mainly in the context of rivers. The best and most authoritative source for information on the effect of bed forms on the behavior of rivers. A heavily mathematical text.

Wohl, Ellen. *A World of Rivers.* Chicago: University of Chicago Press, 2011. The Amazon, Ob, Nile, Danube, Ganges, Mississippi, Murray-Darling, Congo, Chang Jiang, and Mackenzie rivers each have a chapter in this book. Figure 1.1 contains more straightforward and organized information than some full textbooks. Discusses natural history, anthropogenic impact, and the future environment of these ten great rivers. The bibliography is organized by chapter.

Yalin, M. S. *River Mechanics.* New York: Pergamon Press, 1992. A college-level textbook, designed for engineering students, devotes a long chapter to an unusually fundamental treatment of the mechanics of bed forms. Heavily mathematical but with numerous qualitative insights into bed-form behavior. No illustrations.

See also: Alluvial Systems; Beaches and Coastal Processes; Dams and Flood Control; Deep-Sea Sedimentation; Deltas; Desert Pavement; Drainage Basins; Evaporites; Floodplains; Geochemical Cycles; Hydrologic Cycle; Lakes; Reefs; River Flow; Sand; Sediment Transport and Deposition; Surface Water; Weathering and Erosion

RIVER FLOW

Worldwide, rivers are the most important sources of water for cities and major industries. Hydroelectric power is a major source of electrical power, and transport of heavy, bulk goods by river barge is a vital link in most transportation systems. Understanding and predicting low, high, and average flows of rivers is therefore important to the people and industries that depend on them.

PRINCIPAL TERMS

- **discharge:** the total amount of water passing a point on a river per unit of time
- **evapotranspiration:** all water that is converted to water vapor by direct evaporation or passage through vegetation
- **hydraulic geometry:** a set of equations that relate river width, depth, and velocity to discharge
- **hydrograph:** a plot recording the variation of stream discharge over time
- **hydrologic cycle:** the circulation of water as a liquid and vapor from the oceans to the atmosphere and back to the oceans
- **hydrology:** broadly, the science of water; the term is often used in the more restricted sense of flow in channels
- **rating curve:** a plot of river discharge in relation to elevation of the water surface; permits estimation of discharge from the water elevation
- **turbulent flow:** the swirling flow that is typical of rivers, as opposed to smooth, laminar flow

TYPES OF WATER FLOW

There are two very different fundamental types of flow of water. Laminar flow is a smooth flow, in which particles suspended in the water will follow paths that are consistently parallel to each other throughout the flow. Turbulent flow is a complex, swirling flow in which the main flow separates into many different paths and the paths of suspended particles are not consistent with each other throughout the flow. Turbulent flow may have velocity components that are up or down from, or sideways or upstream of, the average flow direction, although the average flow direction is always in the downstream, or downslope, direction. Flow near the bottom and sides of a river or stream with a smooth bed is always laminar, but the zone of laminar flow is very narrow, as frictional forces due to differences of velocity in the flowing stream induce turbulence currents. Turbulent flow thus dominates throughout the cross section of stream flow.

Because flowing water exerts a shear stress, or viscous shear, along the bottom and sides of the river, average flow velocity is least at the bottom and increases upward into the body of the river. Because of energy losses to surface waves, the average turbulent downstream velocity (hereafter referred to simply as velocity) at the river's surface is slightly below the maximum velocity. The maximum velocity occurs at about six-tenths of the river depth above the bottom of the river.

Because of viscous shear between flowing water and the bottom materials, the range of small and large sediment particles that make up most river bottoms are moved by the flowing water. Once in motion, small particles whose settling velocity is less than the upward component of turbulent flow move downstream with the water, settling out only in backwaters, such as the still water behind a dam, where flow velocities become very low. This continuously moving sediment is referred to as suspended load and is restricted, in most cases, to clay- and silt-sized sediments. Sand-sized and larger sediment grains are moved during periods of high flow velocity and dropped where flow velocity decreases. This coarse material is the "bed load." Bed-load transport normally occurs only near the river bed. It is the sediment in transport that does the work of the river as erosion and sediment transport. Erosional features of river valleys, such as canyons and potholes, are produced by the "wet sandblast" of the suspended bed load, a process that is much more effective during periods of high flow velocity.

During periods of rainfall or snowmelt, direct precipitation into streams and runoff from adjacent land provide stream flow. Between periods of rainfall or snowmelt, stream flow comes from the slow seepage of groundwater into surface streams. Small streams, the smallest of which flow only during wet periods, join to form larger streams, which join to form rivers. Because rainfall or snowmelt occurs only occasionally in an area drained by a river (the river's drainage basin), the quantity of water flowing past any point on a river, or any point on any of its tributary streams, varies with time.

DISCHARGE

The quantity of water passing a point on the river is measured in cubic meters per second (or, in common North American and British practice, cubic feet per second) and is termed the discharge. For a period of time after a rainfall or snowmelt event, as, for example, during a flood, discharge increases at all points in the drainage basin. If the flood event occurs in only one part of the drainage basin—say the higher part of the basin with the smaller streams—the increase in discharge will occur first in the higher part of the basin and will occur in the larger streams lower in the basin at some later time.

If the discharge at a given point on a stream is measured continuously over a period of days and the discharge is plotted against time, with discharge on the vertical axis of the graph and time in days on the horizontal axis, the increase in discharge related to a storm or snowmelt (a flood) will appear as a hump in the discharge curve. A graph of discharge with time is called a hydrograph, and a hydrograph that shows a flood-related hump is a flood hydrograph. Flood hydrographs tend to be more pronounced, having a higher curve with steeper sides, on streams near the source of the flood water. Conversely, the flood hydrograph will be longer and less pronounced, having a lower curve with more gently sloping sides, farther downstream. Putting it another way, the flood hydrograph attenuates, or dies out, downstream. The low, flat portion of the hydrograph that measures flow between flood events is called baseflow. Experience with flood hydrographs for a river enables hydrologists to predict the effect of future rainstorms and snowmelts of varying intensity and to predict low flow during prolonged dry periods.

An increase in river discharge is accompanied by an increase in stream velocity. For rivers with sandy bottoms (sandy streambeds), the higher water velocity causes erosion, or scour, of the bottom. That is, the sand begins to move along the bottom with the water, and the river channel becomes deeper. The elevation of the water surface relative to some fixed point on the riverbank also increases. As a rule, the banks are not vertical but sloping, and the increase in elevation of the water surface causes a corresponding increase in width. In summary, an increase in discharge is accompanied by increases in flow velocity, stream width, water surface elevation, and depth of channel (the last two items add up to an overall

increase in depth). A reduction in discharge has the opposite effects, including the deposition of new sand, arriving from upstream, in the channel as the velocity decreases.

HYDRAULIC GEOMETRY

In 1953, Luna Bergere Leopold and Thomas Maddock, Jr., introduced a concept that describes the relationships among the variables that change when discharge changes. The concept is called hydraulic geometry, and it is embodied in the following three equations: $w = aQ^b$, $d = bQ^f$, and $v = kQ^m$, where w is stream width, d is average depth of the stream, v is the flow velocity, and Q is discharge. The coefficients a, b, and k and the exponents b, f, and m are determined empirically, from actual measurement in the field. Since the discharge is equal to the cross-sectional area of the stream (wd) times the flow velocity (that is, $wdv = Q$), $wdv = aQ^b \times bQ^f \times kQ^m = Q$. For this to be true, the product of a, b, and k must be 1 ($abk = 1$), and the sum of the exponents b, f, and m must also be 1 ($b + f + m = 1$). Many field studies have shown these equations to be good approximations of actual variation in width, depth, and velocity with variation in discharge.

The coefficients of the hydraulic geometry equations have little effect, relative to the powerful exponents, and are usually ignored. The exponents of the hydraulic geometry equations depend on the physical characteristics of the drainage basins and stream channels involved, but for a given point on a given stream, average values are $b = 0.1$, $f = 0.45$, and $m = 0.45$, which means that the increase in discharge during a flood event is expressed primarily in increases in depth and flow velocity.

The discharge of rivers increases downstream because of the larger length of stream receiving baseflow and the contribution from many tributaries, and hydraulic geometry equations may also be applied to downstream changes in discharge. Average values for the exponents in the downstream hydraulic geometry equations for width, depth, and velocity are $b = 0.5$, $f = 0.4$, and $m = 0.1$. This phenomenon is a paradox. Casual observation would suggest that small streams in the higher parts of the drainage basins flow faster than the large rivers in the lower parts of the drainage basins. Yet, appearances are deceptive: Water in the wider, deeper channels of the larger streams actually flows faster than does water in the smaller headwater streams.

When a flood flow exceeds the capacity of the river channel, the surface elevation of the river rises above the elevation of the riverbanks, and flooding of the surface adjacent to the stream occurs. This is what has generally been called a flood, or an overbank flood. Overbank floods do serious damage to homes, businesses, industrial facilities, and crops on the flooded areas, and much time and money are devoted to flood prevention. The principal method of flood prevention is the construction of levees, large earthen embankments or concrete walls along the stream bank, at locations where the potential economic loss because of flooding justifies the expense of their construction and maintenance.

STUDY OF RIVER FLOW

Research on flow in rivers, or hydrology, almost invariably involves the determination of flow velocity and discharge. Because discharge (Q) equals stream width (w) times average depth (d) times average flow velocity (v), velocity and discharge are closely related. As implied by the world "average," depth and velocity vary across the width of a river or stream. Velocity is lowest in the shallower parts of the river. Therefore, the cross section of the stream is divided into sections, and the discharge is taken as the sum of discharges of all the sections.

For a relatively small river, a rope or strong cord is stretched across the river and marked at regular intervals, typically 2 meters. The depth is measured at each marked point, and a current meter is used to measure the velocity at each point. The flow in rivers and streams is turbulent, and the current meter actually measures the average downstream component of velocity. Average downstream velocity varies with the depth of the channel and also through the vertical section at any point on the stream, the lowest velocities occurring at the bottom and at the surface. Average velocity at any given vertical section of flow occurs at about $0.6d$ above the bottom, which is where the current meter is positioned. Alternatively, two velocity measurements may be taken, at $0.2d$ and $0.8d$ above the bottom, and averaged. The equation $Q = wdv$, where w is the interval at which measurements were taken, is computed for each section, or interval, across the stream, and all the resultant discharges are summed to obtain the total discharge at the point on the stream, which is now called a station.

This process is laborious. If discharge at a station must be more or less continuously monitored, a quicker method is desirable, which is accomplished by developing a rating curve for the station. Discharge is measured in the manner already described at several different times, with as wide a range of discharges as practical. A staff gauge (a board mounted vertically in the stream and marked in units of length, usually feet in American and British practice) is erected at the station, and the level of the water surface, called the stage of the river, is determined each time the discharge is measured. The rating curve consists of a plot of stage against discharge. Once the rating curve has been determined, discharge is estimated from river stage by use of the rating curve. Because of the scour and fill of the river bottom that occur with each increase and decrease in discharge and velocity, the rating curve is not a straight line. Moreover, because the scour and fill may, over time, change the character of the river channel at the station, it is necessary to actually measure the discharge periodically to check the validity of the rating curve. If large changes in the channel occur, it is necessary to establish a new rating curve.

The U.S. Geological Survey maintains a large number of rating stations, or gauging stations, and periodically reports stream discharges. At most stations operated by the agency, the staff gauge is replaced by a vertical pipe driven into the streambed and perforated near the bed. Water is free to flow in and out of the pipe as river stage changes, but the water surface inside the pipe is not disturbed by surface waves. A cable with a weight at the end is attached to the float, and the cable is passed over a wheel near the top of the pipe. The float is free to move with the water surface inside the pipe and, as it moves, it turns the wheel. Sensitive instruments monitor the position of the wheel and therefore the river stage as well. In this way, the stage is periodically and automatically reported to a central office electronically.

Robert E. Carver

FURTHER READING

Chorley, Richard J., Stanley A. Schumm, and David E. Sugden. *Geomorphology*. New York: Methuen, 1985. A well-referenced older textbook of geomorphology, it nevertheless provides a comprehensive treatment of the theoretical principles of water flowing in river channels. Contains numerous line drawings and working charts and graphs.

Christopherson, Robert W., and Mary-Louie Byrne. *Geosystems: An Introduction to Physical Geography.* Toronto, Ontario: Pearson Education Canada, 2006. An extremely readable and well-illustrated text that discusses water flow in rivers in general terms rather than mathematical specifics, in the overall context of systems functioning on the planet.

Collier, Michael. *Over the Rivers: An Aerial View of Geology.* New York: Mikaya Press, 2008. Discusses the dynamic landscape of the rivers. Explains the processes that shape the landscape and its influence on humans. Written in the popular style. Easily accessible to the general public. Filled with bits of information and extraordinary photographs. Presents multiple examples drawn from the Mississippi River.

Collins, B., and T. Dunne. *Fluvial Geomorphology and River-Gravel Mining: A Guide for Planners.* Sacramento, Calif.: California Department of Conservation, 1990. A thorough look at fluvial systems and geomorphology. Emphasizes design to avoid environmental problems associated with water in all its manifestations. Many worked problems, most involving only basic mathematics.

Darby, Stephen, and David Sear. *River Restoration: Managing the Uncertainty in Restoring Physical Habitat.* Hoboken, N.J.: John Wiley & Sons, 2008. Begins with theoretical and philosophical issues with habitat restoration to provide a strong foundation for decision making. Addresses logistics, planning, mathematical modeling, and construction stages of restoration in later chapters. Rounds out with post-construction monitoring and long-term evaluations to provide a full picture of the habitat restoration process. Highly useful for anyone involved in the planning and implementing of habitat restoration.

Dingman, S. L. *Physical Hydrology.* 2d ed. Long Grove, Ill.: Waveland Press, 2008. A thorough introduction to hydrology that offers a clear development of all the equations that are essential to fluvial hydrology. For full understanding, a year of college calculus is necessary, but about 80 percent of the material can be mastered by a student with knowledge only of algebra and trigonometry. An excellent treatment of the subject, with many answered problems and a helpful annotated bibliography. Accompanied by a CD.

Leopold, Luna B. *A View of the River.* Cambridge, Mass.: Harvard University Press, 2006. A lucid explanation of rivers and their processes. Clearly written and easy to follow. Highly recommended for both beginners and professionals.

_____. *Water, Rivers, and Creeks.* Sausalito, Calif.: University Science Books, 2009. A brief, very readable introduction to hydrology and the study of rivers. Highly recommended for all newcomers to the field and most professionals.

Manning, J. C. *Applied Principles of Hydrology.* 3d ed. Upper Saddle River, N.J.: Prentice Hall, 1997. An excellent short introduction to the principles of surface water and groundwater hydrology. Incorporates very little of the mathematics involved in the two fields, but the descriptions and illustrations of methods of making field measurements are clear and informative.

Newson, Malcolm. *Land, Water and Development: Sustainable and Adaptive Management of Rivers.* 3d ed. London: Routledge, 2008. Presents land-water interactions. Discusses recent research, study tools and methods, and technical issues, such as soil erosion and damming. Suited for undergraduate students and professionals, this text covers concepts in managing land and water resources in the developed world.

Richards, Keith. *Rivers, Form, and Process in Alluvial Channels.* Caldwell, N.J.: Blackburn Press, 2004. A college-level text requiring some familiarity with calculus for complete understanding. Its great strength is the very large number of research papers cited in the text. Conveys a sense of the quantity and type of research that has been done.

Wohl, Ellen. *A World of Rivers.* Chicago: University of Chicago Press, 2011. The Amazon, Ob, Nile, Danube, Ganges, Mississippi, Murray-Darling, Congo, Chang Jiang, and Mackenzie rivers each have a chapter in this book. Figure 1.1 contains more straightforward and organized information than some full textbooks. Discusses natural history, anthropogenic impact, and the future environment of these ten great rivers. The bibliography is organized by chapter.

See also: Alluvial Systems; Beaches and Coastal Processes; Deep-Sea Sedimentation; Deltas; Desert Pavement; Drainage Basins; Floodplains; Floods; Freshwater and Groundwater Contamination Around the World; Lakes; Reefs; River Bed Forms; Sand; Sediment Transport and Deposition; Weathering and Erosion

S

SALINITY AND DESALINATION

Salinity is the total amount of salts dissolved per unit of water; the average salinity of seawater, for example, is 35 grams of salts per kilogram of water. Utilization of saline water for domestic purposes thus requires removal of the dissolved materials. The desalination of saline or brackish water involves costly operations and is typically performed only in coastal or arid regions where alternative water resources are limited or nonexistent.

PRINCIPAL TERMS

- **dissolved matter:** the amount of normally solid materials that are completely dissolved in water
- **evaporation:** the physical process occurring at the water-air interface where water changes its phase from liquid to vapor
- **filtration:** the removal of particulate matter from the water by passing it through a porous medium
- **osmosis:** a natural process whereby the solvent, usually water, in a weak solution migrates across a semipermeable membrane into a similar solution of higher concentration, with the end result being the equalization of the solution concentrations
- **potable water:** freshwater that can be used for domestic consumption
- **reverse osmosis:** in practice, the forced passage of seawater through a semipermeable membrane against the natural osmotic pressure in order to obtain pure water
- **sodium chloride:** the main chemical compound found as dissolved material in seawater
- **suspended solids:** the solid particles that can be found dispersed in the water column
- **water resources:** all the surface water and groundwater that can be effectively harvested by humans for domestic, industrial, or agricultural uses
- **water supply:** the amount of water that is actually delivered to various consumer groups
- **water-treatment plant:** a facility where water is treated by physical and chemical processes until its quality is improved to that of potable water

DISSOLVED SOLIDS

Salinity is one of the most important physical properties of seawater. It is defined as the total amount of dissolved salts found in a unit of water, measured in grams of dissolved matter per kilogram of seawater. The average salinity of seawater is approximately 35 grams per kilogram, corresponding to a concentration of 35 parts of salt per thousand parts of seawater (35 parts per thousand). That is to say, evaporation of all water from 1 kilogram of seawater will, on average, leave 35 grams of dry solids, primarily sodium chloride and other metal salts. The main ionic components of dissolved matter in seawater and the percentages in which they are found in a typical sample are as follows: chloride ions (55.0 percent), sodium ions (30.6 percent), sufate ions (7.7 percent), magnesium ions (3.7 percent), calcium ions (1.2 percent), and potassium ions (1.1 percent). Accordingly, 1 cubic kilometer of typical seawater contains approximately 75 million metric tons of sodium chloride, 11 million metric tons of magnesium chloride, 5 million metric tons of magnesium sufate, 4 million metric tons of calcium sufate, 2.5 million metric tons of potassium sufate, and 344,000 metric tons of calcium carbonate. Depending on the prevailing physicochemical conditions, salinity can vary significantly, from brackish water (2 to 15 parts per thousand) in estuaries and riverine deltas to highly saline water such as in the Mediterranean Sea (38.5 parts per thousand) or Red Sea (42.5 parts per thousand). Even higher levels of salinity prevail in landlocked bodies of water such as the Dead Sea. Atmospheric precipitation or freshwater discharges from inland waters (surface water or groundwater) reduce salinity, while evaporation acts to increase salt content. In spite of the fact that salinity levels vary from one water body to another, the relative abundance of the main dissolved components remains almost unchanged.

The presence of dissolved salts has an effect on the density of seawater. A salinity of 35 parts per thousand amounts to a density difference between fresh and salt waters of approximately 2 percent. Thus, whenever there is a confluence of fresh and salt waters, some interesting phenomena occur. Depending on the degree of energy input by wind, currents, and tidal action, the fresh and salt waters can be thoroughly or partially mixed, or they may remain stratified. Under quiescent conditions, if all other variables (such as temperature and pressure) are the same for both the fresh and salt waters, then the heavier saltwater will sink. In many estuaries with high riverine discharge and low tidal range (such as the Mississippi River), seawater can penetrate many kilometers in the upstream direction, moving along the bottom under the freshwater. This phenomenon is known as a "saline wedge," and the separating interface between fresh and salt waters is called the "halocline." Mixing conditions between fresh and salt waters are important from an ecological point of view, because salinity levels affect the diversity and population of aquatic flora and fauna.

Sea salt is also a major contributor to atmospheric aerosol particles. During wave breaking, characterized by the formation of "white caps," small droplets are carried upward by air currents into the atmosphere. When the droplets evaporate, sea-salt particles of very small sizes (0.5 to 20 micrometers) are transported by the wind over the continents. About 10 percent of the total annual amount of salt that is generated in the oceans (1.8 billion tons) is deposited as airborne sea-salt particles on the continents.

The total volume of oceanic waters is about 1.37 billion cubic kilometers. This volume constitutes approximately 96.5 percent of the total water on Earth. The other major water resources are groundwater, of which 10.53 million cubic kilometers (0.76 percent) is freshwater and 12.87 million cubic kilometers (0.93 percent) is saltwater; and the polar ice, which contains 24.02 million cubic kilometers (1.7 percent) of water. The remaining amount of water is in lakes, rivers, marshes, soil moisture, atmosphere, and biota. Freshwater thus makes up only 2.5 percent of the total amount of Earth's water. Most freshwater supplies are in the polar ice (68.6 percent) and in groundwater (30.1 percent). The percentage of freshwater found in lakes is only 0.26 percent, while the amount found in rivers is even smaller (0.006 percent).

INLAND WATER AND SALINITY MEASUREMENT

Not all inland water is fresh. The amount of the dissolved salts occurring in inland waters, surface or underground, depends on the composition of the soils through which the water passes. Streams and rivers flowing over rocks containing chloride and sodium compounds contribute significantly to the generation of salt. Therefore, some inland waters have a high salt content and are not suitable for any use unless properly pretreated. The most extreme examples of inland brine waters are the Great Salt Lake in Utah (salt concentration of about 120 parts per thousand) and the Dead Sea in the Middle East (salt concentration of about 270 parts per thousand). Salt is also found as surface crust or layers in swamps and dry lake bottoms, particularly in arid climate areas. The famous Bonneville Salt Flats, in Utah, and Death Valley, in California, both reflect the accumulation of various salts over time. The water that periodically inundates these areas transports relatively small amounts of dissolved salts from the surrounding area and forms a landlocked body of water as the runoff collects and pools. When the water evaporates, those salts remain, and have been slowly built up over time to produce the massive deposits of salts for which those regions are known. In coastal regions, excessive pumping of groundwater can lead to seawater intrusion into an aquifer. This can have a long-term negative effect on the water resources of a region, with subsequent devastating impact on the regional economy.

The average amount of freshwater that falls daily on the United States is about 15,750 billion liters. This water feeds the various surface water bodies (lakes and rivers), recharges aquifers, evaporates back to the atmosphere, or flows into the oceans. Therefore, only 2.5 trillion liters of precipitated water can be used for beneficial purposes. From this amount, 1.26 trillion liters is used by industry, 530 billion liters by agriculture, and 94 billion liters by domestic and rural consumers. The daily per-capita water use in the United States is about 7,000 liters. The average domestic water consumption ranges from 75 to 300 liters per day. Thus, the average amount of water used by a person during a seventy-year life span is estimated at 5.6 million liters.

Direct measurement of seawater salinity by evaporation or chemical analysis is too complicated to be used on a routine basis. In the past, salinity (known as "absolute salinity") was estimated in terms of chlorinity. Chlorinity is the amount of chlorine ions plus the chlorine equivalent of bromine and iodine ions. From chlorinity, salinity was estimated by multiplying the value of chlorinity by a factor of 1.80655.

Salinity (known as "practical salinity") is estimated indirectly by measuring the electrical conductivity of the seawater. However, because electrical conductivity is strongly affected by both salinity and temperature, the conductivity readings are properly corrected to compensate for temperature effects.

WATER TREATMENT

Freshwater is a precious commodity that is used for a variety of domestic, rural, industrial, and agricultural purposes. Water is not distributed evenly throughout the world and is subject to short-term and long-term temporal variations. In many regions, the available freshwater resources cannot meet the water demands. After the Industrial Revolution, accelerated anthropogenic pollution added to the water resource problem. In situations of limited water resources, the only alternative solutions are either cleanup and reuse of domestic and agricultural wastewater or, for islands and coastal regions, desalination of seawater. Both of these operations are costly and require construction of appropriate water-treatment facilities. Several countries in the Middle East, including Israel and Saudi Arabia, depend heavily on water desalination for their drinking-water supplies. Under emergency conditions, freshwater is obtained via the use of portable water-purification equipment.

Freshwater can contain a number of impurities that have to be removed or treated before it can be used. These impurities include calcium, magnesium, iron, lead, copper, chloride, sulfate, nitrates, fluorides, sodium, different organic compounds, and suspended solids. Impurities can be hazardous to human health or can give water a disagreeable taste, smell, or appearance. In addition, they can create scaling or corrosive problems in pipes or in machinery that use the water. Because saltwater contains a large amount of dissolved salts, it is always subjected to desalination before use. Generally, the acceptable quality standards for drinking water are 0.5 microgram per kilogram of total dissolved solids and 0.2 microgram per kilogram of chloride.

Water treatment for production of domestic water involves a number of operations such as filtration, softening, distillation, deionization, chemical disinfection, exposure to ultraviolet radiation, and reverse osmosis. The number and the type of operations required depend on the quality and properties of the water supplies. The problem of high salt content can be treated by a variety of methods. Desalination is the process by which dissolved salts are removed from the water; there are a number of desalination methods. Because no one method is applicable in all situations, selection of the most appropriate desalination method is based on such variables as the amount and type of dissolved salts in water, the degree of purification of the water to be produced, and the associated costs. More than one hundred cities worldwide use desalination plants to provide freshwater for their needs.

THERMAL PROCESSING

There are two general methods of desalination: thermal processing (distillation) and membrane separation. The main principle behind thermal processing is as follows: Saltwater is heated until it boils, then the released steam condenses as it cools, forming pure water. Membrane separation is achieved by using reverse osmotic pressure, so that the water passes through a membrane while the salt ions are retained by the membrane.

Distillation, the earliest desalination method, was used in steamships as early as 1884. There are several different thermal processing methods for desalination, such as the thin-film multiple effect distillation (TFMED), multi-stage flash desalination (MSFD), mechanical vapor compression desalination (MVCD), and thermal vapor compression desalination (TVCD). At standard atmospheric pressure (measured at sea level), water boils at 100 degrees Celsius. However, boiling temperature decreases with decreasing pressure. Also, if the water is heated under high pressure at 100 degrees Celsius and is suddenly released into a vacuum chamber, it flashes into vapor. This technique is used in both the TFMED method and the MSFD method, in which the pressure is continuously reduced in sequential stages. The number of sequential stages can range from fifteen to twenty-five. The MVCD and the TVCD methods use compression to increase the pressure and thus increase the temperature of a constant volume of steam. Heating of the steam as it flows through the process facilitates the desalination process. Water obtained through thermal processing can easily have a purity of less than 0.1 microgram per kilogram of dissolved matter. The brine wastewater resulting from desalination of seawater has a salinity of approximately 70 grams per kilogram.

MEMBRANE SEPARATION

Membrane separation includes two major desalination methods: pressure membrane processes (PMP) and electrodialysis reversal (EDR). In PMP, only pure water is able to pass through the membrane, while the majority of the dissolved material is detained by the membrane. The EDR method utilizes ion-specific membranes placed between anodic (positively charged) and cathodic (negatively charged) electrodes. Dissolved material is then collected as the salt ions move under the electric current. Although the EDR method is relatively common, the most widespread desalination methods involve PMP.

There are four pressure-membrane desalination processes: microfiltration (MF), ultrafiltration (UF), nanofiltration (NF), and reverse osmosis (RO). The common principle of these methods is the forced passing (under high pressure) of saline water through a membrane. The main difference among the PMP methods is the size of the particles that are removed from the saline water. For example, MF removes particles larger than 10 microns (1 micron equals 0.000001 meter), UF removes particles of sizes from 0.001 to 10 microns, NF removes particles greater than 0.001 micron, and RO removes particles ranging from 0.0001 to 0.001 micron. Another difference among the PMP methods is the pressure needed for forcing the water through the membrane. MF operates at a pressure of less than 10 pounds per square inch (psi), UF at a range of 15 to 75 psi, NF at a range of 75 to 250 psi, and RO at a range of 200 to 1,200 psi.

Reverse osmosis is an energy-consuming method that can be used very effectively, particularly for production of water for domestic use, whenever good-quality saline water is available. Reverse osmosis can be accomplished using different design modules such as the tubular, the plate-and-frame, the spiral-wound, or the hollow fiber. In all these designs, the water that is allowed to pass through the membrane, the "permeate," is collected as the product water, while the water retained by the membrane forms the so-called concentrate or reject.

There are various types of membranes used for reverse osmosis, such as the cellulose acetate group, which includes cellulose acetate (CA), cellulose acetate butyrate (CAB), and cellulose triacetate (CTA), or polyamide (PA). Production of CA membranes involves four stages: casting, evaporation, gelation, and shrinkage. During the first stage, a solution of cellulose acetate in acetone containing certain additives is cast into flat or tubular thin surfaces. The acetone evaporates, leaving a porous surface. During the gelation stage, the cast is immersed in cold water, forming a gel, while at the same time the additives dissolve in the water. In the last stage, the film shrinks, forcing reduction of the pore sizes. High temperatures result in smaller pore openings.

Electrodialysis is also an effective desalination process whereby ions are separated from the water by being forced through selective ion-permeable membranes under the action of an electric current. The ion-permeable membranes alternate between those allowing only the passage of cations (such as potassium, K^+) and those allowing only the passage of anions (such as chloride, Cl^-).

Another potential methodology for desalination involves freezing of the water. Since ice is theoretically free of any dissolved material, various techniques have been proposed for application of freezing for desalination. However, this method does not have any widespread applicability.

Both the thermal and membrane methods require some form of energy to accomplish desalination. The energy efficiency of the desalination methods is expressed either as the gained output ratio (GOR) or the performance ratio (PR). The GOR is defined as the ratio between the mass of distillate over the mass of the steam. The PR, also known as economy, is estimated as pounds of distillate per 1,000 British thermal units (BTUs) or as kilograms of distillate per 2,326 kilojoules (kJ). Criteria for the selection of a desalination method include energy consumption, process efficiency, operational and maintenance costs, auxiliary services, and growth of demand. Energy is provided mostly by electrically driven pumps, but diesel engines can also be utilized.

SIGNIFICANCE

Domestic (potable) water is a very valuable commodity. Population growth and high demand for water for industrial and agricultural practices have created severe water shortages in many parts of the world. In addition, increased water contamination and extreme hydrologic conditions, such as prolonged drought, can adversely affect the socioeconomic and human health conditions of a region.

In addition, there are other applications that require high-quality water. For example, high-purity water is required by pharmaceutical companies for processing drugs and medications, by hospitals for kidney dialysis, by power and other energy-intensive plants in the form of low-scaling water, and by semiconductor manufacturing for production of high-performance chips.

Since most of the conventional water resources are already under stress, the only alternative solution to the water-resource problem is desalination of the vast oceanic water masses or reuse of wastewater. The various existing thermal or membrane methods can effectively provide high-quality freshwater. However, the high costs associated with these methodologies limit their applicability only to communities that can afford the financial burden. There is ongoing research into improving the efficiency and reducing the cost of existing desalination methods and developing new methodologies. What began as a small distillation process used to provide freshwater to a handful of ships' crew members has evolved into a complex water-treatment operation that supplies freshwater to large populations.

Panagiotis D. Scarlatos

FURTHER READING

Abdelly, Chedly, et al. *Biosaline Agriculture and High Salinity Tolerance.* Boston: Birkhauser Basel, 2008. A compilation of articles discussing the physiology, biochemistry, and ecology of high-salinity ecosystems and halophyte species within those regions. Discusses salinity tolerance at a molecular level. Focuses on resistant plant options for use in agriculture of high-stress locations.

Gunde-Cimerman, Nina, Aharon Oren, and Ana Plemenita. *Adaptation to Life at High Salt Concentrations in Archaea, Bacteria, and Eukarya.* New York: Springer, 2011. Provides information on high-salinity habitats and the halophilic organisms found there. Sections devoted specifically to archaea, bacteria, fungi, protozoa, and viruses follow the environment overview.

Henry, J. G., and G. W. Heinke. *Environmental Science and Engineering.* 2d ed. Upper Saddle River,

N.J.: Prentice Hall, 1996. A lengthy presentation of water quality and wastewater-treatment technological issues, including desalination. Contains a discussion of case studies.

Hogarth, Peter J. *The Biology of Mangroves and Seagrasses.* 2d ed. New York: Oxford University Press, 2007. Examines biology and physiology of saline plant species and discusses community interactions. Expands beyond the basic biology of specific species to cover a broader scope of ecosystem-level diversity and large-scale anthropogenic effects.

Ko, A., and D. B. Guy. "Brackish and Seawater Desalting." In *Reverse Osmosis Technology: Application for High-Purity-Water Production.* New York: Marcel Dekker, 1988. A detailed presentation of technological methods for desalination of brackish and saline waters.

Metcalf & Eddy, Inc. *Wastewater Engineering: Treatment and Reuse.* 4th ed. New York: McGraw-Hill, 2003. A comprehensive discussion of wastewater properties, waste-treatment processes, and associated methodologies. Emphasis on engineering design.

Micale, Giorgio, Andrea Cipollina, and Lucio Rizutti, eds. *Seawater Desalination: Conventional and Renewable Energy Processes.* Berlin: Springer-Verlag, 2009. Presents a number of articles that discuss various desalination technologies from the point of view of whether they function using conventional energy sources or renewable energy sources. Reading level ranges from instructional to highly technical.

National Research Council. *Desalination: A National Perspective.* Washington, D.C.: National Academies Press, 2008. Assesses the current state of desalination technologies and their implementation while also examining such topics as long-term goals, recommendations, funding estimates, and appropriate roles for government and nongovernment agencies.

Porteous, A. *Saline Water Distillation Processes.* London: Longman, 1975. A detailed presentation of the distillation methods used for desalination of saline water.

Ratnayaka, Don D., Malcolm J. Brandt, and K. Michael Johnson. *Twort's Water Supply.* 6th ed. Burlington, Mass.: Butterworth-Heinemann, 2009. Offers a discussion of water-supply systems, including distribution and treatment methodologies.

Rizutti, Lucio, Hisham Mohamed Ettouney, and Andrea Cipollina, eds. *Solar Desalination for the 21st*

465

Century: A Review of Modern Technologies and Researches on Desalination Coupled to Renewable Energies. Dordrecht: Springer, 2007. Part of the NATO Science Series that discusses modern desalination processes driven by renewable energies with regard to the results they have achieved and their future potential.

Segar, Douglas. *Introduction to Ocean Sciences.* 2d ed. New York: W. W. Norton, 2007. Offers comprehensive coverage of all aspects of the oceans and salinity. Readable and well illustrated. Suitable for high school students and above.

Shafer, L. H., and M. S. Mintz. "Electrodialysis." In *Principles of Desalination.* 2d ed. New York: Academic Press, 1980. Provides a detailed description of the electrodialysis method for removal of dissolved matter.

Sincero, A. P., and G. A. Sincero. *Environmental Engineering: A Design Approach.* Upper Saddle River, N.J.: Prentice Hall, 1996. Offers a detailed presentation of water-quality principles and associated water-purification and cleanup technologies and designs.

Talley, Lynne D., et al. *Descriptive Physical Oceanography: An Introduction.* 6th ed. San Diego: Academic Press, 2011. Provides a thorough presentation of seawater properties and salinity distribution in the various seas and oceans.

Tarbuck, Edward J., Frederick K. Lutgens, and Dennis Tasa. *Earth: An Introduction to Physical Geology.* 10th ed. Upper Saddle River, N.J.: Prentice Hall, 2010. Provides a clear picture of earth systems and processes that is suitable for the high school or college reader. Includes illustrations and graphics, as well as an accompanying computer disc. Bibliography and index.

Tebbutt, T. H. Y. *Principles of Water Quality Control.* 5th ed. Woburn, Mass.: Butterworth-Heinemann, 1998. Covers water properties and applied methodologies for water-quality control.

Viessman, W., Jr., and M. J. Hammer. *Water Supply and Pollution Control.* 8th ed. Upper Saddle River, N.J.: Prentice Hall, 2008. Provides thorough quantitative coverage of water-supply issues, water-quality treatment methodologies, and engineering designs.

Warren, John K. *Evaporites: Sediment, Resources and Hydrocarbons.* Berlin: Springer-Verlag, 2006. Discusses a number of evaporitic minerals, with chapters focusing on salts. Discusses chemistry and hydrology, deposit locations, and mining. Does not include photographs, but does have many drawings of geological features.

See also: Acid Rain and Acid Deposition; Aquifers; Artificial Recharge; Climate; Clouds; Dams and Flood Control; Drainage Basins; Floods; Geochemical Cycles; Groundwater Movement; Groundwater Pollution and Remediation; Hydrologic Cycle; Precipitation; Saltwater Intrusion; Severe Storms; Surface Water; Waterfalls; Water Quality; Watersheds; Water Table; Water Wells; Weathering and Erosion

SALTWATER INTRUSION

Saltwater intrusion is the contamination of freshwater aquifers and other freshwater resources by saltwater, rendering them useless for freshwater consumption. Intrusions usually occur in coastal areas and marine islands. Most saltwater intrusion is caused by human activities such as water diversion projects and irrigation, and once started, it can be very difficult, if not impossible, to reverse.

PRINCIPAL TERMS

- **aquifer:** a rock or sediment structure that is saturated with groundwater and is capable of delivering that water to wells and springs
- **brackish water:** water with a salt content between that of saltwater and freshwater; it is common in arid areas on the surface, in coastal marshes, and in salt-contaminated groundwater
- **cone of depression:** a cone-shaped depression produced in the water table by pumping from a well
- **freshwater:** water with less than 0.2 percent dissolved salts, such as is found in most streams, rivers, and lakes
- **freshwater lens:** the shape of the freshwater table in aquifers of coastal areas or marine islands that floats on top of a denser, underlying saltwater
- **groundwater:** water located beneath the ground in interconnected pores beyond the soil-root zone
- **mixing zone:** the area of contact between a freshwater lens and the underlying saltwater
- **saltwater:** water with a salt content of 3.5 percent, such as is found in normal ocean water
- **upconing:** the upward flexure of the mixing zone toward the ground surface produced by excessive groundwater withdrawal by wells, analogous to an inverted cone of depression
- **water table:** the upper surface of groundwater in an aquifer, with a direct connection overhead to the atmosphere such that the water pressure is equal to atmospheric pressure

COASTAL AND MARINE ISLAND AQUIFERS

Saltwater intrusion commonly occurs in coastal and marine island aquifers. In these locations, the freshwater of the groundwater in an aquifer will rest atop underlying saltwater in the aquifer. This layering of freshwater on top of saltwater results from the slightly higher density of the saltwater because of the amount of dissolved salts that it contains. In the coastal regions of continents and marine islands, the freshwater thins and tapers as the coastline is reached, producing a classic lens-shaped cross section to the freshwater body as it floats on the underlying saltwater. For this reason, the freshwater in aquifers in coastal regions is commonly called the freshwater lens.

Ideally, pure freshwater has a density of 1 gram per cubic centimeter. Saltwater, in contrast, has a density of 1.025 grams per cubic centimeter, a density difference of one part in forty. Freshwater floats on saltwater much like a piece of wood floats on water. How high something floats on an underlying, denser liquid depends on the density difference, or contrast, between the floating material and the underlying liquid. In the case of the freshwater lens, the density contrast of one part in forty means that for every centimeter that the freshwater lens floats above the saltwater, it must displace downward into the saltwater at least 40 centimeters. Freshwater is not a solid, like a piece of wood; it is a liquid and will flow unless contained. When a freshwater lens floats on saltwater, the level of the freshwater in the water table is above the level of the saltwater, so it tends to flow in the direction of the source of the saltwater. Typically, that direction is seaward. As the freshwater flows seaward, the lens becomes thinner. This thinning will continue until the lens almost disappears, unless the freshwater lost seaward is replaced by new freshwater entering the lens from sources above or inland of the lens. A freshwater lens is an example of dynamic equilibrium, or stability through motion. A freshwater lens remains stable only if it is recharged by new freshwater at a rate equal to the flow loss of the lens to the sea. This principle of a dynamic equilibrium in the freshwater lens is called the Ghyben-Herzberg principle, for the two scientists who independently discovered the phenomenon.

The boundary between the freshwater lens and the underlying saltwater is called the mixing zone. Other terms used to describe this boundary include the halocline, the diffusion zone, and the dispersion zone, depending on the nature of the process of interest. This boundary can have a variety of characteristics. It can be sharply defined, in which case the change from freshwater to saltwater can occur over a distance of a few centimeters or less, a situation in which the term "halocline" (salt boundary) is typically used. The water can also change from fresh to salt over a broad zone of brackish water meters or tens of meters thick with an ever-increasing salt content. Freshwater and saltwater are miscible liquids and mix very easily. (Oil and water are examples of immiscible liquids, or liquids that do not mix or dissolve each other.) The reasons that the mixing zone can be sharp or broad are not well understood and may be controlled in part by the size, shape, and chemistry of the pores in the aquifer.

Saltwater intrusion occurs when the dynamic equilibrium of the freshwater lens is upset. If the loss of freshwater from the lens is increased or if the flow of new freshwater to the lens is decreased, the lens will thin and, in the process, migrate inland. Inland migration of the freshwater lens means that some portion of the coastal aquifer that once contained freshwater now contains saltwater, as the saltwater replaces or intrudes into the freshwater aquifer. Changes in climate, sea level, or river-flow paths are ways in which this process can occur naturally. Most saltwater intrusion, however, occurs because of human modification of the freshwater flow system.

ACTIVE AND PASSIVE INTRUSION

Active saltwater intrusion occurs when excessive pumping of freshwater wells distorts the freshwater lens by water removal. This distortion can cause two separate problems. The first problem is a decrease in the water available in the freshwater aquifer, causing saltwater to intrude from the ocean direction, pushing the freshwater lens inland. The second situation is called upconing, where excessive pumping from a well produces an inverted cone of depression in the mixing zone. Upconing effectively draws saltwater upward into the freshwater aquifer. Normally, when a well is pumped in an aquifer, the water is removed from the vicinity of the well and is replaced by flow from the surrounding aquifer. Depending on how fast the aquifer transmits water and how fast water is pumped, the water table around the well is lowered in a characteristic way called the cone of depression. If a well is pumped too fast, the cone of depression can reach the bottom of the aquifer, and

the well will go dry. After a period of no pumping, the aquifer will be able to fill the cone of depression enough so that pumping can again produce water.

In a freshwater lens, this situation is doubly complex. The bottom of the freshwater aquifer is essentially the saltwater table, which is at a higher pressure than the freshwater table. As pumping reduces the amount of freshwater pressing down on the saltwater, the pressure of the underlying saltwater is able to rise through an area that reflects the cone of depression formed at the freshwater table. The Ghyben-Herzberg principle requires the mixing zone to rise as the thickness of the freshwater decreases because of pumping. Eventually the bottom of the freshwater well is reached by this upconing of the mixing zone, and the well begins to draw increasingly brackish water and then finally saltwater. When this happens, the well is ruined for further human use. In some cases, cessation of pumping will allow the freshwater lens to reestablish itself, but in most cases, the upconing process produces long-term saltwater contamination of the freshwater lens.

Passive saltwater intrusion can occur from a more subtle distortion of the freshwater lens. Because of the dynamic equilibrium of the lens, it can be distorted not only by freshwater removal at wells but also by interruption of the mechanism by which it is recharged by surface water. Human activities that alter the surface drainage and infiltration of freshwater in the recharge zone of an aquifer will cause the loss of recharge for that aquifer. If recharge is interrupted, the freshwater lens retreats inland as saltwater intrudes into the aquifer. Activities such as the digging of flood-control canals, widespread paving of the land surface, and river diversions can rob the underlying freshwater lens of needed recharge. A long time may pass before the effects of human activities governing recharge are detected in an aquifer, making it difficult to reverse the process.

OTHER EFFECTS

Coastal and marine island regions are not the only areas where saltwater can intrude into a freshwater aquifer. In areas where arid climates predominate, irrigation is often necessary to grow crops. It is not uncommon for irrigation water to be transported into the area by pipeline or canal because the local aquifer cannot withstand the demand for water. In this situation, the excess water on the surface can mobilize the salts in the ground and transport them downward into the water table. This movement is not true saltwater intrusion, but it can result in loss of the freshwater aquifer by salt contamination.

Many types of rock and sediment are deposited in the ocean. At some later time, they may be uplifted from the sea and form dry land that receives rainfall and develops a freshwater aquifer. The deeper regions of these aquifers may contain waters that were left behind from the original marine environment, called connate water. Connate water originated as saltwater, and it can intrude into the freshwater portion of the aquifer during overpumping of the aquifer. The aquifer can thus become contaminated by salt and ruined. In some cases, the deeper waters of an aquifer are brines, where the salt content has become concentrated above that found in the oceans. Brines are potent contaminators of freshwater aquifers because they have such a high concentration of salt.

The intrusion of saltwater into an aquifer can have a major impact on the aquifer material itself. The chemistry of saltwater is very different from that of freshwater. Some aquifer materials can become altered by the intrusion of saltwater, and they will stay altered even if the saltwater is later forced out by replenishment of the original freshwater. Examples of the changes that can occur are shown by aquifers in islands and coastal regions that have developed in limestone strata. In limestone aquifers, both the freshwater lens and the underlying saltwater are usually saturated with the dissolved mineral calcite, which is the principal component of limestone. When freshwater and saltwater mix, however, they are capable of dissolving quantities of calcite that neither one could dissolve alone. The result is the development of areas of dissolved rock in the limestone. The development of caves and the increase in the number of pores in the limestone because of this dissolving process change the characteristics of the aquifer. If the mixing zone moves around because of distortions of the freshwater lens, the aquifer can become fundamentally changed as the area of dissolving reaches more of the aquifer. The changes in sea level during the ice ages caused that to happen in many places. The famous blue holes and underwater caves of the Bahamas owe their origin to this process. Human activity and subsequent saltwater intrusion in limestone coastal areas may be promoting this process today.

STUDY OF SALTWATER INTRUSION

The study of saltwater intrusion is usually a very straightforward task. The major difficulty lies in the change in water use that the public must accept in

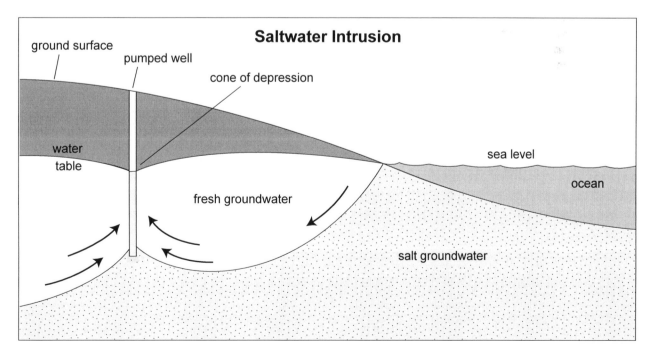

Saltwater Intrusion

ground surface
pumped well
cone of depression
water table
fresh groundwater
sea level
ocean
salt groundwater

order to rectify the problem. The first step in analyzing a freshwater lens is to calculate a water budget for the aquifer. A water budget is much like a bank budget; there are inputs and outputs, and when the two are out of balance, a net change occurs in the budget. In an aquifer, the input is the recharge of the aquifer by freshwater from the surface. This recharge includes rainfall over the area of the aquifer, of which a certain percentage infiltrates the ground to reach the water table. It also includes water brought into the area from other regions by rivers and streams, a certain percentage of which will also sink to the water table. These input values can be measured by taking into account rainfall, evaporation, the use of water by plants (transpiration), and, finally, the water that runs over the ground surface. The difference between how much water comes in and how much is lost to runoff, evaporation, and transpiration is the amount that infiltrates the ground to recharge the aquifer. If the aquifer is in equilibrium, the amount of recharge must equal the amount of discharge.

To measure what is happening down in the aquifer, observation wells are used. These wells identify the location of the water table. If they penetrate deeply enough, they can also tell where the mixing zone and the saltwater are. These wells are not used as a water source but as a means of monitoring the aquifer. If the water table is at a constant level (or seasonally fluctuates about a constant level), the aquifer is in equilibrium, and if the input has been calculated, the output can be estimated. As the aquifer is used as a water supply, the observation wells follow any changes produced in the water table.

Saltwater intrusion is easily detected in observation or supply wells because of the change in salinity that occurs. Sometimes it is detected as a change in the taste of the water, but chemical testing may also be used. Because freshwater is a poor conductor of electricity and saltwater is a good conductor, a relatively simple device called a conductivity meter can be used to check, easily and quickly, the presence of salt in a well. In an observation well, a drop in the water table accompanied by a rise in the mixing zone will be directly measurable, and remediation can begin. Once a supply well has been contaminated by saltwater, however, it is too late to save that well in the short term. It must be shut down and an alternate water supply located. The observation well can predict when saltwater intrusion will damage supply wells

by monitoring the position of the mixing zone and the water table. It is then possible to change water-use patterns at the supply wells, to increase aquifer recharge, or both, thereby preventing a problem. In some cases, the well that is damaged is not the well causing the problem. Imagine a coastal well that is functioning normally. If a well inland of the coastal well pumps too much freshwater, the saltwater will intrude into the aquifer and damage the well closer to the sea long before the inland overpumping well is damaged.

Once a saltwater intrusion problem has been detected or predicted through monitoring of the aquifer, a course of action is needed to rectify the situation. Often the necessary action is relatively simple: Water use can be reduced through conservation, allowing the aquifer to keep the saltwater out of the freshwater lens. This approach results in a reduction in output for the aquifer. Sometimes, however, conservation will not work because demands of necessity are too high. In that case, the situation can be stabilized by increasing the recharge through the development of reservoirs and holding ponds. In extreme cases, water has been brought in by pipeline to an area and recharge accomplished by freshwater injection to the aquifer. When upconing has occurred, it may not be possible to correct the situation by increasing recharge because the freshwater may simply flow around the problem area. It may take many years before the well is again usable.

John E. Mylroie

FURTHER READING

Batu, Vedat. *Applied Flow and Solute Transport Modeling in Aquifers.* Boca Raton, Fla.: CRC Press, 2006. A highly technical text discussing the dynamics of aquifer water flow, flow conditions, solute transport, and sorption principles. Covers aquifer modeling fundamentals, both numerical and analytical approaches, in detail. Contains a list of references and indexing. Best suited for aquifer researchers and advanced graduate students with a background in fluid dynamics or groundwater analysis.

Bear, Jacob, et al., eds. *Seawater Intrusion in Coastal Aquifers: Concepts, Methods, and Practices.* Norwell, Mass.: Kluwer Academic Publishers, 2011. Discusses geophysical and geochemical interactions of seawater and freshwater. Covers management, modeling, and analysis techniques, with strong emphasis on computer programs used. Discusses specific examples of the theories and principles presented, making this text easy to follow and applicable.

Cheng, Alexander H. D., and Driss Oazar, eds. *Coastal Aquifer Management: Monitoring, Modeling, and Case Studies.* Boca Raton, Fla.: CRC Press, 2004. Discusses modeling and monitoring of coastal aquifers and provides case studies with practical application. Each chapter studies a specific hypothesis in coastal aquifer management and saltwater intrusion.

Cooper, H. H., F. A. Kohout, H. R. Henry, and R. E. Glover. *Sea Water in Coastal Aquifers.* Washington, D.C.: Government Printing Office, 1964. A government document and landmark publication on saltwater and coastal aquifers. Contains a succession of four papers by the authors that becomes progressively complex, but the early chapters are very descriptive and useful.

Fetter, Charles W. *Contaminant Hydrogeology.* Long Grove, Ill.: Waveland Press, 2008. A college-level textbook that is extremely readable, with detailed mathematical treatments handled separately from the main text. Provides a good review of hydrology, with technical specifics on the freshwater lens and a general discussion of saltwater intrusion. Good illustrations.

Hunt, Constance Elizabeth. *Thirsty Planet: Strategies for Sustainable Water Management.* New York: St. Martin's Press, 2004. Discusses the hydrologic cycle, components of the cycle, human-induced changes to the cycle, and repercussions of the growing water crisis. Covers floods, climate change, and freshwater ecosystem restoration. Provides a broad overview of hydrology topics of study.

Manning, John C. *Applied Principles of Hydrology.* 3d ed. Upper Saddle River, N.J.: Prentice Hall, 1997. An advanced textbook in scope, detail, and substance, but it is still not very quantitative. Covers a wide variety of water resource topics. Contains many useful examples and sources of data.

Merritt, Michael L. *Assessment of Saltwater Intrusion in Southern Coastal Broward County, Florida.* Tallahassee, Fla.: U.S. Department of the Interior, Geological Survey, 1997. Presents a study, prepared in cooperation with the South Florida Water Management District and Environmental Services, that looks at the occurrence of saltwater encroachment and groundwater pollution in southern Florida. Uses mathematical models to describe the state of saltwater intrusion, future developments, and possible tactics to handle the situation.

Saether, Ola M., and Patrice de Caritat, eds. *Geochemical Processes, Weathering, and Groundwater Recharge in Catchments.* Rotterdam: A. A. Balkema, 1997. A slightly technical compilation that looks at the geochemical cycles and processes associated with catchment basins. Several essays deal with the artificial recharge of groundwater in such systems.

Strahler, Arthur N., and Alan H. Strahler. *Environmental Geoscience: Interaction Between Natural Systems and Man.* Santa Barbara, Calif.: Hamilton, 1973. A college-level text written for the student with a general interest in the topic that details numerous human-geology interactions, including the saltwater intrusion problem.

See also: Aquifers; Artificial Recharge; Dams and Flood Control; Drought; Floods; Freshwater and Groundwater Contamination Around the World; Geochemical Cycles; Groundwater Movement; Groundwater Pollution and Remediation; Hydrologic Cycle; Oceans' Structure; Precipitation; Salinity and Desalination; Seawater Composition; Surface Water; Waterfalls; Water Quality; Watersheds; Water Table; Water Wells

SAND

Sand is the most continental of all sediments. It is important as a source of precious gems and ores, as an abrasive, and as a reservoir for the storage of valuable fluids. Sand dunes form where wind or water deposit sand. Moving dunes can and do overrun cropland and forests, and have many other functions in the dynamics of environmental change.

PRINCIPAL TERMS

- **alluvium:** sediment deposited by flowing water
- **barchan dune:** a crescent-shaped sand dune of deserts and shorelines that lies transverse to the prevailing wind direction
- **cataclastic:** those formative processes of sand that relate to crushing
- **diagenesis:** all physical or chemical changes after deposition
- **endogenetic:** those formative processes of sand that relate to chemical and biochemical precipitation
- **epiclastic:** those formative processes of sand that relate to weathering
- **longitudinal dune:** a long sand dune parallel to the prevailing wind
- **paleocurrent:** the geologic system at the time of deposition
- **precipitate:** to form a solid phase of material from dissolved components, thus separating them from the solution
- **provenance:** all the factors relating to the production of sand
- **pyroclastic:** those formative processes of sand that relate to volcanic action
- **slip face:** the downwind or steep leeward front of a sand dune that continually stabilizes itself to the angle of repose of sand grains
- **star dune:** a starfish-shaped dune with a central peak from which three or more arms radiate
- **stratigraphy:** the internal fabric and structures, the external geometry, and the nature of the basal contact of sand bodies
- **turbidity current:** the movement under gravity of a stream of denser, sediment-bearing fluids through another fluid

FORMATION AND COMPOSITION

Sand is any earth material that consists of loose grains of minerals or rocks that are larger than silt but smaller than gravel. Sand includes those grains that are less than 2.12 millimeters but greater than 0.06 millimeter in diameter. Materials meeting this definition are of widely diverse origins.

There are five processes that lead to the formation and release of sand-sized grains. The first of these processes is weathering, including both disintegration and decomposition. Some rocks crumble by the action of the air, rain, or frost. Decomposition of rocks containing quartz crystal inclusions is probably the origin of most quartz sands. Most of the rock is converted to fine-grained, clay-sized particles, which liberates the inert, undecomposed quartz grains. Sands produced in this manner are called epiclastic sands. The second source of sand is explosive volcanism. The explosive action of volcanoes yields vast quantities of sand-sized debris: glass, crystal fragments, and lava particles. Sands produced in this manner are called pyroclastic sands. Sand-sized materials may also be produced by crushing action, which, as opposed to ordinary abrasion, produces a significant volume of sand. Tectonic movements may crush rocks but do not produce a significant deposit. Glacial crushing, in contrast, does produce a considerable body of sand-sized material as rocks transported by glaciers are ground against other rock. Sands produced in this manner are called cataclastic sands. Much sand-sized material is also produced by chemical and biochemical precipitation. They are generated within the oceanic basins and are not the products of the wastage of landmass. Biochemical and chemical precipitation form oölitic sands that may accumulate in a significant deposit. Sands produced in this manner are called endogenetic sands. The fifth process that may produce sand is pelletization; it involves the sand-sized pellets produced by organisms and the pellets of other origins, such as those that are blown into "clay dunes." Like endogenetic sands, these sands are often found in basins.

Because quartz is the principal product of rock decomposition, it is the principal component of sand. Quartz, a form of silicon dioxide, may be classified in three ways: igneous, including volcanic quartz; metamorphic, including pressure quartz; and sedimentary, including new crystals and overgrowth. One important type of metamorphic quartz is polycrystalline quartz, which includes those grains that are composed of one or more crystal units. Next to quartz, feldspar is the most common mineral of sand. Feldspar is released by the granular disintegration of acidic rock. Several types of feldspar are usually present in sand, although the alkali-rich feldspars seem to be more abundant than the calcareous feldspars. Although mica is conspicuous in some sandstones, it is never a major component because it is derived from igneous rocks. In general, abundant mica points to a metamorphic provenance for sand.

In addition to quartz and feldspar, sandstone usually contains rock particles. These rock particles, most of which are fine-grained, carry their own evidence of provenance. Most common are the shales, clays that have undergone a metamorphic change driven by heat and pressure, which tend to be molded about more resistant quartz. Because they are among the most informative of all the components of sand, any attempt to trace the origin of sand usually begins with an examination of these constituents.

DISTRIBUTION

Sand is distributed across the world. The deep oceanic basins are practically devoid of sand because the grains are too large to be blown or washed to any great distance from the continents before settling due to gravity. Therefore, the principal environments of sand are found on the continents. Sand is produced on the continent and is shifted from higher elevations to lower ones. Only a small amount is carried to the deep sea by turbidity currents that transport sand down the continental slopes to the abyssal plains. The absence of any great quantity of sand on the sea bottom probably results more from an absence of supply than from conditions unfavorable to its accumulation.

The most obvious places to find sand are the rivers and beaches and, to a lesser extent, glacial outwash plains, dunes, and shallow shelf seas. Sand is transported to floodplains and deltas. A little sand also escapes river channels and ends up in swamps and bayous. Shoreline sand includes that which is found in beaches, in lagoons, and on tidal flats. Although windblown dunes are closely associated with beaches and major rivers, the most impressive are found in the dune fields of some desert basins. Marine sands are primarily shelf sands.

Sand is transported primarily by water. It moves mostly along the bottom of a stream as "bed load." The particle size of sand dictates that a very strong turbulent current is required to suspend it in a fluid medium such as water. Thus, sand does not normally move in a continuous manner; instead, sand grains travel in periodic, short jumps along the bottom by a process termed "saltation." The alluvial transport of sand creates forms ranging from small ripples only a few centimeters high to belts many meters high and more than 50 meters thick. A wide range of dunes and bars occur in between.

Sand dispersal on beaches depends on the interaction of shoreline configuration and underwater topography with the energy supplied by waves and currents. As a deep-water wave moves toward a beach, it pushes against the bottom so that the wave tends to parallel the shore. As the water shallows, wave steepness increases, causing loose grains to move back and forth on the bed. This process is called surge transport. In response to passing waves, fluid particles follow a circular path except near the bottom, where the particles move back and forth above the bed, perpendicular to the shoreline. This action, over time, contributes to the continual erosion of larger particles into smaller particles, creating more sand in the process.

Wind transports great quantities of sand in deserts and can also carry inland the sands of beaches that are supplied by currents. When the wind reaches a certain velocity, it exerts sufficient force to cause dry grains of sand begin to roll and accelerate. The round shape of the grains of desert sands can be attributed to this rolling action. Unlike silt and clay, which travel long distances suspended by the wind, sand generally travels by saltation on the ground. The grains are lifted briefly into an arcing trajectory and return to the surface on an elongated, parabolic path.

Turbidity currents are a unique type of transport system for sand. These currents are turbid because of the suspension of fine particles of sand within them, and have an overall density greater than that of the body of water in which they occur. Turbidity currents often form as sediment-laden streams enter an ocean, freshwater lake, or reservoir, in which the turbid water passes beneath the clear, less dense water above. The current slows down as it enters the water body and is maintained as a separate layer of water with a significantly higher density than the overlying water. Under the force of gravity, the turbid layer moves along the floor of the basin until it loses momentum, at which time the suspended material gradually settles. Oceanic turbidity currents may have enough force to extend their flow 150 kilometers or more away from the point of entry.

Diagenesis includes all the changes that sand undergoes after it has been deposited. The major direct evidence of diagenesis in sandstones is the nature of the textural relations between mineral grains and crystals. During diagenesis, original materials are preserved within a matrix that is not original. The most frequently occurring types of replacements are those that preserve faint outlines of the original. The most obvious diagenetic modification is the introduction of cementing agents. Calcite is the most common carbonate mineral cementing sandstone, although silica cementation also occurs frequently. Not all sands undergo diagenesis at the same rate. Sands that are millions of years old may be incoherent, while relatively recent sands may be already bound together.

SAND DUNES

Sand dunes form where wind or water deposit sand. Unlike many other geological processes that produce no visible change in a single human life span, the deposition of sand dunes occurs on a short time line. Dunes are not solely a product of desert dynamics. They also form on the beaches of lakes, rivers, and oceans, on barrier islands and river floodplains, and under water, and have also been observed on Mars. A ready supply of sand and an agent of transportation, such as wind or water, can lead to the formation of a dune. Less than 12 percent of arid lands on Earth are covered by dunes.

Both shoreline and desert sand dunes begin with an obstacle such as a large rock, pebbles, a small sand heap, or vegetation around which sand can be deposited from eddy currents and build up. With constant wind and sand supply, dunes continue to build in size. Some Sahara dunes may reach 100 meters in height, although dunes of 30 meters are more common. Sandbanks Provincial Park in Ontario, Canada, features a sand dune some 450 feet (about 150 meters) in height.

The typical dune shape is distinctive: a long, low-angled windward slope rising to a peak and a steeper leeward slope. Sand grains pushed over the crest eventually settle to a constant 30- to 35-degree angle on the downwind slope. This angle of repose is the maximum stable slope of the intersection of the leeward dune side and the ground. Dunes have several wavelike properties, including crests and wavelength. Different methods of classifying sand dunes have been developed. The most commonly used system distinguishes dunes by shape, sand supply, and orientation to the wind. When sand supply is limited and the wind direction is fairly uniform, a crescent-shaped barchan dune will form. Parabolic dunes occur where vegetation partly covers the sand, often along shorelines. Here, the shape of the dune is similar to the barchan but is oriented in the opposite direction, pointing into the wind rather than away from it. Longitudinal dunes, such as the sinuous line of ridges called seifs in the Sahara Desert, lie parallel to the average direction of prevailing winds. The star dune, formed in a confined basin by variable winds blowing from radically different directions, is the most complex and the least studied of the three types.

Dunes are extremely mobile. During the process of dune growth, as the saltating grains spill over and pile up on the leeward side, or slip face, the entire dune moves downwind. The windward slope, then, is constantly eroding while the sand grains are deposited on the leeward slope. Dunes march forward at a barely detectable 3 meters per year, although dunes in areas of strong, constant winds can move more than 120 meters in one year.

One of the most famous programs of dune stabilization was the United States government's attempt to stabilize 360 kilometers of barrier island beaches off the Atlantic coast. During the 1930's, a sand fence was installed to encourage the development of exceptionally large, artificial dunes. Beach grasses, shrubs, and trees were then planted on the offshore slope. Forty years later, the human-made dunes on Hatteras Island continued to rise in height, but the original beach, 220 kilometers wide, had receded to less than 33 meters, and the marshes behind the towering dunes were drying up. The unnaturally high dunes had prevented sand deposition on the beach and transport of seawater to the marsh at the back of the island. In 1973, the government changed its policy of dune stabilization to allow nature to take its course.

STUDY OF GRAINS

The earliest method of studying the external form of sand grains, which is still used today, involves separating the particles by means of a sieve. Before sifting begins, the sand must be well washed in water and stiffly brushed to detach any mud still sticking to the grains. When dry, the coarsest particles are separated by one sieve and the smallest particles by another so that the sizes of the particles may be compared. The coarse sieve allows grains of 0.36 millimeter in diameter to pass through, and the smaller sieve keeps back all grains that are larger than 0.25 millimeter in diameter. After a sample of medium quality is obtained, it is mixed thoroughly and spread on a horizontal glass plate so that the rounded grains do not separate from the flat and angular grains. The characteristics of the individual grains are then brought into sharp relief with the assistance of a polarizing microscope.

Before the invention of powerful microscopes, the thin-section technique was devised in the nineteenth century to examine the mineral composition of sandstone. A smooth cross section of the stone is obtained in the procedure so that the natural history of the formation may be traced in the various layers of sediment. The thin-section technique has also been applied to igneous rock.

In recent years, sedimentation tubes have been developed. They are gaining in popularity because they provide a more rapid analysis than do sieves. Sedimentation tubes operate on the principle that the sample is introduced at one end of the tube and settles to the other. This method categorizes grains according to their settling velocity, rather than their size.

The question of provenance is one of the most difficult for the sedimentary petrographer to solve because sands being observed are often derived from preexisting sands, and because the source areas may have changed with time. Sedimentary petrographers examine both internal and external evidence as they attempt to trace the "birth" of sediment. Internal evidence is provided by examination of a single grain of sand. A tourmaline grain, for example, may show a secondary growth on a rounded core. This outgrowth may imply weathering and release of the grain, followed by transportation and abrasion, or it might suggest deposition in a new deposit of sand. A more complete analysis of provenance can be made from a sample than from a single grain. If more than one sample is obtained, it is possible to map sedimentary petrologic provinces.

The external evidence relating to provenance is of two types. Regional stratigraphy will contribute to the analysis of provenance by establishing the relative ages of the strata. In order to study the stratigraphy of an area, investigators use a paleogeologic map, which indicates the formations exposed and subject to erosion. Paleocurrent analyses are another important approach to the problem of provenance. They are especially helpful in the study of sandstones of alluvial origin because the up-current direction of these alluvial sands is in the direction of the source.

Once investigators have examined both the internal and external evidence, they present their conclusions as a kind of "flow sheet" or provenance diagram, of which there are two types. The first type is based solely on what can be seen in the rock itself through thin-section analysis. The second type of provenance diagram is based on a study of the thin section and on a knowledge of regional geology and stratigraphy. To construct this type of diagram, any and all manner of geologic data must be pieced together.

SIGNIFICANCE

Sand is economically important because of the mineral content of certain shore and river sands. As the lighter components are removed by the current, the heavier components become concentrated. Some of these deposits, which are called placers, yield diamonds and other gemstones, gold, platinum, uranium, tin, monazite (containing thorium and rare-earth elements), zircon (for zirconium), rutile (for titanium), and other ores. During the California Gold Rush of 1849, millions of dollars worth of gold was taken from placers. In modern times, rare metals for jet engines come from placers in Florida, India, and Australia. The greensands, which are found over the ocean floor, are widely sought after because their green color indicates the presence of potash-bearing material. These sands have been used for agricultural land amendment and for water softening. In addition, potash has been successfully extracted from them. The search for these sands has been refined to an art called alluvian prospecting.

Sands derived from specific minerals are indispensable to certain industries. Very pure quartzose sands are used as a source of silica in the pottery, glassmaking, and silicate industries. Similar sands are required in making the linings for the hearths of acid-steel furnaces. Sands utilized in foundries for making the molds in which metal is cast are those that have a clay-type bond uniting the quartz grains. Quartz sands and garnet sands are also used as abrasives in sandpaper and sand blasting because of their hardness and poor cleavage. They are employed in the grinding of marble, plate glass, and metal. Some sands are used as soil conditioners or fertilizers. Ordinary sands find a multitude of other uses. Sand is an essential ingredient of mortar, cement, and concrete. Sand is also added to clays to reduce shrinkage and cracking in brick manufacture and to asphalt to make "road dressing." Additionally, it is used in filtration and as friction sand on locomotives.

Aside from its usefulness as an additive, sand-based structures also serve as reservoirs for the storage of valuable fluids. The pore systems of sand and sandstones are capable of containing large stores of freshwater, of brines, and of petroleum and natural gas. Sand strata are also conduits for artesian flow. Fluids may also be injected into the sands. Before fluids can be extracted, geologists must become familiar with the shape and porosity of the particular sand reservoir. A working knowledge of diagenesis is essential for geologists who are searching for petroleum deposits.

Geologists and geomorphologists concerned with shore erosion and harbor development are also concerned with sand production, movement, and deposition. In order to solve the problems of shore engineering, some understanding of sand supply and sand deficit or removal is necessary. Geologists must also have a solid understanding of sand as they try to prevent the encroachment of sand on cultivated lands and forests or on roads and other structures. Finally, sand is involved in many aspects of river management.

Alan Brown

FURTHER READING

Blatt, Harvey, Robert J. Tracy, and Brent Owens. *Petrology: Igneous, Sedimentary, and Metamorphic.* New York: W. H. Freeman, 2005. Brings together the major theories of sedimentation. Discusses the formation of sand in terms of modern physics and chemistry. Suitable for college students and geologists. Includes references at the end of each chapter that are very useful.

Chorley, Richard J., Stanley A. Schumm, and David E. Sugden. *Geomorphology.* New York: Methuen, 1985. A well-referenced, though older, textbook, that emphasizes the role and function of weathering sediment transport in all environments and discusses theoretical principles. Includes a particularly lucid description of sand dune formations as aeolian bed forms. Contains numerous line drawings as well as working charts and graphs.

Christopherson, Robert W., and Mary-Louise Byrne. *Geosystems: An Introduction to Physical Geography.* Toronto: Pearson Education Canada, 2006. A well-written and very readable textbook, with numerous references and links to online resources. Presents a detailed discussion of the nature and behavior of sand in the context of physical geography.

Houseknecht, David W., and Edward D. Pittman, eds. *Origin, Diagenesis, and Petrophysics of Clay Minerals in Sandstones.* Tulsa, Okla.: Society for Sedimentary Geology, 1992. A collection of essays written by leading experts in their respective fields. Examines the geochemical and geophysical properties of sand, sandstone, clay minerals, and other sedimentary rocks. Filled with illustrations and includes an index and bibliographical references.

Lade, Poul V., and Jerry A. Yamamuro. "Evaluation of Static Liquefaction Potential of Silty Sand Slopes." *Canadian Geotechnical Journal* 48 (2011): 247-264. Compares sand types and their liquefaction potential.

Murphy, Jessica A. *Sand Dunes: Conservation, Types and Desertification.* New York: Nova Science Publishers, 2011. Presents current research in the study of the conservation, types, and desertification of sand dunes. Discusses a model for plant-based stabilization and the causes and effects of desertification, as well as their use as an industrial resource.

Pettijohn, F. J., Paul Edwin Potter, and Raymond Siever. *Sand and Sandstone.* 2d ed. New York: Springer-Verlag, 1987. Offers an in-depth analysis of sand. A lengthy book that is amply supplemented with photographs, illustrations, and charts. Includes a glossary at the end of each chapter. For college students with a solid background in geology.

Prothero, Donald R., and Fred Schwab. *Sedimentary Geology: An Introduction to Sedimentary Rocks and Stratigraphy.* New York: W. H. Freeman, 2003. Provides a thorough treatment of most aspects of sediments and sedimentary rocks. Well illustrated with line drawings and black-and-white photographs, also contains a comprehensive bibliography. Covers carbonate rocks and limestone depositional processes and environments. Suitable for college-level readers.

Pye, Kenneth, and Haim Tsoar. *Aeolian Sand and Sand Dunes*. Berlin: Springer-Verlag, 2009. Discusses the basic properties and origin of sand grains, the mechanics of sand transport, the formation of sand seas, the dynamics and internal structures of sand dunes, weathering, and diagenesis of dune sand. Includes an extensive bibliography. Written for students, lecturers, and researchers specializing in geomorphology and sedimentology.

Reading, H. G., ed. *Sedimentary Environments: Processes, Facies, and Stratigraphy*. 3d ed. Oxford: Blackwell Science, 1996. Provides a good treatment of the study of sedimentary rocks and biogenic sedimentary environments. Suitable for the high school or college student. Well illustrated, with an index and bibliography.

Reineck, H. E., and I. B. Singh. *Depositional Sedimentary Environment*. 2d ed. Berlin: Springer-Verlag, 1992. Concerned primarily with the various types of sand deposit. Diagrams and photographs help to clarify the technical language. Useful for college students majoring in geology.

Tucker, Maurice E. *Sedimentary Rocks in the Field*. 4th ed. New York: John Wiley & Sons, 2011. Presents a concise account of biogenic sedimentary rocks and other sedimentary rocks. Covers classification of sedimentary rocks well. Briefly discusses depositional environments. Well-selected references. Suitable for undergraduates.

U.S. Minerals Management Service. *Environmental Survey of Potential Sand Resource Sites Offshore Delaware and Maryland*. Herndon, Va.: Office of International Activities and Marine Minerals, 2000. Presents a study of the benthic habitat and species along the continental shelf off Delaware and Maryland. Addresses potential changes to the shelf zone due to dredging and sand mining. Continues with an overview of the study area, methodology, and data analysis of the shelf zone. Includes many excellent images.

Welland, Michael. *Sand: A Journey Through Science and the Imagination*. New York: Oxford University Press, 2010. Presents a scientific and entertaining examination of the nature of sand, from its formation and sedimentary functions to the musical tones emitted by sand dunes in different locations in the world.

_____. *Sand: The Never-Ending Story*. Berkeley: University of California Press, 2011. Discusses the science, geology, and cultural significance of sand as a critical ingredient in many aspects of present-day life. Written for amateur scientists and the general public.

See also: Alluvial Systems; Aquifers; Beaches and Coastal Processes; Deep-Sea Sedimentation; Deltas; Desert Pavement; Drainage Basins; Floodplains; Floods; Hydrologic Cycle; Lakes; Precipitation; Reefs; River Bed Forms; River Flow; Sediment Transport and Deposition; Surface Water; Weathering and Erosion

SATELLITE METEOROLOGY

Satellite meteorology, the study of atmospheric phenomena using satellite data, is an indispensable tool for forecasting weather and studying climate on a global scale.

PRINCIPAL TERMS

- **active sensor:** a sensor, such as a radar instrument, that illuminates a target with artificial radiation, which is reflected back to the sensor
- **albedo:** the percentage of incoming radiation that is diffusely reflected by a planetary surface
- **El Niño:** a periodic anomalous warming of the Pacific waters off the coast of South America; part of a large-scale oceanic and atmospheric fluctuation that has global repercussions
- **geosynchronous (geostationary):** describing a satellite that orbits about Earth's equator at an altitude and speed such that it remains above the same point on the surface of the planet
- **near-polar orbit:** an orbit of Earth that lies in a plane that passes close to both the North and South Poles
- **passive sensors:** sensors that detect reflected or emitted electromagnetic radiation that has issued from another source
- **radiometer:** an instrument that quantitatively measures reflected or emitted electromagnetic radiation within a particular wavelength interval
- **spatial resolution:** the extent to which a sensor is able to differentiate between closely spaced features
- **sun-synchronous orbit:** for an Earth satellite, a near-polar orbit at an altitude such that the satellite always passes over any given point on Earth at the same local time
- **synthetic aperture radar (SAR):** a space-borne radar imaging system that uses the motion of the spacecraft in orbit to simulate a very long antenna

TYPES OF SATELLITES AND INSTRUMENTS

Satellite meteorology is the study of atmospheric phenomena, notably weather and weather conditions, using information gathered by instruments aboard artificial satellites. These satellites, including the International Space Station, are equipped with instruments that monitor cloud cover, snow, ice, temperatures, and other parameters, to give scientists a continuous and up-to-date view of meteorological conditions and activity over a large area. The use of satellite data is an important tool not only for forecasting weather and tracking storms but also for observing climate change over time, monitoring ozone levels in the stratosphere, and studying numerous other aspects of global weather and climate on an ongoing basis.

The satellites from which meteorological measurements are made can be categorized by their orbits. Some weather satellites have a geosynchronous, or geostationary, orbit, meaning that they travel around the globe at an altitude and speed that keep them above the same point over the equator. A near-polar, sun-synchronous orbit, by contrast, is a north-south orbit that passes close to the poles such that a satellite on that orbital path passes over any given location on Earth at the same local time. Geosynchronous satellites have better temporal resolution: They provide updated information for an area every thirty minutes, while near-polar, sun-synchronous satellites may take anywhere from a few hours to several days to transmit updates. However, near-polar satellites have the higher spatial resolution; that is, they are better at providing images in which closely spaced features can be identified. Geosynchronous satellites provide images with comparatively poor spatial resolution because they must orbit at a greater altitude (at least 35,000 kilometers above the surface). Examples of geosynchronous meteorological satellites include the U.S. Geostationary Operational Environmental Satellite (GOES) series, the European Space Agency's METEOSAT series, Russia's Geostationary Operational Meteorological Satellite (GOMS) series, and Japan's Geostationary Meteorological Satellite (GMS), or Himawan, series. Near-polar, sun-synchronous meteorological satellites include the National Oceanic and Atmospheric Administration (NOAA) series of satellites and Russia's Meteor series.

The various orbiting platforms carry different sets of instruments. The weather satellites launched in the 1960's and early 1970's included television camera systems as part of their instrument packages. Later satellites have relied instead on instruments such as specialized radiometers (instruments that measure the amounts of electromagnetic radiation within a specific wavelength range) and radar systems. Radiometers measure such parameters as surface, cloud, and atmospheric temperatures; atmospheric water vapor and cloud distribution; and scattered solar radiation. Radar-system measurements include satellite altitude and ocean-surface roughness. Television cameras and radiometers are examples of passive sensors, which record radiation reflected or emitted from clouds, landforms, or other objects below. Radar systems are active sensors, sending out signals and recording them as they are reflected back. The data collected by a satellite's sensors are transmitted via radio to ground stations. If a near-polar orbiter is not within transmitting distance of a ground station, its onboard data-collection system will store the information until the satellite passes within range.

WEATHER SATELLITES

The Advanced Television Infrared Observation Satellite, or TIROS, and Next-Generation (ATN) near-polar orbiting satellites (NOAA 8 through 14), have carried an assortment of sophisticated instruments. Two of these satellites, NOAA 12 and NOAA 14, remained in operation into the late 1990's. All of the ATN series satellites have included an advanced, very-high-resolution radiometer (AVHRR), which detects specified wavelength intervals within the visible, near-infrared, and infrared wavelength ranges to generate information on sea-surface and cloud-top temperatures and ice and snow conditions; a TIROS operational vertical sounder (TOVS), which measures emissions within the visible, infrared, and microwave spectral bands to provide vertical profiles of the atmosphere's temperature, water vapor, and total ozone content from the ground surface to an altitude of 32 kilometers; and a solar proton monitor, which detects fluctuations in the sun's energy output, particularly those related to sunspot (solar storm) activity. With the exception of NOAA 8 and NOAA 12, all these satellites have included the Earth radiation

budget experiment (ERBE), which uses long-wave and short-wave radiometers to provide data pertaining to Earth's albedo. All but NOAA 8, NOAA 10, and NOAA 12 have carried the solar backscatter ultraviolet (SBUV) radiometer, which measures the vertical structure of ozone in the atmosphere by monitoring the ultraviolet radiation that the atmosphere scatters back into space. Of the ATN series of satellites, NOAA 12 is the only one that has not also carried the Search and Rescue Satellite Aided Tracking (SARSAT) system, which detects distress signals from downed aircraft and emergency beacons from ocean vessels, then relays the signals to special ground stations.

The satellites of the U.S. GOES series that remained in operation in the late 1990's (GOES 8 and GOES 9) are geosynchronous orbiters with their own distinctive instrumentation. Instrumentation aboard GOES 8 (also called GOES-EAST) and GOES 9 (or GOES-WEST) includes a sounder, which uses visible and infrared data to create vertical profiles of atmospheric temperature, moisture, carbon dioxide, and

A hurricane, with the eye in its center, as seen in a satellite image. (PhotoDisc)

ozone; a five-band multispectral radiometer, which scans visible and infrared wavelengths to obtain sea-surface temperature readings, detect airborne dust and volcanic ash, and provide day and night images of cloud conditions, fog, fires, and volcanoes; and a search-and-rescue support system similar to the ones flown on the NOAA near-polar orbiters. The GOES satellites are also equipped with a space environment monitor (SEM), which uses a solar X-ray sensor, a magnetometer, an energetic particle sensor, and a high-energy proton alpha detector to monitor solar activity and the intensity of Earth's magnetic field. The GOES-EAST satellite is positioned above the equator at an approximate longitude of 75 degrees west, while the GOES-WEST satellite orbits above the equator at approximately 135 degrees west longitude. These locations are ideal for monitoring the climatic conditions across North America. From them, GOES-EAST can provide images of storms approaching the eastern seaboard across the Atlantic Ocean during hurricane season (June through November), and GOES-WEST can monitor the weather systems that move in from across the Pacific Ocean, which affect the western seaboard during most of the year. However, when instrument malfunctions impair a satellite's ability to provide data, the National Weather Service can use small rocket engines aboard the satellites to reposition a more functional platform to provide the desired coverage until a replacement satellite can be launched. After the imaging system on GOES 6 failed in 1989, for example, GOES 7 was relocated several times to compensate.

RADAR AND SATELLITE DATA

While operational weather satellites have generally carried radiometers, radar instruments have been part of the instrument package aboard experimental satellites and space shuttle flights. One of the best-known orbiters using active sensors is Seasat, a short-lived experimental craft launched in 1978 to monitor the oceans. During its three months of operation, this Earth-resources satellite provided a wealth of data for meteorological study. Its radar altimeter determined the height of the sea surface, from which data scientists derived measurements of winds, waves, and ocean currents. Its radar scatterometer yielded information on wave direction and size that, in turn, provided insights into wind speed and direction. The most sophisticated of Seasat's active sensors was its

synthetic aperture radar (SAR) system, a radar imaging system that created a "synthetic aperture" of view by using the motion of the platform to simulate a very long antenna. Images of the ocean's surface were obtained from SAR data.

Satellite data have become indispensable to the meteorologist. From orbit, information is readily available for any location on the planet, regardless of its remoteness, inaccessibility, climatic inhospitality, or political affiliation. Satellites yield regular, repeated, and up-to-date coverage of areas at minimal cost. They make it possible to view large weather systems in their entirety, and facilitate meteorological observations on a regional or global basis. Satellites also provide a single data source for multiple locations, alleviating the problem of individual variance of calibration and accuracy that would be associated with separate ground-based observations for each location. However, it is important to note that ground-based stations can make more accurate and detailed observations of a small area, and such details may be lost in a view from space. Important though it is to modern meteorology, the use of satellite data augments, rather than replaces, other methods of study.

WEATHER FORECASTING

Satellite meteorology provides a rapid and relatively inexpensive means of obtaining current and abundant information on temperature, pressure, moisture, and other atmospheric, terrestrial, and oceanic conditions that affect weather and climate. These data, collected in digital form, are readily processed and integrated with other information. Through these ongoing observations from orbit, scientists gain insights into the short-term and long-term implications of major atmospheric phenomena.

Weather forecasting is the best-known application of satellite meteorology. Anyone who has watched a televised weather report is familiar with geostationary satellite images, a series of which are usually presented in quick succession to show the recent movement of major weather systems. Meteorologists use computers to process the vast amounts of data provided by satellites and other information sources, including ground-based stations, aircraft, ships, and buoys. Data processing yields such forecasting aids as atmospheric temperature and water-vapor profiles, enhanced and false-color images, and satellite-image "movies." Computer models of atmospheric behavior also assist the meteorologist in short-range and long-range forecasting.

Satellite images of cloud cover alone yield a wealth of information for the forecaster. By comparing imagery from visible and infrared spectral regions, meteorologists can identify cloud types, structure, and degree of organization, then make assumptions and deductions concerning associated weather conditions. For example, the tall cumulus clouds that produce thunderstorms appear bright in the visible range, as they are deep and thus readily reflect sunlight. These clouds show up in infrared images as areas of coldness, an indicator of the altitude to which the clouds have climbed. Clouds that appear bright in visible-range imagery but that register as warm (low-altitude) in infrared scans may be fog or low-lying clouds. Wispy, high-altitude cirrus clouds, which are not precipitation-bearing, appear cold in infrared images but may not show up at all in visible-range scans.

Weather satellites have proved particularly useful in the science of hurricane and typhoon prediction. These large, violent, rotating tropical storms originate as relatively small low-pressure cells over oceans, where coverage by conventional weather-monitoring methods is sparse. Before the advent of satellites, ships and aircraft were the sole source of information on weather at sea, and hurricanes and typhoons often escaped detection until they were dangerously close to populated coastal areas. Using images and data obtained from orbiting satellites, meteorologists can track and study these storms continuously from their inception through their development and final dissipation. With accurate storm tracking and ample advance warning, inhabitants at risk can evacuate areas threatened by wind and high water, thereby minimizing loss of life.

CLIMATE STUDIES

Meteorological satellites also provide scientists with a view of how human activity affects climate on a local, regional, and even global basis. Terrestrial surface-temperature measurements clearly show urban "heat islands," where cities consistently radiate more heat energy than the surrounding countryside. In images obtained from orbit, thunderstorms can be seen developing along the boundaries of areas of dense air pollution: The haze layer inhibits heating of the ground surface, leading to the unstable atmospheric

conditions that produce rainfall. Satellite imagery has revealed that in sub-Saharan Africa, where the overgrazing of livestock owned by nomads has contributed substantially to the spread of desert areas, the resulting increase in albedo has led to a reduction in rainfall and a subsequent reinforcement of drought conditions. Studies of deforestation in tropical areas have incorporated satellite data in their efforts to determine whether replacing forests with agricultural land affects rainfall by reducing evaporation or altering albedo. Satellite data have also played a major role in the ongoing debates regarding how human activity has affected global temperature trends and the ozone layer.

Satellite meteorology is useful for monitoring the climatological effects of natural occurrences as well. The 1991 eruption of Mount Pinatubo in the Philippines marked the first time that scientists were able to quantify the effects of a major volcanic eruption on global climate. Satellites equipped with ERBE instruments tracked the dissemination of the ash and sulfuric acid particles resulting from the violent eruption. The larger ash particles more readily drift down into the lower portion of the atmosphere, where they are typically removed in precipitation. The smaller sulfuric acid particles, however, can remain suspended in the stratosphere for several years, eventually reaching lower altitudes where they combine with water to produce acidic precipitation. The ERBE instruments measured the amount of sunlight reflected by clouds, land surfaces, and particles suspended in the atmosphere and detected the contribution of suspended particles, clouds, and trace gases such as carbon dioxide to the amount of heat that the atmosphere retained. The eruption was found to have brought about a uniform cooling of Earth, temporarily slowing the ongoing global-warming trend that has been observed since the 1980's.

Another natural phenomenon, El Niño, has also been the subject of satellite-based study. This periodic anomalous warming of the Pacific waters off the coast of South America is part of a large-scale oceanic and atmospheric fluctuation known as the Southern Oscillation, in which atmospheric pressure conditions alternately decline and rise over the eastern Pacific Ocean and Australia and the Indian Ocean. These widespread pressure changes influence rainfall patterns around the world. Satellite measurement of sea-surface temperatures facilitates the early detection of El Niño conditions, and satellite observations on a global basis help scientists to discern the climatic patterns that make up this complex phenomenon.

Meteorological satellites have also been used to gather data pertaining to "solar weather." Using orbiting sensors that detect energetic particles from the sun, as well as more direct imaging methods, scientists can monitor and predict sunspots and other solar activity. The ability to predict the increases in solar emissions that are associated with sunspots allows scientists to anticipate the resulting ionospheric conditions on Earth, the effects of which include magnetic storms and disruption of radio transmissions.

Karen N. Kähler

FURTHER READING

Ahrens, C. Donald. *Essentials of Meteorology: An Invitation to the Atmosphere*. Belmont, Calif.: Brooks/Cole Cengage Learning, 2012. Discusses various topics in weather and the atmosphere. Chapters cover topics such as tornadoes and thunderstorms, acid deposition and other air pollution topics, humidity and cloud formation, and temperature.

Bader, M. J., et al., eds. *Images in Weather Forecasting: A Practical Guide for Interpreting Satellite and Radar Imagery*. New York: Cambridge University Press, 1995. A collection of essays written by leading meteorologists to describe the equipment and techniques used in weather forecasting. Chapters focus on remote sensing, radar meteorology, and satellite meteorology. Color illustrations.

Barrett, E. C., and L. F. Curtis. *Introduction to Environmental Remote Sensing*. 3d ed. New York: John Wiley & Sons, 1992. Discusses weather analysis, forecasting satellite systems, and data applications. Deals with the atmosphere energy and radiation budgets and other aspects of global climatology. Each chapter includes references.

Burroughs, William James. *Watching the World's Weather*. Cambridge, England: Cambridge University Press, 1991. Focuses on the importance of satellite meteorology to an understanding of weather and climate on a global scale. Deals not only with satellites and instrumentation but also with the essentials of meteorology. Includes satellite images, a glossary, a list of acronyms, and an annotated bibliography.

Campbell, Bruce A. *Radar Remote Sensing of Planetary Surfaces*. New York: Cambridge University Press, 2002. Covers methodology and theory of radar remote sensing. Provides examples from Earth, the moon, and other planets. Includes references and indexing.

Campbell, James B., and Randolph H. Wynne. *Introduction to Remote Sensing*. 5th ed. New York: Guilford Press, 2011. Provides an interdisciplinary introduction to the topic, with background information on the electromagnetic spectrum. Covers many aspects of digital imagery, from aerial photography and coverage to image enhancement and interpretation.

Collier, Christopher G. *Applications of Weather Radar Systems: A Guide to Uses of Radar Data in Meteorology and Hydrology*. 2d ed. New York: Wiley, 1996. Offers a detailed look into scientific advancements regarding the tools used in meteorology and hydrology. Focuses on radar meteorology, precipitation measurement, hydrometeorology, and weather forecasting.

Fishman, Jack, and Robert Kalish. *The Weather Revolution*. New York: Plenum Press, 1994. Provides a nontechnical explanation of the basics of meteorology and outlines the evolution of weather forecasting, before and since the advent of weather satellites. The chapter on the development of satellite meteorology discusses programs from TIROS through GOES.

Gurney, R. J., J. L. Foster, and C. L. Parkinson, eds. *Atlas of Satellite Observations Related to Global Change*. Cambridge, England: Cambridge University Press, 1993. Suitable for college-level readers. Includes articles on the stratosphere, the troposphere, Earth's radiation balance, ocean-atmosphere coupling, and snow and ice cover. Illustrated with satellite imagery. An appendix describes selected satellites and sensors.

Hill, Janice. *Weather from Above*. Washington, D.C.: Smithsonian Institution Press, 1991. An overview of U.S. weather satellite programs, intended for a nonscientific audience, that includes a glossary of acronyms, a chronological list of meteorological satellites, and suggestions for further reading. Illustrations include photographs of weather satellites, many from the collection of the National Air and Space Museum.

Kelkar, R. R. *Satellite Meteorology*. Hyderabad: BS Publications, 2007. Traces the history of satellite meteorology as the youngest and fastest-growing branch of the science, to its present state, and speculates on the future. Suitable as a textbook or as a reference work for several related disciplines.

Lillesand, Thomas M., Ralph W. Kiefer, and Jonathan Chipman. *Remote Sensing and Image Interpretation.* 6th ed. Hoboken, N.J.: John Wiley & Sons, 2008. The chapter on Earth resource satellites includes a description of the U.S. NOAA and GOES series of satellites and the Air Force's Defense Meteorological Satellite Program. Earlier chapters provide detailed information on various scanning instruments.

Lubin, Dan, and Robert Massom. *Polar Remote Sensing: Atmosphere and Oceans.* Chichester, England: Praxis Publishing, 2006. A comprehensive multidisciplinary work covering the polar environment, with satellite remote sensing applications to atmospheric chemistry, meteorology, climate study, and physical oceanography.

Lutgens, Frederick K., Edward J. Tarbuck, and Dennis Tasa. *The Atmosphere: An Introduction to Meteorology.* 11th ed. Upper Saddle River, N.J.: Prentice Hall, 2010. Offers an excellent introduction and description of the atmosphere, meteorology, and weather patterns. Suitable for the reader new to the study of these subjects. Color illustrations and maps.

Menzel, W. Paul. *Applications with Meteorological Satellites.* Geneva: World Meteorological Organization, 2001. Presents a NOAA report that discusses the history and evolution of satellite meteorology, data processing, radiation principles, accounting for clouds, measuring surface temperatures, and other techniques used in taking atmospheric measurements. A technical report that provides detailed information best suited for graduate students and professional in the fields of meteorology and satellite imagery.

Monmonier, Mark S. *Air Apparent: How Meteorologists Learned to Map, Predict, and Dramatize Weather.* Chicago: University of Chicago Press, 1999. A college-level text that looks at the satellites and radar systems used to collect meteorological data, as well as the techniques used to interpret that information. Color illustrations, index, and bibliographical references.

Qu, John J., Robert E. Murphy, Wei Gao, Vincent V. Salomonson, and Menas Kofatos, eds. *Earth Science Satellite Remote Sensing. Science and Instruments.* Vol. 1. Beijing: Tsinghua University Press, 2006. A specialist reference work describing the scientific principles of remote sensing by satellite and the instruments used in the process.

Stevens, William Kenneth. *The Change in the Weather: People, Weather, and the Science of Climate.* New York: Random House, 2001. Describes various natural and human-induced causes of changes in the climate. Includes a twenty-page bibliography and an index.

Vallis, Geoffrey K. *Atmospheric and Oceanic Fluid Dynamics: Fundamentals and Large-scale Circulation.* New York: Cambridge University Press, 2006. Begins with an overview of the physics of fluid dynamics to provide foundational material on stratification, vorticity, oceanic and atmospheric models. Discusses topics such as turbulence, baroclinic instabilities, wave-mean flow interactions, and large-scale atmospheric and oceanic circulation. Best suited for graduate students studying meteorology or oceanography.

See also: Atmosphere's Global Circulation; Atmospheric and Oceanic Oscillations; Atmospheric Properties; Barometric Pressure; Climate; Climate Change Theories; Climate Modeling; Clouds; Cyclones and Anticyclones; Drought; Floods; Hurricanes; Hydrologic Cycle; Indian Ocean; Lightning and Thunder; Long-Term Weather Patterns; Monsoons; Observational Data of the Atmosphere and Oceans; Ocean-Atmosphere Interactions; Recent Climate Change Research; Remote Sensing of the Atmosphere; Remote Sensing of the Oceans; Seasons; Severe Storms; Surface Ocean Currents; Tornadoes; Van Allen Radiation Belts; Volcanoes: Climatic Effects; Weather Forecasting; Weather Forecasting: Numerical Weather Prediction; Weather Modification; Wind

SEA LEVEL

Sea level is the average position of the surface of the oceans relative to the land, providing a frame of reference for land elevations and ocean depths. Sea levels change through time, affected by a variety of factors, and these changes have a major influence on the geology of Earth.

PRINCIPAL TERMS

- **continental shelf:** the extension of a continental mass beneath the sea; a flat or gently sloping platform usually 10 to 100 kilometers wide, extending to a depth of 100 to 150 meters
- **eustatic sea-level change:** a change in sea level worldwide, observed on all coastlines on all continents
- **glaciation:** commonly known as an "ice age," the cyclic widespread growth and advance of ice sheets over the polar and high-latitude to midlatitude regions of the world
- **greenhouse effect:** the warming of the atmosphere caused by absorption and re-emission of infrared energy by carbon dioxide and other gases in the atmosphere
- **isostasy:** the passive, vertical rise or fall of the crust caused, respectively, by the removal or addition of a load on the crust
- **local sea-level change:** a change in sea level only in one area of the world, usually by land rising or sinking in that specific area
- **mean sea level:** the average height of the sea surface over a multiyear time span, taking into account storms, tides, and seasons
- **regression:** the retreat of the sea from the land, allowing land erosion processes to occur on material previously below the sea surface
- **tectonics:** the process of origin, movement, and deformation of large-scale structures of the crust
- **transgression:** the advance of the sea over the land, allowing marine sediments to be deposited on what had previously been dry land

CHANGING SEA LEVEL

Sea level is a major aspect of the modern world. The distinction between land and sea depends on the level of the sea. A rise in sea level means the flooding of adjacent low-lying land; a drop in sea level means exposure of some of the sea floor. Much of the world's commerce, food supply, and recreation is associated with shallow coastal waters. The position and rate of change of sea level is important to all these activities, especially as construction has encroached right up to the water's edge in many places. Sea level is most accurately defined as mean (average) sea level, which is the average height of the sea surface measured over an extended period of time for all conditions of tides, seasons, and storms. Land elevations are measured by reference to sea level. Nautical charts, however, use mean low water, the average position of low tide, to measure ocean depths, while mean high water, the average position of high tide, is used for marking the exposure of adjacent land areas. The reason for use of low- and high-tide values, for depth and land, respectively, is purely practical: Successful navigation requires accurate knowledge of water depths and land exposures. By referring depths to mean low tide, ship captains can be more assured that, regardless of tide position, they know the minimum water depth available for their vessels. The same principle applies to land areas: Using a high-tide value to show land allows land users to be sure that the low-lying areas will not flood with the high-tide cycle.

The most fascinating aspect of sea level is that it is not constant. Through time, it can change. The time of change can be hours, days, years, or centuries. When sea level rises and floods the land, it is called a marine transgression. The flooded land becomes part of the ocean environment, and marine sediments are deposited on what was once dry land. Marine regression, by contrast, occurs when sea level drops and the shallow sea floor is exposed. The exposed sea floor becomes part of the land environment and is subject to the same type of erosion processes that function on land. Almost every continental coastal area includes a continental shelf, or a flat-lying or gently sloping portion of the continent that extends under the sea to depths up to 150 meters over a width of several tens of kilometers to over 100 kilometers. The gentle slope of the continental shelf means that a minor rise in sea level results in a major amount of the shelf being drowned; a minor drop in sea level produces a major exposure of the continental shelf sea floor. The rocks of the continents show that over Earth's history, sea level has transgressed onto, and regressed from, the continents many times and to many different levels.

Sea level can be changed in six basic ways: by oscillating the ocean surface; by changing the force of gravity; by moving the land up or down; by changing the characteristics of the ocean water; by changing the amount of water in the oceans; and by changing the volume of the ocean basins. The change in sea level brought about by these six ways results in two major types of sea-level change: local and eustatic. Local sea-level change means that only a specific area of coastline is involved and that coastlines relatively far away or on other continents are not changed. Oscillation of the water surface, changing gravity, and land moving up and down also produce local sea-level change. Eustatic sea-level change means that coastlines around the planet all experience a sea-level change of the same magnitude at the same time. Changing water characteristics, changing the amount of water on the planet, or changing the volume of the ocean basins produces eustatic sea-level change.

LOCAL SEA-LEVEL CHANGE

Sea-level change produced by oscillation of the ocean surface refers to waves, storm surges, and tides. A wave breaking on the beach runs up the beach, then slides back down. Each wave event can be considered a short-term, low-magnitude sea-level change. In extreme cases of large waves, erosion and coastline modification can occur during each sea-level "micro-event." Storm surges are changes in sea level brought about by the movement of surface waters under the influence of strong winds and low atmospheric pressures, such as occurs with hurricanes. Low atmospheric pressure appears to pull sea level up a small amount, though in actuality this is the result of higher air pressure surrounding the system that pushes down on the surrounding water while lower air pressure inside the system allows the interior water to rise. As for the direct effect of wind on water levels, high onshore winds can pile water up on coastal areas by 3 or 4 meters, while offshore winds can lower sea level in the same way but by lesser amounts.

Tides are produced in the oceans by the force of lunar gravity, solar gravity, and by the rotation of the Earth-moon system about its common center of mass. Coastline configuration, latitude, time of the lunar month, and many other factors control the timing and magnitude of ocean tides. Tide characteristics are extremely variable from place to place, but in a given area, the changes in sea level are quite predictable, with magnitudes from a fraction of a meter to more than 10 meters possible. Because ocean surface oscillations are common, low in magnitude, and regular, they are often not recognized as sea-level changes. They are different for every coastline, producing local sea-level change.

The force of gravity is not perfectly uniform over Earth. It depends on the amount of mass beneath the surface and thus, because of tectonics and other activities, may vary by a small amount from location to location. This variation is most marked between the continental landmasses, where there is a great deal more matter to exert gravitational force, and the ocean floors, where there is much less crustal mass. The ocean, as a fluid, responds to the force of gravity: If gravity is slightly weaker in one area than in another, the sea will rise slightly higher; if it is slightly stronger, the sea will sink slightly lower. This sea-level variation occurs only in time frames of millions of years, but it is used to explain local sea levels that are different in certain areas from predicted values.

In many areas, the land itself is moving up or down. This movement has three sources: tectonics, isostasy, and subsidence. Tectonics is the movement and distortion of Earth's crust by convective forces generated within the magma of the mantle, influenced by the thermal activity in the planetary core. Tectonic action is responsible for the formation of volcanoes, mountains, and earthquakes. In an area where tectonic processes are active, the land may be forced up or down, causing it to rise or sink with respect to sea level. In tectonically active areas such as Southern California or in the Mediterranean basin, this type of land movement is common, and sea-level changes of many meters up and down have been historically documented. Isostasy is the vertical movement of the crust downward when a load is applied—as when a glacial mass of ice forms over the land—or its rebound upward when the load is removed. When isostasy occurs in a coastal area, the land will rise or sink, with a subsequent change in sea level. Glaciers are examples of how a load can be applied to the crust, causing isostatic subsidence. When the glacier melts, the load is removed, and the crust can isostatically rebound. This is the process responsible for the gradual rise of the land west of the Niagara Escarpment in southwestern Ontario, Canada, and of the rising east coast of Britain such that thousand-year-old coastal installations now stand as much as 400 meters above sea level. Coral islands and volcanic islands are other examples of a load being placed on the crust, which then isostatically sinks. Land can sink beneath sea level by a process called subsidence. Subsidence is often caused by compaction of the land material, which commonly happens when oil or water is withdrawn from the ground. The loss of the fluid allows the rock to compact, and the overlying land sinks. All three of these methods of moving land up or down occur in localized areas and so result in local sea-level change.

EUSTATIC SEA-LEVEL CHANGE

Changing sea level eustatically, or worldwide, requires changes that affect the oceans as opposed to the land. The ocean basins generally have a fixed volume. If the nature of the water in it is changed, if the amount of water is changed, or if the shape of the container (ocean basin) is changed, sea level will change. The two characteristics of water that control sea level are its temperature and its salinity. For each degree Celsius that the oceans warm, thermal expansion will raise sea level 2 meters due to the lesser density (mass per unit volume) of the water. Increasing the salinity makes the water solution denser and causes sea level to fall. Sea-level variations caused by changes in salinity measure approximately 1 to 2 meters.

The amount of water available to the oceans is changed in three ways: by the growth and melting of glaciers, by steam released from volcanoes, and by water lost to the formation of hydrated crystals in sediments. Glaciation is one of the most important sea-level controls. As ice sheets grow, they are fed by evaporated seawater falling as snow; this seawater is then "trapped" as ice on the continents, and sea level falls by the corresponding amount. This is a negligibly small amount per snowflake, but over thousands and millions of years it has produced glacial coverage up to 4 kilometers in thickness in some places such as Greenland and Antarctica. If the ice melts and the water flows back to the ocean, sea level rises. During the last 2 million years, glaciations have come and gone at least four times, and sea level has risen and fallen over a range of approximately 125 meters. This range is enough to almost totally expose

continental shelves during maximum ice advance on the continents. Only eighteen thousand years ago, sea level was 125 meters below its present level, yet by three thousand years ago, it was essentially at today's level. If the remaining ice on Antarctica were to melt entirely, sea level would rise an additional 60 or more meters, drowning coastal cities worldwide.

The oceans are thought to have originated by the outgassing and release of water as steam from early volcanic activity. Volcanoes are still actively adding water to the oceans. When sediments are deposited in the ocean, they normally contain some entrapped water. Tectonic activity can return these water-bearing sediments back into the crust by the process of subduction. There appears to be a rough balance or equilibrium between water escaping the crust from volcanoes and water returning to the crust through sediment deposition, with no overall sea-level change caused by these processes in the modern world.

Sea level is also affected by changes in the volume of the ocean basins. Continents are continually losing sediments to the sea through processes of erosion. This addition of sediment is slowly filling in the ocean basins, pushing sea level up. At the same time, tectonic activity is distorting the edges of continents, often folding them, which increases the volume of the ocean basins. Tectonic activity in the ocean floor can force the sea floor upward, limiting ocean basin volume. Tectonic activities tend to occur episodically, in fits and starts, rather than as a smooth, continuous process. When tectonics is active, it may increase or decrease ocean volume, causing a drop or rise in sea level. Sediments deposited on the ocean floor may be plastered back onto the continents by tectonic activity, first decreasing and then increasing ocean basin volume. Sea-level changes, in response to sediment balance and tectonic location and magnitude, occur slowly over millions of years.

STUDY OF SEA LEVEL

When sea level changes, it leaves an imprint on the land. Transgressing ocean waters erode the land surface with waves and then, as waters deepen again, deposit marine sediments. When regression occurs, the shallowing water leads to wave erosion of the sea floor. Further regression exposes the sea floor to the air and to erosion by wind, rain, and running water from precipitation. Casual examination of the continents reveals clear evidence of past marine transgression and regression. Limestones, marine shales, and marine sandstones are common around the world on the dry land of the continents. They range in age from billions of years old to only a few hundred years old. The sea has transgressed and regressed many times in Earth's history. The timing and exact nature of the sea-level change may be more difficult to determine. In the Bahamas, fossil corals exist several meters above sea level. By sampling the corals and dating them by means of trace amounts of radioactive elements in the samples, scientists can determine their age. In this case, their age is about 125,000 years. Therefore, more than 100,000 years ago, the land to which the fossil coral is attached was under water. Did the land rise, or did the water drop? Measurement of tectonic activity shows that the islands of the Bahamas are not rising or sinking. Examination of the history of glaciation shows that 125,000 years ago, ice sheets had melted back a little more than they are presently. From this information, scientists concluded that the coral grew when sea level was eustatically higher than it is today.

Further evidence of sea-level change can be obtained by examining the tectonic, deposition, and erosion history of the planet. Examination of major episodes of tectonic activity, sediment deposition, and erosion can allow the construction of graphs showing how sea level rose and fell, in general terms, over much of Earth's history. Most of the sea-level changes preserved in the rock record were tectonically generated. Glaciation has occurred only a few times in the past, and the sea-level changes caused by glaciation have left a unique and distinctive record in rock structures.

If sea level never changed, the geology of all surface rocks would be very simple. There would be no exposed marine rocks at all. If there were no tectonics to help drive sea-level change, the continents would eventually erode to sea level. Earth would eventually become a flat, relatively featureless place.

John E. Mylroie

FURTHER READING

Coe, Angela L., ed. *The Sedimentary Record of Sea-Level Change.* New York: Cambridge University Press, 2003. Discusses changes in sea level throughout time, as well as the factors influencing the sea level, including ice ages and sedimentation. Includes multiple case studies, chapter summaries, references, and an index. Suited for undergraduates and graduate students.

Davis, Richard A., Jr. *Sea-Level Change in the Gulf of Mexico.* Hong Kong: Everbest Printing, 2011. Provides a brief description of the change in sea level over time in the Gulf of Mexico. Causes and the rate of change are covered at the beginning to provide a foundation for the discussion of sea-level measurements during early history, glacial times, melting times, current times, and the future.

De Angelis, Hernan, and Pedro Skvarca. "Glacier Surge After Ice Shelf Collapse." *Science* 299 (2003): 1560-1562. Discusses the ice shelf of West Antarctica. Presents the argument that instability within the ice sheet will result in sea-level changes.

Kelley, Joseph T., Orrin H. Pilkey, and J. A. G. Cooper. *America's Most Vulnerable Coastal Communities.* Boulder, Colo.: Geological Society of America, 2009. A Geological Society of America Special Paper that warns of the impending rise in sea level over the next few decades. Uses case studies of ten U.S. coastline communities, Puerto Rico, and some western European beachfronts to emphasize the nature of the approaching problem and the inadequate responses to it.

Kennet, James P. *Marine Geology.* Englewood Cliffs, N.J.: Prentice Hall, 1982. A college-level text on the geology of the oceans that assumes some science background on the part of the reader. Contains an excellent, in-depth overview of sea-level change.

Komar, Paul D. *Beach Process and Sedimentation.* Upper Saddle River, N.J.: Prentice Hall, 1998. Offers extensive treatment of waves, longshore currents, and sand transport on beaches. Presents and elaborates upon equations and mathematical relationships. College-level material. Intended for those interested in the specifics of coastal processes.

Montgomery, C. W. *Environmental Geology.* 9th ed. Columbus, Ohio: McGraw-Hill, 2010. An introductory college text that discusses the causes and ramifications of the greenhouse effect.

Pilkey, Orrin H., and Rob Young. *The Rising Sea.* Washington, D.C.: Island Press, 2009. Presents a discussion based on the prediction that ocean sea levels will rise by at least 2.5 meters over the next 100 years, due to the effects of global warming. Intended for all readers as a first step in understanding the danger.

Sinha, P. C., ed. *Sea Level Rise*. New Delhi: Anmol Publications, 1998. A collection of essays that reviews the continuing debate over changes in sea level, taking into account changes in the atmosphere and climate caused by global warming and the greenhouse effect. Also looks at the effects that sea-level change may have on the environment.

Stowe, Keith. *Exploring Ocean Science*. 2d ed. New York: John Wiley & Sons, 1996. An introductory text that provides the layperson with a good discussion of ice volumes and sea level.

See also: *AR4 Synthesis Report*; Beaches and Coastal Processes; Carbonate Compensation Depths; Cyclones and Anticyclones; Deep Ocean Currents; Groundwater Pollution and Remediation; Gulf Stream; Hurricanes; Hydrothermal Vents; Monsoons; Ocean-Atmosphere Interactions; Ocean Pollution and Oil Spills; Oceans' Origin; Oceans' Structure; Ocean Tides; Ocean Waves; Remote Sensing of the Oceans; Saltwater Intrusion; Seamounts; Seawater Composition; Surface Ocean Currents; Surface Water; Tsunamis; Turbidity Currents and Submarine Fans; Water Wells; World Ocean Circulation Experiment

SEAMOUNTS

Seamounts, formed by undersea volcanoes, are far more numerous and much larger than their volcanic counterparts on land. Some may become large enough to rise above sea level as islands for a brief period, but almost all eventually resubmerge as guyots or atolls. Radiometric dating of seamounts has helped to verify the theory of continental drift.

PRINCIPAL TERMS

- **atoll:** a tropical island on which a massive coral reef, often ringlike, generally rests on a volcanic base
- **basalt:** a rock that results when lava rich in iron and magnesium and low in silica is cooled rapidly; it has a fine-grained, dark-colored appearance
- **guyot:** a drowned volcanic island with a flat top caused by wave erosion or coral growth
- **hot spot:** a column or plume of molten rock that rises from deep within the mantle and can cause volcanic eruptions if it penetrates the lithosphere
- **hyaloclastite:** the rock type that results when lava is chilled rapidly and explosively beneath the sea at shallow depths, resulting in a fragmented, glassy texture
- **lava:** magma that has erupted from a volcano
- **lithosphere:** the rigid outermost layer of Earth that floats on the softer layer (the asthenosphere) beneath; it is thinner under the oceans than on the continents
- **magma:** a general term for molten rock within the mantle layer
- **midocean ridge:** a roughly linear, submarine mountain range where new seafloor lithosphere is created by the process of seafloor spreading
- **pillow lavas:** lavas that have been rapidly cooled by water as they erupt and consequently develop crusted, rounded, or pillow-shaped structures

ORIGIN AND GROWTH

Seamounts are volcanoes that rise from the sea floor but lack sufficient height and land area to be classified as islands. Like their volcanic counterparts on land, seamounts are roughly conical or domelike in shape, and many have craters at the top. Compared to volcanoes on the continents, seamounts are much larger and higher, and may rise to as much as 10,000 meters above the ocean floor. A seamount that has a flat top is called a guyot. Almost all guyots were islands at one time, and they acquired their flat tops through the erosive action of waves, the growth of corals, or a combination of both processes. The islands also may have undergone resubmergence caused by the subsidence or sinking of the sea floor or by eustatic rise in sea level. The tops of some guyots can be as much as 3,000 meters below present sea level, but most are about 1,000 meters deep. A guyot that is less than 200 meters deep is called a bank. Seamounts and guyots are a prominent feature of the ocean floor, particularly in the southwestern Pacific Ocean, although a great many also exist in the Atlantic Ocean. Some, including the Grand Banks found some distance off the coast of Newfoundland, Canada, are associated with vast midocean ridges, but many rise from the deep, flat sections of the ocean floor known as the abyssal plains. Some seamounts are isolated, others occur in clusters and form a large volcanic plateau, and still others form a long chain.

Little is known regarding the origins of seamounts. It is known, however, that magma (molten rock) rising through the sea floor squeezes its way beneath the saturated but relatively buoyant bottom sediments and then crystallizes. After many of these intrusions, a solid base is built up, and cone development can begin. The magma that makes up seamounts is not of the explosive variety, so seafloor eruptions are relatively quiet affairs. In fact, the water pressure in the deep ocean is so great that the gas and steam normally associated with volcanoes on the continents cannot escape. Instead, the lava (magma that has escaped the interior) oozes out quietly in submarine flows. Because deep seawater is quite cold, the lava is chilled very rapidly; often, the lava cools into wrinkled, glassy crusts that enclose round blobs. These structures, common on the sea floor, are known as lava pillows. The rock that makes up the pillows is a dark, fine-grained rock known as basalt, which is rich in iron and magnesium-bearing minerals.

As the seamount grows, its increasing size begins to bring it nearer the sea's surface and consequently into areas of lower water pressure. At a depth of about 2,000 meters, the gases associated with the lava and the heated seawater itself can begin to expand and explode violently as the lava cools, resulting in a glassy, fragmented structure known as hyaloclastite. It is also at these or shallower depths that the submarine eruption may be noticed by passing ships as an area of dark, turbulent water, floating fragmented and bubbly rocks called pumice, and gas and ash clouds at the surface. During both of these stages, magma may continue to be injected along cracks and layers inside the growing seamount and crystallize internally. If the magma finds a place where it can escape along the sides or base of the mountain, a flank eruption may build a parasitic cone.

The next stage in the growth of a seamount, when the eruption is close to sea level, is critical. The effects of the exploding gases, combined with the effects of wave erosion on the loose, fragmented debris, tend to prevent the seamount from emerging above the water to become an island. If the volume of lava erupted is sufficient to keep pace with these destructive forces, however, subaerial lava flows may begin to cover the hyaloclastites with an armor plating that is resistant to wave erosion, and a volcanic island is born.

EROSION AND SUBSIDENCE

During its life as an island (which is likely to be only a few million years, a relatively brief period compared to its life as a seamount and guyot), the mountain is attacked by wind, running water, and glaciers (depending on its latitude). All these factors tend to reduce its elevation even as subsequent eruptions may build it up. If the conditions are tropical, coral reef growth may encrust the wave-battered shores. Every island eventually succumbs, however, to the combined effects of erosion and subsidence (sinking) of the sea floor that begin to submerge it once again. Coral growth may be able to keep pace with the effects of subsidence for a time. Sometimes, this extensive coral growth results in a completely coral-capped volcano known as an atoll. Many atolls in the South Pacific have more than 1,000 meters of massive coral growth above their volcanic bases.

If coral growth cannot keep pace with the rate of seafloor subsidence, the island or atoll becomes submerged once again, this time in the form of a bank and then finally as a guyot once it reaches a depth of 200 meters. The mountain erodes gradually on the sea floor: The sides are subject to erosion by currents,

crumbling, and slumping, and the rocks undergo chemical reactions with the seawater. The entire mountain is also gradually buried in the ubiquitous "rain" of dust and the tiny remains of microscopic plants and animals, which cap the top and drape the sides in thick layers of fine sediments.

CONTINENTAL DRIFT

No guyot lasts for a very long period of geologic time, however, because all are eventually carried by continental drift to subduction zones along the edges of continents, where the sea floor is effectively recycled as it moves downward into the mantle below the continental mass. The study of seamounts and guyots has helped to verify the idea of continental drift (plate tectonics) and to show how fast plate movement occurs. The sea floor consists of one or more slabs (plates) of quasi-rigid rock 50 to 80 kilometers thick. The oceanic lithosphere, as it is called, is created at the great midocean ridges, where two plates are being driven apart from each other by convection currents in the underlying magma. Magma wells up to fill the gap thus created. As the magma cools and crystallizes, it is added to the slab and becomes part of the plates. Thus, new seafloor lithosphere is added to both of the diverging plates at midocean ridges. Sometimes, a seamount will grow at the midocean ridge (Iceland is an example of a volcanic island in this location) and actually become split in half as the two plates pull apart.

The slabs of oceanic lithosphere are able to slide about on a slippery zone in the upper mantle, known as the asthenosphere, just as slabs of ice on a winter pond can drift on the water. Where stresses push two plates together, one is forced to override the other. The plate that is forced underneath (subducted) plunges deep into the asthenosphere and eventually melts. Because oceanic lithosphere is thin and dense compared to continental lithosphere, it is the sea floor that gets subducted, or recycled, most often. Thus, the sea floor, carrying its seamounts, is geologically much younger than the continents.

HOT SPOTS

Although some seamounts erupt near midocean ridges, many that erupt far from plate boundaries are associated with hot spots. Hot spots, or plumes, are believed to be long, narrow fountains of magma that rise from deep within the mantle, well below the asthenosphere. These magmas have a chemical composition that is quite different from that of the magma of the midocean ridges. Seamounts are generally made up of alkaline basalts (basalts enriched in the elements sodium and potassium compared to midocean-ridge basalts).

The upwelling plume of magma at the hot spot has a dramatic effect on the seafloor lithosphere passing over it. The rising plume pushes the lithosphere upward as much as 1,000 to 1,500 meters into a broad arch or swell and heats the lithosphere from below, making it thin and stretched. Finally, if magma can break through the weakened lithosphere, a seamount is born. Eventually, however, the oceanic lithosphere is carried by plate motion away from the hot spot, which, unlike the lithosphere, has a relatively fixed location. The seamount or volcanic island begins to move, along with the lithosphere in which it is embedded, down the side of the bulge caused by the upwelling magma. In addition, the heavy burden of a large volcano on the thin oceanic lithosphere causes it to sag downward into the soft asthenosphere below. Both of these effects combine to pull a seamount downward or to submerge an island into a guyot.

At the same time that the old volcano is moving off the hot spot and subsiding, magma may continue to erupt through the new lithosphere over the hot spot, and a new volcano will emerge next to the old one. Over time, repeated eruptions as the plate slowly moves over a stationary hot spot create a type of submarine volcanic chain called an island arc. The shape of the arc reflects the direction of movement of the plate over the plume below. In this way, over millions of years, a whole chain of seamounts, some of which may have been islands at one time, extend from the location of the hot spot in the direction of plate motion for thousands of kilometers. It was in this fashion that the Hawaiian Islands and the closely related Emperor Seamounts were formed as the Pacific plate was pulled over a hot spot in a northwesterly direction toward the subduction zone near the Aleutian Islands of Alaska.

Sara A. Heller

FURTHER READING

Bardintzeff, Jacques-Marie, and Alexander R. McBirney. *Volcanology.* 2d ed. Burlington, Mass.: Jones & Bartlett Publishers, 2000. A comprehensive if somewhat technical treatment of volcanoes, volcanic landforms, magma, volcanic rocks, and types of eruptions. Discusses the intraplate volcanism that produces seamounts and guyots and compares it to volcanism at midocean ridges. Includes examples and methods of study. Bibliography, index. Suitable for the college-level reader.

Bull, William B. *Tectonic Geomorphology of Mountains: A New Approach to Paleoseismology.* Malden, Mass.: Wiley-Blackwell, 2007. Provides technical coverage of topics in paleoseismology. Contains information on uplifting, mountain formation, tectonic activity, and fault scarps. Recommended for graduate students and practicing paleoseismologists.

Edwards, John. *Plate Tectonics and Continental Drift.* North Mankato, Minn.: Smart Apple Media, 2006. Provides an excellent overview of the basic principles and history of Alfred Wegener's theory of continental drift. Suitable for all readers.

Garrison, Tom S. *Essentials of Oceanography.* 6th ed. Belmont, Calif.: Brooks/Cole Cengage Learning, 2012. Suitable for students taking an introductory course in oceanography. Represents a streamlined version of the author's larger comprehensive textbook, and discusses many aspects of the ocean environment.

_____. *Oceanography: An Invitation to Marine Science.* Belmont, Calif.: Brooks/Cole, Cengage Learning, 2010. Provides excellent coverage of plate tectonics, ocean formation, seafloor spreading, and island arc formation. Covers topography and bathymetry of deep-ocean basins. Includes abundant diagrams to aid readers from the layperson to advanced undergraduates.

Harris, Peter T., and Elaine K. Baker, eds. *Seafloor Geomorphology as Benthic Habitat.* New York: Elsevier, 2011. Discusses benthic ecology, habitat mapping, biodiversity, and community structure of seamounts, sea beds, reefs, fjords, and hydrothermal vents. Examines case studies and discusses methodologies of seafloor studies.

Hekinian, R. *Petrology of the Ocean Floor.* New York: Elsevier, 1982. A comprehensive, detailed, and rather technical textbook covering the chemical, mineral, textural, and genetic aspects of the rocks of the sea floor. Contains chemical analyses from a number of seamounts, as well as a few photographs of rock samples. Discusses the magma sources for the sea floor. Appendices, index. Suitable for the college-level reader.

Keating, Barbara H., Patricia Fryer, Rodney Batiza, and George W. Boehlert, eds. *Seamounts, Islands, and Atolls.* 2d ed. Washington, D.C.: American Geophysical Union, 1988. Contains a collection of twenty-six technical articles concerning seamounts and related features, which generally focus on a particular seamount or group of seamounts and demonstrate the use of a particular method of study such as sonar, geophysics, sediment analysis, or geochemistry. Discusses the effect of seamounts on ocean circulation and biology. No index or general conclusions. Suitable for the college-level reader.

Kennish, Michael J. *Practical Handbook of Marine Science.* 3d ed. Boca Raton, Fla.: CRC Press, 2001. Covers marine geology topics such as seafloor topography, sediments, plate tectonics, midocean ridges, and hydrothermal vents. Best suited for advanced undergraduates and graduate students. Provides references for each chapter.

King, Cuchaine A. M. *Introduction to Marine Geology and Geomorphology.* London: Edward Arnold, 1974. Covers the geologic origins of submarine landforms and their methods of study. Contains chapters on plate tectonics, continental margins, ocean sediments, sea-level changes, and the landforms of the open oceans such as seamounts, guyots, and atolls. Extensive bibliography and index. Suitable for the college-level reader.

Menard, H. W. *Islands.* New York: W. H. Freeman, 1986. An up-to-date, nontechnical, and well-illustrated volume describing the geological influences on islands, seamounts, and guyots, with emphasis on continental drift. Discusses the birth and development of submarine volcanoes and their tectonic effects on the oceanic crust. Index. Suitable for the college-level reader.

Nairn, Alan E. M., Francis G. Stehli, and Seiya Uyeda, eds. *The Ocean Basins and Margins. Vol. 7A, The Pacific Ocean.* New York: Plenum Press, 1985. Summarizes the geology of various regions of the Pacific Ocean. Summarizes knowledge about several chains of seamounts in the Pacific and what they reveal about hot spots and the motion of the Pacific plate. Extensive references. Suitable for the college-level reader.

Pitcher, T. J. *Seamounts: Ecology, Fisheries and Conservation.* Oxford: Blackwell Publishing, 2007. Written by fifty-seven of the world's leading experts on seamounts. Offers a complete discussion of their formation and distribution over the sea floors of the world's oceans, as well as their value and importance as oceanic resources.

Schwartz, M. *Encyclopedia of Coastal Science.* Dordrecht: Springer, 2005. Contains many articles specific to ocean and beach dynamics. Also discusses coastal habitat management topics, hydrology, geology, and topography. Articles may run multiple pages and include diagrams. Each article has bibliographical information and cross-referencing.

Seibold, E., and W. H. Berger. *The Sea Floor: An Introduction to Marine Geology.* 3d ed. New York: Springer-Verlag, 2010. A well-illustrated text about the landforms of the sea floor and continental margins, seafloor sediments and biota, and how sediments can be used as indicators of past climates. Contains a brief section on seamounts. Appendices, index. Suitable for the college-level reader.

Yuen, David A., Shigenori Maruyama, Shun-ichiro Karato, and Brian F. Windley, eds. *Superplumes: Beyond Plates Tectonics.* Dordrecht: Springer, 2007. A rather technical book composed of learned papers discussing the theory and techniques of study of superplumes emanating from the outer core below the South Pacific Ocean, Africa, and the Mid-Atlantic Ridge.

See also: Atmosphere's Evolution; Beaches and Coastal Processes; Carbonate Compensation Depths; Deep Ocean Currents; Greenhouse Effect; Gulf Stream; Hydrothermal Vents; Ocean Pollution and Oil Spills; Ocean-Atmosphere Interactions; Oceans' Origin; Oceans' Structure; Ocean Tides; Ocean Waves; Sea Level; Seawater Composition; Sediment Transport and Deposition; Surface Ocean Currents; Tsunamis; Turbidity Currents and Submarine Fans; World Ocean Circulation Experiment

SEASONS

Seasons are the two (fair and rainy) or four (spring, summer, autumn, and winter) periods of the year that are typically distinguished by specific types of atmospheric conditions. Many plant and animal life cycles and periods of activity are based on the seasons, which, in turn, are defined by the relative positions of Earth and the sun.

PRINCIPAL TERMS

- **autumnal equinox:** the day that the sun passes directly over the equator in the southward direction, producing day and night of equal length and marking the beginning of autumn; in the Northern Hemisphere, the date is about September 21, and in the Southern Hemisphere, it occurs about March 21
- **equator:** the line of latitude on Earth that is exactly halfway between the North and South Poles
- **monsoon:** a wind system that results in an annual cycle of fair weather followed by rainy weather
- **perihelion:** the point in a planet's orbit at which it is closest to the sun
- **summer solstice:** the day when the sun is directly over the Tropic of Cancer in the Northern Hemisphere; in the Southern Hemisphere, the day when the sun is directly over the Tropic of Capricorn
- **Tropic of Cancer:** a line of latitude 23.5 degrees north of the equator; the most northerly latitude on Earth at which the noon sun passes directly overhead
- **Tropic of Capricorn:** a line of latitude 23.5 degrees south of the equator; the most southerly latitude on Earth at which the noon sun passes directly overhead
- **vernal equinox:** the day that the sun passes directly over the equator in the northward direction, producing day and night of equal length and marking the beginning of spring; in the Northern Hemisphere, the date is about March 21, and in the Southern Hemisphere, it is about September 21
- **winter solstice:** the diametric opposite of the summer solstice, occurring in the Northern Hemisphere when the sun passes directly over the Tropic of Capricorn, and in the Southern Hemisphere when it passes over the Tropic of Cancer

ENERGY FROM THE SUN

The seasons are the natural, weather-related divisions of the year. In the North and South Temperate Zones of Earth, the four seasons of spring, summer, autumn, and winter are the normal progression of annual climatic change. These represent distinct phases in tne weather patterns of those regions, each lasting approximately three months. As latitudes change, however, seasonal variations of weather, as well as the length of the seasons, change to reflect local conditions. At latitudes increasingly distant from the equator, colder weather becomes more dominant and warmer seasons become shorter and cooler. At latitudes approaching the equator, however, warmer conditions dominate and colder seasons shrink to nonexistence. In tropical areas, the seasons may be classified merely as "rainy" and "dry" according to the amounts of rainfall and sunshine that are received.

The seasons and their weather patterns all result from the variable distribution of energy from the sun according to the relative positions and motions of the sun and Earth. The seasons change because the solar energy received increases and decreases in an annual cycle. This cycle results from Earth's axis being tilted at an angle of 23.5 degrees relative to the plane formed by Earth's orbit around the sun.

Earth makes a complete orbit around the sun every 365 days, 5 hours, and 49 minutes. As it does so, the tilt of Earth's axis does not appreciably change. Thus the north end of the axis tilts toward the sun in June; six months later, when Earth has traveled to the opposite point in its orbital path, the north end of the axis tilts away from the sun.

Light and solar energy are most intense when they strike Earth directly, perpendicular to the planet's surface, because its energy is then the most concentrated. Light falling at an oblique angle is spread out as it strikes the surface and is thus more diffuse and less effective in delivering heat to the surface. When the North Pole tilts toward the sun, more sunlight falls on the Northern Hemisphere than the Southern Hemisphere. This sunlight is more direct; that is, it hits the ground surface exactly vertically at the Tropic of Cancer on the summer solstice. This results in two factors that together cause the warmer weather of summer: The sun is higher in the sky than it is in autumn and winter, and the number of hours of daylight is increased. The higher the sun is in the sky, the more concentrated is its heat and thus the warmer that part of the surface becomes.

A common misconception is that summer occurs because Earth is closer to the sun. In fact, Earth is closest to the sun (at perihelion) about January 3 of each year, which is winter in the Northern Hemisphere. Earth is farthest from the sun on about July 3. Earth's orbit is an ellipse (an elongated circle), but the shape of this ellipse is so nearly circular that its effect (that is, the variation in distance to the sun) is not as important a factor in Earth's weather as is the angle at which the sunlight strikes Earth. This angle is greatest in the Northern Hemisphere in June, when the sun shines directly over the Tropic of Cancer, and greatest in the Southern Hemisphere in December when the sun shines directly over the Tropic of Capricorn. It takes an enormous amount of solar energy to warm Earth's atmosphere, lakes, oceans, and land, and thus the warmest part of summer does not occur on the summer solstice itself, but instead about one month later.

EFFECTS OF LATITUDE

Latitude affects seasonal change in two ways. One of these is the number of hours of daylight. As one goes from the equator (0 degrees latitude) toward either of the poles, the latitude increases until one is at the poles, where the latitude is 90 degrees. On the day of the summer solstice, daylight is at a maximum for areas north of the equator and at a minimum for areas south of the equator. The farther north one goes on that date, the longer the daylight. At 20 degrees north of the equator (approximately the latitude of Mexico City), daylight on that date is 13 hours and 12 minutes long; at 40 degrees north (approximately the latitude of New York, Rome, or Beijing), it is 14 hours, 52 minutes; at 60 degrees north (approximately the latitude of Anchorage or Oslo), daylight is 18 hours and 27 minutes.

The opposite is true at the winter solstice. At 20 degrees north of the equator, daylight on that date is 10 hours and 48 minutes long; at 40 degrees north, it is 9 hours, 8 minutes; at 60 degrees north, daylight lasts only 5 hours and 33 minutes. Therefore, the closer one is to the poles, the more extreme the variations of daylight and darkness.

The other way that latitude affects seasonal change is the angle of incoming sunlight. As one goes north from the Tropic of Cancer (or south from the Tropic of Capricorn), the angle of incoming solar light decreases. Even though far northern areas have extremely long periods of daylight from May to July, the angle of sunlight is so low that the solar energy is spread very thinly across the surface. Therefore, Earth does not receive as much heat in those locations and, thus, summer temperatures in the region never get very high.

Two other common misconceptions are that the sun is straight overhead at noon every day and that it rises due east and sets due west every day. In fact, the sun is never straight overhead at any part of any day in any location north of the Tropic of Cancer or south of the Tropic of Capricorn. The location of sunrise and sunset changes with the seasons. In June, the sun rises in the northeast and sets in the northwest, while in December it rises in the southeast and sets in the southwest. The exact location is dependent upon latitude. The only days on which the sun rises due east and sets due west are the vernal and autumnal equinoxes.

OTHER FACTORS AFFECTING SEASONS

Seasons and seasonal weather are affected by other factors such as altitude, nearby mountain ranges, ocean currents, and proximity to water. Mountains lose heat in a particular manner, and the air at the top of a mountain is much cooler than at the bottom. A typical example is Mount Kilimanjaro in Tanzania, the bottom of which is located in a tropical rainforest but the top of which is covered by snow and ice.

The Gulf Stream in the Atlantic Ocean absorbs a great deal of solar energy as it passes through tropical areas near Florida. It then flows northeastward, carrying its relatively warm water to Western Europe. Western Europe thus generally experiences much warmer weather than areas of eastern North America at the same latitude. The same process occurs in the Pacific Ocean, where the Japan Current carries warm water to the western North American shore near the states of Oregon and Washington.

Mountain ranges often deplete air currents of their moisture and deprive downwind areas of rainfall. The Cascade Mountains, for example, force moist Pacific air upward as it passes over them to the east. This causes the air to cool, its contained water vapor to condense, and rain to fall on the windward side of the mountains, a region known as a "rain shadow." When the air gets to the other side of the mountain range, much of its moisture is gone, and the potential for rainfall is much lower. These factors cause western Oregon and western Washington to get much more rainfall than most places in North America but leave Idaho and Montana with very little.

Lakes and oceans heat up more slowly than land areas do. As a result, land areas near large bodies of water do not experience the extremes of heat and cold that areas farther from the water do. For example, downtown Chicago, which is at the Lake Michigan shoreline, does not get as cold on a winter night as Batavia, Illinois, which is 57 kilometers west of the Chicago lakefront. For the same reason, downtown Chicago does not get as hot on a summer afternoon as does Batavia.

Many areas near the tropics do not experience the four seasons already described but rather have an annual pattern of dry and wet seasons. In southern Asia, for example, the lower angle of the sun in the winter causes temperatures to cool below the temperature of the nearby warm Indian Ocean. This causes winds to blow off the land toward the ocean and results in several months of fair or dry weather. By summer, the higher sun has caused the continent to warm a little above the temperature of the ocean, and the wind pattern is reversed. Moist, warm air then flows from the ocean to the land, causing heavy rainfall; this type of cyclical wind system is called a "monsoon." The name also is given to the rains caused by this system.

STUDY OF THE SEASONS

The ability to predict the seasons accurately was vitally important to early civilizations. Because of their dependence upon farming, ancient peoples had to know when a river would flood and when to plant their crops. Primitive peoples noted that the appearance of certain constellations, and the locations of sunrise and sunset, varied when warmer or cooler weather could be expected.

Several early civilizations, including those of Egypt, Babylon, India, and China, have left indirect evidence of astronomical writings from as early as 2500 B.C.E. Stonehenge, built in southwest England in about 1800 B.C.E., has a large stone that marks the direction of sunrise at the summer solstice. Medicine wheels made by Native Americans two thousand years ago also show the direction of the summer solstice sunrise.

A critical barrier in defining the seasons was the difficulty of determining the exact length of one year. For many centuries, astronomers and civil rulers tried to define the year based on a number of lunar months. It is interesting to note that the Mayan civilization developed a calendar that agrees with present-day calculations of the length of a year to a high degree. The Egyptians, who needed a means to forecast the flooding of the Nile, may have been one of the earliest civilizations to rely on a solar calendar. By the year 46 B.C.E., however, errors in the accepted calendar were so great that Julius Caesar redefined the year, entirely independently of the moon, as 365 days, with one extra day added every four years, to

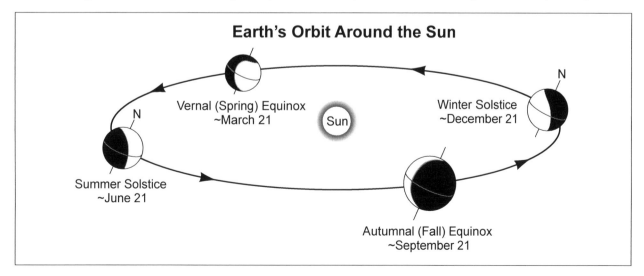

Earth's Orbit Around the Sun

Vernal (Spring) Equinox ~March 21

Sun

Winter Solstice ~December 21

Summer Solstice ~June 21

Autumnal (Fall) Equinox ~September 21

create what is known as the Julian calendar. The Gregorian calendar, adopted in 1582 and still used today, corrected a small error in the Julian calendar by eliminating the extra day from would-be leap years that are divisible by one hundred but not by four hundred.

An understanding of the causes of seasonal change begins with an understanding of the relative positions and motions of the sun and Earth. In the sixth century B.C.E., Pythagoras theorized that Earth was a sphere resting in the center of the universe. Even though several of his students believed that the apparent movements of the sun and the stars were caused by the movement of Earth, that explanation was rejected by many people, including Aristotle. The Greek astronomer Ptolemy confirmed Aristotle's geocentric views. His *Almagest* was the standard work on astronomy for 1,400 years.

In 1543, Nicolaus Copernicus published his explanation of the sun-centered solar system and a new explanation for the changing of the seasons. His text shows the position of the tilted Earth in relation to the sun at the two equinoxes and solstices.

Although Copernicus's heliocentric solar system and explanation for the seasons are commonly taught in schools today, his ideas did not win general acceptance for nearly two hundred years. Galileo Galilei's use of the telescope confirmed Copernicus's theories, as did Sir Isaac Newton's 1687 theory of gravitation. The last minor obstacle to universal acceptance of the Copernican system was the fact that the distant stars did not appear to move as Earth revolved around the sun. That opposition disappeared after Friedrich Bessel's 1838 discovery of stellar parallax, which confirmed that those stars do move, albeit by very small amounts.

SIGNIFICANCE

An understanding of the seasons is just as important to modern civilization as it was to ancient ones. Today, the need for an understanding of seasons is more complex but just as vital. A knowledge of the seasons and the length of a growing season still affects decisions about which crops can be planted in a given area. Certain crops require longer growing seasons—typically described in terms of "heat units"—than others and must be grown in southern areas; some perennial flowers, such as tulips, require a cold dormant period and cannot be grown in areas without a

cold winter season. Homeowners who purchase trees and other living plants from landscaping catalogs need to know about their seasonal climates in order to buy plants suited to local conditions. Knowing how high the sun will be in the summer can help a homeowner or a landscape architect to decide the best location for shade-producing trees so that they do not interfere with a sun-loving vegetable garden.

Seasonal changes of the sun can help the environmentally conscious architect to decide where to place windows and whether to design roof overhangs. For example, in summer, when most new houses and office buildings will likely be using air conditioning, midday sunlight streaming in windows can drive up interior temperatures and the amount of electricity required to maintain a cool interior temperature. To minimize this, homes and other buildings can be designed with roof overhangs that shade the windows from direct sunlight. In winter, when the buildings could use this sunlight to keep down heating costs, the sun will be farther south and thus lower in the sky. If well designed, a roof overhang can shade windows from the high summer sun while allowing in light from the low winter sun. Numerous other features that are dependent on seasonal variations for their effectiveness are now incorporated into the design of energy-efficient structures.

Kenneth J. Schoon

FURTHER READING

Ahrens, C. Donald. *Meteorology Today: An Introduction to Weather, Climate and the Environment.* 8th ed. Belmont, Calif.: Thomson Brooks-Cole, 2007. One of the most widely used and authoritative introductory textbooks for the study of meteorology and climatology. Explains complex concepts in a clear, precise manner, supported by numerous images and diagrams. Discusses seasonal effects as the fundamental driving force of atmospheric events.

Banerjee, Subhankar. *Arctic National Wildlife Refuge: Seasons of Life and Land.* Seattle: Mountaineers Books, 2003. A photographic journey through the Arctic National Wildlife Refuge supplemented with a narrative documenting the land, animals, and people of this region. Demonstrates the seasonal variations in the land and biology.

Christopherson, Robert W., and Mary-Louise Byrne. *Geosystems: An Introduction to Physical Geography.* Toronto: Pearson Education Canada, 2006. A highly readable introductory textbook that describes the relationship between the sun and Earth as what produces the seasons and places their relative positions as the driving principle of atmospheric activity.

Emiliani, Cesare. *Planet Earth: Cosmology, Geology, and the Evolution of Life and Environment.* Cambridge, England: Cambridge University Press, 1992. A large, comprehensive book containing basic information about matter and energy, many aspects of the physical and historical Earth, and a large section about Earth's relationship to the universe.

Henes, Donna. *Celestially Auspicious Occasions: Seasons, Cycles, and Celebrations.* New York: Berkley, 1996. Looks at the history, rituals, and mythology surrounding seasons. Well illustrated and contains a bibliography.

Humphreys, Jay. *Seasons of the Sea.* Sarasota, Fla.: Pineapple Press, 2001. Provides a different perspective of seasonal changes to look at the changes occurring off the coast of Florida. Discusses the seasonal changes in each region of Florida with sections devoted to specific species of the area. Begins each chapter with a discussion of the region's coastline. Includes suggested readings and an index.

Lambert, David, and the Diagram Group. *Field Guide to Geology.* 2d ed. New York: Facts on File, 2007. A profusely illustrated book about the earth, its seasons, rocks, erosional forces, and geological history. Contains a list of great geologists (including Copernicus) and a list of geologic museums, mines, and spectacular geologic features. Indexed. Useful to the amateur geologist or interested layperson.

Lau, William K. M., and Duane E. Waliser. *Intraseasonal Variability in the Atmosphere-Ocean Climate System.* 2d ed. New York: Springer-Verlag, 2012. A multiauthored work intended for an advanced technical audience, with comprehensive reviews of intraseasonal variation employing a balance of observation, theory, and modeling.

Mason, Betsy. "Season of Fire." *Discover* 24 (2003): 32-39. Presents a nontechnical account of geologist Steve McNutt and his identification of patterns in the activity of the volcano Mount Pavlof. Discusses the hypothesis that there is a volcano season.

Montgomery, Sy. *Seasons of the Wild: A Year of Nature's Magic and Mysteries.* Buffalo, N.Y.: Firefly, 1995. A part of the Curious Naturalist series that focuses on the seasonal changes that occur in North America throughout the course of one year. Presents observations and knowledge in a way that is interesting to readers who may not otherwise be interested to read about the natural history of seasons. Illustrations.

Stevens, William Kenneth. *The Change in the Weather: People, Weather, and the Science of Climate.* New York: Random House, 2001. Describes various natural and human-induced causes of changes in the climate. Includes a twenty-page bibliography and an index.

Weber, Lyne, and Jim Weber. *Nature Watch Austin.* Austin: Texas A&M University Press, 2011. Discusses the ecological changes that take place throughout the year in Texas. Focuses on wildlife, although the introduction and many sections throughout discuss geology, erosion, the water cycle, meteors, and climate. Filled with information, photographs, diagrams, and suggestions for further research. References are organized by subject and the text is well indexed.

See also: Atmospheric and Oceanic Oscillations; Atmospheric Properties; Barometric Pressure; Climate; Clouds; Cyclones and Anticyclones; Drought; Greenhouse Effect; Hurricanes; Lightning and Thunder; Monsoons; Ozone Depletion and Ozone Holes; Satellite Meteorology; Severe Storms; Tornadoes; Van Allen Radiation Belts; Volcanoes: Climatic Effects; Weather Forecasting; Weather Forecasting: Numerical Weather Prediction; Weather Modification; Wind

SEAWATER COMPOSITION

The properties of seawater are determined primarily by the properties of pure water, and secondarily by its nature as a solution. Because water is a liquid and has great capacity as a solvent, seawater is well mixed and salty due to the ions that have been dissolved from the rocks of the continental crust. Seawater is a source of mineral wealth for humankind.

PRINCIPAL TERMS

- **element:** one of a number of substances composed entirely of atoms that cannot be broken into smaller particles by chemical means
- **free oxygen:** the element oxygen by itself, not combined chemically with a different element
- **hydrosphere:** the areas of Earth that are covered by water, including the oceans, seas, lakes, and rivers
- **mineral:** an inorganic substance occurring naturally and having definite physical properties and a characteristic chemical composition that can be expressed by a chemical formula
- **nodule:** a lump of mineral rock typically found on the ocean floor
- **primary crystalline rock:** the original or first solidified molten rock of Earth
- **salinity:** a measure of the quantity of dissolved solids in ocean water, typically given in parts per thousand by weight
- **weathering:** the breaking down of rocks by chemical, physical, and biological means

THE FORMATION OF EARTH

The hydrosphere consists of the water areas of Earth, which include ponds, lakes, rivers, groundwater, and the oceans. The oceans form the largest portion of the hydrosphere, covering 71 percent of Earth's surface. The composition of Earth's water derives from the circumstances surrounding the formation of the solar system and the planet Earth.

In the beginning, it is hypothesized that a mass of gases and space dust came together and gravitational eddies eventually formed separate clouds of aggregate materials, which presumably later consolidated into planets. When the young planetary mass started to cool, it formed a crust, which being thin, allowed heat, molten material, and gaseous material to escape from the interior through numerous cracks. The gaseous material formed the first atmosphere, probably made up primarily of hydrogen and helium molecules. These molecules, being fairly light in weight and highly energized by atmospheric temperatures and incoming solar radiation, were probably lost to space. Eventually, they were replaced by other gases derived from the interior by the ongoing volcanic activity as the planet's surface continued to cool. This subsequent atmosphere was composed mainly of carbon dioxide and water vapor, with higher percentages of other gases released from entrapment in rock structures than are found today. The water in the oceans and all other water on the planet are believed to have been released from within the mineral structures of the material from which the planet formed.

Clouds formed from the condensing water vapor in the ancient atmosphere, shielding Earth's surface and allowing less than 60 percent of the sun's energy to penetrate. As the surface continued to cool, the water vapor condensed into liquid and began to fall and accumulate in depressions. With widespread volcanic activity continuing, water vapor was continuously being released, along with smaller amounts of carbon dioxide, chlorine, nitrogen, and hydrogen gas, which then underwent chemical reactions driven by sunlight to produce methane and ammonia. As the surface continued to cool, vast amounts of condensation eventually formed the oceans. Geologic evidence shows that the oceans have existed for at least 3 billion years. This evidence comes in the form of algal fossils presumed to have grown in a marine environment.

Earth's crust was formed by primary crystalline rocks, the first molten material that solidified into rock as the planet cooled. These rocks were weathered and eroded into the particles that became deposited and slowly dissolved in water, carried into the ocean basins, and accumulated. Also carried into the ocean were great loads of particulate material weathered from the primary crystalline rocks and deposited as sediments. Thus the components of the primary rocks were freed by chemical weathering and dissolved in ocean water or chemically bonded with sediments and carried into the ocean by rivers. The chemical weathering took place because of the different compounds in the atmosphere, some of which combined with water vapor to form acidic rainwater ranging in strength from only slightly acidic solutions of carbonic acid to solutions of much stronger nitric and sulfuric acids. Each of these various acidic solutions had the ability to leach out various metallic ions, such as sodium, potassium, magnesium, iron, and others, from the materials that they contact. Seawater gained its characteristic saltiness through these processes.

Comparing the discharge of gases by hot springs in the United States to the average rate throughout the 3 billion years of the oceans' existence shows that enough water vapor is produced to fill the oceans to one hundred times their present volume. Water therefore must be recycled and not all newly formed; the excess amount does not represent new water released from the original crystallization of magma. Only 1 percent of this water requires such an origin to account for the present volume of the oceans.

Water on land comes daily from the sea. The seas hold about 4.4 billion cubic meters of saltwater. Of this amount, about 12 million cubic meters enters the atmosphere each year through evaporation and is returned by rainfall and the flow of rivers, and about 3 million cubic meters descends each year over continents, replenishing ponds, lakes, and rivers.

GASES AND SOLIDS IN SEAWATER

Ocean water is a mixture of gases and solids dissolved in pure water (96 percent pure water and 4 percent of dissolved elements, by weight). Nearly every natural element has been found or is expected to be found in seawater, although some occur only in very small amounts. The most abundant mineral found in ocean water is sodium chloride (familiar as common table salt), which makes up 85 percent of the dissolved minerals. It is interesting to note that the composition of human blood is very similar to that of seawater; in it are all the elements of the sea, dispensed in different proportions.

The seven most abundant minerals in seawater include sodium chloride, 27.2 parts per thousand; magnesium chloride, 3.8 parts per thousand; magnesium sulfate, 1.7 parts per thousand; calcium sulfate, 1.3 parts per thousand; potassium sulfate, 0.9 part per thousand; calcium carbonate, 0.1 part per thousand; and magnesium bromide, 0.1 part per thousand. It is important to note that these "minerals" do not occur in the form suggested by their molecular formulas,

but as the component ions dissolved in water. Six ionic species actually make up 99.3 percent of the total mass of the dissolved material: chlorine, 55.2 percent; sodium, 30.4 percent; sulfate, 7.7 percent; magnesium, 3.7 percent; calcium, 1.2 percent; potassium, 1.1 percent; and others, 0.7 percent.

The salinity of seawater is fairly uniform across the oceans at different latitudes and at various depths, mainly because of winds, waves, and currents. Local variations in mineral content are attributed to freshwater streams entering oceans, glacial melt, and human activity, but the variations overall are small. The salinity averages about 35 parts per thousand. This has been verified by the *Glomar Challenger* expedition, using Nansen bottles to take samples of seawater at different depths around the world and salinometers to measure salinity, as well as many other types of tests. There is more variation of salinity at the surface than at depths because of freshwater (rivers, glacial melt) entering the ocean at a given location, plus the biological activity and climate at different latitudes.

In areas where freshwater is entering the ocean, the salinity will decrease. Biological activity changes the salinity according to which species and how many marine plants and animals reside in the area. In climates that are hot and dry, the rate of evaporation is high and rainfall is low, so the ratio of dissolved salts to water is higher, making the water more saline (saltier). Similarly, in the polar regions in winter, the water freezes but the minerals do not, which changes the water-to-mineral ratio and thus increases salinity. In most climates, rainfall is greater than evaporation, thus diluting seawater and decreasing salinity.

The most abundant dissolved gases in the ocean are nitrogen, carbon dioxide, and oxygen. The amount varies with depth, and as oxygen and carbon dioxide are vital to life, most living plants and animals are found in the top 100 meters of the ocean, or the sunlight penetration layer. The amount of dissolved gases will also vary with temperature. Warm water holds less dissolved gas than cold water because cold water is heavier and sinks, carrying oxygen-rich water to the ocean depths, which, in turn, allows fish and marine life to live in the deepest parts of the ocean. At the surface, gases (oxygen and carbon dioxide) are exchanged between the ocean and the atmosphere as well as between the plants and animals that live in the top layers of the ocean, where the most abundant life is found. Marine plants take in carbon dioxide along with water and then, with the aid of sunlight, produce the sugar glucose and oxygen in the process called photosynthesis. Marine animals and photosynthetic plants take in oxygen and exhale or release carbon dioxide in the process called respiration.

Most precipitation that falls finds its way back to the ocean largely by rivers, bearing salts from soils and rock in solution. Many things affect the salinity of the ocean, including the exchange of water between the ocean and the atmosphere, which is determined by climate, and the absorption of salts by plants and animals. Considering the history of ocean salinity, one might ask if the oceans have possessed a relatively uniform salinity throughout their history or if they are becoming more saline. By far the most important component of salinity is the chloride ion, which is produced in the same manner as water vapor. The ratio of chloride ions to water vapor has not fluctuated throughout geologic time, so scientists conclude, on the basis of present evidence, that ocean water salinity has been relatively constant over the lifetime of the oceans.

It is now evident that the oceans became salty early in their history because of weathering by acidic rainfall and the erosion of primary crystalline rock. Also, through continual volcanic activity, water vapor and gases were amply supplied to the atmosphere to aid in this weathering and eroding process. These particles were carried to the ocean and dissolved in seawater, making the water salty. This process has been going on since the formation of the oceans, so it is safe to assume that the ocean has been salty since it was formed approximately 3 billion years ago.

Comparing the salinity of oceans both past and present by studying vents and hot springs, the salinity appears to maintain a certain balance. Salinity ranges between 33 and 38 parts per thousand, by weight. This variation is caused by atmospheric effects at different latitudes, by freshwater entering into the oceans from rivers and glacial melt, and by biological activity in the ocean itself as plants and animals remove minerals needed for their growth and development (photosynthesis, respiration, shell building, and so on) from the seawater and put into it other forms (waste products, skeletal structures, shells, casts, and so on). In local areas, such as bays, coves, and estuaries, the salinity of seawater is further affected by human activities such as industry and agriculture, and by the pollution from these activities.

STUDY OF SEAWATER COMPOSITION

The investigation of seawater composition is accomplished primarily by collecting samples of seawater at different depths around the world and then measuring the salinity of the samples. A variety of instruments are used to collect samples. Nansen bottles are special metal cylinders fastened at a measuring point on a strong wire, which is then lowered into the sea to the desired depth. A messenger weight is dropped down the wire; when it strikes the bottle, it releases a catch. The bottle then turns upside down, and its valves close, trapping the water at that depth inside. The Nansen bottle commonly used does not seal completely, however; a better apparatus is the Fjorlie sampler or Niskin bottle. The Fjorlie sampler or Niskin bottle is attached to a line at both ends with spring-closing hinged ends. A messenger closes the bottle with a good seal.

Corrosion of metal-lined samplers may cause changes in the water composition in an hour or so. Copper, zinc, lead, and iron in metal linings often contaminate seawater samples. Plastics have solved this problem for both collection and storage of seawater. It is also necessary to filter out any organic matter that could alter the seawater composition. For maximum accuracy of testing, samples should be tested as soon as possible and not stored.

A salinometer is used to electronically measure salinity. It is easy to use and gives immediate readings. Because the ions dissolved in seawater affect its properties as a conductor of electricity, the more ionic mineral matter in the sample, the better it conducts. The results are then compared to a table of standard measurements to obtain the sample's salinity.

Joyce Gawell

FURTHER READING

Attenborough, David. *The Living Planet.* Boston: Little, Brown, 1984. Tells the story of Earth, how it came to be, and how it has been shaped and continuously altered by volcanism, mountain building, weathering, erosion, and the drifting of the continents. Also explores the interactions of the living species with their environments. Explores each environmental niche from the Arctic to the dry deserts and the freshwater ecosphere to the open ocean, as well as the artificial environment created by humans to make life fit their needs and desires.

Davis, Richard A., Jr. *The Ocean.* San Francisco: W. H. Freeman, 1972. A book-format reprint of the September 1969 issue of *Scientific American*, which was devoted to the oceans. Includes articles covering a wide range of subjects and oceanic research, from the origin of the oceans and deep-ocean floor to seawater chemistry and marine resources. Reading level is senior high and above.

Emerson, Steven, and John Hedges. *Chemical Oceanography and Marine Carbon Cycle.* New York: Cambridge University Press, 2008. Provides a good overview of geochemistry topics in oceanography. Discusses chemical composition, thermodynamics, carbonate chemistry, the carbon cycle, and calcium carbonate sedimentation. Appendices follow the chapters they pertain to. Contains excellent indexing.

Garrison, Tom S. *Essentials of Oceanography.* 6th ed. Belmont, Calif.: Brooks/Cole Cengage Learning, 2012. Written to provide a basic understanding of the formation and function of the world's ocean environments for students undertaking an introductory course in oceanography.

Grasshoff, Klaus, Klaus Kremling, and Manfred Ehrhardt, eds. *Methods of Seawater Analysis.* 3d ed. New York: Wiley-VCH, 1999. A widely used college text that is completely revised and extended, devoting more attention to the techniques and instrumentation used in determining the chemical makeup of seawater. Illustrations, bibliography, and index.

Harrison, Roy M. *Principles of Environmental Chemistry.* Cambridge, England: Royal Society of Chemistry, 2007. Discusses chemistry of the atmosphere, freshwater, oceans, and soils. Also discusses biogeochemical cycling and environmental organic chemistry. Suited for undergraduates and graduate students with a chemistry background.

Hester, R. E., and R. M. Harrison. *Chemistry in the Marine Environment.* Cambridge, England: Royal Society of Chemistry, 2000. Discusses ocean-atmosphere interactions, along with radioactive isotopes, contaminants, and pollutants. Provides a glimpse at the various chemicals found in seawater.

Marshall, John, and R. Alan Plumb. *Atmosphere, Ocean and Climate Dynamics: An Introductory Text.* Burlington, Mass.: Academic Press/Elsevier, 2008. An introductory university-level textbook written to provide a grasp of the interactions of oceans and atmosphere both past and present. Assumes a certain amount of mathematical background on the part of the reader.

Pickard, G. L., and W. J. Emery. *Descriptive Physical Oceanography: An Introduction.* 5th ed. Oxford, England: Pergamon Press, 1995. Offers a thorough presentation of seawater properties and salinity distribution in the various seas and oceans.

Segar, Douglas. *An Introduction to Ocean Sciences.* New York: Wadsworth, 1997. Provides comprehensive coverage of all aspects of the oceans and salinity. Readable and well illustrated. Suitable for high school students and above.

Spaulding, Nancy E., and Samuel N. Namowitz. *Earth Science.* Boston: Houghton Mifflin Harcourt, 2004. Used in the ninth through twelfth grades in the public school system. Covers the complete spectrum of the physical and biological relationships of Earth, plus the position and relationship of Earth in space. Contains an excellent section on the composition and environmental structure of the world's oceans. An excellent reference text for the layperson, readily available in most public school libraries.

Steele, John H., Steve A. Thorpe, and Karl K. Turekian, eds. *Marine Chemistry and Geochemistry.* New York: Academic Press, 2010. Pulls articles in from the Encyclopedia of Ocean Sciences to provide a topic-specific compilation of oceanography articles. Discusses the chemistry of seawater, radioactive isotopes in the oceans, pollution, and marine deposits.

Tarbuck, Edward J., and Frederick K. Lutgens. *Earth: An Introduction to Physical Geology.* 6th ed. Upper Saddle River, N.J.: Prentice Hall, 1999. Provides a clear picture of earth systems and processes. Suitable for the high school or college reader. Includes an accompanying computer disc in addition to its illustrations and graphics. Bibliography and index.

Trujillo, Alan P., and Harold V. Thurman. *Essentials of Oceanography.* 10th ed. Upper Saddle River, N.J.: Prentice Hall, 2010. Designed to give the student a general overview of the oceans in the first few chapters. Follows up with a well-designed, in-depth study of the ocean—involving chemistry of the ocean, currents, air-sea interactions, the water cycle, and marine biology—and a well-developed section on the practical problems resulting from human interaction with the ocean, such as pollution and economic exploitation.

Usdowski, Eberhard, and Martin Dietzel. *Atlas and Data of Solid-Solution Equilibria of Marine Evaporites*. New York: Springer, 1998. Offers the reader an illustrated guide to seawater composition, including phase diagrams of seawater processes. Accompanied by a CD-ROM that reinforces the concepts discussed in the chapters.

Williams, Richard G., and Michael J. Follows. *Ocean Dynamics and the Carbon Cycle: Principles and Mechanisms*. New York: Cambridge University Press, 2011. Provides the fundamentals of oceanography. Discusses both biological and chemical aspects of ocean dynamics. Deals with carbonate chemistry and the carbon cycle in oceans.

See also: Bleaching of Coral Reefs; Carbonate Compensation Depths; Deep Ocean Currents; Geochemical Cycles; Gulf Stream; Hydrothermal Vents; Ocean-Atmosphere Interactions; Ocean Pollution and Oil Spills; Oceans' Origin; Oceans' Structure; Ocean Tides; Ocean Waves; Reefs; Sea Level; Seamounts; Surface Ocean Currents; Tsunamis; Turbidity Currents and Submarine Fans; World Ocean Circulation Experiment

SEDIMENT TRANSPORT AND DEPOSITION

Flowing water, wind, and glaciers move sediment from where it is produced by rock weathering to sites of deposition in river basins, lakes, and the oceans. Much of the world's landscape is shaped directly or indirectly by the movement of sediment. Interpretation of sedimentary deposits, modern and ancient, rests on the understanding of sediment transport and deposition.

PRINCIPAL TERMS

- **bed load:** sediment in motion in continuous or semicontinuous contact with the sediment bed by sliding, rolling, or hopping (saltation)
- **bed shear stress:** the force per unit area exerted by the flowing fluid on the sediment bed, averaged over an area that is large compared to individual bed particles
- **competence:** a concept that expresses the ability of a fluid stream to move particles of a given size
- **debris flow:** a flowing mass consisting of water together with a high concentration of sediment with a wide range of sizes, from fine muds to coarse gravels
- **saltation:** a mode of sediment transport in a moving fluid, in which sediment particles move forward in discrete increments rather than continuously, often as one particle bumps into another and drives it forward
- **sediment discharge:** the rate of transport of sediment past a planar section normal to the flow direction, expressed as volume, mass, or weight per unit time; also called sediment transport rate
- **sediment discharge formula:** a formula or equation designed to predict the sediment discharge that would be observed for a given combination of flow conditions and sediment characteristics
- **suspended load:** sediment in motion above the sediment bed, supported by the vertical motions of turbulent eddies
- **threshold of movement:** the conditions for which a flow is just strong enough to move the sediment particles at the surface of a given sediment bed

MOVEMENT OF SEDIMENT

Weathering of bedrock exposed on the continents produces solid particles of mineral or rock, ranging in size from the finest clay to large boulders. In most places, sediment moves slowly downslope toward stream channels, largely by the direct or indirect effects of gravity. Sediment transport by fluids is highly dependent upon the density and viscosity of the fluid. Fine sediments may be transported by moving air from any location. Once in stream channels, sediment particles of different sizes are moved with varying degrees of efficiency by flowing water.

A flow of water or air exerts a force on a solid particle resting on a loose bed of similar particles. This force, which arises both from the friction of the flowing fluid and from the existence of relatively high fluid pressure on the upstream side of the particle and relatively low pressure on the downstream side, tends to move the particle in the direction of the flow. This force commonly has an upward component, termed lift, as well as a downstream component, termed drag. When the fluid force on the bed particle, which is counteracted by the weight of the particle, is sufficient to lift the particle up from its underlying points of support or to rotate the particle downstream around its points of support, the particle begins to move downstream. This condition is called incipient movement, and the overall force per unit area, or stress, that the flow exerts on the bed under those conditions is called the critical or threshold bed shear stress. Another way of looking at incipient movement is defined in terms of competence: the point at which fluid shear stress is just able to initiate the movement of particles of a given size in a sediment bed.

WATER AND AIR TRANSPORT

Once a sediment particle is set in motion by a flow of water, it is likely to move by some combination of sliding, rolling, or hopping close to the bed. The material in this kind of motion is called bed load. If turbulent eddies in the flow have upward speeds greater than the downward settling speed of the particles relative to the fluid in their immediate vicinity, some of the moving particles are swept up into the flow to travel long distances downstream before returning to the bed. The material in this kind of motion is called the suspended load. As the strength of the flow increases, a larger percentage of the load travels in suspension, but bed load is always present near the bed even in strong flows. Suspended particles are not floating in the fluid stream. Rather, they are suspended in the fluid due to the upward force exerted by turbulence currents and are continuously settling downward relative to surrounding fluid. Ultimately, they are redeposited on the bed after traveling distances ranging from less than 1 meter (for coarser particles) to hundreds or even thousands of kilometers (for the finest particles).

The sediment particles transported by water range in size from the finest clay sizes (of the order of 1 micrometer in size) through silts (a few tens of micrometers) to sands (of the order of 1 millimeter) and gravels (coarser than a few millimeters). Clays and silts are carried mostly in suspension and are deposited only where current velocities are very small. Sands are transported both as bed load and in suspension, depending on the strength of the flow, and gravels are transported mainly as bed load.

In air, the most prominent mode of sediment particle movement is saltation, in which the particles are briefly lifted off the bed to move in a regular arching trajectory upward at a fairly large angle to the bed, and then downward at a fairly small angle to the bed. Saltating sand grains under the influence of strong winds commonly rise no more than 1 or 2 meters above the sand surface while traveling as much as several meters downwind. Sands and even small gravel particles are transported in saltation; finer particles are put directly into suspension by the wind.

In the oceans, sediment is moved not only by unidirectional currents but also by oscillatory flow resulting from the passage of wind-generated waves at the sea surface. Moreover, unidirectional flows and oscillatory flows can be superposed to produce combined flows, in which the water at the bed has an oscillatory motion but undergoes net movement in some direction as well. The concepts of threshold, bed load, and suspension apply to oscillatory and combined flows as well as to unidirectional flows.

DISCHARGE AND DEPOSITION

The time rate at which sediment is carried across some planar section, real or imaginary, normal to the flow direction is called the sediment transport rate, or sediment discharge. It is expressed as either mass, weight, or volume of sediment per unit time. The transport rate of the bed load and of the suspended load can be considered either separately or together as the total transport rate. The sediment transport

rate, expressed per unit width normal to the flow direction, is a steeply increasing function of the bed shear stress or the flow velocity. The great mathematical complexity of turbulent flow carrying discrete solid particles has hindered development of theories to predict the sediment transport rate as a function of sediment characteristics and flow conditions. A large number of formulas or equations, often called sediment discharge formulas, have been developed to predict the sediment transport rate. All have been built around one or another physically plausible mechanism that provides the general mathematical form of the equation. The specific form of the equation is then found by fitting or adjusting coefficients in the equation so that the equation conforms to some set of actual measured data on transport rates. None of these sediment discharge formulas is significantly better than any other, and there can be differences by as much as a factor of ten in predicted transport rates.

The volume concentrations of suspended sediment in most flows of water in rivers or in the oceans, as expressed in volume of sediment per unit volume of water-sediment mixture, is usually no more than a few percent. In certain situations, however, water-saturated masses of sediment can begin to flow even on a gentle slope of 1 or 2 degrees by liquefaction, either spontaneously or induced by earthquake shocks. Such flows, called debris flows, may have sediment concentrations of up to 70 percent by volume. Debris flows can be formed either on the land surface or under water.

A fluid medium is not essential for sediment transport. The force of gravity itself is often sufficient to induce the movement of significant quantities of sediment, at least for short distances. Soil creep on hillsides is the primary example of this influence, while the collapse of sediment structures such as sand dunes and the wholesale movement of sediments of many sizes in a landslide are also well-known events.

Glaciers are locally responsible for the transport of significant volumes of sediment. Glaciers derive most of their sediment load from erosion of the bedrock or from preexisting sediment beneath the glacier, although valley glaciers can carry on their upper surface large quantities of sediment that fall from the valley walls. Glaciers are far less selective of the sediment sizes they carry than are flows of water or air, which is understandable given the

A glacier transported this very large piece of sediment, leaving it to stand alone after the ice melted, in this case almost precariously balanced. Such boulders are called "erratics" because they seem unrelated to the surrounding landscape. (U.S. Geological Survey)

order-of-magnitude difference between the viscosities of liquid water and solid ice.

Transported sediment is ultimately redeposited in some way. Deposition is always associated with one or both of two kinds of changes in the flow. One of these is temporal. There is a net loss of load everywhere from the flow to the bed over time, as the flow becomes weaker. An example is redeposition of sediment picked up by a river flood as the flood subsides. The other change in flow, which is usually more important in building thick deposits of sediment, is spatial. The flow becomes weaker in the downstream direction, causing the sediment transport rate to decrease in the downstream direction. The only way the sediment transport rate can decrease downstream is for sediment to go into storage at all points on the bed, thus building up the bed. An example is the expansion and weakening of flow in a river delta, where a river meets a large lake or the ocean.

STUDY OF SEDIMENT

Sediment transport is studied in natural flows, in laboratory tanks, and by computer modeling. Laboratory studies have the advantage that the conditions of sediment transport can be closely controlled,

so that the various factors thought to be important in determining the mode and rate of sediment movement can be varied independently. The disadvantage of laboratory work, aside from necessarily small physical scales of the flow, is that the phenomenon may be too simplified to simulate natural flow environments well. In the laboratory, sediment transport and deposition are studied mostly in open channels, called flumes, in which a flow of water is passed over a sediment bed. Flumes range from a few meters to more than 100 meters long, from about 10 centimeters to a few meters wide, and from several centimeters to about 1 meter deep. The water is usually recirculated from the downstream end to the upstream end to form a kind of endless river. The sediment may also be recirculated, or it may be fed at the upstream end and caught in a trap at the downstream end. In laboratory flumes, the sediment movement may be observed visually or photographed either through a transparent sidewall or from the water surface if suspended sediment is not abundant.

Measurement of sediment transport rates is notoriously difficult, not only in natural flows but also in the laboratory. In flumes and in some specially instrumented rivers, it is possible to pass the flow over or through a section where all of the sediment in transport as bed load is extracted for measurement. In general, however, bed load must be measured using traps of various designs that are lowered to the bottom, opened for a certain time interval, and then brought back to the surface. The problem is that such samplers tend to distort the flow and therefore the sediment movement in their vicinity, and there is usually no good way of estimating and correcting for that effect.

In both the laboratory and nature, suspended load is usually sampled by extracting samples of the suspensate (water plus sediment) at several levels in the flow by sucking or siphoning through small-diameter horizontal tubes with their opening facing upstream. Care must be taken to match the extraction speed to the local flow speed to minimize overcatching or undercatching. Both in rivers and in shallow marine environments such as beaches, the direction and rates of sediment movement have been estimated by the placement of plugs of sediment tagged with short-lived radioisotope tracers and taking closely spaced sediment samples in the surrounding area at some later time, after the tagged sediment has been dispersed by transport. Measurements of this kind have the advantage of integrating the transport over a long time period.

SIGNIFICANCE

Because most of Earth's topography is produced by erosion, transport, and deposition of particulate material derived from weathering of bedrock, consideration of sediment transport is essential in any attempt to account for how the landscapes of Earth develop through time. Even in the driest of deserts, most geological work is accomplished by running water: On the rare occasions of heavy rains, the abundant loose sediment produced by weathering is entrained and transported by floods. Erosion and deposition of sediment in rivers and estuaries in the processes of channel shifting lead to great changes in river geometry on time scales that range from days to decades. These changes often make it difficult to maintain navigable channels in rivers and harbors. The useful water-storage life of reservoirs is determined by the rate of transport of sediment from upstream in relation to the reservoir capacity. Because of saltation, reservoir life is typically limited to a few decades rather than to hundreds of years. Rivers

downstream of reservoirs commonly experience a substantial lowering of the level of the riverbed as the now sediment-free flow seeks to pick up new sediment, leading to what is called degradation.

In coastal zones, sediment is transported by tidal currents in shifting tidal channels and by nearshore currents of various kinds that flow parallel to open shorelines. Sediment movement along open shorelines is augmented greatly by the effect of waves: The strong oscillatory bottom flows produced by waves tend to suspend the sediment, which then can be carried for some distance even by unidirectional currents too weak to move sediment by themselves. Understanding of the rates of sediment erosion, transport, and deposition is essential for dealing with problems of shoreline changes in the coastal zone.

The sedimentary record of Earth is the outcome of sediment transport and deposition, in the same ways that are observed in the present day. Understanding modern processes of sediment movement and deposition is essential in interpreting the ancient depositional environments in which Earth's sedimentary record was produced. Understanding of the controls on the complex geometry of sediment bodies—ultimately a matter of sediment transport and erosion—plays an important role in petroleum exploration because petroleum is commonly found in porous sedimentary rocks that were formed by particle-by-particle deposition of sediments in river systems and in the oceans.

John Brelsford Southard

FURTHER READING

Allen, John R. *Principles of Physical Sedimentology.* Caldwell, N.J.: Blackburn Press, 2001. Offers a lucidly written introduction to the movement and deposition of sediment for sedimentology students at the college level and beyond. Chapters on sediment transport and deposition are moderately mathematical but contain unusually clear qualitative discussions of the physical effects.

Blatt, Harvey, Robert J. Tracy, and Brent Owens. *Petrology: Igneous, Sedimentary, and Metamorphic.* New York: W. H. Freeman, 2005. A textbook on sedimentology aimed at the upper college level. The chapter on sediment movement, a self-contained treatment on fluid flow and sediment transport, is somewhat mathematical but is an excellent starting point for someone looking for fundamentals.

Chorley, Richard J., Stanley A. Schumm, and David E. Sugden. *Geomorphology.* New York: Methuen, 1985. A well-referenced, though older, textbook, that emphasizes the role and function of sediment transport in all environments; theoretical principles are closely discussed. Contains numerous line drawings as well as working charts and graphs.

Harvey, A. M., A. E. Mather, and M. Stokes, eds. *Alluvial Fans: Geomorphology, Sedimentology, Dynamics.* Special Publication 251. London: Geological Society of London, 2005. A compilation of articles discussing the advancements in alluvial fan research. Examines a wide range of rivers. Discusses characteristics of alluvial fans, processes affecting the alluvial fans, and the resulting ecological impacts.

Hsu, Kenneth J. *Physics of Sedimentology.* 2d ed. New York: Springer, 2010. Written by a knowledgeable professor with strong teaching skills. Discusses the physics and mathematics of sedimentary rock dynamics assuming the reader's understanding begins at the middle school level. Designed for a university-level course. Each chapter contains suggested readings, and includes a subject index, references, and appendices.

Joseph, P. *Deep-Water Sedimentation in the Alpine Basin of SE France.* Special Publication 221. London: Geological Society of London, 2004. A compilation of articles discussing stratigraphy, depositional models, and basin-floor topography. Articles are very technical. Best suited for researchers.

Leeder, Mike R. *Sedimentology and Sedimentary Basins: From Turbulence to Tectonics.* 2d ed. Hoboken, N.J.: John Wiley & Sons, 2011. A college-level text on sedimentology, with separate chapters on fluid flow and sediment transport. Uses some mathematics, but the treatment remains coherent.

Middleton, Gerard V., and John B. Southard. *Mechanics in the Earth and Enviromental Sciences.* New York: Cambridge University Press, 1994. Contains several chapters on the fluid dynamics of sediment-transporting flows. Written for nonspecialists who have at least an elementary knowledge of calculus. Deals with sediment transport, with emphasis on important physical effects.

Niedoroda, Alan W. "Shelf Processes." In *Encyclopedia of Coastal Science.* Edited by M. Schwartz. Dordrecht: Springer, 2005. Describes the properties of water in the continental shelf zone. Covers waves, currents, and sediment transport.

Prothero, Donald R., and Fred Schwab. *Sedimentary Geology: An Introduction to Sedimentary Rocks and Stratigraphy.* New York: W. H. Freeman, 2003. Provides a thorough treatment of most aspects of sediments and sedimentary rocks. Well illustrated with line drawings and black-and-white photographs. Also contains a comprehensive bibliography. Deals with carbonate rocks and limestone depositional processes and environments. Suitable for college-level readers.

Pye, Kenneth. *Aeolian Dust and Dust Deposits.* London: Academic Press, 1987. An excellent reference about airborne transport and sediment deposition.

Pye, Kenneth, and Haim Tsoar. *Aeolian Sand and Sand Dunes.* Berlin: Springer-Verlag, 2009. Discusses the characteristics and classification of sand. Covers the mechanics of sand transport and sand dunes.

Reading, H. G., ed. *Sedimentary Environments: Processes, Facies, and Stratigraphy.* Oxford: Blackwell Science, 1996. Offers a good treatment of the study of sedimentary rocks, sedimentary transport, and biogenic sedimentary environments. Suitable for the high school or college student. Well illustrated, with an index and bibliography.

Schreiber, B. C., S. Lugli, and M. Babel, eds. *Evaporites Through Space and Time.* Special Publication 285. London: Geological Society of London, 2007. A compilation of articles focused on the study of evaporates. Covers tectonics, depositional models, and includes articles discussing specific basins.

Vanoni, V. A., ed. *Sedimentation Engineering.* 2d ed. New York: American Society of Civil Engineers, 2006. An engineering reference manual, aimed at students and practicing engineers, that deals with the fundamentals of sediment-transport mechanics from an applied standpoint. The best and most authoritative source for information on the engineering aspects of sediment movement. Emphasis is on engineering practice, but without slighting basic understanding of the physical effects. Heavily mathematical.

See also: Alluvial Systems; Beaches and Coastal Processes; Dams and Flood Control; Deep-Sea Sedimentation; Deltas; Desert Pavement; Drainage Basins; Floodplains; Lakes; Reefs; River Bed Forms; River Flow; Sand; Weathering and Erosion

SEVERE AND ANOMALOUS WEATHER IN RECENT DECADES

Severe storms and meteorological events in and around the United States in the last few decades have led to greater concern about climate change and sustainable development. Highly publicized tornadoes, nor'easters and other snow and ice storms, hurricanes, and cyclones have cost billions in monetary damage and have led to significant human casualties. Scientists, emergency professionals, and political leaders are working to understand these phenomena and how they affect developed areas. Such studies could help introduce systems and protocols that warn citizens and protect against weather-related disasters.

PRINCIPAL TERMS

- **El Niño:** meteorological condition in which the waters of the eastern, tropical Pacific Ocean are warmed by the atmosphere
- **Fujita scale:** scale that rates the severity of tornadoes based on the amount of destruction they cause
- **La Niña:** meteorological condition in which the waters of the eastern, tropical Pacific Ocean are cooled by a lack of radiation from the atmosphere
- **nor'easter:** severe storm in which storm fronts combine off the Atlantic seaboard, resulting in a circulating, high-precipitation storm
- **Saffir-Simpson scale:** system used to categorize the strength of a hurricane or typhoon based on wind speed

TORNADOES

An unpredictable and incredibly destructive weather phenomenon is the tornado, which is a vortex of violently circulating winds associated with severe storms. Tornadoes are formed when systems of warm and cold air intersect to form powerful storm clouds known as mesocyclones. The mix of warm and cold air, resulting in strong updrafts and downdrafts, cause the air near the surface to spin.

Scientists are learning more and more about how tornadoes form and move. Such knowledge has helped meteorologists and emergency personnel to alert at-risk residents, giving them time to take shelter before the arrival of a tornado. However, science has not reached a point at which tornadoes can be accurately predicted.

In 1971, University of Chicago researcher Tetsuya Fujita developed what would be called the Fujita scale, which assesses the strength of a tornado based predominantly on the amount of damage it causes. An EF-0 tornado (with winds ranging between 64 and 116 kilometers, or 40 and 72 miles, per hour), for example, may strip shingles from a house, knock over television antennae, and cause tree damage.

Meanwhile, an EF-5 tornado, the most powerful type on record, can contain sustained winds between 400 and 500 km (about 250 to 310 mi) per hour or more, destroying homes and large structures and causing wide swaths of damage.

In recent years a number of severe tornadoes (categorized EF-3 or higher) have touched down in the United States. For example, on May 22, 2011, a seemingly unremarkable storm system formed over southeastern Kansas. This storm quickly intensified into a supercell (a thunderstorm that contains a mesocyclone), generating small tornadoes. A massive, wedge-shaped funnel cloud (a cone-shaped, circulating cloud emanating downward from a mesocyclone that, when it reaches the ground, becomes a tornado) dropped from the storm and headed from the southwest in a northeasterly direction—the general trajectory on which tornadoes travel—to the city of Joplin, Missouri. At its apex, the EF-5 wedge (which actually contained multiple vortices) was approximately 1 km (0.62 mi wide), cutting a swath of devastation through the southern area of the city of 49,000 people. About 160 people were killed and another 1,150 were injured by the twister, which caused approximately $3 billion in damage; almost seven thousand homes were destroyed.

The Joplin tornado was preceded by another major storm, an EF-4 tornado that leveled a large portion of Tuscaloosa, Alabama, in April 2011. Nearly three hundred people were killed, thirty-two of whom were in Tuscaloosa, where the tornado cut a swath nearly 1.5 km (1 mi) wide in some areas.

The Joplin and Tuscaloosa tornadoes were among the 1,691 confirmed tornadoes that touched down in 2011, 59 of which were deemed "killer tornadoes" by the National Oceanic and Atmospheric Administration (NOAA). Since the start of the twenty-first century, this total number has been exceeded twice only: The year 2004 had about 1,800 tornadoes in the United States and 2008 had about 1,700 tornadoes.

HURRICANES AND TYPHOONS

Hurricanes and typhoons are some of the most destructive natural forces on Earth. Like tornadoes, these massive storms (which are both identified scientifically as cyclones) feature high winds but also include extremely large amounts of precipitation. This combination of wind and water is potentially devastating for any area in its path.

Cyclones are tropical storms, forming over the warm waters of the Atlantic and Pacific oceans near the earth's equator. The warm, moist air in these areas rises upward, creating areas of low pressure beneath the developing system. Air from nearby systems with higher pressure rushes into these lower-pressure areas. This air is quickly warmed and sent into the growing clouds (formed as the rising, moist air cools off). This constant updraft causes the clouds to start spinning counterclockwise if the system is above the equator and clockwise if below the equator.

The spinning eventually creates an eye in the center of the storm; the eye is a region in which the sky is clear and winds are calm. Outside the eye, winds continue to build as more air rushes into the low-pressure system through the eye and along the ocean surface. Once winds in the storm reach speeds of 63 km (39 mi) per hour, the system is classified as a tropical storm. At 120 km (74 mi) per hour, the system becomes a cyclone, or hurricane in the Atlantic and eastern Pacific oceans and typhoon in the central and western Pacific.

There are five categories in which hurricanes and typhoons are classified. According to the Saffir-Simpson scale, the weakest of these storms, category 1, has sustained winds of between 120 and 153 km (74 and 95 mi) per hour, while the strongest type, category 5, has sustained winds of more than 250 km (155 mi) per hour. At the beginning of the annual Atlantic and Pacific cyclone seasons (June 1 through November 30 and April through December, respectively), a list of names (developed by the World Meteorological Organization) is available for each storm once it reaches tropical storm status.

Hurricane Andrew, which reached Florida and Louisiana in 1992, was at its strongest a category 4 storm. Hurricane Katrina, which reached the Gulf region in 2005, was a category 5, as was Hurricane Camille in 1969. (This storm's final wind speed could not be determined because the storm had destroyed all available measuring devices.)

Because they are oceanic storms, hurricanes and typhoons will quickly weaken once they reach land. However, even a weak hurricane can cause massive damage, generating a storm surge (high water caused by a cyclone's wind and low pressure) and triggering coastal flooding. Such a storm also can produce several inches of rain in a short of time, causing coastal and inland flooding.

Using computer modeling, remote sensor technologies, and other meteorological tools, scientists work to predict the number of cyclones that will occur in a given season. Prediction is important, not only because it will help scientists, public safety officials, and private citizens take stock of emergency measures but also because it could help researchers develop technologies that could weaken such storms before they strike land. This latter endeavor has received much attention in recent years, although most scientists agree that prediction is a theoretical and not a practical field of science.

SEVERE WINTER STORMS

Some forms of severe and anomalous weather occur in the winter, producing heavy snow, ice, and high winds. Blizzards, for example, are massive winter storms in which sustained winds of 56 km (35 mi) per hour or higher are coupled with snowfall.

The more common type of condition associated with blizzards is heavy snowfall of 30 centimeters (1 foot) or more. However, ground blizzards, in contrast, do not produce as much snow; instead, they have strong winds that kick up snow that is already on the ground. Whether the snow falls from the sky or is blown from the ground, one of the most common features of a blizzard, in addition to high winds, is extremely poor visibility of 0.5 km (0.25 mi) or less. The severe winds and poor visibility characteristic of a blizzard make these storms extremely dangerous.

Some unusual winter weather patterns do not produce a large amount of snow; rather, they produce rapid changes in temperature, which cause rain that already has fallen to quickly freeze. Ice storms occur when warm, moist air typically driven from the south comes into contact with colder weather patterns. Such systems may produce freezing rain, which is rain that freezes once it contacts a colder surface. One of the best-known examples of a severe storm in the last two decades is a system that led to the accumulation of nearly 7 cm (3 in) of solid ice in northern New York and New England and parts of Canada in 1998. That storm snapped trees and telephone wires, caused power outages for millions of people, and caused more than $3 billion in damage. It also led to the death of nearly forty people.

Another type of severe weather system, the nor'easter, continues to garner study, especially because it affects more people and has a wider geographic effect, particularly in the northeastern United States, than both tornadoes and hurricanes. A nor'easter is a strong storm that involves the interplay of cold air from Canada with the warm air of the Atlantic Ocean. The two fronts create a slow-moving, counterclockwise storm that features high winds and heavy precipitation.

Nor'easters are frequently known as winter storms, although they occur year-round. One of the most famous examples of a nor'easter is the so-called perfect storm of October, 1991, which caused damage from as far south as Florida and as far north as Maine. This storm was so powerful that a hurricane actually formed inside the larger nor'easter. This hurricane was never named, becoming one of only eight unnamed cyclones since the naming practice was introduced in the 1950's; a more pressing need was to track the major storm and the devastation it caused.

CLIMATE CHANGE

The high number of devastating tornadoes, nor'easters, and hurricanes since the early 1990's may be attributed to a number of atypical (although not unnatural) factors. For example, two critical phenomena, El Niño and La Niña, are well-known contributors to weather patterns.

El Niño, a warming trend in the eastern tropical Pacific, is known to contribute to the creation of storms with heavy precipitation. La Niña, in contrast, is a period marked by cooler water temperatures that brings colder, drier air along the jet stream (the band of air currents that proceeds from the west to the east), and causes periods of cooler air in the United States.

El Niño and La Niña are cyclical events caused by the interaction of the atmosphere and the surface of the ocean in the tropical Pacific. However, a growing school of scientific thought, concerned with global warming and climate change, argues that the longtime emission of greenhouse gases into the

atmosphere has caused the atmosphere to increase in temperature. Such changes are theorized to foster El Niño and La Niña conditions more frequently than in previous centuries. Such shifts could lead to more severe droughts and to severe hurricanes, tornado-producing storms, flooding, and blizzards. Many scientists attribute the occurrence of high-profile and devastating storms in recent decades to this trend. Although data are not complete (tornadoes, for example, are too difficult to predict and model), researchers continue to seek direct connections between global warming and severe weather.

Michael P. Auerbach

FURTHER READING

Burt, Christopher C. *Extreme Weather: A Guide and Record Book.* New York: Norton, 2007. The author of this book argues that, based on scientific evidence and observations of the many devastating weather events have occurred in recent decades, the global climate is changing, creating an environment in which extreme weather events will continue to be more frequent than in years past.

D'Aleo, Joseph S., and Pamela G. Grube. *The Oryx Resource Guide to El Niño and La Niña.* Westport, Conn.: Greenwood Press, 2002. An extensive review of the occurrences, causes, and effects of El Niño and La Niña in the last several centuries. Provides examples of extreme weather caused by these phenomena.

Mogil, H. Michael. *Extreme Weather: Understanding the Science of Hurricanes, Tornadoes, Floods, Heat Waves, Snow Storms, Global Warming, and Other Atmospheric Disturbances.* New York: Black Dog & Leventhal, 2007. Provides a comprehensive review of extreme weather events. Also offers thoughts on storm and disaster preparedness in the face of such weather.

Repetto, Robert, and Robert Easton. "Climate Change and Damage from Extreme Weather Events." *Environment* 52, no. 2 (2010): 22-33. In this article, the authors describe severe weather events as they relate to global warming and climate change. Repetto and Easton attempt to draw links between global warming and the increase in weather disasters in recent decades.

Zielinski, Gregory A. "A Classification Scheme for Winter Storms in the Eastern and Central United States with an Emphasis on Nor'easters." *Bulletin of the American Meteorological Society* 83, no. 1

(2002). The author of this article argues for the creation of a classification system for nor'easters and similar storm systems. He argues that the frequency and destructive nature of these storms warrant the creation of a scale akin to the Fujita scale for tornadoes and the Saffir-Simpson hurricane scale.

See also: *AR4 Synthesis Report*; Atmospheric Properties; Barometric Pressure; Beaches and Coastal Processes; Climate; Climate Change Theories; Climate Modeling; Clouds; Cyclones and Anticyclones; Dams and Flood Control; Deltas; Drought; Earth-Sun Relations; El Niño/Southern Oscillations (ENSO); Floodplains; Floods; Global Energy Transfer; Global Warming; Gulf of Mexico; Gulf Stream; Hurricane Katrina; Hurricanes; Hydrologic Cycle; Impacts, Adaptation, and Vulnerability; IPCC; Lightning and Thunder; Long-Term Weather Patterns; Monsoons; Ocean-Atmosphere Interactions; Precipitation; Recent Climate Change Research; Remote Sensing of the Oceans; Satellite Meteorology; Seasons; Severe Storms; Surface Ocean Currents; Tornadoes; Tropical Weather; Tsunamis; Weather Forecasting; Weather Forecasting: Numerical Weather Prediction; Weather Modification; Wind

SEVERE STORMS

A severe storm is a violent weather phenomenon that has a specific structure, often associated with air circulating in a cyclonic or anticyclonic manner, and heavy precipitation. Winds affected by a storm are often of high velocity, a factor used to differentiate among storm stages.

PRINCIPAL TERMS

- **blizzard:** a winter storm characterized by cold wind having a minimum velocity of 56 kilometers per hour, large amounts of blowing snow, and low levels of visibility
- **Doppler radar:** a radar method that uses the Doppler shift to measure the speed of targets moving either toward or away from the radar
- **Doppler shift:** a phenomenon in which the wavelength of electromagnetic radiation (or other type of wave) is lengthened by reflection from a surface moving away from the source or shortened by reflection from a surface moving toward the source
- **downburst:** a severe localized downward outflowing of air and associated wind shear below a thunderstorm
- **glaze:** a coating of ice formed on exposed objects by the freezing of a film of supercooled water deposited by rain, drizzle, or fog
- **hurricane:** a severe tropical cyclone, typically between 500 and 600 kilometers in diameter, with winds in excess of 65 knots (74 miles or 120 kilometers) per hour
- **ice storm:** a storm characterized by a fall of freezing rain, with the formation of glaze on objects below
- **rawinsonde:** a radiosonde with a radar target attached so that it can be tracked for collection of wind information
- **tornado:** a violent rotating column of air that forms and extends downward from a cumulonimbus cloud and has the appearance of a funnel, rope, or column that touches the ground
- **vortex:** the center of a whirling or rotating fluid, typically with low pressure in the center due to loss of the fluid mass in that locus by centrifugal force

WINTER STORMS

A storm is a disturbed state of the atmosphere that has an impact on the ground surface with powerful and potentially destructive weather. Some types of storms are confined to certain seasons or locations, and others can occur anywhere. Among the storms occurring in the atmosphere are winter storms, thunderstorms, tornadoes, and tropical cyclones. Winter storms in particular can be quite severe, destructive, and life-threatening. Two types of winter storm can be particularly catastrophic: ice storms and blizzards.

The term "ice storm" is given to rain that falls from the atmosphere in liquid form and freezes when the water comes in contact with a surface having a temperature of 0 degrees Celsius or lower. This form of precipitation is also known as freezing rain. In order for freezing rain to occur, the surface temperature of the ground must be below 0 degrees Celsius, and above-freezing temperatures must be present aloft. Snowflakes fall through the layer of warmer air and are melted. The resulting raindrops then cool as they pass through the colder air near the surface, losing most or all of their latent heat content such that they freeze quickly on impact with any cold surface. This kind of precipitation produces layers of solid ice, called glaze, that coat streets, trees, automobiles, and power lines, sometimes to thicknesses of more than 2 centimeters. The added weight of the ice has been sufficient to collapse vulnerable structures, and has been the cause of major power disruptions in eastern North America as electrical grid towers fell under the additional load.

A blizzard is characterized by a strong wind with a velocity of 56 kilometers per hour or higher, temperatures lower than –7 degrees Celsius and enough snow to restrict visibility to less than 150 meters. The high winds coupled with the low temperature produce extreme windchill factors, while the amount of falling or blowing snow driven by the wind can produce total whiteout conditions. Blizzards are associated with midlatitude cyclones. The type of cyclone most likely to produce blizzard conditions is one with a surface low pressure connected with a low pressure in the upper air at the level of the jet stream.

The area of heaviest snowfall in a cyclone is within about 200 kilometers north of the low-pressure center. The heavy snow results from moist air from the south turning counterclockwise around the low-pressure center. Farther to the south, usually along the cold front, sleet and freezing rain may occur. Sleet, like freezing rain, occurs when above-freezing temperatures are present aloft; only the raindrops freeze before reaching the surface. The strongest winds are behind the cold front, and blizzard conditions are most likely to occur there.

THUNDERSTORMS

A thunderstorm is a violent disturbance in the atmosphere and typically occurs along a weather front. These storms are especially frequent when a cold front moves into a mass of warm, moist air. Associated features of thunderstorms include lightning, thunder, occasionally hail, and frequently heavy precipitation, although in dry climates precipitation at the surface may not occur. When temperatures in the atmosphere decrease rapidly with height, the atmosphere is unstable. Moreover, if the air is moist, a considerable amount of energy is stored inactively in the water vapor, and this energy will be released when the vapor changes to liquid water or ice. When this moist, unstable air is given an initial lift by unequal heating of the ground surface, a mountain range, or an advancing front, a rising air current is set in motion. As long as the rising air is less dense than the surrounding air, it will continue to rise. As the water vapor is condensed, air density is decreased, and a towering thunderhead cloud forms.

Conditions favorable for the formation of thunderstorms most often occur in warm, moist tropical air. For this reason, thunderstorms form most frequently in states bordering the Gulf of Mexico and are also frequent around the Great Lakes region in North America. Thunderstorms are divided into two basic types, termed local and organized thunderstorms. Local storms are isolated, scattered, and usually short-lived. Normally they occur on warm summer afternoons near the time of the peak daily temperature. Organized thunderstorms are long-lived and occur over larger areas than local storms. They form in rows called squall lines, along cold fronts, occasionally along warm fronts, and adjacent to mountain peaks.

The initial stage of thunderstorm formation is the cumulus stage, in which the cloud is dominated by updrafts. Precipitation does not occur in this stage, but as the cloud gets larger, the updrafts get stronger and more widespread. In the top of the cloud, where liquid water and ice crystals are abundant and where buoyancy is less, a downdraft is initiated. As soon as the downdraft starts, the second stage in the life cycle is reached, called the mature stage.

The most violent weather in the thunderstorm occurs during the mature stage. Both a strong updraft and downdraft exist in the cloud formation, and heavy rain is produced in the downdraft side. Also associated with the downdraft are strong wind gusts at the surface. Depending on the strength of upper winds and downdraft currents, surface winds may range from cool, gentle breezes to strong blasts of air. Gradually, the downdraft spreads throughout the cloud, and the dissipating stage is reached. In this stage, the storm is characterized by weak downdrafts and light rain.

Hazards other than strong winds and heavy rain associated with thunderstorms are lightning and hail. Lightning occurs because of the separation of positive and negative charges within clouds, between clouds, and between the clouds and the ground. When the electrical potential of a charge is sufficient to overcome the insulating effect of the air, a lightning stroke results. Thunder is caused by a rapid expansion of air as a lightning bolt—which is several times hotter than the sun's surface—passes through it. Hail is formed as an ice crystal is buffeted about within a cloud and successive layers of ice are added to the developing hailstone as supercooled water is encountered within the cloud. The eventual size of a hailstone depends on the length of time it undergoes these conditions during its passage through the cloud.

TORNADOES AND HURRICANES

Tornadoes are also associated with severe thunderstorms. They are small, powerful storms usually less than 0.5 kilometer in diameter but, at times, may extend for 1 kilometer or more. A tornado may have the shape of a funnel, rope, or cylinder extending from the base of a thunderstorm cloud to the surface of the ground. The tone of the tornado depends on its background, the debris, and condensed moisture within it. A blue sky behind a tornado makes it appear dark, whereas intense rain behind it makes it look white. The funnel will appear dark when it is filled with debris and dust sucked up from the surface.

The motion of a tornado is highly variable, averaging 65 kilometers per hour, but some tornadoes have been observed to travel as fast as 110 kilometers per hour. Inside, the storm winds, which almost always turn in a counterclockwise direction, may whirl around the center in excess of 500 kilometers per hour. Within a tornado are smaller, more intense vortices called suction vortices. There may be anywhere from one to three such vortices in a tornado. When there is more than one suction vortex, they rotate around a common center and account for total destruction in one area, while only meters away there is little or no damage.

Tornadoes occur in many parts of the world, but the topography and pressure patterns of the central United States are especially suited to tornado formation, such that the region extending northeast from Texas through southwestern Ontario, in Canada, is often referred to as "tornado alley." The Rocky Mountains block winds from the west. High pressure in the Atlantic at 30 degrees north latitude causes warm, moist air from the Gulf of Mexico to flow northward. The jet stream, flowing over the mountains, is colder and drier, making for an extreme vertical contrast in the two air masses. When unstable air rises, the contrast provides conditions for an explosive upward movement of air. Another aspect of the tornado is the low pressure in the center. Pressure here often approaches 800 millibars, whereas average sea-level pressure is 1,013 millibars.

Tornado occurrence follows the seasonal migration of the jet stream. In winter, the jet stream is closer to the Gulf of Mexico, and the Gulf States are then most prone to tornadoes. In spring, the southern plains states are most likely to experience tornadoes, and in late spring and summer, the northern plains and eastern United States are most prone. May is the peak month of occurrence, and Texas, because of its size, has more tornadoes than any other state. When storms are averaged over area, however, Oklahoma ranks first.

Hurricanes are tropical cyclones that occur in the Atlantic Ocean and Gulf of Mexico. Their counterparts in the Pacific Ocean are typically referred to as cyclones and typhoons. A hurricane goes through a four-stage development. Stage one is the tropical disturbance, in which a low-pressure center has some clouds and precipitation but no enclosed isobars (lines connecting points of equal pressure) and only light winds. The second stage is the tropical depression, with lower pressure in the center and at least one enclosed isobar but with winds less than 60 kilometers per hour. Third is the tropical storm stage, with winds between 60 and 120 kilometers per hour around a low-pressure center with several enclosed isobars. The storm is given a name in this stage. Fourth is the tropical cyclone or hurricane stage, with pronounced rotation around a central core or eye. Winds are sustained at speeds in excess of 120 kilometers per hour, circling as bands in toward the center. Hurricanes form over warm oceans and derive most of their energy from water with temperatures greater than 26.5 degrees Celsius. These storms form only in late summer and fall. Because the motion of a hurricane is affected by the Coriolis force, hurricanes are not seen to form closer than 5 degrees of latitude to the equator, where the Coriolis force is not sufficient to induce rotation. Hurricanes have no fronts and are smaller than a midlatitude cyclone, while central pressures are lower and winds are stronger.

STUDY OF STORMS

One of the first major investigations into the nature of thunderstorms was undertaken from 1946 to 1947 during what was called the Thunderstorm Project. The project consisted of flying instrument-bearing aircraft through thunderstorms to obtain various kinds of data. The study also was augmented by collection of data from various instruments such as radar, radiosondes, and ground-based instruments. Much was learned about thunderstorm structure, internal activity, and life cycle from this investigation. It was largely through the Thunderstorm Project that the cumulus, mature, and dissipating stages in a thunderstorm's life cycle were identified. Aircraft are also used to fly through hurricanes for the purpose of collecting storm data.

One device used in data collection in the upper atmosphere is the rawinsonde, which is a package of weather instruments attached to a balloon that is sent aloft. The rawinsonde has instruments to record temperature and humidity, a reflector for collecting wind data by ground-based radar, and a transmitter to send data to recorders in the weather station. Rawinsonde stations are spaced several hundred kilometers apart and are released only twice daily at 0000Z and 1200Z (the time in Greenwich, England). Thus, the rawinsonde is limited, because data collected in this manner are insufficient to make precise forecasts of severe thunderstorms or tornadoes hours in advance.

Another valuable meteorological tool is radar, which can be used to detect and observe storms hundreds of kilometers away from a station. A radar set sends out pulses of radio waves through an antenna that rebound from objects including raindrops, cloud drops, ice crystals, and hail. A radio receiver intercepts the returning pulses between transmitted pulses, and these are recorded.

Doppler radar is a particularly useful forecasting tool, especially for severe thunderstorms and tornadoes. Doppler radar sends out continuous radio waves instead of pulses, and uses the Doppler effect on reflected radio signals to measure speeds of objects moving toward or away from the radar antenna. Targets such as cloud drops, raindrops, and other liquid or solid particles reflect radio waves, so the direction of air movement can be discerned. Thus, air that is whirling within a storm can be detected by the appearance of shortened wavelength on one side of a central point and lengthened wavelength on the other side. Doppler radar can identify and locate a tornado within a thunderstorm as much as fifteen to twenty minutes before the funnel touches the ground. A network of Doppler radars is in place across North America, providing meteorologists with a great deal of information regarding storms and weather patterns.

Satellites are another useful tool for detecting and observing middle-latitude cyclones, thunderstorms, and hurricanes. Several meteorological satellites have been placed in orbit over the years, beginning with the Television Infrared Observation Satellites (TIROS). Satellites such as the Applications Technology Satellites (ATS) and Synchronous Meteorological Satellites (SMS) are in geosynchronous orbit, which means they make one revolution of Earth in a twenty-four-hour period so that they remain over the same location on the surface. These satellites sense conditions on and above Earth and send coded information back to weather stations. The information is transformed into the weather images that are frequently shown on television. Images and measurements are taken in both the visible and infrared wavelength ranges. Both wavelengths can produce visible images, but infrared sensors detect the temperature differences of objects. These images provide information on midlatitude cyclones, thunderstorms, and hurricanes.

SIGNIFICANCE

Storms occur somewhere in the country nearly every day. They can be quite destructive and are often life-threatening, although they are at the same time beneficial as essential components of the water cycle. One dangerous aspect of storms is lightning, and about fifty-five people are killed in the United States each year from lightning strikes.

Thunderstorms, on an annual basis, can cause more cumulative damage than other storms simply because there are so many of them. In addition to lightning, thunderstorms can produce heavy downpours of rain, which can cause flash flooding. Hailstorms are also associated with thunderstorms. Hail often destroys crops and can cause damage to buildings, automobiles, and other structures. Strong gusts of wind on the downdraft side of a thunderstorm often do appreciable damage to vegetation, especially trees, and to buildings. Downbursts—air that rushes out of a thunderstorm downdraft and spreads out laterally near the surface—are particularly hazardous to aircraft taking off or landing and have caused several plane crashes.

Tornadoes are generally associated with severe thunderstorms, although they also occur in conjunction with hurricanes. They are difficult to forecast and often appear quickly, without warning. More tornadoes occur annually across the contiguous United States than in any other country, averaging between seven hundred and one thousand such storms each year. Deaths from tornadoes average more than one hundred per year, and property damage caused by a tornado is typically valued in the millions of dollars. The conditions for the formation of storms that generate tornadoes migrate with the movement of jet stream, and the month of May has more tornadoes than any other, although June has more days on which tornadoes occur.

Hurricanes are normally limited to late summer and fall, although they have occurred as late as December. Global climate changes and rising ocean temperatures have brought about a significant extension of the hurricane season. Hurricanes are not as intense as are tornadoes but, being thousands of times larger and of much longer duration, they cause more damage. They form most frequently in the Gulf of Mexico and the Atlantic Ocean, but similar storms also form in the Pacific Ocean. The most damaging aspect of a hurricane is the tidal surge that accompanies it. Surges have been as high as 8.5 meters and have carried floods inland for several kilometers. The damage from Hurricane Camille in 1969, which had a storm surge of more than 7.5 meters, totaled some $1.5 billion. More recently, in 2005, Hurricane Katrina struck the Louisiana coast, flooding the city of New Orleans. Katrina boasted sustained winds of almost 280 kilometers (175 miles) per hour, pushing a storm surge of up to 8.5 meters (28 feet). More than 1,500 people were killed by the storm and property damage amounted to more than $80 billion. High-velocity winds also cause considerable damage, and the damage is more widespread than surge damage.

Ice storms occur most often in the eastern and southern states and have been responsible for power outages when power lines break and towers collapse under the added weight of accumulated glaze. Ice storms are also very hazardous to transportation due to slippery road conditions. Blizzards occur in the northern United States. Blizzard winds can reach hurricane force, and because of drifting snow and low visibility, travelers can become stranded. Because of the cold temperatures, people lost in blizzards frequently suffer severe frostbite or die from hypothermia.

Ralph D. Cross

FURTHER READING

Ahrens, C. Donald. *Essentials of Meteorology: An Invitation to the Atmosphere.* Belmont, Calif.: Brooks/Cole Cengage Learning, 2012. Discusses various topics in weather and the atmosphere. Chapters cover topics such as tornadoes and thunderstorms, acid deposition and other air pollution topics, humidity and cloud formation, and temperature.

Balogna, Julie, and Christopher K. Passante. *The Complete Idiot's Guide to Extreme Weather.* New York: Alpha Books, 2006. Examines extreme weather conditions around the world.

Bluestein, Howard B. *Tornado Alley: Monster Storms of the Great Plains.* New York: Oxford University Press, 2006. A compilation of excellent color photographs that capture the power of storms and tornadoes in the American Midwest. Describes the hazards involved with these storms, as well as the factors that cause them.

Dunlop, Storm. *The Weather Identification Handbook.* Guilford, Conn.: Lyons Press, 2003. Provides a simple and useful guide to various atmospheric objects, patterns, dynamics, and phenomena. Begins with identification of cloud formations, followed by optical phenomena such as rainbows, and discusses various weather patterns and events. Best used as a reference for the weather enthusiast as an introduction to the study of meteorology.

Erickson, Jon. *Violent Storms.* Blue Ridge Summit, Pa.: TAB Books, 1990. Deals with severe storms and provides good background material on storms in general. Written on a general level and easily understood by the layperson. Illustrated with diagrams and black-and-white and color photographs.

Gibilisco, Stan. *Violent Weather, Hurricanes, Tornadoes, and Storms.* Blue Ridge Summit, Pa.: TAB Books, 1984. An excellent book on storms of all kinds. Nontechnical but goes into considerable detail on storm types. Written in a style easily understood; suitable for the layperson, yet rigorous enough to be included on college reading lists. Illustrated with diagrams and black-and-white photographs.

Grazulis, Thomas P. *The Tornado: Nature's Ultimate Windstorm.* Norman: University of Oklahoma Press, 2003. Elucidates the formation and life cycle of tornadoes, their structure, and wind speeds. Examines related areas such as forecasting, risks and safety measures, and many common myths about tornadoes. Includes accounts of some of the deadliest tornadoes in history.

Lighthill, James, and Robert Pearce, eds. *Monsoon Dynamics.* New York: Cambridge University Press, 2009. Discusses atmospheric and oceanic influences on monsoons. Discusses tropical climatology, such as drought and rainfall patterns, temperature oscillations, and wave dynamics. Contains articles focusing on the dynamics in India, the Indian Ocean, and eastern Africa. A technical text best suited for researchers, graduate students, and professional meteorologists.

MacGorman, Donald R., and W. David Rust. *The Electrical Nature of Storms.* New York: Oxford University Press, 1998. Describes the atmospheric conditions and electrical conditions that create thunderstorms, hailstorms, lightning, tornadoes, and hurricanes. Discusses the ways in which violent weather affects the environment and humans.

Mooney, Chris. *Storm World: Hurricanes, Politics, and the Battle Over Global Warming.* Orlando, Fla.: Harcourt, 2007. Presents a succinct overview of the title topics, and covers the debate over whether global warming is increasing the frequency and ferocity of hurricanes and other severe storms.

Rosenfeld, Jeffery. *Eye of the Storm: Inside the World's Deadliest Hurricanes, Tornadoes and Blizzards.* Cambridge, Mass.: Basic Books, 2003. Provides a detailed inside look at the title phenomena. Gives the reader a foundation in the properties of these atmospheric phenomena.

Samaras, Tim, Stefan Bechtel, and Greg Forbes. *Tornado Hunter: Getting Inside the Most Violent Storms on Earth.* Washington, D.C.: National Geographic Society, 2009. Offers a close-up account of tornadoes, their study, and some of the people who risk the storm to understand its secrets.

Schneider, Bonnie. *Extreme Weather: A Guide to Surviving Flash Floods, Tornadoes, Hurricanes, Heat Waves, Snowstorms, Tsunamis and Other Natural Disasters.* Basingstoke, England: Palgrave Macmillan, 2012. Presents vivid explanations of how, when, and why major natural disasters occur. Discusses floods, hurricanes, thunderstorms, mudslides, wildfires, tsunamis, and earthquakes. Presents a guide of how to prepare for and what to do during an extreme weather event, along with background information on weather patterns and natural disasters.

Schneider, Stephen Henry, and Michael D. Mastrandrea. *Encyclopedia of Climate and Weather.* 2d ed. New York: Oxford University Press, 2011. Provides over 300 succinct articles discussing basic and advanced topics in weather, climate, and meteorology. Contains cross-referencing and a bibliography of related resources. Also provides a glossary and list of abbreviations.

Sheets, Bob, and Jack Williams. *Hurricane Watch: Forecasting the Deadliest Storms on Earth.* New York: Vintage Books, 2001. Provides a history of the study of hurricanes. Discusses modeling of hurricanes. Includes many excellent appendices of the strongest, deadliest, most damaging hurricanes. Also includes appendices of hurricane names, probabilities, and costs. Written for the layperson with some more technical portions, yet still easily accessible.

See also: Atmosphere's Structure and Thermodynamics; Atmospheric and Oceanic Oscillations; Atmospheric Properties; Barometric Pressure; Climate; Clouds; Cyclones and Anticyclones; Drought; Earth-Sun Relations; Gulf Stream; Hurricane Katrina; Hurricanes; Lightning and Thunder; Long-Term Weather Patterns; Monsoons; Remote Sensing of the Oceans; Satellite Meteorology; Seasons; Tornadoes; Tropical Weather; Van Allen Radiation Belts; Volcanoes: Climatic Effects; Weather Forecasting; Weather Forecasting: Numerical Weather Prediction; Weather Modification; Wind

SURFACE OCEAN CURRENTS

Ocean currents represent a dynamic system that, along with atmospheric circulation, helps to distribute heat evenly across the planet. Responding to the seasons, ocean currents play important roles in climate, marine life, and ocean transportation.

PRINCIPAL TERMS

- **core ring or core eddy:** a mass of water that is spun off of an ocean current by that current's meandering motion
- **Coriolis effect:** the apparent deflection of any moving body or object from its linear course, caused by Earth's rotation
- **current:** a sustained movement of seawater in the horizontal plane, usually wind-driven
- **drift:** a movement similar to a current but more widespread, less distinct, slower, more shallow, and less easily delineated
- **gyre or gyral:** the very large, semiclosed surface circulation patterns of ocean currents in each of the major ocean basins
- **heat budget:** the balance between the incoming solar radiation and the outgoing terrestrial reradiation
- **planetary winds:** the large, relatively constant prevailing wind systems that result from Earth's absorption of solar energy and that are affected by Earth's rotation
- **thermohaline circulation:** any circulation of ocean waters that is caused by variations in the density of seawater resulting from differences in the temperature or salinity of the water

OVERVIEW

The "heat budget" of Earth results in a temperature range that makes life on the planet possible. Ocean currents play a vital role in the heat budget. These currents are major determinants of climates and strongly influence the distribution of marine life. Ocean currents must be studied in relation to other aspects of the environment with which they interact. The currents are, for example, closely associated with atmospheric circulation, because the planetary winds are the prime movers of the currents. The friction of the wind blowing over the ocean surface began the slow, shallow movement of surface waters that eventually became a global circulation of immense volumes of seawater. There are also deeper ocean currents that are much slower moving and are difficult to monitor, whose significance, therefore, is less well understood. In part, the deep currents derive from the physical fact that water is continuous in structure, such that water moved from one location must be replaced by water from a different location. The deep currents, however, are primarily caused by thermohaline circulation, driven by slight differences in seawater densities resulting from differences in temperature and salinities. The shallow, wind-driven currents—the ones affecting the surface waters—although they may be hundreds of meters deep, are effectively independent of such deep ocean currents.

The most significant features of ocean currents are their geographic locations and their directions of flow. It is helpful to recognize overall patterns. There are large-circulation gyres in each of the major ocean basins, discernible as an apparent overall circular movement of surface waters. These gyres, or gyrals, move clockwise in the Northern Hemisphere and counterclockwise in the Southern Hemisphere. The North Central Atlantic Gyre, for example, located east of the United States, is one of the best known and most studied. The Florida Current (part of the Gulf Stream system) is on the west side of the gyre and is a warm current flowing generally northward. The Canaries Current, on the east side of the gyre, is a cold current that flows generally southward. The North Atlantic Drift and the North Equatorial Current form the eastward and westward components of the gyre, respectively. The result of circulation in the gyre is that warm water from the equatorial region is transported poleward to heat-deficient areas. Simultaneously, the Canaries Current transports colder water back toward the equator. The ocean currents thus help to distribute surface and atmospheric heat more evenly throughout the world. In the Atlantic Ocean south of the equator, a large gyre moves counterclockwise. The warm Brazil Current on the west side of the gyre flows southward, transporting heat away from the equator. The Benguela Current on the east side of the gyre moves colder water toward the equator.

In the Pacific Ocean, similar patterns of clockwise and counterclockwise gyres are apparent. North of the equator, the Japan Current (also known as the Kuroshio) transports warm water toward the pole, and the California Current moves colder water toward the equator. In the Pacific Ocean south of the equator, the cold, nutrient-rich Humboldt Current flows northward off the west coast of South America and is renowned historically as one of the most fertile commercial marine fishery areas in the world. The Indian Ocean possesses similar gyres, although the attenuated portion north of the equator presents some special features.

Wind and Solar Energy

The forces that drive the oceanic current circulations are the planetary winds. The planetary winds are in turn driven by solar energy. The ocean currents, therefore, are sun-driven as sunshine energizes the Gulf Stream and the other currents. Some general principles about Earth's heat budget can be stated. The sun heats Earth, its atmosphere, oceans, and land, but each portion heats differently. The atmosphere, the most fluid and most responsive of the three, has developed large bands of alternating pressure belts and wind belts, such as the Northeast Trade Winds and the Prevailing Westerlies. The Northeast Trade Winds lie between 5 and 25 degrees north latitude. The winds flow predominantly from the northeast and form one of the most constant of the wind belts. The friction of the wind moving over the ocean surface causes the surface waters to move with the wind, but because of the Coriolis effect, caused by Earth's rotation, the movement of the water current in the Northern Hemisphere tends to be about 45 degrees to the right of the winds that cause the current. The resultant current, the North Equatorial Current, is fragmented into different oceans because of the intervening continents. Largely as a result of the Coriolis effect, the current deflects to its right and, in the Atlantic Ocean, eventually becomes the Gulf Stream. In the Pacific Ocean, the comparable current is the Japan Current. One can thus see the origins of the clockwise gyrals in the Northern Hemisphere. Another wind belt in the Northern Hemisphere, the prevailing westerlies, is located between 35 and 55 degrees north latitude. These winds are not as constant as the northeast trade winds, and they flow prevalently from the west. The correlation of the latitudes of the westerlies and the west-to-east-moving currents of the gyres is apparent. The currents slow down and become more widespread, shallower, and less distinguishable but are urged on toward the east by the Westerlies. The North Atlantic Drift and the North Pacific Current result from this relationship.

Northern Hemisphere

Again analyzing the North Central Atlantic Gyre, the blocking position of the Iberian Peninsula causes the North Atlantic Drift to split, part moving southward toward the equator as the cold Canaries Current and part moving poleward into the Arctic Ocean as the warm Norwegian Current. The Canaries Current merges into the North Equatorial Current to complete the gyre. The temperature characterizations of currents and drifts as "warm" or "cold" are relative. There are no absolute temperature divisions. Some warm currents are actually lower in temperature than some cold currents. For example, the Norwegian Current is considered a warm current only because it is warmer than the Arctic water into which it is entering. Only a few degrees above freezing in winter, the Norwegian Current nevertheless transfers significant amounts of heat into these high latitudes and moderates the winter temperatures in Western and Northern Europe. A compensating movement of cold water out of the Arctic is accomplished by the southward flowing Labrador Current between Greenland and North America.

The Gulf Stream is the world's greatest ocean current. There is, however, some confusion about what constitutes the Gulf Stream. The Gulf Stream is generally taken to include the entire warm-water transport system from Florida to the point at which the warm water is lost by diffusion into the Arctic Ocean. It would thus include both the North Atlantic Drift and the Norwegian Current. Technically, the Gulf Stream is a smaller segment of that transport system—the portion off the northeast coast of the United States. The Gulf Stream system thus includes the Florida Current, the Gulf Stream, the North Atlantic Drift, and the Norwegian Current.

Southern Hemisphere

Ocean current patterns in the Southern Hemisphere are almost a mirror image of those in the Northern Hemisphere, adjusted for differences in the configuration of the continents. The southeast trade winds drive the South Equatorial Current, while the Coriolis effect causes it to deflect to the left. Resultant gyres are counterclockwise, but again, the poleward-moving currents transfer the heat away from the equator, and the equatorward-moving currents return colder water. In general, cold currents are richer in nutrients, have a higher oxygen content, and support a greater amount of life than warm currents. Most products of the world's commercial fisheries are yielded by cold waters. In contrast, cold currents offshore are associated with desert climates onshore. The atmospheric circulations that drive the ocean currents also create conditions that are not conducive to precipitation in the latitudes of these cold currents. Examples are the Sahara Desert adjacent to the Canaries Current, the Atacama Desert adjacent to the Humboldt Current, the Sonoran Desert adjacent to the California Current, and the Kalahari Desert adjacent to the Benguela Current.

There are other currents that are sporadic in occurrence, such as the warm El Niño current that periodically develops off the west coast of northwestern South America for reasons that are not well understood. Numerous small local currents are also caused by tides, storms, and local weather conditions.

STUDY OF OCEAN CURRENTS

The study of ocean currents has acquired new significance as scientists have discerned the role of the currents in climate and marine life. Information comes from many sources. One of the earliest attempts to identify and chart an ocean current was made by Benjamin Franklin when he was postmaster general of colonial America. His map of the Gulf Stream was published in 1770 and has proved to be remarkably accurate when one considers his sources of information. Franklin noted that vessels sailing westward from England to America in the midlatitudes of the Atlantic Ocean were taking longer than ships moving eastward and longer than ships moving westward but in lower latitudes. He correctly concluded that the vessels were moving against a slow, eastward-moving current.

Since that time, vast amounts of data have been acquired to detect, measure, and chart the currents. One of the early methods still employed is the use of drift bottles. Sealed bottles are introduced into the sea at various locations and dates and are allowed to float with the currents. Finders are requested to note the date and location of the bottle-find and to return the data to the address in the bottle. Ocean current data have also been obtained serendipitously through the loss of floating goods in midocean shipping accidents. The points of landfall of such materials, as well as of materials washed out to sea by some natural disaster such as a tsunami, provide important information about the surface movement of ocean waters. Various types of more technologically advanced current meters are also used. Some are moored to the sea bottom and can transmit results by radio. It is difficult for a ship at sea to measure currents because the ship itself is drifting with the current. Currents are generally very slow and difficult to measure. A few currents may be measured at 6 to 8 kilometers per hour, but much more common are those less than 1 kilometer per hour. The average surface velocity of the North Atlantic Drift is about 1.3 kilometers per hour. The currents also vary in width and depth. The Florida Current off Miami is about 32 kilometers wide, 300 meters deep, and moving at about 5 to 8 kilometers per hour. It transports more than 4 billion tons of water per minute. The volume of flow is more than one hundred times that of the Mississippi River. As the flow proceeds north and then east as the North Atlantic Drift, it spreads, thins, slows, and splits into individual meandering flows that are difficult to follow. Spin-off eddies, or "core rings," occur that can persist for months.

One useful method of tracking ocean currents is to be able to identify water of slight temperature variations and salinity differences. When the flow movement is so slow as to be practically undetectable with current meters, the slight temperature and salinity differences can be used as "tracers" to identify current movements. This method is also used in identifying the even slower-moving deep-ocean currents. More recently, advanced satellite imagery and high-altitude aerial photography have become extremely important in monitoring ocean currents. Using sensors that detect radiation at selected bands of the electromagnetic spectrum, satellites collect data on broad patterns of seawater temperatures and thus help scientists to understand the movements and extent of the currents. This type of sea monitoring is also useful in detecting any changes that might occur in the oceans in the future.

SIGNIFICANCE

Ocean currents play a vital role in the environment. Along with atmospheric circulation, ocean currents serve to distribute the heat absorbed from the sun to different parts of the world. Immense volumes of relatively warm seawater are slowly moving poleward, transporting heat from the heat-surplus equatorial regions to the heat-deficient regions nearer the poles. Cold-water currents in turn move colder water back toward the equator. Although neither solar energy nor rainfall is evenly distributed over the planet, the mixing actions of the ocean currents function to keep the global environment in a steady state. These moderating effects of the ocean currents affect the climates of coastal areas in the middle and high latitudes, especially in Europe. The densely populated nations of northwestern Europe experience much milder winters than would otherwise be expected for such high latitudes. Northwestern North America similarly benefits.

Life in the sea is also aided by this current-driven ocean water mixing. In addition to heat, ocean currents distribute oxygen and nutrients, the result being the formation of certain areas in the oceans where very favorable life-supporting conditions occur. These fertile areas of mixing are concentrated sources of commercial marine fishery products. Where mixing is limited, nutrient-poor regions arise in the ocean such as the Sargasso Sea, located in the center of the North Central Atlantic Gyre. Global warming may alter ocean currents, creating a further need to study these currents and their effects on climate and marine life.

John H. Corbet

FURTHER READING

Broecker, Wally. *The Great Ocean Conveyor.* Princeton, N.J.: Princeton University Press, 2010. Discusses ocean currents, focusing specifically on the great conveyor belt. Written by the great ocean conveyor's discoverer. Explains the conception of this theory and the resulting impact on oceanography. Written in a manner easy to follow with some background in science, yet still relevant to graduate students and scientists.

Clarke, Allan J. *An Introduction to the Dynamics of El Niño and the Southern Oscillation.* Burlington, Mass.: Academic Press, 2008. Presents the physics of ENSO, including currents, temperature, winds, and waves. Discusses ENSO forecasting models. Provides good coverage of the influence ENSO has on marine life, from plankton to green turtles. Each chapter has references, and there are a number of appendices and indexing. Best suited for environmental scientists, meteorologists, and similar academics studying ENSO.

Colling, Angela. *Ocean Circulation.* 2d ed. Oxford: Butterworth-Heinemann, 2001. A well-illustrated textbook for the Open University Oceanography course that discusses the effects of ocean circulation as reflected in various phenomena. Discusses surface currents and deep water currents, with focus on the North Atlantic Gyre, Gulf Stream, and equatorial currents. Discusses the El Niño phenomenon as well as the great salinity anomaly.

Gross, M. Grant. *Oceanography: A View of the Earth.* 7th ed. Englewood Cliffs, N.J.: Prentice Hall, 1996. A general introductory text for oceanography that is well illustrated in all aspects of the study of the oceans. Explains and maps ocean currents. Relates both horizontal and vertical aspects of oceanic circulation to winds, temperatures, and salinities. Comprehensive and easy to read. Contains a glossary and an index.

Ingmanson, Dale E., and William J. Wallace. *Oceanography: An Introduction.* 5th ed. Belmont, Calif.: Wadsworth, 1995. Provides a general introduction to oceanography. Written as an introductory college text but can be read by the high school student who is interested. Well illustrated, with important terms in bold print. Includes a glossary, and each chapter contains a list of further readings.

Schwartz, M. *Encyclopedia of Coastal Science.* Dordrecht: Springer, 2005. Contains many articles specific to ocean and beach dynamics. Discusses coastal habitat management topics, hydrology, geology, and topography. Articles may run multiple pages and have diagrams. Each article has bibliographical information and cross-referencing.

Stowe, Keith. *Exploring Ocean Science.* 2d ed. New York: John Wiley & Sons, 1996. An introductory text for college students who have little background in the sciences. Discusses oceanic and atmospheric circulation, dealing specifically with surface ocean currents. All chapters include review questions and suggestions for further reading. Includes a glossary.

Sverdrup, Keith A., Alyn C. Duxbury, and Alison B. Duxbury. *An Introduction to the World's Oceans.* 8th ed. Boston: McGraw-Hill, 2004. Includes a clearly written section on the planetary winds and their effects on ocean currents. Maps the general patterns of ocean-current circulation and uses diagrams to explain the Coriolis effect. Lists suggested readings.

Talley, Lynne D., et al. *Descriptive Physical Oceanography: An Introduction.* 6th ed. San Diego: Academic Press, 2011. Covers only the physical aspects of oceanography in a less comprehensive and more technical manner than general-introduction oceanography texts. Presents a detailed description of ocean circulation, both surface currents and deep currents. Includes details on the types of current meters and the methods of current measurements. Includes an extensive bibliography.

Thurman, Harold V., and Alan P. Trujillo. *Introductory Oceanography.* 10th ed. Upper Saddle River, N.J.: Prentice Hall, 2003. Provides an introduction to oceanography that is comprehensive but not too technical for the general reader. Very well illustrated and includes some high-quality color maps and diagrams. Each chapter includes questions and exercises and also lists references and suggested readings. Addresses the circulations of the ocean currents according to the major ocean basins, with maps and diagrams for each basin.

Trujillo, Alan P., and Harold V. Thurman. *Essentials of Oceanography.* 10th ed. Upper Saddle River, N.J.: Prentice Hall, 2010. Discusses the topic of deep ocean currents in the broader context of the whole ocean and oceanography using a systems approach that is amenable to use by all students.

Ulanski, Stan. *The Gulf Stream: Tiny Plankton, Giant Bluefin, and the Amazing Story of the Powerful River in the Atlantic.* Chapel Hill: University of North Carolina Press, 2008. Discusses the hydrodynamics of the Gulf Stream, followed by the biology, and lastly the impact of this current on humans through history. An interesting compilation of the known information on the Gulf Stream current written for the general public.

Voituriez, Bruno. *The Gulf Stream.* Paris: UNESCO, 2006. Offers an analytical narrative that examines complex scientific information to describe the causes and dynamics of the Gulf Stream through the history of its discovery and exploration.

See also: Barometric Pressure; Carbonate Compensation Depths; Climate; Climate Change Theories; Deep Ocean Currents; Gulf Stream; Hydrologic Cycle; Hydrothermal Vents; Ocean-Atmosphere Interactions; Ocean Pollution and Oil Spills; Oceans' Origin; Oceans' Structure; Ocean Tides; Ocean Waves; Remote Sensing of the Oceans; Saltwater Intrusion; Sea Level; Seamounts; Seawater Composition; Tsunamis; Turbidity Currents and Submarine Fans; World Ocean Circulation Experiment

SURFACE WATER

Surface water supplies are among the most basic needs of humankind, but water resources are unevenly distributed in both location and time. Surface water includes the oceans, but the term is generally used to refer to non-oceanic water that is most abundant in lakes, both fresh and saline. Streams and rivers are sources of freshwater that are constantly replenished.

PRINCIPAL TERMS

- **deranged drainage:** describing a landscape whose integrated drainage network has been destroyed by irregular glacial deposition, yielding numerous shallow lake basins
- **drainage basin:** the land area that contributes water to a particular stream or river system; the edge of such a basin is a drainage divide
- **lake basin:** an enclosed depression on the land surface in which surface waters collect; basins are created primarily by glacial activity and tectonic movement
- **saline lake:** a lake with elevated levels of dissolved solids, primarily resulting from evaporative concentration of salts; saline lakes lack an outlet to the sea
- **stream:** a body of flowing water that delivers surplus water from the land to the sea; this term covers all such moving water, including creeks and rivers
- **throughflow:** the subsurface movement of surplus water through the soil to a stream

OVERVIEW

Surface water is a crucial commodity for human beings, plants, and animals, but it is available in only a limited quantity. Furthermore, it is unevenly distributed geographically and temporally, such that vast areas experience perennial, seasonal, or intermittent shortages, while other regions have excessively abundant water. Replenishment of surface water supplies through the hydrologic cycle assures that water will always be available, though not necessarily at the time and place that it is needed or in the desired quantity.

Surface waters include water in freshwater lakes and streams, and in saline lakes such as the Great Salt Lake, the Caspian Sea, and the Dead Sea. Research by the U.S. Geological Survey has revealed that at any given moment, only about 0.001 percent of all water is fresh surface water; a similar amount is held in saline lakes. The total volume of water present in freshwater lakes and streams is nonetheless impressive, equaling more than 125,000 cubic kilometers.

Humankind is dependent on surface waters for a wide variety of uses besides direct consumption, including irrigation of crops, generation of electricity, industrial activities, food processing, transportation, and recreation. In moderate climatic zones, humans may ingest only 3 to 4 liters of water per day to survive, and typically less, but water use in even the least industrialized societies is far higher than that rate. The annual per capita water consumption in underdeveloped nations is approximately 350 cubic meters annually. In the United States, the annual consumption of water exceeds 2,300 cubic meters per person per year. Only one-tenth of this water is consumed domestically, with the remainder going to irrigation, industry, and the generation of electricity. As developing nations become industrialized, their demands for usable water are increasing significantly.

RUNOFF

Surface waters are produced and replenished through precipitation and diminished by evaporation, infiltration to subsurface storage, and return flow to the sea. Precipitation falling on forest or complete grass cover is intercepted by vegetation. Interception is of great importance because it reduces the kinetic energy of raindrops considerably, reducing their erosive potential. This water eventually drops off leaves or runs down the branches of trees, bushes, and blades of grass, where it encounters the ground surface. Studies of steep forested terrain at Coweeta Hydrologic Laboratory in North Carolina revealed that no measurable overland flow was generated in seven years of observation. All runoff reaching the stream channels first infiltrated the soil, later to reemerge in drainageways. It is now believed that all storm flow and base flow of streams draining forested landscapes is generated by infiltrated water, which moves in the shallow unsaturated zone as throughflow, displacement flow, saturated flow in fluctuating belts adjacent to streams, or slow groundwater seepage. In arid areas or on lands disturbed by farming, paving, or compaction, infiltration is greatly reduced, and surface waters are largely direct surface runoff or overland flow. Runoff generated by overland flow reaches stream channels much more quickly than that which moves by sub-surface routes, and it is less substantially depleted by evapotranspiration (the combined loss of water by direct evaporation and transpiration, which is the process by which plants expel water as vapor in their metabolic functions).

All the land area that contributes runoff to a particular stream constitutes the watershed, or drainage basin, of that particular stream. Land-use changes within the watershed will affect the runoff timing, volume, and water quality of the stream. Activities outside the watershed do not ordinarily influence runoff rates or volumes within the watershed. Thus, the watershed is the basic unit of study in most hydrologic investigations.

The global pattern of seasonal and annual runoff is quite complex; the amount of runoff at any location is determined as much by rates of evapotranspiration as it is by the amount of precipitation that falls. Plants obtain water from soil moisture, water that adheres to particles in the soil in much the same way that a sponge holds water. Runoff is surplus water left over after soil moisture is completely replenished. Thus, the tropical and subtropical regions, which receive abundant rainfall, do not necessarily experience the highest rates of runoff, because high temperatures throughout the year cause high rates of evapotranspiration, greatly reducing the water surplus.

The average depth of runoff is approximately 27 centimeters, but there is considerable variation from that average. Only a few areas in the world produce more than 100 centimeters of annual runoff. They include tropical areas such as Central America, the lower Amazon basin, equatorial West Africa, Bangladesh and northeast India, Madagascar, and the East Indies, where exceptionally heavy precipitation overcomes the effects of high evapotranspiration. Outside of the tropics, annual runoff in excess of 100 centimeters occurs primarily in coastal alpine settings, where cool temperatures and forced lifting of moisture-laden air over mountain ranges produce high rates of runoff. Such areas include coastal Alaska and British Columbia, Norway, Chile and Argentina, Tasmania, and New Zealand. Each of these belts of exceptionally heavy runoff is surrounded by areas receiving 50 to 100 centimeters of runoff per year. The largest areas in this range are the Amazon basin, the Congo basin, Southeast Asia, the Appalachians, and Japan.

Areas producing less than 10 centimeters of runoff per year are extensive. The largest such contiguous area covers Africa north of 10 degrees north latitude, the Arabian peninsula, Iran, Afghanistan, Pakistan, and much of interior Asia. The interior of North America west of the hundredth meridian produces little runoff except from the higher mountain ranges, and the Atacama and Patagonian regions of South America also yield less than 10 centimeters of runoff per year. Water is a scarce commodity in all these areas, except where unusually abundant groundwater occurs or where streams such as the Nile River pass through.

The large remaining continental areas generally produce in the range of 25 to 50 centimeters of runoff per year. Such moderate rates of runoff still produce substantial streams when drainage basins are large. Eastern North America, northern Europe and Asia, East Asia, most of India, eastern Australia, and East Africa are included in this category. Surface water shortages in these regions occur primarily in watershed divide areas and during seasonal and intermittent droughts.

MOUNTAINS, STREAMS, AND LAKES

In alpine areas, the snowpack generated by winter storms provides the majority of the stream flow. Conversely, areas on the lee side of such mountain ranges are deprived of moisture through the rain-shadow effect. The net result of heavy precipitation in the mountains, accompanied by cool temperatures and reduced evaporation rates, is that mountain ranges are islands of moisture that generate abundant stream flow during the spring melt. The numerous streams generated by snowmelt flow to the lower, drier adjacent areas and provide them with a source of usable freshwater. Almost all of the streams of the western United States are generated in this manner: the Colorado, the Snake and Columbia, the Missouri, the Arkansas, the Sacramento, and the Rio Grande being but a few examples. The mountain regions of Europe, Africa, Asia, and Australia perform a similar function for adjacent lowlands. When a stream from such locations flows through arid lands, it is especially valued and is known as an exotic stream. Prominent examples include the Nile, Indus, and Colorado Rivers.

The five largest streams of the world account for more than one-third of the world's total stream flow. The Amazon River alone accounts for almost 20 percent of the world's stream flow, as it drains the largest watershed in the world and gathers waters from the largest tropical rainforest. The Amazon watershed is almost as large as the forty-eight contiguous states of the United States and, 800 kilometers above the mouth of the river, its channel averages 2.5 kilometers wide and 50 meters deep. The discharge of the next largest stream, the Congo River, is only one-quarter as great, while the discharge of the mighty Mississippi River is only one-tenth that of the Amazon. The combined discharge of all the world's streams is roughly 30 percent of the precipitation that falls on the continents; the remainder is returned directly to the atmosphere by evaporation and by transpiration.

Freshwater lakes cover some 1.5 percent of the land surface and contain the vast majority of liquid freshwater, a total of approximately 125,000 cubic kilometers. Saline lakes contain only slightly less water, storing an average of 105,000 cubic kilometers of water. Although the freshwater lakes are generally of greater utility to humans, the saline lakes provide important resources as well, including fish, salt, and magnesium.

Lakes occur where natural basins have developed, such that ponding of surface waters occurs. Because the normal cycle of fluvial (stream-related) erosion of the landscape does not produce such depressions, extensive areas of the continents are without naturally occurring lakes. The vast majority of lake basins were produced by the erratic deposition and scouring action of glaciers, but almost two-thirds of the water held in lakes is contained in six structural basins: the Caspian Sea, the Aral Sea, and Lakes Baikal, Tanganyika, Nyasa, and Victoria. These structural basins were produced by a combination of the downfaulting of basins and uplift of adjacent terrain. Lake Baikal in Siberia contains almost one-fifth of the world's liquid freshwater, because of its large size and depth exceeding 1,700 meters. The rift valleys of east Africa, formed by the downfaulting of linear basins associated with the rending of the continent by plate tectonic movement, contain a series of large, deep freshwater lakes.

Glaciers passing over North America scoured out preexisting river valleys to form deep depressions, which were further deepened (relative to their outlets) by postglacial tilting and deposition of recessional moraines. The Great Lakes were formed in this way, as were Canada's Lakes Winnipeg and Winnipegosis, Great Slave Lake, and Great Bear Lake, along with several hundred thousand smaller lakes. Hundreds of thousands of lakes were formed in the recently glaciated terrains of Europe and North America by erratic deposition of loose materials by glaciers. Such uneven deposition eradicated the well-integrated preglacial drainage networks of the areas affected, leaving vast areas of uneven topography with many shallow depressions, which are now filled with water. This type of hydrologic system is referred to as a deranged drainage system.

Preferential solution of certain areas of limestone and other soluble rock types often results in collapse features known as dolines, or sinkholes. When these depressions are filled with impermeable clays, or where the regional water table is high, the depressions tend to hold water. The Lake District of north-central Florida provides numerous examples of such lakes. Other causes of lake basins include landslides, volcanic flows (Lake Tahoe), volcanic eruption and collapse (Crater Lake), scouring by wind, and meteorite impact. More than 100,000 small, elliptically oriented lake basins, most of them now dry, occur on the coastal plain of the United States from New Jersey to Georgia. The origin of the Carolina Bays has been vigorously debated. Human-made lakes are increasingly common on the landscape, built by damming streams to produce reservoirs for water supply, flood control, power generation, transportation, and recreation.

Lake basins are sediment traps because flowing water entering a lake quickly loses velocity and drops its sediment load. As a result, only the largest and deepest lakes last more than a few thousand years, making them among the most ephemeral geographic features on the landscape over geologic time.

Study of Surface Water

People have been concerned with the origins and volumes of stream flow since the beginnings of civilized culture, as many early civilizations began on the banks of alluvial streams. The ancient Egyptians kept detailed records of the dates and heights of the annual floods of the Nile from as early as 3500 B.C.E., dependent as they were upon its delivery of water and nutrient-rich sediment for agricultural activities. Modern hydrologists depend upon similar measurements for much of their research. At more than 16,000 stream sites in the United States alone, gauging stations measure the height of the stream surface every fifteen minutes. These stage recordings are converted to flow rates on the basis of the previously measured cross-sectional area of the stream channel below each gauge height and the flow velocity. These measurements may be recorded on paper at the gauging station, to be retrieved later, or are sent electronically to the managing agency. The stream-flow data are stored in a computer for later tabulation and retrieval. Lake levels are similarly monitored and converted into water volume contained in the lake. In the United States, most stream and lake gauges are operated by the U.S. Geological Survey (USGS), which issues annual reports for all its gauges, organized and distributed by state (available from state offices of the USGS upon request). In addition, the flow data are stored in a computer system that is capable of providing much more detailed flow statistics than the printed reports. Stream gauges provide valuable warning of approaching floods in some locales. The cities of Bath, England, and Gatlinburg, Tennessee, have been heavily damaged by floods in the past but now have electronic gauges upstream that warn of approaching floods. More commonly, such readings are used to allocate limited water resources to downstream claimants.

Hydrologists frequently plot stream-flow rates against time to produce a graphical representation of discharge that is called a hydrograph. Analysis of the hydrograph can provide a wealth of information concerning stream-flow generation and timing mechanisms. By analyzing the form of the hydrograph of a small storm, it is possible to forecast the runoff characteristics of a large storm, such as the peak rate of flow and the time of peak flow.

In order to study how stream flow is generated, hydrologists employ a variety of research methods. On small upland catchments, dye tracers are often used to determine paths and rates of movement. Dye tracers are also used in tracking the paths of disappearing streams in regions of soluble rock. To determine how much water is being added to or lost from a stream channel through bank seepage, stream reach surveys, which involve stream gauging along successive longitudinal segments of a stream between tributaries, are undertaken.

In areas where snowmelt is an important component of stream flow, regular snow surveys are carried out. Most commonly, this involves manual coring of the snowpack along predetermined transects to determine both the snow depth and the water content of the snow. Depth gauges can be checked electronically from low-flying planes at some locations, and telemetered weighing devices are also used. In the most remote areas, where manual surveys are not possible, aerial photogrammetry and satellite imagery are of great utility in determining snowpack extent and water content. Such information is critical in formulating a basic understanding of snowmelt hydrology as well as for allocating stream flow to irrigators and determining how much flood storage is needed in downstream reservoirs.

SIGNIFICANCE

Water is a critical commodity in even the most primitive society. In warm weather, humans require a continual intake of water in order to maintain body functioning and, in very hot climates, cannot survive much longer than a day without water. In agricultural and industrial societies, immense quantities of water are needed for the production and processing of food and the manufacture of various goods, and delivery of it must be reliable. A single hectare of cotton grown in Arizona requires on the order of 15 million liters of water per year, while the production of a metric ton of steel requires roughly 250,000 liters. The production of a single Sunday newspaper typically involves the use of more than 1,000 liters of water. As a result of water-intensive agriculture and industry, the annual per capita use of water in the United States exceeds 2,300 cubic meters. In order to increase standards of living around the world, large quantities of water are needed for a variety of agricultural, industrial, and domestic purposes. In a world with more than 7 billion inhabitants, the acquisition of such volumes of water is increasingly difficult, and many experts believe that water supplies will be one of the primary limitations on future population growth. Water shortages have already constrained industrial and agricultural expansion in many areas.

Surface water is unevenly distributed across the globe. Some locations have such a problem with excess water that vast areas are not arable and remain largely uninhabitable. Such an area is western Siberia, where more than 2 million square kilometers of land is annually flooded for extended periods by the Ob and Yenisei Rivers. Far larger areas are without adequate water supplies, many of them in Africa and Asia, the regions of the world with the greatest population pressures. The largest proportion of liquid surface water is in freshwater lakes, but only ten lakes account for two-thirds of all such water. Thus a few areas (such as the Great Lakes area) are very well endowed with lake waters, while most parts of the world have very little. Most freshwater lakes are very small, contain small volumes of water, are very easily fouled, and are short-lived. Human-made reservoirs are no exception.

The second most voluminous source of surface water is saline lakes. The Caspian Sea alone contains three-fourths of such water supplies, with lesser bodies such as the Aral Sea, Great Salt Lake, and Dead Sea falling far behind. These bodies of water are not potable, or suitable for drinking, but they greatly influence local weather patterns and provide many important resources.

Although they contain far less water at any given time than do fresh or saline lakes, streams are the most important component of the surface water system because of the tremendous volumes of water that they convey throughout the year. Although not as limited in extent as lake water, stream flow exhibits great discrepancies in abundance across the globe. The equatorial zone is very well endowed with stream flow, as are the midlatitudes in general, but vast areas of the subtropical arid belts have very little. Some such areas are blessed with exotic streams, which flow from areas having higher, cooler, wetter climatic regimes.

Michael W. Mayfield

FURTHER READING

Brimblecombe, Peter, et al., eds. *Acid Rain: Deposition to Recovery.* Dordrecht: Springer, 2010. A compilation of articles from *Water Air, & Soil Pollution: Focus*, discussing acid rain from various perspectives. Discusses agriculture, human impact, ecological impact, wet versus dry deposition, soil chemistry, and surface water quality.

Chapra, Steven C. *Surface Water-Quality Modeling.* Waveland Press, 2008. Covers mixed systems, non-mixed systems, contaminants, and sampling. Discusses water chemistry, biology, and ecosystems, as well as mathematical modeling using computer applications. A good text for hydrologists and advanced undergraduate students.

Christopherson, Robert W., and Mary-Louise Byrne. *Geosystems: An Introduction to Physical Geography.* Toronto: Pearson Education Canada, 2006. A highly readable, introductory college-level text that builds on the concept of surface water as an integral and primary component of all geographic systems.

Dodds, Walter K., and Matt R. Wiles. *Freshwater Ecology: Concepts and Environmental Applications of Limnology.* 2d ed. Burlington, Mass.: Academic Press, 2010. Covers the physical and chemical properties of water, the hydrologic cycle, nutrient cycling in water, as well as biological aspects. Written by two of the leading scientists in freshwater ecology. An excellent resource for college students. Each chapter has a short summary of main topics.

Fairbridge, Rhodes W., and Reginald W. Herschy, eds. *The Encyclopedia of Hydrology and Water Resources.* Boston: Kluwer Academic, 1998. Serves as a great reference tool for anyone interested in the study of hydrology. Includes sections devoted to surface water and groundwater, as well as water resources. Suitable for college-level readers. Illustrations and maps.

Hunt, Constance Elizabeth. *Thirsty Planet: Strategies for Sustainable Water Management.* New York: St. Martin's Press, 2004. Discusses the hydrologic cycle, components of the cycle, human-induced changes to the cycle, and repercussions of the growing water crisis. Also covers floods, climate change, and freshwater ecosystem restoration. Provides a broad overview of hydrology topics of study.

Jones, J. A. A. *Global Hydrology: Processes, Resources, and Environmental Management.* Essex, England: Longman, 1997. Looks at the science of hydrology and the environmental issues and aspects relevant to it. Also focuses on water resource management and development. Suitable for the nonscientist. Illustrations, maps, index, and bibliographical references.

Knight, Gregory, Ivan Raev, and Marieta Staneva, eds. *Drought in Bulgaria.* Hants, England: Ashgate Publishing Limited, 2004. Presents the occurrence of drought in Bulgaria as a case study to provide information on prospective future global conditions. Discusses geological, economic, and ecological impacts of drought in Bulgaria from 1982 to

1994. Describes the effect of drought on managed forests, croplands, natural forests, and surface water. Concludes with policy and conservation recommendations for the future.

Kovar, Karel, et al., eds. *Hydrology, Water Resources, and Ecology in Headwaters.* Wallingford, England: International Association of Hydrological Sciences, 1998. A collection of essays that focuses on water supplies, resources, and water resource development. Pays a great deal of attention to water ecology as well as a nice overview of hydrology in general.

Leopold, Luna B. *Water: A Primer.* San Francisco: W. H. Freeman, 1974. Offers a general treatment of water and the hydrologic cycle written for the general public. Thorough but easy to follow, well illustrated, and contains numerous examples of the phenomena presented. Suitable for high school-level readers.

Manning, John C. *Applied Principles of Hydrology.* 3d ed. Upper Saddle River, N.J.: Prentice Hall, 1996. Designed to be used as the text for a general college course in hydrology. Less quantitatively oriented than most engineering hydrology texts, yet quite thorough. Suitable for high school students and above.

Mays, Larry W. *Ground and Surface Water Hydrology.* Hoboken, N.J.: John Wiley & Sons, 2011. A comprehensive college-level textbook that stresses the fundamental principles of hydrologic processes relevant to groundwater and surface water by making extensive use of Internet resources and discussing newer topics in hydrology such as remote sensing and GIS; covers all principal climate types.

Newson, Malcolm. *Land, Water and Development: Sustainable and Adaptive Management of Rivers.* 3d ed.

London: Routledge, 2008. Presents land-water interactions. Discusses recent research, study tools and methods, and technical issues, such as soil erosion and damming. Suited for undergraduate students and professionals. Covers concepts in managing land and water resources in the developed world.

Palmer, Tim. *Endangered Rivers and the Conservation Movement.* Lanham, Md.: Rowan and Littlefield Publishers, 2004. Provides a detailed account of the history and progress of the conservation movement working for the retention of free-flowing rivers throughout the United States. Offers a view of the social aspects of surface water hydrology.

Pielou, E. C. *Fresh Water.* Chicago: University of Chicago Press, 1998. Examines and evaluates all sources of freshwater, including glaciers, lakes, and rivers. Pays special attention to the measures being taken to preserve and protect freshwater resources.

Scott, Ralph C. *Physical Geography.* New York: John Wiley & Sons, 1988. A very thorough, well-illustrated text in general physical geography. The chapters on streams and stream-flow generation are especially well written, and the full-color illustrations are very helpful. Suitable for high school students and above.

See also: Aquifers; Artificial Recharge; Dams and Flood Control; Floods; Freshwater and Groundwater Contamination Around the World; Geochemical Cycles; Groundwater Movement; Groundwater Pollution and Remediation; Hydrologic Cycle; Precipitation; Rainforests and the Atmosphere; Salinity and Desalination; Saltwater Intrusion; Seawater Composition; Waterfalls; Water Quality; Watersheds; Water Table; Water Wells

T

TORNADOES

Tornadoes are small, violent, rotating storms that may produce devastating wind velocities of more than 400 kilometers per hour. The force of the cyclonic wind in a strong tornado can demolish well-built structures, and people in a tornado's path are at severe risk of physical harm and death.

PRINCIPAL TERMS

- **cold front:** the transition zone or zone of contact between two air masses when cold air moves into a region occupied by warmer air
- **Coriolis effect:** a phenomenon in which, because of the planet's rotation, an apparent force is exerted on objects in motion, causing them to deflect from their intended path to the right in the Northern Hemisphere or to the left in the Southern Hemisphere
- **cumulonimbus cloud:** also called "thunderstorm cloud"; a very dense, tall, billowing cloud form that develops an anvil-shaped head due to high-altitude wind shear, and normally accompanied by lightning and heavy precipitation
- **dust devil:** a rotating column of air rising above a hot ground surface, made visible by the dust it contains; it is much smaller than a tornado, having winds of less than 60 kilometers per hour, and causing little or no damage
- **hurricane:** a huge, tropical low-pressure storm system with sustained winds in excess of 118 kilometers per hour, formed over warm ocean surface water and powered by thermodynamic heat transfer from the water
- **squall line:** any line of vigorous thunderstorms created by a cold downdraft that spreads out ahead of a fast-moving cold front
- **unstable air:** a condition that occurs when the air above rising air is unusually cool so that the rising air becomes relatively warmer and accelerates upward
- **vortex:** the central, low-pressure axis of any rotating fluid, as occurs in whirlpools and tornadoes
- **waterspout:** a tornado that exists over water; less violent and smaller waterspouts form in fair weather just as dust devils do over dry land

TORNADO FORMATION AND CLASSIFICATION

Tornadoes are relatively small, localized low-pressure areas associated with powerful thunderstorms under cumulonimbus clouds. For its size, the tornado is the most violent of the whirlwinds. The "typical" tornado is 250 meters in diameter, with whirling winds of about 240 kilometers per hour. The twisting funnel cloud typically travels at about 65 kilometers per hour over the surface and lasts ten minutes, moving, in North America, along a northeasterly track. Very large, devastating tornadoes are relatively rare but have almost unbelievable destructive power. The Tri-State Tornado of March 18, 1925, touched down near Ellington, Missouri, at 1:00 P.M. and ripped a trail of havoc for 352 kilometers across southern Illinois, finally breaking up at 4:30 P.M. near Princeton, Indiana. The storm killed 695 people and injured 2,027. Damage, calculated in 1970 dollars, was $43 million. Compared with other tornadoes, it raced along the ground, averaging well over 100 kilometers per hour.

Tornadoes are most consistently associated with fast-moving cold fronts that sweep across the midsection of the United States, drawing warm, moist, tropical air from the Gulf of Mexico. The cold front is usually associated with a strong low-pressure storm system that rotates counterclockwise as it swirls across land in the prevailing westerly wind pattern. The counterclockwise rotation of the low-pressure system brings cold air in behind, which wedges underneath the warm Gulf air that is drawn in ahead of the storm center. When heavy, cold air wedges under the less dense warm, tropical air, the warm air is forced to rise. If the air is unstable, the cloud will accelerate upward, making a towering thundercloud. The upward surge stops only when the cloud has penetrated the excessively cold upper air. If the cloud tops can penetrate the tropopause at an altitude above 11 kilometers, severe storms, including supercells that spawn tornadoes, are possible. These high cloud tops indicate unstable air at abnormal heights, and occasionally the unstable conditions can drive storm cloud tops to 20 kilometers or higher. A high-altitude zone of strong wind from the west (the "jet stream") tends to increase the chance for violence when associated with a storm system.

Tornadoes are classified by their maximum wind velocity, which occurs on the skin of the spinning funnel. T. T. Fujita, of the University of Chicago, developed a scale from 1 to 5, or weakest to strongest. Tornadoes consisting of winds below 116 kilometers per hour are ranked "F0" (the F standing for Fujita) and induce slight damage (broken street signs and branches); F1 tornadoes have winds of 116 to 180 kilometers per hour and can cause trees to snap and windows to break; F2 tornadoes have winds of 181 to 253 kilometers per hour and cause considerable damage, with sufficient power to uproot trees; F3 tornadoes have winds of 254 to 332 kilometers per hour and cause severe damage, powerful enough to flip over cars or knock down brick walls; F4 tornadoes, with winds of 333 to 419 kilometers per hour, are devastating, destroying frame houses; and finally, the strongest of tornadoes, with wind velocities above 419 kilometers per hour, are capable of destroying steel-reinforced buildings and are designated F5. More than one-half of all tornadoes reported are in the F0 to F1 range of intensity; however, nearly 70 percent of all fatalities are caused by tornadoes of F4 to F5 intensity. Only 2 percent of tornadoes are in the upper range. In the years from 1960 to 1985, the average number of tornado deaths in the United States was 88 per year.

Multiple tornadoes can occur when the weather conditions are ideal for severe weather. The worst twenty-four hours on record was April 3 to April 4, 1974, when a remarkable 148 tornadoes struck eleven states, centered on Kentucky. Canada also reported an abnormally high number of tornadoes during that episode. The swarm of funnels claimed 300 lives and left 5,500 injured.

OCCURRENCE AND DAMAGE

Tornadoes have been reported in each of the fifty states, but they are rare in Alaska and the mountainous portions of the western United States. From 1953 to 1976, only one tornado was reported in Alaska, and only fourteen from the whole state of Nevada. No doubt more twisters may have occurred in these sparsely inhabited states, but conditions generally are not favorable for the formation of tornadoes in these areas. Central Oklahoma has the highest incidence of tornadoes, with more than nine twisters annually for every 26,000 square kilometers. For the whole state, the average is about fifty per year. The area from Fort Worth, Texas, through northwestern Nebraska has been dubbed Tornado Alley because the storms develop there so consistently. The four-state zone has more than five tornadoes per year for each 26,000 square kilometers. Other particularly vulnerable areas include the Texas Panhandle near Lubbock, northeast Colorado, parts of Iowa, most of Illinois and Indiana, most of the Florida peninsula, parts of Georgia, and most of southern Alabama. The United States accounts for 75 percent of all tornadoes globally.

Southwest of Howard, South Dakota, on August 28, 1884, a tornado stirs the ground in this oldest known photograph of a tornado. (National Oceanic and Atmospheric Administration)"

Conditions that favor the formation of tornadoes include broad flatlands with no obstructions to the flow of surface wind; an elevation near sea level to allow the full height of the atmosphere for the development of towering clouds; a position on a large continent where very cold air from the north can be swept into a low-pressure storm system that has access to hot, humid tropical air to the south; a southward bulge of strong jet stream currents aloft; and springtime weather patterns that provide intense low-pressure systems that can penetrate rather close to the Gulf of Mexico coast of the United States. March through July is the peak season, with May the most tornado-prone month. Winter tornadoes are mostly confined to the Gulf of Mexico coast, and the frequency moves north and swings toward Kansas as springtime progresses. By July and August, the area of tornado danger spreads through the northeastern states and into southern Canada. Oklahoma is in or near the worst areas most of the year. Most of the storms occur during the late afternoon, at the climax of daily heating, although a really violent frontal advance occasionally will generate night and early-morning tornadoes.

Some of the damage caused by tornadoes results from the rapid passage of low pressure. Most houses are built to withstand downward pressure from much water, snow, or wind against the structure, especially weight on the roof. When a tornado passes over a house, however, the low pressure above, countered with high pressure inside that cannot leak out quickly enough plus wind pressure under the eaves, causes the house to appear to "explode" from within. A rapid pressure drop of 10 percent would give the pressure inside a house a lifting force of nearly 1 metric ton per square meter. The roof is lifted slightly off the supporting walls, which, in turn, fall outward. The roof then drops back onto the interior of the house or blows away.

Whirlwinds can develop multiple vortices. Around the core of the funnel cloud, it is possible for high-speed "suction spots" to develop that might have wind velocities 100 kilometers per hour faster than the average velocity of the whirling funnel. Tornado paths observed in open ground often reveal a swirling pattern of streaks or scratches in the soil. On a larger scale, these suction traces match the paths of greatest destruction along the tornado's path. Even in the much smaller dust devils, multiple vortices have been observed. Two or more small dust columns may rotate around the perimeter of the central column of a dust devil. Hurricane Celia, which struck near Corpus Christi, Texas, in 1971, approached landfall with only 145-kilometer-per-hour winds, but the core (eye) of the storm broke into multiple vortices at Corpus Christi, and the damage was more typical of winds of 250 kilometers per hour. The hurricane was expected to cause minor damage, but the center behaved more like a cluster of F2-scale tornadoes and caused extensive damage, even to well-built structures.

STUDY OF TORNADOES

Although meteorologists are quite successful at predicting the general region where tornadoes are likely to occur, they have not been so successful at measuring the wind velocities and air pressure in tornadoes. The storms are so small and so violent that it is nearly impossible to get instruments into their direct path and have the instruments able to survive the passage of the funnel. The few weather stations that have been hit by tornadoes were destroyed or lost power to record the data. Barographs have recorded a drop in pressure of about 1 centimeter of mercury in about thirty seconds during the passage of tornadic storms.

Many of the best measurements of tornadoes are from indirect methods, such as calculating the wind velocity required to cause the kinds of destruction observed. Close estimations of wind velocity can be calculated from steel towers that have been toppled or from railroad boxcars that have been tipped over. Reinforced concrete grain silos have been ripped apart, and walls have collapsed in enough storms to get a large collection of approximate values. Surprisingly, a fairly reliable set of data involves the penetration of straw or splinters into wood surfaces. These projectiles are so small that they are quickly accelerated up to the velocity of the wind, and they are so common that most storms will hurl vast numbers of them at a variety of fixed targets. Experiments reported in 1976 provide many examples of the penetration of straw and toothpicks into all varieties of wood, both wet and dry. The data indicate that a velocity of 30 meters per second (108 kilometers per hour) is sufficient to drive a toothpick into soft pine. Broom straws need about twice as much velocity as do toothpicks to penetrate wood.

Meteorologists continue to improve their ability to forecast, locate, and track tornadoes. Space satellites, a worldwide network of manned weather stations, and sophisticated computer systems enable meteorologists to "see" weather as it develops. Balloons carry instrument packages aloft twice a day from about 90 of the 250 weather stations of the continental United States. The balloons give wind, humidity, temperature, and pressure data for all of the lower atmosphere where storms develop. Forecasters can determine which levels of the atmosphere are unstable and where the moist air is likely to be forced aloft with conditions that can generate violent storms. When dangerous storms begin to develop, Doppler radar is available in most parts of the nation. Doppler radar detects the wind component parallel to the radar beam, then examines the pattern of the wind field to find locations of potential tornadoes. The radar helps to spot hail formation while other instruments monitor the location and frequency of lightning. All these clues to violent storms focus attention on the parts of storms that might spawn tornadoes. Critical information can be relayed to news services, which, in turn, can warn citizens who are in danger.

SIGNIFICANCE

There is no end to the documented stories of strange phenomena caused by tornadoes. Many instances are recorded where heavy boards have punched through steel plate or metal pipes. Automobiles have been pounded and rolled into battered wads of twisted steel by the storms, and some vehicles have been thrown into upper stories of buildings. Wire fences have been ripped up and wound into prickly balls up to 16 meters in diameter. Strange objects, such as animals, trash barrels, photographs, or blankets, may be picked up in one area by a tornado and deposited many kilometers away. A survivor of a tornado near Scottsbluff, Nebraska, reported seeing a head-sized boulder whirling around his car after the funnel engulfed the auto and its two occupants. After witnessing the flying boulder, the man was hurled from his car and nearly killed, regaining consciousness in a hospital. His passenger, also ejected from the car, died. The auto was destroyed and deposited in a nearby field.

The National Weather Service usually can predict severe weather regions several hours in advance, but the exact location of a tornado must wait for a visual sighting or the occurrence of a tornado signature on Doppler radar. When threatening storms develop, it is wise to monitor local weather broadcasts and to keep a lookout for the characteristic funnel cloud. Often the twister is causing major damage long before the dust swirl on the ground ever connects with the descending visible funnel. Usually a tornado will travel toward the northeast along the ground at about 60 kilometers per hour. The storms move erratically but do not alter course very much, and if the funnel appears to be heading toward the observer, it might be possible to leave the area of greatest danger by moving away in a direction perpendicular to the path of the storm. Attempting to escape a tornado, however, is often more dangerous than taking some protective measures, because drivers trying to flee tornadoes in cars are often involved in serious accidents resulting from panic. Conditions of traffic, congestion, and available time should be considered before attempting to run from a twister. Those in buildings should try to get to lower floors or in narrow, confined corridors. Above all, windows should be avoided: Many serious injuries during tornadoes result from flying pieces of glass. Taking shelter under heavy tables or inside a sturdy tub can prevent some injury from falling beams or masonry. Tornadoes tend to stay on or even above the ground surface, so a depression, pit, culvert, gutter, or ditch may provide safety. A deep storm cellar with a latched door provides excellent protection. A mobile home is perhaps the worst place to seek shelter from a tornado, due to their light and consequently weak construction. Automobiles also are not safe; cars are easily overturned and are often beaten into shapeless masses by tornadoes. Flying debris causes most of the injuries in tornadoes, and shelter should include protection from tumbling containers, planks, sections of fence, branches, splinters of glass, and other items that could be ripped loose by the storm.

Dell R. Foutz

FURTHER READING

Ahrens, C. Donald. *Essentials of Meteorology: An Invitation to the Atmosphere.* Belmont, Calif.: Brooks/Cole Cengage Learning, 2012. Discusses various topics in weather and the atmosphere. Chapters cover topics such as tornadoes and thunderstorms, acid deposition and other air pollution topics, humidity and cloud formation, and temperature.

_____. *Meteorology Today: An Introduction to Weather, Climate and the Environment*. 8th ed. Belmont, Calif.: Thomson Brooks-Cole, 2007. One of the most widely used and authoritative introductory textbooks for the study of meteorology and climatology. Explains complex concepts in a clear, precise manner, supported by numerous images and diagrams. Includes extensive discussion of tornadoes and tornado science.

Bluestein, Howard B. *Tornado Alley: Monster Storms of the Great Plains*. New York: Oxford University Press, 1999. An excellent compilation of color photographs that capture the power of storms and tornadoes in the American Midwest. Describes the hazards involved with these storms, as well as the factors that cause them.

Brooks, H. E., C. A. Doswell III, and M. P. Kay. "Climatological Estimates of Local Daily Tornado Probability for the United States." *Weather Forecasting* 18 (2003): 626-640. Discusses patterns of tornado events across time and space. Discusses new data analysis techniques, along with conclusions drawn from the resulting maps. Some knowledge of map rendering is helpful.

Grazulis, Thomas P. *The Tornado: Nature's Ultimate Windstorm*. Norman: University of Oklahoma Press, 2003. Elucidates the formation and life cycle of tornadoes, their structure and wind speeds, and examines related areas such as forecasting, risks and safety measures, and many common myths about tornadoes. Includes accounts of some of the deadliest tornadoes in history.

Kennedy, A., J. M. Straka, and E. N. Rasmussen. "A Statistical Study of the Association of DRCs with Supercells and Tornadoes." *Weather Forecasting* 22 (2007): 1191-1199. Discusses the descending reflectivity core of a supercell. Evaluates the use of DRCs in determining tornado-genesis and now-casting of tornadoes.

Kukushkin, A. B., and V. A. Rantsev-Kartinov. "Evidence for Skeletal Structures in Tornado and the Probable Role of Nanodusty Plasma in Severe Weather Phenomena." *31st EPS Conference on Plasma Physics: Europhysics Conference Abstracts* 28G: O5.08. Discusses new research on the formation of tornadoes. Uses information from tornadoes over the past century combined with new analyses to potentially develop techniques of early tornado diagnostics.

Lutgens, Frederick K., and Edward J. Tarbuck. *The Atmosphere: An Introduction to Meteorology*. 11th ed. Upper Saddle River, N.J.: Prentice Hall, 2010. A college textbook written by the authors of other introductory Earth science books that are very understandable for beginners. A profusely illustrated book that has twelve pages devoted to tornadoes. Contains a glossary and seven separate appendices to explain everything from metric conversions to the reading of daily weather charts.

MacGorman, Donald R., and W. David Rust. *The Electrical Nature of Storms*. New York: Oxford University Press, 1998. Describes the atmospheric and electrical conditions that create thunderstorms, hailstorms, lightning, tornadoes, and hurricanes. Discusses the ways in which violent weather affects the environment and humans.

Prothero, Donald R. *Catastrophes!: Earthquakes, Tsunamis, Tornadoes, and Other Earth-Shattering Disasters*. Baltimore: Johns Hopkins University Press, 2011. Provides a detailed and clear explanation of the many natural and anthropogenic disasters facing our planet. Each chapter is devoted to a different catastrophe, including earthquakes, volcanoes, hurricanes, ice ages, and current climate changes.

Rosenfeld, Jeffrey O. *Eye of the Storm: Inside the World's Deadliest Hurricanes, Tornadoes, and Blizzards*. Cambridge, Mass.: Basic Books, 2003. A must-read for students and meteorologists filled with accounts of storms and their powers of destruction. Focuses on the aftermath of deadly storms but also does a nice job explaining the conditions that create weather systems of such power. Well-illustrated.

Samaras, Tim, Stefan Bechtel, and Greg Forbes. *Tornado Hunter: Getting Inside the Most Violent Storms on Earth*. Washington, D.C.: National Geographic Society, 2009. A close-up account of the drive to understand tornadoes, and some of the people who risk the fury of the storm to seek out its secrets.

Schneider, Bonnie. *Extreme Weather: A Guide to Surviving Flash Floods, Tornadoes, Hurricanes, Heat Waves, Snowstorms, Tsunamis and Other Natural Disasters*. Palgrave Macmillan, 2012. Presents vivid explanations of how, when, and why major natural disasters occur. Discusses floods, hurricanes, thunderstorms, mudslides, wildfires, tsunamis, and earthquakes. Provides background information on weather patterns and natural disasters, and a guide of how to prepare for and what to do during an extreme weather event.

See also: Air Pollution; Atmosphere's Evolution; Atmosphere's Global Circulation; Atmosphere's Structure and Thermodynamics; Atmospheric and Oceanic Oscillations; Atmospheric Properties; Auroras; Barometric Pressure; Climate; Clouds; Cyclones and Anticyclones; Drought; Greenhouse Effect; Hurricanes; Lightning and Thunder; Monsoons; Ozone Depletion and Ozone Holes; Remote Sensing of the Atmosphere; Satellite Meteorology; Seasons; Severe Storms; Van Allen Radiation Belts; Volcanoes: Climatic Effects; Weather Forecasting; Weather Forecasting: Numerical Weather Prediction; Weather Modification; Wind

TROPICAL WEATHER

The tropical zone is the area surrounding the equator that is exposed to direct solar rays during part of the year. Tropical areas receive higher annual precipitation and experience low variation in temperature between seasons. Localized low-pressure systems in the ocean can develop into weather disturbances when the temperature of the ocean increases. As temperature and pressure continue to increase, weather disturbances develop into tropical depressions and tropical storms.

PRINCIPAL TERMS

- **circulation cell:** zones of concentrated air circulation caused by the rotation of the earth and the cyclic distribution of heat through the atmosphere
- **cold front:** area in which a dominant stream of colder air pushes under a pocket of warmer air, causing the warm air to rise and leading to precipitation at the leading edge of the front
- **easterly waves:** localized zones of low pressure oriented parallel to the earth's rotational axis and moving from east to west across the ocean; they form an important generative component of tropical weather patterns
- **Intertropical Convergence Zone:** low-pressure area created by the interaction of the tropical circulation cells on either side of the equator and by differential heating of the equatorial atmosphere
- **monsoon:** period of increased precipitation caused by the differential distribution of heat and pressure between the lithosphere and hydrosphere
- **storm surge:** rising water levels beneath and surrounding the warm core of a tropical storm system related to the effects of low- and high-pressure interactions within the storm
- **tropical cyclone:** tropical storm marked by clear rotation around a central, warm column of air and wind speeds above 119 kilometers (74 miles) per hour
- **tropical zone:** area between the Tropic of Cancer and the Tropic of Capricorn that falls directly under the sun during a part of the year
- **troposphere:** lowest level of Earth's atmosphere lying between 0 and 10 km (0 and 6 mi) above sea level within which weather patterns develop
- **warm front:** area in which a dominant warm current of air rises over a pocket of cold air to cause condensation and precipitation at the trailing edge of the front

ORIGIN OF TROPICAL WEATHER

The tropical zone is the portion of the earth that surrounds the earth's equator. The zone ranges from approximately 23.5 degrees north (the Tropic of Cancer) to 23.5 degrees south (the Tropic of Capricorn).

Because of the relationship between the rotation of the earth and its orbit around the sun, the portion of the earth that lies directly under the sun varies between the Tropics of Cancer and Capricorn during the year. The tropical zone can be described as the portion of the earth that lies directly under the sun for some portion of the year.

In general, the tropics receive high annual precipitation and relatively stable temperatures that vary little between seasons. Rather than having warm and cold seasons, tropical areas have wet and dry seasons because precipitation in the tropics varies more markedly throughout the year than does temperature.

Weather patterns within the tropics are caused by the differential distribution of solar energy. Solar radiation strikes the earth along the tropical zone, exciting the atoms of atmospheric gases, which causes them to vibrate and collide with one another. In the lowest level of the atmosphere, called the troposphere, excited pockets of atmospheric gases rise because they lose density and pressure as they spread. The gases continue to rise until they reach the limit of the troposphere, the tropopause, where, because the atmosphere is highly stratified, warm air is forced toward the poles.

As warm air moves toward the Tropics of Capricorn and Cancer it gradually cools and condenses and falls to the surface. By approximately 30 degrees north and south, tropical air currents moving close to the surface converge with cooler air moving toward the equator from the poles. Some of the tropical air is pushed back toward the equator, thus constituting a circulation cell, which is a pattern of rising and falling air currents that cycles air between the surface and the tropopause.

Two tropical or Hadley cells move air from the equator to about 30 degrees north and south and back. A portion of the tropical air from the Hadley cells continues moving toward the poles, cycling through two additional circulation cells and thereby distributing the solar energy contained within tropical air over the surface of the earth.

LOW-PRESSURE SYSTEMS AND STORM GENERATION

Directly over the equator, where the northern and southern tropical cells meet, is the area called the Intertropical Convergence Zone (ITCZ). This zone is known colloquially as the doldrums.

The ITCZ does not remain directly over the equator because the position of the sun relative to the earth changes during Earth's orbit. The ITCZ therefore migrates with the seasons, moving through an area that takes the zone between 5 and 10 degrees north or south of the equator. The ITCZ migrates north in the summer months and south in the winter months, corresponding to temperature variations, increases in precipitation, and increased storm activity.

The ITCZ receives the highest level of solar heating during the year and therefore develops into a low-pressure area as the air within the ITCZ loses density in response to solar excitation. Low-pressure areas are characterized by cloud cover and strong winds. Because the earth rotates counterclockwise, the winds spreading from the ITCZ are deflected relative to the poles; this a phenomenon known as the Coriolis effect, which causes the ITCZ winds to move to the northeast and southeast from the equator. These winds, called the trade winds, carry air currents toward the ends of the tropical zone, where they gradually cool, thereby increasing in both density and pressure. This creates two high-pressure areas, called the subtropical high-pressure zones, which shift (along with the migration of the ITCZ) between 10 and 30 degrees north and south of the equator.

Weather fronts develop at the point where low- and high-pressure systems meet. A cold front is an area in which a dominant stream of cold air pushes under a bed of warmer air at its leading edge. This causes warm air to rise and condense rapidly; as the water vapor condenses, precipitation develops along the leading edge of the cold front.

A warm front is an area in which dominant streams of warm air encounter pockets of cold air. The warm air rises over the cold air, thereby leading to the condensation of water vapor and precipitation following in the wake of the front. In general, rising air produces rainfall while falling air creates dry conditions.

TROPICAL MONSOONS

Monsoons are seasonal variations in precipitation that accompany the movement of the ITCZ. Monsoons result from the differential heating of the ocean and nearby landmasses and from changes in the direction of wind patterns. Monsoon seasons are the periods of highest annual precipitation during the year. Monsoons affect portions of Africa, Asia, North America, and South America.

Through most of the year, wind currents typically move from the continents to the ocean. In the summer months, the solid materials of the continental crust heat faster and reach higher average temperatures than the liquid water of the ocean, which disseminates and thereby regulates heat more efficiently. As this occurs, a low-pressure area develops over the land as hot air disperses into the atmosphere. This causes a reversal in the direction of prevailing winds, as cooler air pockets over the ocean are drawn over the land. The mixture of warm and cool air rises and leads to condensation and precipitation moving inward over the continent. This continues until heat levels reach equilibrium between the two areas and the monsoons begin to abate.

Monsoons also occur in the winter because the land loses heat more rapidly than does the water, thereby producing a high-pressure system over the land. When this reaches a certain level, warmer air pockets over the ocean are drawn over the land and begin to rise, again blending with cooler air to produce precipitation. These two systems are responsible for the seasonal cycle of monsoons alternating with dry seasons in the tropics.

TROPICAL STORMS

Tropical storms develop within the trade winds out of localized disturbances called easterly waves, which are troughs of low pressure moving from east to west across the ocean. Easterly waves develop when a portion of the ocean is heated such that water vapor begins to rise from the surface through evaporation, thereby reducing pressure along a narrow band. As this zone of low pressure moves, the area behind it forms into a zone of divergence, where the winds flow out of the system.

To the front of the wave, a zone of convergence forms, where high- and low-pressure winds meet and spiral upward. This spiraling, rising column of current, which carries significant moisture from evaporated water vapor, is the origin of tropical storms.

The defining characteristic of a tropical storm is the column of warmer air at the center of the storm known as the core, which creates the differential pressure and density that drive the continued movement of the system. For a tropical storm to develop, the water underlying the storm system must be 26 degrees Celsius (79 degrees Fahrenheit) or warmer, with high local humidity levels. When these factors merge with local weather disturbances, a tropical storm can develop.

PHASES OF TROPICAL STORMS

Tropical storms begin as smaller, localized tropical disturbances. In most cases, tropical disturbances result in isolated thunderstorms that dissipate as the warm currents at the core are drawn into the upper troposphere. If the localized pressure difference grows, the storm becomes a tropical depression, which has a more defined core and wind speeds between 37 and 63 kilometers (23 and 39 miles) per hour. At this point, the tropical storm is generally given an identification number by meteorological organizations and is tracked for further developments.

When wind speeds increase to between 64 and 118 km (40 to 73 mi) per hour, the storm is reclassified as a tropical storm or tropical cyclone. At this point, the storm system is designated with a unique name and may pose a serious threat to coastal settlements. Cyclones with wind speeds exceeding 119 km (74 mi) per hour are called mature tropical cyclones and are characterized by a well-defined core, which is sometimes called the eye of the storm. Mature tropical cyclones that develop in the eastern part of the Pacific basin or in the Atlantic basin are called hurricanes, while those that develop in the western portion of the Pacific basin are called typhoons.

Once a cyclone forms, it will move in response to changes in local wind speed and pressure. The path of a cyclone is highly unpredictable, which increases the danger they pose to terrestrial ecosystems and human settlements. Cyclones can change speed and direction rapidly and without significant warning, making it difficult to predict the path that the cyclone

will take. In general, most of the storms that originate above the equator tend to move northwest while those below the equator move southwest.

Tropical storms follow seasonal patterns, which are related to the north and south variation of the ITCZ. The peak for cyclones in the Southern Hemisphere falls between January and March, while the peak for cyclones in the Northern Hemisphere falls between June and November. The northwest Pacific basin is the most active area for tropical cyclones, with storms forming during any month of the year. Most cyclones are active for less than one week, though particularly strong storms have lasted for nearly one month before dissipating. Tropical storms dissipate when the latent heat energy in the ocean and atmosphere is reduced to such level that the storm can no longer sustain its motion.

The National Weather Service in the United States names each tropical storm using a system of alternating male and female names chosen to reflect the alphabetical position of the storm for that year. The first named storm in any year will therefore be given a name beginning with the letter *A*. If the last storm of the preceding year was given a male name, then the new storm will be given a female name and vice versa. The list of potential names is recycled through a six-year period. When a hurricane causes significant damage to human settlements, the name of the hurricane may be retired from the list of potential storm names. Hurricane Allison (2001) and Hurricane Agnes (1972) are two hurricanes whose names have been retired from usage because of the level of damage wrought by those storms.

In some hurricanes wind speeds can exceed 180 km (112 mi) per hour, which is sufficient to destroy buildings and fell trees. When a cyclone is active, water levels in the area directly beneath and around the eye of the storm rise in response to the low pressure of the core, creating what is called a storm surge. Many hurricane- or typhoon-related deaths result from flood waters that accompany the storm surge. Hurricane Katrina, which hit the Atlantic and Gulf coasts of the United States in 2005, caused more than $80 billion in damage and led to nearly two thousand deaths.

In addition, approximately 25 percent of hurricanes that impact the continental surface have associated tornadoes, which are vortexes of wind currents that can move over dry land. Associated tornadoes can spread wind damage for miles surrounding the impact zone.

Micah L. Issitt

FURTHER READING

Ahrens, C. Donald. *Essentials of Meteorology: An Invitation to the Atmosphere.* 6th ed. Belmont, Calif.: Brooks/Cole, 2011. Covers the major principles in meteorological science, including methods used to study and predict changes in weather patterns. Discusses a variety of factors influencing the development of tropical weather patterns.

Anthes, Richard A. *Meteorology.* 7th ed. Upper Saddle River, N.J.: Prentice Hall, 1997. Introductory text to meteorological research and methods written for students with basic understanding of mathematics and physics. Contains a discussion of tropical weather patterns and how they develop.

Barry, Roger C., and Richard J. Chorley. *Atmosphere, Weather, and Climate.* 8th ed. New York: Routledge, 2003. Introductory text covering weather patterns and climate change. Contains descriptions of many of the phenomena that lead to tropical weather patterns.

Burroughs, William James. *Climate Change: A Multidisciplinary Approach.* 2d ed. New York: Cambridge University Press, 2007. College-level text covering climate change phenomenon and research methodology. Chapter 10 contains a discussion of tropical weather patterns and tropical storms.

Kshudiram, Saha. *Tropical Circulation Systems and Monsoons.* New York: Springer, 2010. Detailed text covering the development of weather systems in tropical environments, including a complex discussion of the physics of tropical storms, monsoons and other tropical weather phenomenon.

Ruddiman, William F. *Earth's Climate: Past and Future.* New York: W. H. Freeman, 2001. Introduction to climate research and meteorological science written for the general audience. Includes a discussion of tropical weather systems and their social and economic effects.

See also: Atlantic Ocean; Atmospheric and Oceanic Oscillations; Atmospheric Properties; Barometric Pressure; Beaches and Coastal Processes; Climate; Clouds; Cyclones and Anticyclones; Earth-Sun Relations; El Niño/Southern Oscillations (ENSO); Floods; Global Energy Transfer; Global Warming; Gulf of Mexico; Gulf Stream; Hurricane Katrina; Hurricanes; Hydrologic Cycle; Impacts, Adaptation, and Vulnerability; Indian Ocean; IPCC; Lightning and Thunder; Long-Term Weather Patterns; Monsoons; Ocean-Atmosphere Interactions; Pacific Ocean; Precipitation; Rainforests and the Atmosphere; Remote Sensing of the Oceans; Satellite Meteorology; Seasons; Severe Storms; Surface Ocean Currents; Tornadoes; Weather Forecasting; Weather Forecasting: Numerical Weather Prediction; Weather Modification; Wind

TSUNAMIS

A tsunami is a series of potentially catastrophic ocean waves most commonly caused by movement of the sea floor associated with large earthquakes. Once known as tidal waves, tsunamis have resulted in thousands of deaths, primarily around the Pacific Ocean.

PRINCIPAL TERMS

- **bore:** an unusually large advancing wave of water leading a sudden rise in water level that may be produced by the rising tide, a tsunami, or a seiche in an estuarine stream
- **seiche:** an oscillation in a partially enclosed body of water, such as a bay or estuary
- **tsunami warning:** the second phase of a tsunami alert; it is issued after the generation of a tsunami has been confirmed
- **tsunami watch:** the first phase of a tsunami alert; it is issued after a large earthquake has occurred on the sea floor

CAUSES OF TSUNAMIS

Giant ocean waves that were once, incorrectly, called tidal waves or seismic sea waves have resulted in thousands of deaths in countries around the Pacific Ocean. These destructive waves are now generally known as tsunamis. In the simplest terms, a tsunami is a series of waves usually caused by violent movement of the sea floor.

The movement at the sea floor that causes the tsunami can be produced by three different types of violent geologic or seismic activity. By far the most common and, therefore, the most important of these is submarine faulting, which occurs when a section of the ocean floor is thrust upward or suddenly drops at a subduction zone fault. Such fault movements are accompanied by earthquakes. Probably the second most common cause of tsunamis is sudden landslide by which a mass of rock and earth falls suddenly into a body of water. A tsunami may be generated by a landslide starting above sea level and then plunging into the sea, or by a submarine landslide. The highest tsunami waves ever officially reported were produced by a landslide at Lituya Bay, a confined fjord in Alaska, on July 9, 1958. A massive rock slide at the head of the bay produced a tsunami wave that attained a high-water mark more than 500 meters above the shoreline.

The third major cause of tsunamis is nearshore or submarine volcanic activity. In most cases, the flank of a volcano is suddenly uplifted or depressed, producing a tsunami in much the same way as faulting activity does. However, tsunamis have also been produced by the actual explosion of submarine or shoreline volcanoes. In 1883, the violent explosion of the famous island volcano Krakatau sent tsunami waves as high as 40 meters crashing ashore in Java and Sumatra, killing more than 36,000 people.

Although tsunamis caused by landslides or volcanic activity may become very large near their sources and may cause great damage there, they have relatively little energy. They decrease rapidly in size in the deep waters of the open ocean, becoming small or even unnoticeable at any great distance. As they approach land and enter shallower waters again, their size increases according to the kinetic energy that they have retained. The giant tsunami waves that cross entire oceans are almost all caused by submarine faulting associated with large subduction earthquakes. Most tsunamis occur in the Pacific Ocean because the Pacific Ocean basin is surrounded by a zone of very tectonically active features, such as deep ocean subduction trenches, explosive volcanic islands, and dynamic mountain ranges.

CHARACTERISTICS OF TSUNAMIS

Tsunami waves are very different from ordinary ocean waves, most of which are caused by the wind blowing over the water. Wind-generated waves rarely have a wavelength (distance from crest to crest) greater than 300 meters. Tsunami waves may have a wavelength of as much as 160 kilometers. Wind-generated ocean surface waves never travel at more than about 100 kilometers per hour and are usually much slower. In the deep water of an ocean basin, tsunami waves may travel at 800 kilometers per hour, but are often only 50 centimeters high, thus passing unnoticed by ships at sea.

A tsunami is not a single giant wave but rather consists of a series of several waves, perhaps ten or more, that form what is called a tsunami wave train. These individual waves follow one behind the other, between five and ninety minutes apart. When tsunami waves move into shallower water and approach shore, they start to change. The shape of the near-shore sea floor has an effect on how tsunami waves behave. The waves tend to be smaller near small, isolated islands, where the bottom drops away quickly into deep water. Near large islands, such as the main Hawaiian Islands, the waves are strongly influenced by the bottom; they bend around the land and may be reflected from the shoreline. The reflected waves may augment other waves and create extremely large wave heights in unexpected places. As video records of the 2011 tsunami that struck Japan indicate, the tsunami wave does not appear like a typical wind-driven wave breaking on the shore, but more like an abrupt, massive increase in sea level as the water rushes inland.

Though it is not yet possible to accurately predict the production, size, or effects of tsunami waves as they arrive in coastal areas, prediction of the velocity of tsunamis is made possible by their great wavelength. To understand how the arrival time of a tsunami is determined, it is necessary to look at ocean waves in general. Oceanographers divide waves into various categories based on the relationship between wavelength and the depth of water through which they are passing. When the water depth is less than one-twentieth of the wavelength, the waves are known as shallow-water waves, and their speed is determined solely by the depth of water. Knowing the water depth, one can calculate the velocity of any shallow-water wave. Tsunami waves may have a wavelength of more than 160 kilometers, and if the water depth is less than one-twentieth of the 160-kilometer wavelength, or 8 kilometers, then the tsunami waves would be shallow-water waves. Most of the deep Pacific Ocean basin is less than 5 kilometers deep, so most tsunamis there are shallow-water waves. To determine the speed of such tsunamis, all that is necessary to know is the depth of the water through which they pass. In most of the deep Pacific Ocean, this speed works out to be around 725 kilometers per hour, but it will vary depending on the exact water depth along the path of the tsunami.

EFFECTS OF TSUNAMIS

As the waves approach the shore, frictional effects of contact with the sea floor begin to affect the tsunami waves, and they travel progressively more slowly, with the forward speed dropping to around 65 kilometers per hour. At this point, the wave height usually begins to increase dramatically. A tsunami wave that was 50 centimeters high at sea may reach a height of 10 meters or more at the shoreline.

Like storm waves, tsunami waves are often more severe on headlands, where the wave energy is concentrated. The presence of a well-developed coral reef off a shoreline also appears to have a strong effect on tsunami waves. The reef may serve to absorb a significant amount of the wave's energy, reducing its height and the intensity of its impact on the shoreline. Unlike ordinary waves, however, tsunamis are often quite large in bays. In this way, tsunami waves somewhat resemble tides.

Another wave phenomenon may also be produced in bays when a tsunami strikes. The water in any basin, be it a small bay or a large sea, will tend to oscillate back and forth with a fixed period determined by the size and shape of the basin. This oscillation is known as a seiche. A tsunami wave may initiate a seiche, and if the following tsunami wave arrives in conjunction with the next natural oscillation of the seiche, the water may reach even greater heights than the tsunami waves alone, by the wave property of constructive interference. Much of the great height of tsunami waves in bays may be explained by this constructive combination of a seiche wave and a tsunami wave arriving simultaneously.

The popular image of a tsunami wave approaching shore is a nearly vertical wall of water, similar to the front of a breaking wave in the surf. Actually, most tsunamis do not form such wave fronts; the water surface instead is very close to horizontal, and the surface itself moves up and down. The waves arrive like a very rapidly rising tide. Under certain circumstances, however, an arriving tsunami wave can develop an abrupt, steep front that will move inland at high speeds. This phenomenon, generally encountered only as a tidal phenomenon, is known as a bore.

Bores produced by tides occasionally occur in the mouths of rivers. Well-known examples occur on the Solway Firth and the Severn River in Great Britain, on the Petitcodiac River in Maine, near the mouth of the Amazon River in Brazil, and, most strikingly, on the Chientang River in China, where the bore may attain a height of nearly 5 meters. In place of the usually gradual rise of the tide, the onset of high tide is

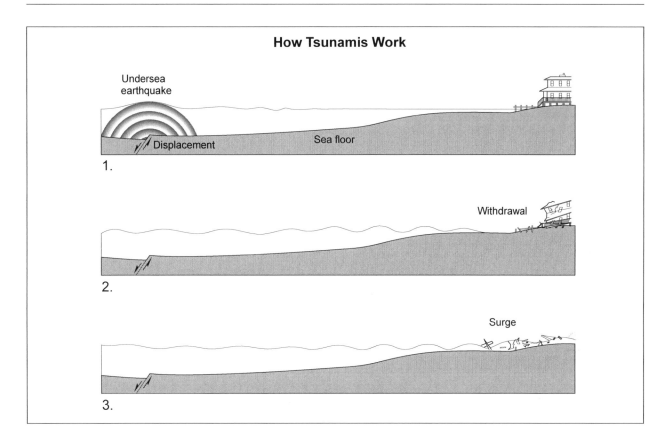

How Tsunamis Work

Undersea
earthquake

Displacement

Sea floor

1.

Withdrawal

2.

Surge

3.

delayed by the outflow of the estuary and augmented by a funneling effect as the stream width becomes narrower. When the high tide does arrive, it comes in very quickly, and the rapidly moving wall of water is followed by a less steep, but still quite dramatic, rise in the water level, accompanied by swift upstream currents.

Because the height of tsunami waves is strongly influenced by the submarine topography and shape of the shoreline and by reflected waves, and because they may be further modified by seiches, tides, and wind waves, the actual inundation and flooding produced by a tsunami may vary greatly from place to place over even a short distance. Though the image of a bore is the most dramatic—and such a wall of water can raze nearly everything in its path—it is the flooding and backwash effect of a tsunami that cause the most damage. Two different terms are often used to describe the extent of tsunami flooding: "inundation" and "run-up." Inundation is the depth of water above the normal level and is usually measured from sea level at average low tide. Inundation may

be measured at any location reached by the tsunami waves. Run-up is the inundation at the maximum distance inland from the shoreline reached by the tsunami waters.

The withdrawal of the tsunami waves can cause significant damage. As the water rapidly withdraws toward the sea, the force of its movement scours out bottom sediments, undermines the foundations of buildings, and carries almost everything in its path out to sea. Entire beaches have been known to disappear as the sand is carried out to sea by the withdrawing tsunami waves, as have thousands of people, cars, trucks, houses, boats, and any other material caught in the retreating backwash.

STUDY OF TSUNAMIS

The best way to learn about tsunamis is to study the tsunami waves themselves. Much of this work is being carried out in the Hawaiian Islands because of their susceptibility to tsunamis from all parts of the Pacific Ocean basin and because Hawaii is the headquarters of the Pacific Tsunami Warning System. Because tsunamis are, fortunately, not everyday events, it is imperative to collect the most information possible from each occurrence. When a tsunami is en route to the Hawaiian Islands, trained observers head toward preselected shoreline vantage points, where time-lapse surveillance cameras are set up to film the waves. Portable tsunami gauges are deployed from piers and in designated shoreline areas. These gauges sense the change in water pressure as the waves pass over them and record their measurements.

Patrol aircraft take to the air before the arrival of the first waves. The aircraft fly at an altitude of 300 meters in a racetrack pattern over critical shoreline areas, covering the same spot every fifteen minutes. Special cameras mounted in the belly of each plane take 480 exposures on 70-millimeter film, documenting the arrival of each tsunami wave on the shores of the islands.

After a tsunami, a ground survey and damage assessment are conducted by a team from the U.S. Army Corps of Engineers, which is joined by volunteers from the American Society of Civil Engineers. A post-tsunami aerial photographic survey is undertaken jointly by the Navy, the Coast Guard, and the Civil Air Patrol, using National Weather Service U-2 surveillance aircraft.

Laboratory techniques have also been employed to study tsunami waves. Much of the damage caused by tsunamis results from the run-up of the giant waves on shore. Various modeling techniques have been used to try to simulate the run-up phase. One such technique, called hydraulic modeling, uses a physical scale model. Hilo Bay on the island of Hawaii is particularly sensitive to tsunami waves. After the disastrous tsunami of 1960, a hydraulic model of the bay was constructed. The model measured 25 by 19 meters and represented the triangular shape of Hilo Bay. Model tsunami waves were produced by releasing water from large tanks according to a program. Experiments with this hydraulic model have shown that almost any wave that enters the bay either hits downtown Hilo directly or is bounced off the northeast coast into the town. Sometimes the direct and reflected waves interact constructively to produce especially large waves in the center of the bay.

Another type of model being increasingly used to study tsunamis is the numerical model, which uses high-speed digital computers to calculate mathematical simulations of tsunami waves. The models,

however, are only as accurate as the data on which they are based, and these data can only come from measurements and observations of actual tsunamis. A recent improvement in data collection has been the use of satellites to transmit data from remote tide stations.

Satellite-telemetered tide stations have been installed at some twenty-five sites across the Pacific. These stations operate on their own independent power sources, secure from electricity outages that may result from earthquakes. Sea-level measurements are made every two seconds and averaged over a three- or four-minute interval, and the data are routinely transmitted by satellite to the Pacific Tsunami Warning Center every three to four hours. In the event of a tsunami wave, however, an "event detector" almost instantaneously sends a message to the warning center over a special emergency satellite channel.

Even more sophisticated measuring devices are being tested, including devices that do not have to be installed on land. A warning system has been proposed that would be based on the detection of tsunamis by highly sensitive bottom-pressure gauges located on the midocean sea floor. According to specialists, a tsunami wave as small as 1 centimeter could be detected with such instruments. In fact, a small tsunami resulting from an earthquake in Mexico on March 14, 1979, was successfully measured using a device on the sea floor 3,000 meters deep, off Baja California. To study how tsunami waves change upon entering shallow water, an observational program has been conducted off the Galápagos Islands, with instruments at depths of 3,000 meters, 10 meters, and 1 meter.

In addition to seafloor tsunami detectors, seismographs have been deployed on the ocean bottom. The Japanese have successfully operated a permanent ocean-bottom seismograph system off the southern coast of central Honshu. Attached to their seismographs is a tsunami gauge. In the future, the system will ultimately use both shore-based and ocean-bottom earthquake and tsunami sensors that transmit real-time data via satellite to the center, where computers will provide scientists with the information they need to issue confirmed tsunami alerts. These efforts will increase their knowledge of tsunami wave generation, propagation, and run-up.

Walter C. Dudley, Jr.

FURTHER READING

Adams, W. M., and N. Nakashizuka. "A Working Vocabulary for Tsunami Study." *Tsunami Hazards* 3 (1985): 45-51. Provides an elementary scientific discussion of the different terms used to describe tsunami waves and their effects.

Bernard, Eddie N., and Allan R. Robinson. *The Sea, Volume 15: Tsunamis.* Cambridge, Mass.: Harvard University Press, 2009. Presents a discussion of all aspects of tsunamis, from the geophysical properties of their generation and propagation, to applications of tsunami forecasting and warning systems. Part of an oceanography reference series.

Chester, Roy. *Furnace of Creation, Cradle of Destruction.* New York: AMACOM Books, 2008. Discusses the turbulent processes of the planet. Covers earthquakes, volcanoes, and tsunamis in reference to plate tectonics, natural disasters, and prediction and mitigation efforts. Multiple chapters explore seafloor spreading. Also discusses hydrothermal activity. Takes on an immense range of content, but still explains concepts clearly and with detail.

Clague, John, Chris Yorath, and Richard Franklin. *At Risk: Earthquakes and Tsunamis on the West Coast.* Vancouver: Tricouni Press. 2006. Geared to the lay person, with a good amount of technical depth. Presents an overview of seismology and historical perspective of geology research in Cascadia.

Dudley, W. C., and M. Lee. *Tsunami!.* 2d ed. Honolulu: University of Hawaii Press, 1998. Includes eyewitness accounts of tsunamis striking the Hawaiian Islands. Provides a thorough, nontechnical explanation of the generation, propagation, and run-up of tsunami waves and an account of the origin and operation of the Pacific Tsunami Warning System. Includes maps, charts, and numerous photographs of tsunamis and their devastating effects.

Finkl, Charles W., ed. *Coastal Hazards: Prediction, Susceptibility, and Mitigation.* Charlottesville, Va.: Coastal Education and Research Foundation, 1994. A volume from the Coastal Research series that focuses on techniques used to prepare for such coastal hazards as tsunamis and hurricane landfall. Illustrations, maps, index, and bibliography.

Guidoboni, Emanuela, and John E. Ebel. *Earthquakes and Tsunamis in the Past: A Guide to Techniques in Historical Seismology.* New York: Cambridge University Press, 2009. Discusses paleoseismology as a field of study, providing background information for topics to follow. Focuses on interpretation and analysis of historical data. Final chapters provide conclusions pulled from actual data. Contains a glossary, a bibliography and references, and indexing.

Joseph, Antony. *Tsunamis: Detection, Monitoring and Early Warning Technologies.* Burlington, Mass.: Academic Press/Elsevier, 2011. The first professional reference book of its kind, focusing on international and regional tsunami warning systems, with numerous resources for readers.

Myles, Douglas. *The Great Waves.* New York: McGraw-Hill, 1985. Relates the history of tsunamis from the beginning of recorded history to the mid-1980's. Discusses the nature and origins of various tsunamis and provides personal accounts of people affected by the tsunami disasters.

O'Laughlin, Karen Fay, and James F. Lander. *Caribbean Tsunamis: A 500-Year History from 1498-1998.* Dordrecht: Kluwer Academic Publishers, 2003. Aimed at the advanced reader in areas of specific application as well as the general public, characterizing the nature of Caribbean tsunamis, their scientific aspects, and their role in policy determination.

Prothero, Donald R. *Catastrophes!: Earthquakes, Tsunamis, Tornadoes, and Other Earth-Shattering Disasters.* Baltimore: Johns Hopkins University Press, 2011. Provides a detailed and clear explanation of the many natural and anthropogenic disasters facing our planet. Each chapter is devoted to a different catastrophe, including earthquakes, volcanoes, hurricanes, ice ages, and current climate changes.

Satake, Kenji, ed. *Tsunamis: Case Studies and Recent Developments.* Dordrecht: Springer, 2005. Geared to professionals in the field of tsunami research, although nonspecialists should find the book of interest as well.

Schneider, Bonnie. *Extreme Weather: A Guide to Surviving Flash Floods, Tornadoes, Hurricanes, Heat Waves, Snowstorms, Tsunamis and Other Natural Disasters.* Basingstoke, England: Palgrave Macmillan, 2012. Presents vivid explanations of how, when, and why major natural disasters occur. Discusses floods, hurricanes, thunderstorms, mudslides, wildfires, tsunamis, and earthquakes. Provides background information on weather patterns and natural disasters, and a guide of how to prepare for and what to do during an extreme weather event.

Sutton, Gerard K., and Joseph A. Cassalli, eds. *Catastrophe in Japan: The Earthquake and Tsunami of 2011.* Hauppauge, N.Y.: Nova Science Publishers, 2011. A compilation of reports on the effects of the 2011 earthquake in Japan and the resulting tsunami, including the impact on agriculture and the economy. Focuses on the nuclear crisis following the earthquake and tsunami. One chapter describes the events within the nuclear power plant resulting from the natural disaster.

Tsuchiya, Yoshito, and Nobuo Shuto, eds. *Tsunami: Progress in Prediction, Disaster Prevention, and Warning.* Boston: Kluwer Academic Publishers, 2010. A thorough book that provides information on advancements made in the study of tsunamis. Pays special attention to the technologies and procedures used to predict tsunamis, warn populations of their approach, and prevent damage. Color illustrations, maps, bibliographical references.

See also: Atmosphere's Global Circulation; Atmosphere's Structure and Thermodynamics; Carbonate Compensation Depths; Climate; Deep Ocean Currents; Gulf Stream; Hydrothermal Vents; Ocean-Atmosphere Interactions; Ocean Pollution and Oil Spills; Oceans' Origin; Oceans' Structure; Ocean Tides; Ocean Waves; Remote Sensing of the Oceans; Sea Level; Seamounts; Seawater Composition; Surface Ocean Currents; Turbidity Currents and Submarine Fans; Wind; World Ocean Circulation Experiment

TURBIDITY CURRENTS AND SUBMARINE FANS

Turbidity currents are a major mechanism whereby sediment from nearshore areas is transported to deeper parts of the oceans. This sediment often accumulates as part of large depositional systems called submarine fans, which could well be exploited as a major source of petroleum at some time in the future.

PRINCIPAL TERMS

- **abyssal plain:** the flat, sediment-covered area of the sea floor that merges with the base of the continental rise
- **continental margin:** the area that separates the emergent continents from the deep sea floor, generally consisting of the continental shelf, continental slope, and continental rise
- **continental rise:** the broad and gently sloping ramp that rises from the abyssal plain to the base of the continental slope; submarine fans are found here
- **continental shelf:** the gently seaward-sloping submerged edge of a continent that commonly extends to a depth of about 200 meters or to the edge of the continental slope
- **continental slope:** the relatively steep region of the continental margin between the continental shelf and the continental rise
- **gas hydrates:** relatively stable, often crystalline, molecular combinations of water and hydrocarbon gases, especially methane, that form on the ocean floor due to the elevated pressure conditions
- **submarine canyon:** a submerged, V-shaped canyon cut into the continental shelf and continental slope, through which turbidity currents funnel into the deeper parts of the oceans
- **turbulent flow:** a high-velocity sediment flow in which individual sediment particles move in very chaotic directions above the sea floor

DEVELOPMENT OF THE CONCEPT

A turbidity current is a dense mass of water and sediment that flows downhill along the bottom of an ocean or any other standing body of water such as a lake. Turbidity currents may reach high speeds and are capable of carrying large quantities of sediment, and of eroding or scouring the ocean floor as they move.

The concept of the turbidity current has a long history. In the late nineteenth century, geologists observing the waters of the Rhone River entering Lake Geneva noted that instead of mixing with the lake water, the river water moved along the bottom of the lake in a channel. This behavior was interpreted to reflect the elevated density of the cold, sediment-laden Rhone River water. These dense, bottom-hugging currents were called "density currents." It was suggested in the late 1930's that dense currents composed of sediment and water could be produced by wave activity on the continental shelves, the flat or gently sloping submerged edges of the continents, during periods when global sea level is lower than it is today. Furthermore, it was postulated that these dense, turbulent mixtures of suspended sediment and water would flow across the continental shelves and down large canyon-like features into deeper parts of the ocean.

From the 1930's to the 1950's, researchers conducted numerous laboratory studies to test the hypothesis that turbidity currents could actually erode the ocean floor and produce such features as submarine canyons on the continental shelf. This work was done by pouring muddy water into the end of an inclined flume (a long, straight trough in which the hydrodynamic properties of moving fluids can be studied) in order to produce artificial turbidity currents. Results of these investigations indicated that sediment in a turbidity current moves in a very chaotic or random pattern, much like the movement of snow and other materials in an avalanche. Additionally, geologists recognized that turbidity currents can move rapidly and that their velocity is dependent upon the slope of the sea bottom along which they move as well as the density of the sediment-water mixture.

These experimental studies also yielded insight into the nature of the sedimentary deposits that accumulate from turbidity currents. These deposits, referred to as turbidites, form as graded beds, sedimentary layers in which the largest or most coarse-grained sediment particles are concentrated at the bottom of the bed and grade gradually upward to the smallest or most fine-grained sediment at the top. The graded nature of the bedding was deduced correctly to be a consequence of a reduction in the flow velocity of the turbidity current upon reaching the very gentle slopes that are typical of the bottom of the ocean, so that the largest sediment particles settle out of the current to the bottom of the ocean first, followed by progressively finer particles. Thus, each turbidity current produces a single-graded bed or turbidite.

Geologists working in the field began to realize that the graded beds such as those produced in laboratory studies could be observed in sequences of sedimentary rocks exposed on land in various mountain belts throughout the world (the Appalachians, Apennines, and Carpathians). Moreover, oceanographic research demonstrated the presence of turbidite sands in some of the deepest areas of the modern oceans. It is now apparent that turbidity currents are and were a dominant, if not the dominant, mechanism of sediment transport from shallow-water environments on the continental shelf to the deeper parts of the ocean. Evidence of this includes the recovery of shallow-water organic remains from very deep parts of the oceans far removed from land. The laboratory studies and subsequent oceanographic research indicated that turbidites differ from most other sedimentary deposits in that they are nearly instantaneous deposits that may accumulate over a period of just a few hours to a few days. Moreover, turbidity currents are quite capable of eroding the great submarine canyons that cut into many continental shelves.

CAUSES OF TURBIDITY CURRENTS

Downhill movement of turbidity currents can be triggered by various causes. Commonly, earthquakes affecting the continental shelves will cause sediment on the continental slope—the part of the continental margin characterized by an increase in gradient immediately seaward of the continental shelf—to slide downslope, thereby mixing with seawater to form a turbidity current. A rapid sequence of successive breaks in transatlantic cables on the continental margin bordering southern Newfoundland was apparently caused by the downslope movement of a dense, turbulent mixture of seawater and sediment generated from the continental shelf and slope in response to the Grand Banks earthquake of November 8, 1929. Those cables closest to the point on the ocean floor directly above the earthquake, the epicenter, broke first, whereas cables farther from this point broke later. The breaking of the cables indicated the

erosive capability of turbidity currents. Subsequent drilling of that part of the ocean floor traversed by the turbulent flow recovered a 1-meter-thick graded bed containing shallow-water organic remains; this discovery strengthened the argument that the flow was indeed a turbidity current. The earthquake-induced turbidity current averaged 27 kilometers per hour, although it reached velocities in excess of 70 kilometers per hour in steeper parts of the continental margin, and it covered an area of more than 195,000 square kilometers.

Turbidity currents can also be generated by wave activity on continental shelves, an idea, as already noted, that was postulated in the 1930's. More specifically, large waves produced during great storms such as hurricanes are capable of creating the turbulence required to mix sediment and seawater, thereby creating a turbidity current. An equally plausible mechanism of turbidity-current generation involves oversteepening of the continental slope by the sudden addition of sediment. This is especially common where large rivers deposit their sediment load near the head of a submarine canyon.

The rate at which turbidity currents are generated was greatest during periods when sea level was much lower than it is today. This was especially typical of glacial periods, when more seawater was locked up in the enlarged polar ice caps, resulting in the lowering of the global level of the oceans. During these times of lowered sea level, rivers were capable of transporting their sediment loads directly across the previously submerged continental shelf into the head of a submarine canyon. There, the sediment mixed with seawater and was fed, via the submarine canyon, directly into the deeper parts of the ocean as turbidity currents. When sea level rose and the shoreline retreated landward as the exposed continental shelf was once again submerged, the river was cut off from the canyon head, thereby precluding the infusion of sediment directly to the canyon and reducing the likelihood of turbidity-current generation.

CHARACTERISTICS OF SUBMARINE FANS

Turbidity currents triggered on continental shelves or continental slopes move downhill until they reach a point at which the reduced gradient of the ocean floor causes a reduction in the velocity of the sediment flow. This leads to deposition of a graded bed or turbidite. Many turbidite deposits that are funneled through submarine canyons ultimately accumulate as part of large fan-shaped or cone-shaped sediment bodies called submarine fans. The submarine fans, which spread outward from the mouths of the submarine canyons, merge with the bottom of the continental slope and comprise the continental rise, the broad, gently sloping feature that rises from the abyssal plain of the ocean floor and merges with the base of the continental slope. Where submarine canyons are close together along the continental shelf and continental slope, the attached submarine fans may coalesce to form a wide, laterally extensive continental rise.

In general, submarine fans are subdivided into three major morphologic elements or parts: the upper fan, midfan, and lower fan. The upper fan, also referred to as the inner fan, is typically characterized by a single submarine channel that is connected to the submarine canyon. Upper fan channels range from 2 to 18 kilometers wide and may be as deep as 900 meters. The single channel is commonly flanked on both sides by levees, low ridges that run along the length of the channel. Most of the sediment transported through the upper fan channel via the submarine canyon is deposited into the midfan, that area of the submarine fan composed of raised, lobelike sequences of turbidites called depositional lobes. The depositional lobes are fed by numerous shallow and unstable distributive channels that branch off the main upper fan channel. Because these channels are generally relatively shallow (several tens of meters deep), they are more likely to be filled in during passage of extraordinarily dense turbidity currents. When that happens, the channels are abandoned and subsequent turbidity currents erode or scour out new channels in adjacent areas of the midfan portion of the submarine fan. The lower fan is characterized by a smooth ocean floor that passes imperceptibly seaward into the abyssal plain. The low gradient of the lower fan relative to that of the midfan leads to a much-reduced abundance of turbidites in the lower fan. Turbidite deposits are not common on the abyssal plain because ocean floor gradients in this area are typically too low to sustain movement of the dense sediment cloud.

Submarine fans display great variations in size. The Bengal Fan, in the Bay of Bengal in the northeast Indian Ocean, is the largest submarine fan. Its total length exceeds 3,000 kilometers. The main or upper fan channel ranges from 13 to 18 kilometers wide and from 150 to 900 meters deep. Most submarine fans, however, are much smaller than the Bengal Fan.

The growth of submarine fans, because they are major sites of turbidite sedimentation, is controlled by variations in sea level. As noted previously, turbidity currents are generated more frequently during periods of low sea level. Accordingly, submarine fans are likely to grow fastest, as manifested by increased rates of turbidite sedimentation, during periods of low global sea level. Indeed, geologists have demonstrated that the Mississippi submarine fan, which is fed by the Mississippi River, was the site of abundant turbidite sedimentation at the end of the most recent ice age, approximately 15,000 to 20,000 years ago, when sea level was as much as 120 to 130 meters lower than it is today. Since then, the rate of turbidite sedimentation has dropped off greatly as sea level gradually rose, and the shoreline retreated landward to its present position.

Gary G. Lash

Further Reading

Black, J. A. *Oceans and Coasts.* Dubuque, Iowa: Wm. C. Brown, 1986. A high school or beginning-level college text that provides a discussion of continental margin environments as well as an overview of turbidity currents and submarines.

Huneke, Heiko, and Thierry Mulder. *Deep Sea Sediments.* Amsterdam: Elsevier, 2011. Discusses the results of recent exploration techniques for the study of deep-sea sediments, including sediment fans, based on industrial interest in such sediments. Geared to specialists in the field of ocean sedimentology.

Kennish, Michael J. *Practical Handbook of Marine Science.* 3d ed. Boca Raton, Fla.: CRC Press, 2001. Covers marine geology topics such as seafloor topography, sediments, plate tectonics, midocean ridges, and hydrothermal vents. Best suited for advanced undergraduates and graduate students. Provides references for each chapter.

Leeder, Mike R. *Sedimentology and Sedimentary Basins: From Turbulence to Tectonics.* Oxford: Wiley-Blackwell, 2011. Intended for an audience of senior undergraduate and graduate students, academics, and industry professionals. Uses a general science narrative approach to address the principles and processes of the subject area.

McKinney, Frank. *The Northern Adriatic Ecosystem: Deep Time in a Shallow Sea*. New York: Columbia University Press, 2007. Covers the paleogeography of the Adriatic Sea. Discusses the succession of the ecosystem as the sea's geography changed. Discusses oceanography topics such as circulation and sedimentation. Topics are well described and logically ordered. Accessible to undergraduates.

Oceanography Course Team. *Ocean Circulation*. 2d ed. Oxford: Butterworth-Heinemann, 2001. Discusses surface currents and deep water currents, with focus on the North Atlantic Gyre, Gulf Stream, and equatorial currents. Discusses the El Niño phenomenon as well as the great salinity anomaly. Provides a good introduction to oceanography.

Ross, D. A. *Introduction to Oceanography*. 5th ed. New York: Harper-Collins College Publishers, 1995. An oceanography textbook that offers a good discussion of continental margin environments, including the shelf, slope, and rise as well as the abyssal plain. Also discusses turbidity currents and submarine fans. Suitable for high school or first-year college students.

Schulz, Horst D., and Matthias Zabel. *Marine Geochemistry*. 2d ed. Berlin: Springer-Verlag, 2006. Discusses physical and chemical properties of marine sediments, diagenesis, bacteria, and biogeochemistry, as well as phosphorus, nitrogen, oxygen, sulfur, methane, iron, carbonates, sulfur, boron, and manganese. Final chapter covers marine sediment models. Well suited for undergraduate and graduate students with some geology or chemistry background.

Schwartz, M., ed. *Encyclopedia of Coastal Science*. Dordrecht: Springer, 2005. Contains many articles specific to ocean and beach dynamics. Also discusses coastal habitat management topics, hydrology, geology, and topography. Articles may run multiple pages and have diagrams. Each article has bibliographical information and cross-referencing.

Shanmugam, G. *Deep-Water Processes and Facies Models: Implications for Sandstone Petroleum Reservoirs*. Amsterdam: Elsevier, 2006. Discusses criteria for recognizing deposits from gravity-, thermohaline-, wind-, and tide-driven processes in deep-water sediments and environments using data from thirty-five case studies that cover thirty-two sandstone petroleum reservoirs. Intended for advanced students of deep-water sedimentology and petroleum geology.

Talley, Lynne D., George L. Pickard, William J. Emery, and James H. Swift. *Descriptive Physical Oceanography: An Introduction*. 6th ed. London: Elsevier, 2011. An introductory college-level textbook for students who will specialize in the field of oceanography.

Thurman, H. V., and Alan P. Trujillo. *Introductory Oceanography*. 10th ed. Upper Saddle River, N.J.: Prentice Hall, 2003. Offers a good overview of the science of oceanography. Provides a discussion and diagram of turbidity currents and the submarine canyons they create. Well illustrated and contains a helpful glossary.

Walker, Roger G. *Facies Models: Response to Sea Level Change*. 2d ed. Tulsa, Okla.: Society of Economic Paleontologists and Mineralogists, 1992. Contains an excellent discussion of turbidites and their environments of deposition. Perhaps the best feature is the reading lists, which contain references on the history and philosophy of the turbidity current concept, hydrodynamic properties of turbidites, and submarine fans. Best suited for the first-year or second-year college student.

See also: Carbonate Compensation Depths; Deep Ocean Currents; Gulf Stream; Hydrothermal Vents; Ocean-Atmosphere Interactions; Ocean Pollution and Oil Spills; Oceans' Origin; Oceans' Structure; Ocean Tides; Ocean Waves; Remote Sensing of the Oceans; Sea Level; Seamounts; Seawater Composition; Surface Ocean Currents; Tsunamis; World Ocean Circulation Experiment

V

VAN ALLEN RADIATION BELTS

The Van Allen radiation belts are regions of the magnetosphere that trap high-energy particles from space. The particles that make up the ionic content of the inner belt are energetic protons, while the outer belt consists mainly of electrons and is subject to day-night variations.

PRINCIPAL TERMS

- **electrons:** subatomic particles that have one unit of negative charge
- **magnetic field:** magnetic lines of force that are projected from a planet's interior and out into space
- **plasma:** a state of matter consisting of ionized gases
- **protons:** positively charged subatomic particles, the antimatter counterpart of electrons

CHARACTERISTICS

The Van Allen radiation belts consist of toroidal, or doughnut-shaped, structures that exist within the magnetic field. The inner belt begins at an altitude that varies between 250 kilometers and 1,200 kilometers, depending on latitude, and extends to an altitude of about 10,000 kilometers. The ionic particles that make up this inner belt are energetic protons. Within the inner belt is another belt consisting of ionized nitrogen, neon, and oxygen believed to have originated as neutral atoms from the interstellar medium that have penetrated into the solar system. Before entering the magnetic field, these neutral atoms were ionized by solar ultraviolet radiation. The outer belt consists mainly of electrons and extends from the boundary of the inner belt outward to about 60,000 kilometers. During times of extensive solar activity, the outer belt may expand outward to more than 80,000 kilometers..

The particles in the Van Allen belts travel along a spiral or corkscrew-shaped path along the magnetic lines of force. The spirals are small compared to the scale of the entire magnetic field, and they curve to follow the field lines. As the lines of force converge toward a pole, the field becomes more intense. As a result, the particles travel in a tighter spiral as they approach the pole. Eventually, the converging tubes of magnetic force will cause the particles to be reflected back toward the equator and on to the opposite pole. The point of closest approach to a pole is the "mirror point" of the particle. The transit time between mirror points is about one second.

In addition to bouncing back and forth between mirror points, the particles undergo a slow lateral drift. The basic curvature of the path of a spiraling

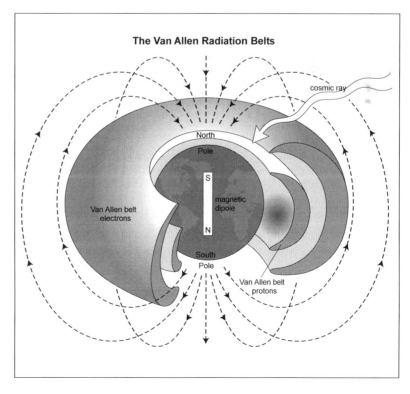

The Van Allen Radiation Belts

particle depends upon the local strength of the magnetic field. The particles in the inner belt follow a tighter spiral, as the field nearest the planet is stronger. Because there is a slight difference in the curvatures of the spirals in the inner and outer belts, the particles drift laterally. Because the charges of protons and electrons are opposite, they spiral in opposite directions. The drift direction is also opposite; the protons tend to drift westward and the electrons eastward. This counteracting drift leads to a uniformity of the radiation belts.

At the end of each path, some particles penetrate through the mirror point and descend into regions of higher atmospheric density. These particles interact with particles of atmospheric gases. Particles of radiation lose energy as a result of these collisions, and after a period of days or weeks, they are lost to the lower atmosphere, only to be replaced by more particles from the sun.

A large influx of particles from the sun will, in turn, cause large numbers of particles to collect in the upper atmosphere. The resulting interactions with oxygen and nitrogen atoms produce the colorful auroras. In the Northern Hemisphere, this phenomenon is called the "aurora borealis" or "northern lights"; in the Southern Hemisphere, the display is called the "aurora australis" or "southern lights."

The auroral displays are usually pink, blue, and green streaks or curtains of light. The emission of light is the result of collisions between particles of radiation from the Van Allen belts and atoms of gas in the atmosphere. When a particle of radiation strikes an atom of gas, the orbiting electrons of the atom absorb the energy of the collision. They then jump to a higher energy level. After remaining there for only a fraction of a second, the electrons fall back to the lowest energy level, or the "ground state." When they do this, light is released at a wavelength that represents the difference in energy between the excited state and the ground state.

Formation

The Van Allen radiation belts exist because of three natural phenomena: the solar wind, cosmic rays, and the magnetic field that surrounds the planet. As a result of the enormous heat in the sun's upper atmosphere, atoms of gas are given enough energy to escape the sun's gravity and move off into space. The solar wind, as this phenomenon has become

known, consists of a plasma with a temperature near 100,000 kelvin. The plasma contains charged particles, including protons, electrons, and ions of heavier elements, mainly helium. After the plasma escapes from the sun's upper atmosphere, it flows outward into space. Because the plasma conducts heat well, the temperature remains high even after it has traveled a great distance from the sun. The velocity of the solar wind increases as it expands radially outward. The speeds are near 300 kilometers per second at a distance of 30 solar radii from the sun and nearly 400 kilometers per second at the distance of Earth.

When the plasma reaches Earth, the density of the plasma is only about 5 particles per cubic centimeter at times of relatively little solar activity. This density changes considerably at times of peak solar activity. As the solar wind arrives at Earth, it encounters the magnetic field. The edge of the magnetic field, the bowshock, deflects the solar-wind particles away from Earth, but many protons and electrons penetrate into the magnetosphere where they become trapped. It is these trapped particles from the solar wind that make up the bulk of the Van Allen radiation belts.

A steady contribution to the inner radiation belts is made by cosmic rays. Cosmic rays consist of the nuclei of atoms and come to Earth from two different sources. Some are hurled into space from the surface of the sun during violent eruptions such as solar flares; others come from the depths of space.

Some cosmic rays have energies sufficient to penetrate the magnetosphere and reach the surface. Others collide with particles of atmospheric gas and release a shower of secondary radiation. The principles of the interaction of cosmic-ray particles with the magnetic field are the same as for the trapped particles of solar radiation.

The lifetimes of particles trapped in the Van Allen belts are highly variable. Under conditions of minimum solar activity, some particles remain trapped for months or years. Because the radiation belt density is fairly low, collisions that would send particles out of the belt are rare. An individual particle's lifetime is therefore determined by the height of its mirror points above the densest part of the atmosphere. The higher the mirror points, the less chance that the particle of radiation will collide with an atom of atmospheric gas.

The mechanism of loss and replenishment of particles in the radiation belt is not well understood.

Several mechanisms work to distribute particles of various energies to different parts of the belts. The continuous supply of solar-wind particles from the sun appears to be a necessity. Apparently, low-energy solar-wind particles enter the magnetosphere and are accelerated to energies necessary to become radiation-belt particles. Changes in the magnetic field can excite the electrons in the outer belt to speeds approaching the speed of light.

STUDY OF RADIATION BELTS

Radiation in space consists of electromagnetic waves from the sun; highly energetic protons, electrons, and atomic nuclei that make up the solar wind; cosmic rays both from the sun and outer space; and trapped particles within the Van Allen radiation belts. The ground surface is protected from these forms of radiation by the atmosphere and its magnetic field. Astronauts flying in space, however, have a much more significant risk. If a spacecraft is in orbit at an altitude lower than the altitude of the inner Van Allen belt, then there is no danger to the astronaut from the trapped particles of radiation. Although the radiation intensity of the inner belt is fairly constant, the intensity in the outer belt is much more sensitive to what is happening on the surface of the sun. Activities on the sun such as solar flares will result in a considerable fluctuation in the radiation intensity at this higher level. During periods of peak solar activity, the radiation in the outer belt could give an unprotected astronaut a fatal level of radiation exposure. The cabin of a spacecraft offers some protection; however, when a particle strikes the spacecraft wall, it produces a shower of secondary radiation by a process known as "bremsstrahlung."

High-energy particles are capable of damaging human organisms. High-speed, high-energy particles pass through the body, colliding with and knocking electrons out of atoms that make up the cells. This results in chemical changes to the components of the cells.

Even on the surface of the planet, humans are subjected to a certain amount of background radiation. The cells of the body regularly absorb radiation, die, and regenerate. The body has acquired immunity to this type of radiation. When the body is exposed to additional high-energy ionizing radiation, however, the cells may not be able to replace themselves because of damage to the nuclei that control the cell.

Another possibility would be the uncontrolled reproduction of the damaged cells and the spread of a cancer.

The best way to protect an astronaut from the effects of the Van Allen radiation belt is shielding, although shielding of the entire spacecraft is impractical because of the mass of the materials used in making the shield. It is generally more feasible to have a small portion of the spacecraft protected; the area must be large enough to provide a safe haven for the entire crew until the time of danger has passed. In August 1972, a major solar flare occurred. A detailed study of the radiation released from that event showed that a shield of aluminum 0.2 meter (20 centimeters or about 8 inches) thick would be required to provide the necessary protection to keep astronaut exposure rates below the established limits.

During the Apollo missions, spacecraft trajectories were planned that avoided regions with the highest concentrations of radiation. Also, most of the missions were launched after the peak of the solar cycle. As a result of these precautions, the astronauts were exposed to about the same radiation dosages as someone would receive from a diagnostic X ray.

The inner Van Allen radiation belt interacts with the upper atmosphere in the polar regions to produce the aurora borealis in the Northern Hemisphere and the aurora australis in the Southern Hemisphere. Although the auroras are sometimes visible all over the globe, their regular and most frequent appearances are confined to the Arctic and Antarctic zones. The greatest frequency of the aurora in the Arctic region appears within a zone that lies from 15 to 30 degrees from the north magnetic pole.

In the region of the auroral zone, viewing an auroral display can be a nightly event. The development of an auroral exhibition may be described by the following sequence. After sunset, a faint arc becomes visible in the northern sky. The arc remains stable for hours, with only a slight amount of movement. Suddenly, its lower border becomes more intense, and the arc breaks up into a series of parallel rays. The rays increase in color and intensity, and bundles of rays move along the arc. The arc then splits up into rays and draperies that fill the sky with dancing movements. The entire display usually lasts only minutes before the forms fade away. The faint arc again becomes visible in the northern sky. This display may be repeated several times during the night. A faint luminosity covers the northern sky after a particularly powerful auroral display. This phenomenon has given the aurora borealis the additional name the "northern dawn."

These colorful displays are produced when electrons and protons drop into the inner radiation belt and collide with atoms of atmospheric gases. The gas atoms become excited by these collisions and when they return to their stable forms, visible light is emitted.

The trapped particles that make up the Van Allen belts are held in close proximity to Earth by the magnetic field. Geophysical studies have concluded that the planet's magnetism is generated within the liquid iron-and-nickel outer core rather than the solid inner core or the rock that makes up the mantle and the crust. The molten outer core flows at a rate of several kilometers per year in massive convective currents.

These currents, along with the rotation of the planet, create electrical currents that, in turn, create the magnetic field. It has been found that other planets that have strong magnetic fields—Jupiter, for example—also have radiation belts similar to Earth's Van Allen radiation belts.

SIGNIFICANCE

The history of the study of near-Earth radiation goes back to the early 1950's. During those years, scientists launched instrument packages into the upper atmosphere using a combination of balloons and rockets. A balloon would lift a small rocket up to an altitude of about 25 kilometers, then the rocket would ignite and carry the package to an altitude of from 95 to 115 kilometers. The purpose of these tests was to monitor cosmic-ray intensities at high altitudes and latitudes. By doing so, scientists hoped to learn more about how cosmic rays are deflected by the magnetic field and absorbed in the atmosphere.

In 1953, a rocket launched into the northern auroral zone yielded a radiation count far greater than expected. It was proposed that since other instrument packages launched into regions both north and south of the zone revealed no anomalous data, there must be a connection between the high radiation count and the aurora. It was believed that the auroras were caused when showers of particles from the sun entered the atmosphere along magnetic lines of force. During the International Geophysical Year (1957-1958), further tests were completed in the

polar regions. The tests revealed that the radiation included energetic protons and electrons.

It was during the International Geophysical Year that a series of orbiting satellites were to be launched. It was decided that radiation-detecting instruments would be placed aboard these satellites. Before any American satellites could be orbited, the former Soviet Union launched Sputnik 1. Moreover, the first American launch attempts, using the Vanguard rocket, were a complete failure as most of the rockets exploded on the launch pad. In January 1958, the Jupiter-C rocket successfully carried the Explorer 1 satellite into orbit, and with it a cosmic-ray detector.

The first reports from Explorer 1 indicated that radiation intensity increased with altitude. The data were somewhat incomplete, as they could be retrieved only when the satellite was near a tracking station. A later satellite, Explorer 3, carried a tiny magnetic tape recorder. This device could record data during an entire orbit and then send it upon receiving a radio command. The data from Explorer 3 confirmed that the radiation increased with altitude and eventually went to zero. Scientists subsequently determined that the zero reading on their radiation counters was anomalous; the counters were actually being overloaded by radiation. The satellites had found a major new phenomenon: particles of radiation trapped in the magnetic field.

Data from satellites and lunar probes carrying more advanced instrument packages eventually revealed the existence of two belts of trapped radiation. Since their discovery in 1958, the radiation belts have been thoroughly mapped by space probes. Knowledge of the Van Allen belts is essential because of the effects of ionizing radiation. Orbiting satellites are especially vulnerable to sudden changes in the Van Allen belts. The 1996 failure of Anik E1, a Canadian telecommunications satellite, was believed to have been caused by such a change. On May 19, 1998, a sudden change in the magnetic field caused electrons in the outer belt to accelerate to just under the speed of light, causing the Galaxy 4 telecommunications satellite to fail abruptly, resulting in a loss of service to 45 million customers. Because of the energy of the electrons traveling at these speeds, prohibitively expensive, heavy shielding would be required to completely protect sensitive satellites.

David W. Maguire

FURTHER READING

Beatty, J. Kelly, Carolyn Collins Petersen, and Andrew Chaikin, eds. *The New Solar System.* 4th ed. Cambridge, Mass.: Sky Publishing, 1999. A well-illustrated, somewhat technical volume that consists of a collection of essays by various experts in solar system research. Topics include the sun, planets, moons, comets, asteroids, and meteorites.

Bone, Neil. *Aurora: Observing and Recording Nature's Spectacular Light Show.* New York: Springer, 2007. Includes a discussion of the interaction between the sun and the atmosphere of Earth. Explains the causes of auroras, and provides details from professional studies, amateur observations, and forecasting. Discusses historical references and auroras on other planets.

_____. *The Aurora: Sun-Earth Interactions.* 2d ed. New York: Wiley, 1996. A college-level text that provides the perfect introduction to the origins, physics, and significance of auroras. Suitable for the reader with no prior knowledge in the field. Color illustrations, bibliographical references, and index.

Bryant, Duncan Alan. *Electron Acceleration in the Aurora and Beyond.* Philadelphia: Institute of Physics, 1999. Offers a good look into the geophysics of auroras that explains the relationship between the electron and the aurora in a somewhat technical manner. Recommended for the advanced reader with much interest in the field. Color illustrations, index, and bibliography.

Damon, Thomas D. *Introduction to Space.* 4th ed. Malabar, Fla.: Krieger Publishing Company, 2011. A well-written, well-illustrated volume that covers various topics relevant to spaceflight. Covers the history of spaceflight, propulsion systems, orbits, satellites, and living and working in space. Limited math equations. Well suited for high school and undergraduate students.

Formin, L. I. *Cosmic Rays in the Earth's Atmosphere and Underground.* Dordrecht: Kluwer Academic Publishers, 2004. Presented in four parts, with the first being an overview of cosmic ray research and theory. Discusses the influences and effects of cosmic rays on the atmosphere and atmospheric effects in subsequent parts.

Giacomelli, Giorgio, Maurizio Spurio, and Jamal Eddine Derkaoui. NATO Scientific Affairs Division. *Cosmic Radiations: From Astronomy to Particle Physics.* Dordrecht: Kluwer Academic Publishers, 2001. Discusses neutrino oscillations, high-energy cosmic rays, and other non-accelerator-based particle physics, along with research geared toward the discovery of new particles and phenomena. Intended for a technical audience.

Holmes-Siedle, A. G., and L. Adams. *Handbook of Radiation Effects.* 2d ed. London: Oxford University Press, 2002. Provides a broad overview of radiation topics. Discusses radiation in the environment, both in space and on Earth, as well as the basic physics behind radiation and the effects of radiation on other materials. Also covers the relationship between radiation and optics.

Paschmann, Götz, Stein Haaland, and Rudolf Treumann, eds. *Auroral Plasma Physics.* Dordrecht: Kluwer Academic Publishers, 2003. Takes a technical approach to the discussion of aurora phenomena. Chapters cover remote sensing of auroral arc and the physics behind the colorful phenomena, as well as study methods and measurements. Requires some background in physics. Does not provide much information on the fundamentals of physics.

Plummer, Charles C., Diane H. Carlson, and Lisa Hammersley. *Physical Geology.* 13th ed. Columbus, Ohio: McGraw-Hill, 2009. Offers a general introduction to physical geology intended for use at the college-freshman level. Contains many tables, illustrations, and photographs; also includes a glossary and an index.

Van Allen, James A. *Origin of Magnetospheric Physics.* Iowa City: University of Iowa Press, 2004. Discusses the research of Van Allen, including discovery of the radiation belts. Contains many diagrams and is accessible to both undergraduate students and astrophysicists.

_____. "Radiation Belts Around the Earth." *Scientific American* 200, no. 3 (March, 1959). Written by Van Allen, who designed the experimentation that discovered the radiation belts that bear his name. Contains both a history of the study of radiation and a technical description of the radiation belts.

Wentzel, Donat G. *The Restless Sun.* Washington, D.C.: Smithsonian Institution Press, 1989. A well-written volume intended for the layperson that describes, in nonmathematical terms, internal and external solar processes.

Zeilik, Michael, and Elske V. P. Smith. *Introductory Astronomy and Astrophysics.* 4th ed. Independence, Ky.: Brooks/Cole Cengage Learning, 1998. A text for an introductory college course on astrophysics. Well illustrated with graphs, drawings, and photographs. Includes problem sets at the end of each chapter. Assumes some knowledge of advanced mathematics.

See also: Atmospheric and Oceanic Oscillations; Atmospheric Properties; Auroras; Climate; Clouds; Cosmic Rays and Background Radiation; Drought; Earth-Sun Relations; Hurricanes; Lightning and Thunder; Monsoons; Satellite Meteorology; Seasons; Severe Storms; Tornadoes; Volcanoes: Climatic Effects; Weather Forecasting; Weather Forecasting: Numerical Weather Prediction; Weather Modification; Wind

VOLCANOES: CLIMATIC EFFECTS

Studies of volcanic activity confirm the existence of a significant relationship between the effects of an eruption and long-term climatic conditions.

PRINCIPAL TERMS

- **aerosol:** an aggregate of dispersed gas particles suspended in the atmosphere for varying periods of time because of their small size
- **atmosphere:** the thin layer of nitrogen, oxygen, and other gases surrounding Earth, whose density decreases rapidly with height
- **climate:** the sum total of the weather elements that characterize the average condition of the atmosphere over a long period of time for any one region
- **greenhouse effect:** the retention of solar heat in the lower atmosphere caused by the absorption and reradiation of infrared energy from the surface by various gases, creating an insulating effect similar to a greenhouse
- **ozone layer:** a region of the stratosphere, around 60 kilometers in altitude, containing ozone that absorbs ultraviolet radiation from the sun
- **stratosphere:** the atmospheric layer above the troposphere, characterized by little or no temperature change with altitude
- **sulfur dioxide:** a colorless, nonflammable, suffocating gas formed when sulfur is oxidized
- **tropopause:** the transition zone at the top of the troposphere between the troposphere and the stratosphere
- **troposphere:** the lowest layer of atmosphere where temperature generally declines with altitude, containing about 95 percent of the mass of the atmosphere and the site of most atmospheric turbulence and weather features

ATMOSPHERIC ENVIRONMENT

Scientists have speculated for centuries on the impact of volcanic eruptions on the climate, and historical figures as early as Benjamin Franklin have noted the possible link between an eruption and climatic conditions. Two years after the 1873 explosion of Liki Fissure, in Iceland, Franklin suggested that the blue haze that lingered over the city of Paris during his stay there was caused by the Icelandic event. He believed the "fog," as he termed it, caused a decline in the temperature by absorbing portions of sunlight that otherwise would have reached the ground surface.

Technological advances such as satellite imagery have made it possible for scientists to pinpoint more precisely which types of matter injected into the atmosphere by a volcano have the greatest effect. Initially, researchers believed it was the amount of gas and ash hurled into the atmosphere that determined the impact. However, scientists have come to learn that it is the types of gases that are the critical determining factor. The molten rock of a volcano contains a variety of gases that are released into the atmosphere before, during, and after an eruption. They range from water vapor to dense clouds of sulfur. Other gases include carbon dioxide, sulfur dioxide, hydrogen sulfide, hydrogen, fluorine, chlorine, carbon monoxide, and hydrochloric acid, along with smaller amounts of other chemical compounds.

Exposure to the acid gases such as sulfur dioxide, hydrogen sulfide, and hydrochloric acid can be life threatening, while exposure to fluorine is particularly dangerous. One of the most serious hazards posed by a volcano is the large amount of carbon dioxide it can emit during an eruption. Since it is heavier than air, carbon dioxide tends to settle in lower elevations. As a result, numerous people residing near erupting volcanoes have been asphyxiated. When a volcano erupts, its immediate effect on the local area is evident, as it spews a great amount of ash, volcanic gases, and heat into the atmosphere. Violent eruptions usually are accompanied by thunderstorms, lightning, and torrential rains. In some cases, the intense heat can generate powerful whirlwinds, strong enough to topple nearby trees and destroy wildlife. Volcanic plumes also contain droplets of water in which acid gases have dissolved. These droplets eventually fall to the ground in the form of acid rain, which can have a corrosive effect on a variety of metal objects and other materials. Exposure to significant amounts of volcanic gases also can have a lethal effect on most varieties of vegetation.

Along with the research into the makeup of gases has come a greater awareness of the long-term effects on climatic patterns. The volcanic dust released into the lower atmosphere can create a temporary cooling effect by producing an ash cloud that blocks the sunlight. However, the ash particles are quickly washed out by the abundant supply of water and rain contained in the lower atmosphere. The majority of ash clouds stop rising at the troposphere, where they encounter increased air temperatures. Dust particles thrown into the stratosphere can linger for several weeks or months before they settle back to the surface.

For many years scientists believed that volcanic ash was the most important factor in climatic changes. They since have discovered that of all the ingredients tossed into the air, it is the volcanic gases that exert the greatest influence on climatic conditions. Specifically, the key factor is the conversion of the gases into sulfuric acid aerosols that are capable of remaining in the atmosphere for months. The droplets, though tiny in size, are able to reflect significant amounts of sunlight and have been detected at altitudes as high as 25 kilometers. They not only are able to cool the troposphere by reflecting solar rays back into space, but also can warm the stratosphere by absorbing infrared radiation. The reflective effect is particularly strong when it occurs in normally cloudless areas. It has been estimated that the aerosols can increase the planet's reflectivity, or albedo, by nearly 20 percent. Although aerosols eventually grow large enough to fall back to the surface from their own weight, the process can take years because of the rarefied and dry conditions in the stratosphere, which slows their growth. Aerosol cloud eruptions occur on an average of once every ten to twenty years, with major eruptions taking place at a rate of nearly one every one hundred years.

Only those volcanic eruptions that emit significant amounts of sulfur compounds have an effect on the global climate. Smaller eruptions can create atmospheric effects similar to the larger explosions if they release large concentrations of sulfur-rich elements directly into the stratosphere. Also, eruptions occurring at high latitudes have less impact on climatic conditions than those at lower latitudes, where air currents are greater. The aerosols travel more quickly around the globe when moving in an easterly or westerly direction. If they are traveling in a north-south direction, the movement is much slower, with many of the aerosols becoming confined for years in a zone surrounding the polar cap.

MEASUREMENT METHODS

There are two primary indices that are used to measure the probable impact of volcanic activity. The first is the Dust Veil Index (DVI), which is based on an estimate of the volume of material injected into the atmosphere, surface temperatures, and the amount of sunlight reaching the surface. This index is derived from observations made at midlatitudes and thus is not entirely representative of the global scenario. The second index is the Volcanic Explosivity Index (VEI), which is based on the magnitude, intensity, dispersion, and destructiveness of an eruption. Other measurements of impact include tree-ring records, ice-core readings, and solar radiation measurements.

In addition to the impact indices, four primary methods are used to determine the volume and composition of gases that are emitted during large volcanic eruptions. The first is an examination of the composition and amount of aerosol layers in polar ice cores that are identified as being related to volcanic eruptions. Second is a comparison of gases from eruptions and glass inclusions in crystals that had formed in the volcanic rock prior to the event. The third is measurements of eruptions from satellite imagery, and the fourth is measurements of volcanic aerosols from the surface. Scientists have had some success with using a laser instrument that sends out a pulsing light beam, which reflects back when it detects aerosols. This method enables researchers to construct a profile indicating the density and height of the aerosols.

Ice core readings are especially beneficial in providing a clear record of older eruptions. Atmospheric aerosols from nearly every historic event have shown up in deep drillings of the polar ice. Since they tend to accumulate in layers, the ice cores offer clear annual records of climate and weather. As the aerosols fall to the ground surface over the poles, they begin to soil the surface snow with acid fallout in a process called sedimentation, by which thin layers of debris are formed. Over time, the snow becomes compacted into glacial ice and can be detected through electrical conductivity measurements. Some ice core discoveries have provided records going back more than 100,000 years.

Satellite measurements have enabled scientists from the U.S. Geological Survey to determine the amounts and compositions of gases emitted by several active volcanoes in the United States. Satellite sensors detected up to 1 million metric tons of sulfur dioxide tossed into the stratosphere during the main eruption of Mount St. Helens in 1980. Of particular benefit are the satellite observations conducted by the National Aeronautical and Space Administration's (NASA) Total Ozone Mapping Spectrometer (TOMS) instrument, which have helped to measure sulfur dioxide levels in the atmosphere following major events. TOMS was instrumental in tracking the band of sulfur dioxide across the Pacific produced by the eruption of Mount Pinatubo in the Philippines in 1991. Altogether, TOMS has made more than one hundred observations of volcanic events, including a major eruption of Chile's Cerro Hudson volcano in 1991. These measurements allow scientists to compare volcanic emissions of sulfur dioxide with injections of the gas from industrial plants and other human-based activities. Through comparative studies of volcanic activity, researchers are able to examine the effects of past and future eruptions with the aim of determining whether human or natural activities ultimately pose the greater threat to the environment.

HISTORICAL RECORD

Though less documented than modern eruptions, the larger historic events offer substantial proof of volcanic effects on climate for the simple reason they were bigger and left a more easily detectable trail of evidence.

By drilling into the sea floor south of Haiti and uncovering evidence of ash, researchers concluded that massive volcanic eruptions in the Caribbean Basin more than 55 million years ago created a sudden temperature inversion in the ocean waters that led to one of the most dramatic climatic changes in history. Scientists discovered distinctly colored volcanic ash layers that were far different from the sediments located above and below them. The period when the ash layers were deposited corresponds with a time of rapid warming globally. The presence of the ash indicates that a gigantic eruption took place just as the warming began. Scientists believe that the dust and gases from the eruptions initially cooled the atmosphere, increasing the density of seawater to the point where it sank into the deep ocean. The descending water, in turn, warmed the ocean floor and melted deposits of methane sediments, which then

bubbled up into the air, creating a greenhouse effect that warmed the world. Evidence also indicates that the process resulted in the extinction of nearly one-half of all deep-sea animals, victims of asphyxiation because of the lower solubility of oxygen in the suddenly warmer waters. Conversely, the evolution of new plant and animal species, including many primates and carnivores, was accelerated. Scientists already were aware that volcanic eruptions had occurred in the North Atlantic Ocean nearly 61 million years ago and believe that the Caribbean Basin event somehow may have acted in connection with these earlier eruptions.

In another major undersea discovery, scientists suspect that the islands of Tonga and Epi, located about 1,930 kilometers east of Australia, were the products of a massive eruption that took place around the year 1453. During the course of their research, scientists found that the entire stretch of sea floor separating the two islands was a crater more than 11 kilometers in width. They also uncovered charred vegetation that was carbon-dated between 1420 and 1475. To further narrow down the date of the eruption to 1453, they analyzed ice cores from Greenland and Antarctica; tree-ring records from California, Europe, and China; and reports of worldwide crop conditions during the period.

In 1815, the volcano Tambora erupted in Indonesia, precipitating one of the clearest examples of an eruption-induced global cooling event. The volcano emitted a massive column of solid material into the upper atmosphere. The aerosol veil extended to both hemispheres with effects that lasted well into the following year. The aftereffects were such that the year 1816 came to be known as "the year without a summer." In some regions of New England, up to 15 centimeters of snow fell in the month of June. There were numerous other reports of abnormally cool weather, including record low temperatures that forced people to wear coats and gloves in July. The average temperature in the Northern Hemisphere was reduced by as much as 0.5 degree Celsius, and parts of the United States and Canada experienced unusual summer frosts and crop failure. In Europe, the unusually cold readings resulted in widespread famine, though at the time the connection with the volcanic veil went unrecognized. Researchers identified the Tambora eruption from evidence uncovered in ice cores in Antarctica and Greenland. The event coincides with the fact that the decade between 1810 and 1820 is considered perhaps the coldest on record.

The famous 1883 eruption of Krakatau in Indonesia marked perhaps the first time researchers became fully involved on a worldwide basis with a volcanically induced atmospheric event. Much of the global interest could be attributed to the advances in telegraphic communication, which enabled scientists to share their observations of the spectacular sunsets and other visible phenomena arising from the eruption. Measurements indicated that Krakatau generated a cloud of approximately 21 cubic kilometers of matter. Witnesses in the area recalled dramatic displays of lightning in the cloud veil and a strong odor of sulfur in the air. Researchers believe that the ash cast into the upper atmosphere by the eruption and the ensuing dust veil led to worldwide decreases in incoming solar radiation. Mean annual global temperatures fell close to 0.5 degree Celsius in 1884, with the cooling period extending through the remainder of the 1880's. In 1884, there was a marked increase in the number of storms in the United States. Record snowfalls, an unusually high number of tornadoes, torrential rains, and severe flooding caused widespread damage. The abnormal atmospheric conditions attributed to Krakatau included brilliant sunsets and a blue or green tinge to the sun, depending on which part of the globe the observation was made. In 1888, the Royal Society of London published a volume that documented the eruption and formally established the connection between major volcanic activity and subsequent changes in worldwide atmospheric conditions.

By historic standards, the eruption of Mount Pinatubo may appear insignificant, but it stands as a watershed event in the ability of scientists to monitor the interaction of a volcanic cloud and the upper atmosphere. The eruption is believed to have sent nearly 20 billion kilograms of sulfur dioxide about 20 to 27 kilometers into the atmosphere, resulting in 30 billion kilograms of sulfuric acid aerosols. For several months the TOMS instrument tracked the sulfur cloud created by Pinatubo with images verifying that its particles circled the globe in about three weeks, forming an almost continuous band.

The Pinatubo eruption had a gigantic atmospheric impact. The year following its eruption turned out to be one of the coldest on record. Temperature measurements in the lower and middle atmospheres indicated a change of nearly 0.5 degree Celsius between 1991 and 1992. By 1994, readings revealed that the volcano's effect had waned and that global temperatures had returned to previous levels.

SIGNIFICANCE

Much has been learned and much remains a mystery concerning the chemical and physical processes that occur between a volcanic eruption and climatic change. It is an area of intense study because of the belief among scientists that the balance of the global climate is dependent on the phenomenon of volcanism. The atmosphere essentially was developed through intermittent volcanic emissions of carbon dioxide and water vapor, along with nitrogen and possibly methane. There is no reason to believe that the relationship between the two forces has changed in any dramatic way.

Volcanic eruptions can be an agent for global cooling or global warming, depending on their interactions with other environmental elements. The historical record indicates that when the atmospheric balance is threatened by natural or human forces, the consequences can be severe. To most people, fractions of degrees may not appear significant, but in the grand scheme of the environment, they can produce dramatic effects. During the ice ages, the global temperature was only about 5 degrees Celsius cooler than it was at the close of the twentieth century. Scientists believe that a global rise in temperature of as little as 3 degrees Celsius could bring about dramatic changes, including accelerated glacial melting, rising sea levels, more frequent and more severe storms, and droughts. The temperature increase during the twentieth century is considered by many as evidence that the human production of greenhouse gases such as carbon dioxide is affecting the climate. However, it also is believed that multiple eruptions of large volcanoes over a long period of time can raise the carbon dioxide levels enough to cause substantial global warming. To add to the equation, studies also indicate a possible association between other volcanic vapors and the depletion of the ozone layer. A few researchers have even advanced the idea that there is a link between volcanism and El Niño, the periodic warm ocean conditions that appear along the tropical west coast of South America. A number of eruptions have preceded El Niño in years past, leading to speculation that volcanic gases may trigger or strengthen the phenomenon.

Major events such as the Caribbean Basin volcanic eruption pose a special problem for climatic equilibrium. The sudden warming of the deep ocean resulting from a series of large volcanic eruptions is a scenario that scientists believe could recur, causing a major disruption of atmospheric circulation. In attempting to trace the connections between volcanic activities and climate, scientists have begun to think in global terms and to look upon their task as an interdisciplinary effort. In so doing, they have been able to make significant strides in developing the depth of understanding necessary to form reasonably accurate forecasts of future catastrophic events.

William Hoffman

FURTHER READING

Christopherson, Robert W., and Mary-Louise Byrne. *Geosystem: An Introduction to Physical Geography*. Toronto: Pearson Education Canada, 2006. A highly readable and well-illustrated book that delivers a thorough overview of the various systems that interact to make up the physical environment. Closely discusses the effects of volcanism on climate.

de Boer, Jella Zeilinga, and Donald Theodore Sanders. *Volcanoes in Human History: The Far-Reaching Effects of Major Eruptions*. Princeton, N.J.: Princeton University Press, 2002. Provides an overview of volcanism followed by specific volcanoes and eruptions. Includes the interaction of human history and volcanic activity. Covers the Hawaiian Islands, Crete, Vesuvius, Iceland, Tambora, Krakatau, Pelée, Tristan da Cunha, and Mount St. Helens.

Decker, Robert W., and Barbara Decker. *Volcanoes*. 4th ed. New York: Freeman, 2005. An introductory work on the study of volcanoes that contains a concise chapter, with clear illustrations, on the connection between volcanic eruptions and climate.

Fisher, Richard V., Grant Heiken, and Jeffrey B. Hulen. *Volcanoes: Crucibles of Change*. Princeton, N.J.: Princeton University Press, 1997. Covers a long list of volcanoes, from Mount Vesuvius to Mount St. Helens. A segment on the effects of volcanic gases helps explain the complex interactions among gaseous, liquid, and solid volcanic matter, the surrounding atmosphere, and solar radiation.

Francis, Peter, and Clive Oppenheimer. *Volcanoes*. 2d ed. New York: Oxford University Press, 2004. Covers volcanic activity from lava flows to pyroclastic currents. Provides many examples from Hawaii, Italy, Ethiopia, Japan, Mount St. Helens, and Krakatau. Written for the layperson, but some knowledge of geology is helpful.

Kuhn, Gerald G. "The Impact of Volcanic Eruptions on Worldwide Weather." *Twenty-first Century Science and Technology* (Winter, 1997-1998): 48-58. A well-documented article that provides a comprehensive review of the evidence supporting a link between volcanic activity and climatic changes. Gives special attention to a wide range of weather-related abnormalities associated with the aftereffects of specific events.

Marti, Joan, and Gerald Ernst. *Volcanoes and the Environment*. New York: Cambridge University Press, 2005. Presents a discussion of the various ways in which volcanism affects terrestrial, aquatic, and atmospheric environments, from both historical and present-day perspectives. Provides information on volcanoes from the physical mechanisms and behaviors to hazards and effects on humans and nature. Written for students and geologists studying environmental science and geology.

Oppenheimer, Clive. *Eruptions That Shook the World*. New York: Cambridge University Press, 2011. Describes the mechanics of volcanoes and different types of eruptions. Also describes the effects of eruptions on the atmosphere, humans, and other organisms. Examines specific volcanoes and provides an appendix of major eruptions.

Robinson, Andrew. *Earth Shock*. London: Thames and Hudson, 1993. Offers an interdisciplinary look at the forces of nature, including volcanoes and their impact on the global climate. Probes the interrelationships among the various natural disasters with a lucid style, supported by ample illustrations and charts.

Savino, John, and Marie Jones. *Supervolcano*. Franklin Lakes, N.J.: New Page Books, 2007. Discusses the classification of supervolcanoes and their eruptions. Describes the effects of volcanic eruptions on climate and the ecosystem. Includes a glossary, bibliography, further resources, and indexing.

Siebert, Lee, Tom Simkin, and Paul Kimberly. *Volcanoes of the World*. 3d ed. Berkeley: University of California Press, 2010. Reviewed as "the most comprehensive source on dynamic volcanism," presenting chronological, statistical, environmental, and historical information about volcanism over the past ten thousand years.

Sparks, R. S. *Volcanic Plumes.* New York: Wiley, 1997. Examines the basic geological principles and dynamics behind the volcanic plumes and their impact on the surface environment. Focuses on how the plumes interact with the atmosphere and then disperse before depositing their debris and gases.

Winchester, Simon. *Krakatoa: The Day the World Exploded, August 27, 1883.* New York: Harper-Collins Publishers, 2003. An excellent and entertaining description and placement of the violent eruption of Krakatoa within the context and theory of plate tectonics as a planetary process. Well researched. Includes historical observation of atmospheric and climatic events.

See also: Atmosphere's Global Circulation; Atmospheric and Oceanic Oscillations; Climate; Clouds; Drought; Hurricanes; Lightning and Thunder; Monsoons; Precipitation; Satellite Meteorology; Seasons; Severe Storms; Tornadoes; Van Allen Radiation Belts; Weather Forecasting; Weather Forecasting: Numerical Weather Prediction; Weather Modification; Wind

WATERFALLS

Waterfalls are created by the free flow of a stream over a discontinuity in the streambed. The fall may be perpendicular and free from the rock surface or may run across the rock, frequently in a series of small falls, with the water essentially in free fall under the force of gravity. Waterfalls attract viewers for their scenic and aesthetic qualities, but they also possess scientific value as an aid in the interpretation of earth history and economic importance as possible sites for the generation of hydroelectric power.

PRINCIPAL TERMS

- **cascade:** a small waterfall or series of small falls
- **cataract:** most frequently, an overwhelming flood or a great volume of flow over a cliff; sometimes, however, the term is used interchangeably with "cascade"
- **grade:** a hypothetical uniform profile of a stream seeking to achieve quasi-equilibrium; the slope of the streambed between its highest and lowest points
- **knickpoint (or nickpoint):** an abrupt change in the stream profile, generally caused by a resistant rock layer that retards the rate of erosion
- **rapids:** a turbulent flow in a stream caused by obstructions and constrictions of the channel or by resistant rock layers
- **riffles:** a smaller version of rapids, a turbulent flow between calm pools, found in nearly all streams for hydraulic reasons
- **tectonics (tectonic activity):** vertical or horizontal movements in the earth's crust, displacing rocks, landforms, and stream gradients

CHARACTERISTICS

Waterfalls occur at breaks in the relatively smooth profiles or streambed slopes of streams. The break in slope may be minor and result in only a riffle, or slight roughening of the water surface. All streams possess riffles, which result from the hydraulic action that permits streams to carry sediment. Rapids are the result of a more profound interruption of the profile, often sufficient to block the passage of most boats. Rapids are an indication that the streambed has encountered erosion-resistant bedrock, boulders, or other obstructions. Some purists maintain that true waterfalls exist only where water falls free of its streambed, plunging downward through the air. Except for the largest and most spectacular falls, however, free fall is generally a function of the amount of discharge in the stream channel, varying with weather and climate, and the topography through which the streambed passes. Most of the world's streams have dry spells every year. During those drought periods, a free-falling waterfall may become a cascade, a cataract, or even rapids. The Great Falls of the Potomac River dried up to very weak rapids during a late 1960's drought, but it was still an obstruction to navigation and a potential site for waterpower development, possessed scenic appeal, and presented evidence to geologists of the underlying rock structure and its place in deciphering earth history. These are the major reasons why people are interested in waterfalls, whether they are 1,000 meters high or less than 10, and whether they are free-falling or are better described as cascades, cataracts, or rapids.

FORMATION

Streams, on their route to the sea, lake, or some other termination, cut downward through loose sediments and bedrock, by eroding and transporting some of this material as their sedimentary load. If the materials through which they are eroding are relatively soft or weak, the stream ultimately will achieve grade, denoted by a smooth, upwardly concave profile. Waterfalls are an indication that something has prevented the stream from achieving an equilibrium between its discharge, or quantity of flow, and the sediment load that it carries. The cause may lie in the structure of the underlying rocks, with particularly resistant layers being encountered in the downward course of erosion. Frequently, the stream cannot achieve a smooth profile because of some event of geologic history, such as rapid tectonic uplift or glacial deepening of a major valley. Most surface relief is a consequence of tectonic activity in the past few million years, particularly the uplifting of terrain. This length of time is insufficient for streams to achieve even quasi-equilibrium or grade in the highlands of the world, where complex geology often exposes rocks of varying resistance to weathering and stream erosion. Resistant rock layers may be sandstones, as in much of the Appalachian Mountains and Colorado Plateaus, or dolomite such as that which forms the Niagara Escarpment, over which the Niagara River falls.

The effects of simple erosion are not in itself sufficient to describe the formation and evolution of waterfalls, however. The geologic history of the Niagara River and Niagara Falls, for example, is more complicated than merely the encountering of a resistant dolomite rock layer by the downward cutting river. Continental glaciation of the eastern and central United States and Canada obliterated the pattern of preglacial stream drainage, and the roughly twelve thousand years that Niagara Falls has been in existence is insufficient time for that stream to achieve grade. Similarly, the head of navigation on the Mississippi River is at St. Anthony Falls in Minneapolis, Minnesota; upstream of the falls, the Mississippi flows on a new, postglacial course. The head of navigation of the Ohio River is the falls at Louisville, Kentucky, only a short distance upstream from the mouth of the Ohio, where it joins the Mississippi. This peculiar situation led geologists to search for the preglacial Ohio River, which was discovered buried by glacial sediments in northern Indiana and Ohio. Niagara Falls, St. Anthony Falls, and the falls of the Ohio at Louisville may be considered as large and dramatic knickpoints, or breaks in the smooth stream profile. Knickpoints migrate upstream as erosion proceeds on its path toward grade or quasi-equilibrium, eventually becoming smaller and smaller until they are eliminated as significant breaks in the stream profile.

Waterfalls therefore represent unusual and temporary geologic circumstances and contribute to scientific knowledge both in the quest for explanation of each individual waterfall and in the contribution to understanding of the geologic history of a region. The largest number of waterfalls worldwide undoubtedly occur in younger, recently uplifted mountains that have been subjected to alpine glaciation. Just as major rivers have greater eroding capability than their tributaries, so larger valleys are occupied by larger glaciers capable of cutting deeper into the bedrock. The glaciers of tributary valleys are much smaller and have less potential for erosion than those in the main valleys. After the glaciers melt, the streams occupying the tributary valleys are left hanging, and they descend to the main stream as waterfalls. Hanging tributary valleys also occur in unglaciated uplands, but they are far more common in the spectacular scenery of alpine mountains, especially in the world's major fjord regions: Alaska and British Columbia, Norway, Chile, and New Zealand's South Island.

SCENIC APPEAL

The scenic appeal of waterfalls is the reason most people find them of interest. The sheer grandeur of the falling water inspires artists, photographers, and writers, whose products enhance the waterfalls' fame and encourage multitudes to experience the view personally. The attraction of waterfalls is a significant factor in decisions to visit state and national parks and even roadside waysides. Tourist counts are notoriously unreliable, but it is safe to say that millions have visited Niagara Falls, owing in part to its location near large population centers of the United States and Canada. By contrast, Victoria Falls on the Zambezi River in southern Africa, Angel Falls in Venezuela (the world's highest at 979 meters), the Iguazu Falls on the border of Argentina and Brazil, and Guaira Falls on the upper Parana River between Brazil and Paraguay all possess spectacular characteristics, but they are located too far from large centers of population to be visited easily.

There is also disagreement as to which waterfall has the greatest discharge. Unlike the height of a waterfall, which is static unless a catastrophic rockfall occurs, stream discharge is variable throughout the year, and from dry years to wet years. Nearly all waterfalls occur in places with seasonal precipitation or in environments where the winter precipitation is in the form of snow, leading to spectacular flows during the snowmelt season but disappointing conditions when the stream is chiefly ice. Niagara retains an appeal when it is frozen, but the weather outside is generally uncomfortable at that time of year, and most tourists visit during the warm season. Thousands of people annually register disappointment at the appearance of Yosemite Falls and the other falls of Yosemite National Park during the long, dry summers.

This is a characteristic of waterfalls in regions of alpine glaciation; they are frozen in winter and are most spectacular during the short snowmelt season of spring and early summer.

Tropical waterfalls, such as those of Africa, South America, and India may have tremendous discharges during the rainy season but much lower flows during the dry season. One of Niagara's great advantages as a tourist attraction is that it has huge natural reservoirs upstream in the form of the Great Lakes, which ensure an even discharge year after year, wet season and dry.

RATING SYSTEMS

Arguments concerning which waterfall among the giants is greatest frequently involve rating systems employing the height of the falls, its width, its discharge, and other quantifiable factors. Curiously, vista, or the opportunity to view the falls from a particular point, is often overlooked. Whereas Niagara Falls, for example, can be observed from several viewpoints, all of which overwhelm the observer with the view of a tremendous amount of water cascading over the edge of the escarpment into a broad open basin, the much wider Victoria Falls, in Africa, descends into a complicated narrow chasm or canyon and little of Victoria Falls can actually be seen from one point on the surface. This is also true of Iguazu Falls, which is up to several kilometers wide and consists of as many as twenty cataracts. Aircraft flights are the best way to observe these giants and are, in fact, the only way to experience more than a small fraction of those falls.

A hypothetical rating system may be required to incorporate many points of consideration, such as the amount of time a waterfall is in full flow each year and availability to the general public as an attraction. In addition, aesthetic and therefore highly subjective considerations may come into play, such as which waterfalls are the most beautiful, or inspiring, or dramatic. These and other considerations can be important if decisions must be made by government agencies regarding the protection of a particular waterfall. In actuality, such scenarios confront many water projects, which must procure a favorable ratio of benefits to costs in order to survive. The allocation of limited financial resources increasingly involves such decisions.

HYDROELECTRIC POWER

The height of waterfalls creates another area of interest: the potential for hydroelectric power generation. "Head" is the term used to describe the difference in elevation between the water level at the top of a fall and that at the bottom. The higher the head, the greater the potential energy of position, which can be converted into electrical energy as the water descends. It must be emphasized that the waterfall itself is not harnessed. Rather, the difference in water levels, or the head, is harnessed by diverting water from the upper level to flow downward through penstocks to the lower level. The potential energy of the water at the upper level is thus converted to kinetic energy, and the momentum of the moving water is utilized to drive hydroelectric generators. Niagara Falls was for years the world's largest single hydroelectric generating facility, and it is still among the largest of hydroelectric projects. Most of the waterfalls of the tropics have a potential for power generation, but this has not yet been developed extensively. Europe, Japan, the United States, and Canada have the most fully developed hydroelectric generating capacities. Regions of alpine mountain glaciation have particularly high potential. The economic benefits of this aspect of waterfalls can be enormously significant locally, and frequently nationwide, although highly industrialized nations with significant numbers of automobiles demand far more energy than waterpower can generate. Most hydroelectric power generation today is actually not from natural waterfall sites but from what can be called "artificial waterfalls": the creation of head by the construction of a high dam within a narrow valley or gorge.

At the beginning of the Industrial Revolution, before the development of electricity and its distribution through transmission lines, water-power sites provided the energy for countless small factories and mills. Many of these were the sites of small waterfalls and rapids, such as along the Fall Line of the Piedmont of the southeastern United States. The Great Falls of the Potomac are an example of such a site. The development of electrical transmission lines freed industry from these locations near falls and rapids and allowed an expansion throughout the countryside. The smaller water-power sites fell into disuse, and only a few have been preserved for historic reasons. The larger sites, such as Niagara Falls, remain an important part of the economy.

Neil E. Salisbury

FURTHER READING

Beisel, Richard H., Jr. *America's Top 100 Western Waterfalls.* Parker, Colo.: Outskirts Press , 2008. A guidebook for waterfall enthusiasts, providing historical and sightseeing information about each waterfall classified according to the International Waterfall Classification System.

Benn, Douglas I., and David J. A. Evans. *Glaciers and Glaciation.* 2d ed. London: Hodder Education Publishers, 2010. A comprehensive account of the formation and evolution of glaciers. An easily understandable book that describes the natural processes of glaciation and the creation of waterfalls. Suitable for the high school reader and above. Color illustrations, index, and a large bibliography.

Berton, Pierre. *Niagara: A History of the Falls.* New York: Kodansha International, 1997. Provides the reader with a complete and entertaining history of Niagara Falls. Filled with illustrations and maps that complement the text and make it easily understood and enjoyed by readers of all levels. Index and bibliography.

Boyle, Godfrey, ed. *Renewable Energy.* 2d ed. New York: Oxford University Press, 2004. Provides a complete overview of renewable energy resources. Chapters discuss solar energy, bioenergy, geothermal energy, hydroelectric energy, tidal power, wind energy, and wave energy. Discusses the basic physics principles, technology, and environmental impact. Each chapter has references and a further reading list. An excellent starting point, although, the advanced technical details of these power supplies are limited.

Corrigan, Patricia, and Geoffrey H. Nash. *Waterfalls.* New York: Chelsea House, 2007. Provides detailed information about the world's "top ten" waterfalls, including their location, size, source, volume, appearance, geologic characteristics, history, and the local climate. Written for middle school and high school students.

Easterbrook, Donald J. *Surface Processes and Landforms.* 2d ed. Upper Saddle River, N.J.: Prentice Hall, 1999. A not-overly-technical discussion of how waterfalls and rapids relate to attempts by streams to achieve equilibrium and a graded profile. Suitable for college-level readers.

Fairbridge, Rhodes W., and Reginald W. Herschy, eds. *The Encyclopedia of Hydrology and Water Resources.* Boston: Kluwer Academic, 1998. The entry on waterfalls provides a succinct but illuminating classification of waterfalls and a brief description of rates of recession of falls, centering on Niagara with a comparison to the Nile. Suitable for college-level readers.

Forrester, Glenn C. *Niagara Falls and the Glacier.* Hicksville, N.Y.: Exposition Press, 1976. A highly readable account of the geological context of Niagara Falls, together with a discussion of the role of glaciation in the origin and development of the falls. Includes considerable information on hydropower developments and measures taken to preserve the falls. Well illustrated, with photographs and diagrams. Suitable for high school readers.

Janssen, Sarah, ed. *The World Almanac and Book of Facts, 2011.* Mahwah, N.J.: World Almanac Books, 2011. Contains a succinct listing of the world's most famous waterfalls, including their heights and certain other characteristics.

Lawton, Jerry. *Waterfalls: The Niagara Escarpment.* Richmond Hill, Ontario: Boston Mills Press, 2000. While Niagara Falls is the most well known, a number of other waterfalls flow over the extent of the Niagara Escarpment in southwestern Ontario. Guides the reader to thirty of them, providing historical and geological information as well as sightseeing tips for each one.

Pavlopoulos, Kosmas, and Niki Evelpidou. *Mapping Geomorphological Environments.* New York: Springer, 2009. Contains a chapter discussing fluvial environments and processes. Discusses glacial formations and the waterfalls of glacial state park. Describes many other geologic formations and examines mapping methodologies.

Snead, Roman E. *World Atlas of Geomorphic Features.* Huntington, N.Y.: Robert E. Krieger, 1980. Includes a readable discussion of the nature of major waterfalls of the world, as well as a listing of more than seventy major worldwide waterfalls and more than thirty major U.S. waterfalls. Accompanying maps show the general location of each falls and, in addition, regions where smaller waterfalls are common. Suitable for high school readers.

See also: Alluvial Systems; Aquifers; Artificial Recharge; Dams and Flood Control; Floods; Freshwater and Groundwater Contamination Around the World; Groundwater Movement; Groundwater Pollution and Remediation; Hydrologic Cycle; Precipitation; Salinity and Desalination; Saltwater Intrusion; Sediment Transport and Deposition; Surface Water; Water Quality; Watersheds; Water Table; Water Wells

WATER QUALITY

The term "water quality" refers to the fitness of water for a defined use such as human consumption, and is measured in terms of chemical, physical, and biological parameters. Standards against which the quality of water is compared are neither universal nor constant and depend upon who has established the standards and for what purpose.

PRINCIPAL TERMS

- **concentration:** amount of a specific substance present in a given volume of sample water; commonly used units include milligrams per liter or micrograms per liter
- **contaminants:** solutes introduced into the hydrologic environment as a result of human activity, without regard to degree of degradation
- **detection limit:** the lowest concentration of a constituent that can be reliably detected
- **maximum contaminant level goals (MCLGs):** nonenforceable health goals based on the levels of contaminants that cause no negative health effects
- **maximum contaminant levels (MCLs):** enforceable standards for drinking water established by government regulatory agencies, such as the U.S. Environmental Protection Agency under the Safe Drinking Water Act
- **national primary drinking water standards:** the list of MCLs and MCLGs for organic and inorganic constituents; the list also includes various standards for asbestos fibers, turbidity, bacteria, viruses, and radioactive-emitting constituents, established using less common concentration units
- **pollution:** the presence of environmental components that are not naturally present; contaminant levels at objectionable concentrations

CHEMICAL ANALYSIS OF WATER

Pure water, composed only of molecules of dihydrogen oxide (H_2O) and nothing else, does not exist in nature. Even rainwater contains measurable amounts of dissolved constituents in the range of 10 milligrams per liter. Water is of acceptable quality for a defined use or purpose if, on analysis, constituents in it do not exceed prescribed concentrations. Water quality describes the fitness or suitability of water for a specific use, based upon chemical, physical, and biological parameters. Significant differences have arisen among scientific and engineering disciplines and government agencies as to which indicators are appropriate for the evaluation of water quality. The results of an analysis of a water sample are commonly presented as indicators of water quality without the provision of a context of use or standards.

Standards against which the quality of water is compared are neither universal nor constant and depend upon who has established the standards and for what purpose. Legal standards prescribed by regulation are binding. They prescribe conditions not to be exceeded for a water resource and allow penalties to be assessed for violations. Standards are subject to change over time as more becomes known about the health effects of exposure to various contaminants, as analysts are able to detect ever smaller quantities of contaminants, and as governments apply standards to more situations.

This methodology of listing constituents and concentrations that must not be exceeded has undergone constant evolution. Prior to the establishment of formal criteria, odor, color, taste, turbidity, and temperature were measures commonly used in assessing the desirability of a drinking-water source. By 1784, less direct chemical criteria involving the ability of a sample to dissolve soap without forming lumps or a residue were applied to establish whether water was drinkable. Chemical criteria alone, however, are insufficient for establishing a water supply as both drinkable and safe. The relationship between disease and pollution by human and animal wastes had been recognized for centuries. An early method of measuring the bacterial quality of water, for example, relied on observing the length of time that a stored water sample remained free of visible growths. This was eventually replaced by techniques to identify and count bacteria, and to compare measurements to a standard.

U.S. GEOLOGICAL SURVEY AND U.S. PUBLIC HEALTH SERVICE

The U.S. Geological Survey (USGS) first reported chemical analyses of natural waters in 1879 and, by 1901, had published more than twenty-five reports on the geologic control and on the chemical and physical properties of natural water. At that time, many water sources were pristine, unaffected by human activity. The composition (quality) of waters from lakes, rivers, and wells resulted solely from reactions with gases in the air and minerals in soil and rock. The major dissolved constituents, those generally with concentrations of more than 1 milligram per liter, are calcium, magnesium, sodium, potassium, bicarbonate, carbonate, chloride, sulfate, nitrate, and oxygen; these constitute up to 99 percent by weight of the dissolved matter in pristine waters. Under less common natural situations, other constituents such as iron or fluoride may exceed 1 milligram per liter concentration. Minor constituents are detected in pristine natural waters if sought by analysis. Only some of the major constituents, such as sulfate and chloride, are included in either the U.S. primary (enforceable) or secondary (nonenforceable) drinking-water standards. Canadian standards are generally the same as U.S. standards, with only minor differences. Other major constituents are listed in the standards of other organizations, such as the World Health Organization or the European Community.

After 1901, the USGS expanded its activities to include pollution studies, recognizing that sewage and industrial wastes were degrading the quality of water and adversely affecting municipal water supplies. In 1905, the USGS began the first monitoring program to assess the quality of streams and lakes, efforts that led to estimates of the amounts of dissolved and suspended matter carried to the oceans by rivers.

The U.S. Public Health Service (USPHS) was established in 1912 and was directed to study sanitary water quality. The U.S. Geological Survey continued to studying water supplies for public use and for agricultural and industrial purposes, and maintained limited networks to evaluate trends in water quality. In the United States, formal chemical water-quality standards originated by action of the USPHS in 1914. Dissolved constituents believed to be harmful to humans were identified, and maximum allowable concentrations were established. Water exceeding the limits could not be used for food preparation or for drinking water on passenger trains (interstate carriers) crossing state lines. The USPHS standards were widely, although unofficially, regarded as the basis for acceptability of a water supply for human consumption. The standards were expanded both in the number of constituents covered and in lowered permissible concentrations in 1925, 1942, 1946, and 1962. The final set of standards promulgated by the USPHS, issued in 1962,

considered bacterial quality; physical characteristics of turbidity, color, and odor; chemical characteristics, some mandatory and others recommended; and radioactivity. In earlier times of pristine sources in protected watersheds, water that required no extensive treatment was available, and one set of standards was sufficient for both raw water and drinking water. By 1962, modern civilization had affected most water sources, and raw water from degraded sources had to be treated so that the standards for drinking water were met at the point of delivery.

ENVIRONMENTAL PROTECTION AGENCY

By the 1960's, industrial manufacturing of new chemical products and by-products, as well as the generation of waste, had resulted in contamination and pollution, with many materials found to be persistent in the environment and affecting surface and groundwater supplies. Efforts to restrict the degradation of water sources were under way in specific geographic areas ranging from small drainage basins to interstate commissions for river basins. The Environmental Protection Agency (EPA) was established in 1970 and given the task of setting goals and standards and identifying sources of polluting effluents. Federal legislation, including the U.S. Water Quality Act and the Clean Water Act, led to broadened activities in documenting quality, mandating treatment and recovery, and requiring the establishment of standards for discharged waters. The National Pollutant Discharge Elimination System (NPDES) was established for all point source discharges into U.S. waters, and required permits, reporting, and effluent limitation. For situations where the limitations were not stringent enough to improve the quality of receiving waters, treatment was required. The EPA was charged with developing a wide array of water-quality standards. An understanding of the degree to which the nation's waters are contaminated and what the water quality trends are was seen as essential to management decisions. The USGS was thus brought back into the process of monitoring surface and groundwater supplies, looking at contamination to a greater extent than before. The agency established the National Water Quality Assessment Program (NAWQA) to systematically study the quality of U.S. water, stream basin by stream basin.

The first set of drinking-water standards to be established by the EPA became effective in 1977, under the mandates of the 1974 U.S. Safe Drinking Water Act. Among the inorganic contaminants, fluoride and mercury were newly added to the earlier USPHS standards, nitrate became a mandatory rather than recommended standard, and radioactive sources were redefined. This came about in large part because of better information about the risks and health effects of those contaminants. The standards have undergone changes and extensions since 1977, including modifications authorized by the Safe Drinking Water Act Amendments of 1996. A prior mandate of the EPA to regulate twenty-five new contaminants every three years has been set aside, replaced by a mandate to review at least five contaminants for possible regulation every five years, in consideration of the following criteria: whether the contaminant adversely affects human health; whether it is known or substantially likely to occur in public water systems with a frequency and at levels of public health concern; and whether regulation of the contaminant presents a meaningful opportunity for health-risk reduction. In addition, there are provisions for monitoring unregulated contaminants, creating an accessible database, and disclosing violations to the public served by water systems within twenty-four hours.

Domestic use, including drinking water, is considered by many to be the most essential use of water, and standards for drinking water receive the greatest attention. Water-quality requirements for other purposes may be more restrictive (for example, for high-pressure boiler water) or less restrictive (for example, for hydraulic cement manufacture) than standards for domestic use.

APPLICATION OF WATER-QUALITY STUDIES

In the earth sciences, water-quality studies generally have a focus beyond determining whether a water source is suitable for a given purpose. Larger questions of regional water quality, such as determining how and why water with certain characteristics is associated with a specific rock type, or explaining how and why groundwater evolves chemically as it slowly moves through an aquifer, are examples of applications that center on understanding natural processes. The contamination and pollution of water resources have drawn considerable attention, leading to studies of the transport of pollutants by water. One example of applications of the methodology from the earth sciences should illustrate the disciplinary perspective.

Of the major constituents in natural waters, only sulfate is listed in the national primary drinking water standards. Sulfate in drinking water produces laxative effects and an unpleasant taste. It is listed in the nonenforceable national secondary drinking water standards for taste and laxative effects at a concentration of 250 milligrams per liter and is prohibited by the primary standards at 400 to 500 milligrams per liter. The sources of the sulfate are listed as "natural deposits."

As a result of the Safe Drinking Water Act and using data from the U.S. Geological Survey, a series of state maps was compiled to show the regional variation in concentration of major dissolved constituents in well water. A zone of high-sulfate water extends from Lake Erie across northwest Ohio and into east-central Indiana. Water from wells in this area is of generally unacceptable quality. From the perspective of the earth sciences, it was important to build upon the recognition of this zone in order to determine probable cause. Obviously, such a study cannot exclude areas from which groundwater just passes the standards. Results from this study provide an understanding of the geologic controls on the system. High-sulfate water is recovered from shallow wells in glacial deposits and also from wells in a deeper bedrock aquifer. The situation is explained in part by the presence of gypsum and anhydrite, both calcium sulfate minerals, in a sedimentary terrain characterized by shale and dolomite units. Glacial activity eroded formerly exposed bedrock of shale and anhydrite, moved it, and redeposited it as unconsolidated material over undisturbed bedrock, also containing anhydrite and dolomite. High values of sulfate in the water, at some wells exceeding 1,000 milligrams per liter, would ordinarily not be possible because of the solubility limits of calcium sulfate minerals. In such waters, magnesium values were elevated, and calcium values were lower than expected. The conclusion is that in order for such high values of sulfate to exist in the water, a process known as dedolomitization is taking place, in which dolomite, a calcium magnesium carbonate mineral, is dissolved, and calcite, a calcium carbonate mineral, is deposited, in effect adding magnesium and removing calcium from the water. Without this process, such high values of sulfate would not normally be possible due to the very low solubility of many sulfate minerals.

CONTAMINATED WATERS

Contaminated waters may be safe to drink, but typically are not. In addition to the constituents derived from natural sources, these waters contain (by definition) constituents derived from a variety of human activities, such as improperly treated sewage, storage tanks that have leaked, improper disposal of hazardous wastes, and agricultural practices. Many of the chemicals involved, such as various herbicides and pesticides, are manufactured synthetically and do not occur in nature. Standards for safe drinking water for most of these constituents range generally from tenths to several hundred micrograms per liter.

Maximum contaminant levels (MCLs) are derived from studies of risk to humans consuming two liters of water a day over a lifetime of seventy years. Based upon extrapolations of animal studies for a given contaminant, an increased cancer risk to humans of one in one million over a lifetime leads to the standard. By statute, no cancer risk is to be tolerated, but the technology does not exist to totally eliminate the very small concentrations of many contaminants in water resources. Thus, the maximum contaminant level goal is generally zero for MCLGs but a small actual concentration for MCLs.

Other water-quality standards, including national effluent standards for limiting the discharge of pollutants into surface waters, have been established or enforced as a result of a number of federal laws and resultant regulations, including the Clean Water Act, which addresses water pollution from point and nonpoint sources; the Comprehensive Environmental Response, Compensation and Recovery Act (the "Superfund" Act), which mandates cleanup of hazardous-waste sites and leaking tanks; the Resource Conservation and Recovery Act, which defines and requires tracking and proper disposal of hazardous wastes; the National Environmental Policy Act, which establishes the need for environmental impact statements for federally controlled or subsidized actions; the Endangered Species Act, which protects some habitats; and the Wild and Scenic Rivers Act, which limits development along some rivers. States in some instances have established water-quality standards similar to or more restrictive than the ones put forth by federal agencies.

Management of water quality for effluents takes place through regulations applied to discharges from or into three distinct sites. End-of-pipe standards specify levels that must be met at the point from which effluent is discharged from an industrial facility. Technology-based standards impose regulations on a discharging facility. Assimilative capacity standards define the water-quality conditions that a receiving body of water (stream or lake) must not exceed. Dischargers to the stream or lake are identified, and those causing the stream or lake to exceed standards are required to manage the quality of their discharges.

Robert G. Corbett

FURTHER READING

Berner, E. K., and R. A. Berner. *The Global Water Cycle.* Englewood Cliffs, N.J.: Prentice Hall, 1987. An interdisciplinary text that provides chemical characterization of water as rain, soil and groundwater, river water, lakes, estuaries, and oceans, and reports the relative importance of natural and human processes in the cycling of elements through the hydrologic cycle.

Brimblecombe, Peter, et al., eds. *Acid Rain: Deposition to Recovery.* Dordrecht: Springer, 2010. Discusses acid rain from various perspectives. Covers agriculture, human impact, ecological impact, wet versus dry deposition, soil chemistry, and surface water quality.

Fetter, C. W. *Contaminant Hydrogeology.* Long Grove, Ill.: Waveland Publishing, 2008. An applied text for hydrogeologists and engineers that presents technical information on the collection and interpretation of data from contaminated groundwater sites and options for remediation of those sites.

Hem, J. D. *Study and Interpretation of the Chemical Characteristics of Natural Water.* 3d ed. United States Geological Survey Water-Supply Paper 2254. Washington, D.C.: U.S. Government Printing Office, 1992. Provides an introduction to water chemistry. Written to serve geologists and hydrogeologists who need to evaluate water quality. Provides practical information about low-temperature aqueous geochemistry using real-world examples. Offers an extensive list of references.

Mays, Larry W. *Water Resources Engineering.* Hoboken, N.J.: John Wiley & Sons, 2011. Considered the leading resource on the principles and practices of water resource engineering, with new and updated graphics integrated into each chapter, with a focus on sustainability. Written for water resource engineers.

Moore, John E. *Field Hydrogeology.* 2d ed. Boca Raton, Fla.: CRC Press, 2012. Provides practical information on field investigation, aquifer testing, and groundwater quality testing. Discusses planning and report writing in detail. Also provides case studies from around the world. Best suited for students learning the planning and investigation of field hydrology.

Novotny, Vladimir. *Water Quality: Diffuse Pollution and Watershed Management.* 2d ed. Hoboken, N.J.: John Wiley & Sons, 2003. Describes many topics related to nonpoint source pollution. Discusses causes of water pollution, water quality statistics, the water cycle, erosion, and soil pollution. Provides good descriptions of management practices and mitigation. Includes environmental assessment and modeling.

Perry, J., and E. Vanderklein. *Water Quality: Management of a Natural Resource.* Cambridge, Mass.: Blackwell Science, 1996. Claims that water quality is basically a social and political concern. Presents a nonmathematical but comprehensive treatment of the subject, addressing broad issues such as ecological responses to stress, cultural dimensions of water-quality policy, and global implications of change. Reviews the evolution of the concepts of water quality and management and provides a perspective that could serve as a framework for further changes. Extensive bibliography.

Schmoll, Oliver. *Protecting Groundwater for Health: Managing the Quality of Drinking Water Sources.* London: IWA Publishing, 2006. Delivers, in a single comprehensive framework, information and tools that can be used by everyone from staff to top managers involved in groundwater source management projects.

Steenvoorden, J. H. A. M., and Theodore Endreny, eds., *Wastewater Re-Use and Groundwater Quality.* Wallingford, England: International Union of Geodesy and Geophysics, 2004. Presents a number of learned articles on the title topic, examining the practices of wastewater reuse and their impact on the environment.

Thompson, Stephen A. *Hydrology for Water Management.* Rotterdam: A. A. Balkema, 1999. A thorough account of hydrology, groundwater flow, and stream flow focused on the management of water supplies in efforts to keep them free of pollutants and available to the largest number of people possible. Illustrations, maps, index, and bibliography.

U.S. Geological Survey. Office of Water. *The Quality of Our Nation's Water: Nutrients and Pesticides.* Creston, Va.: USGS Information Services, 1999. A government report that summarizes the extent of water pollution as compiled from reports from the states from 1990 through 1998 generated under the requirements of the Clean Water Act. Defines water-quality concepts and uses and summarizes pollutants and sources. Discusses methods used to collect nutrient and pesticide data.

Vigil, Kenneth M. *Clean Water.* 2d ed. Corvallis: Oregon State University Press, 2003. Written for the general public and intended to explain issues related to water quality. Covers water chemistry, microbiology, and watershed management. Includes a glossary, indexing, an additional reading list, and Internet resources.

See also: Aquifers; Artificial Recharge; Atmosphere's Global Circulation; Climate; Dams and Flood Control; Floods; Freshwater and Groundwater Contamination Around the World; Geochemical Cycles; Groundwater Movement; Groundwater Pollution and Remediation; Hydrologic Cycle; Ocean-Atmosphere Interactions; Precipitation; Salinity and Desalination; Saltwater Intrusion; Surface Water; Waterfalls; Watersheds; Water Table; Water Wells

WATERSHEDS

A watershed, or drainage basin, is a region that is drained by a stream, lake, or other type of watercourse. The land is divided into millions of watersheds of varying sizes and shapes, all of which act as collectors of runoff that flow from higher to lower elevations. Most watersheds join other larger watersheds and eventually flow into the oceans.

PRINCIPAL TERMS

- **base flow:** that portion of stream flow that is derived from groundwater
- **discharge:** the volume of water per unit time that flows past a given point on a stream
- **drainage divide:** the ridge of land that marks the boundary between adjacent watersheds
- **interior drainage:** watersheds in arid areas where the runoff does not flow into the oceans
- **perennial stream:** a stream that has water flowing in it throughout the year
- **relief:** the difference in elevation between the highest and lowest points of land in a particular region
- **runoff:** that portion of precipitation in a watershed that appears directly in surface streams without having first entered into the groundwater
- **stream:** water flowing in a relatively narrow but clearly defined channel from higher to lower elevations under the influence of gravity

CHARACTERISTICS

The term "watershed" has several meanings. The term is derived from the German term *Wasserscheide*, which means "water parting," or the line or ridge of higher ground that separates two adjoining drainage basins. This definition is also used in Great Britain, where "watershed" refers to a drainage divide between adjacent drainage basins. The usage of the term in the United States and by several international agencies has been modified to refer to the land area that is drained by, or that contributes water to, a particular stream, lake, or other body of water. For this discussion, the term will refer to the region that serves as the collecting system for all the water that is moving downslope from higher to lower elevations on its eventual path to the ocean. In this physical context, which is governed by topography, the terms "watershed" and "drainage basin" are synonymous.

The relationship of watersheds to topography was recognized many years ago. Philippe Buache in 1752 presented a memoir to the French Academy of Sciences in which the concept of the topographic unity of a watershed was outlined. This concept was followed by European cartographers of the late eighteenth and early nineteenth centuries who prepared maps that showed the major drainage basins of each country. Although these early cartographers would often exaggerate the height of the divides between watersheds, the basic concept was to show how the land was divided into a variety of drainage basins that acted as efficient collection systems for runoff resulting from precipitation.

Watersheds transport water from upland areas to lower elevations in a variety of pathways. The most obvious path is by perennial streams that flow in channels. This form of surface runoff includes not only overland flow, which is the water moving over the ground surface, but also base flow, which comes from that portion of the precipitation that has infiltrated through the soil into the underlying groundwater that enters the stream at some downgradient point. Thus, surface runoff from a watershed is a mix of "stormflow" or "quick flow," which occurs right after a precipitation event, and base flow from groundwater, which takes a more time to join the surface water. The rates at which surface water and groundwater move through a watershed depend upon many factors, such as precipitation amounts and intensity, geology, soils, topography, and vegetation.

STREAM CHANNELS

Stream channels vary enormously in length and width, from a minor erosion channel that can easily be stepped over to rivers such as the Mississippi, which is as wide as 1.5 kilometers before it empties into the Gulf of Mexico, and the Amazon, which becomes several kilometers wide before entering the Atlantic Ocean. Watersheds also have an enormous range in length, area, and discharge. By far, the largest watershed in the world is the Amazon, with a drainage area of 6,150,000 square kilometers, approximately one-third of the entire area of South America. The second- and third-largest watersheds in the world are the Zaire in Africa (3,820,000 square kilometers) and the Mississippi in the United States (3,270,000 square kilometers). Thus, the Mississippi River watershed, which includes the Missouri River, drains an astonishing 40.5 percent of the entire area of the contiguous United States.

The Amazon is also the largest river in the world in terms of discharge, averaging 6,300 cubic kilometers per year. The second- and third-largest dischargers in the world are the Zaire and the Orinoco in Venezuela (1,250 and 1,100 cubic kilometers per year, respectively). The longest rivers in the world are the Nile in Africa (6,671 kilometers), the Amazon (6,300 kilometers), the Yangtze in China (6,276 kilometers), and the Mississippi (6,019 kilometers). At the other end of the spectrum are innumerable small streams that are in the headwaters of their watersheds near the divides, some with lengths of only a few meters.

Although there is obvious variation in shape from watershed to watershed, most tend to be pear-shaped. This shape is the most probable one to occur, as ground slopes and branching stream networks naturally evolve over time to dispose of the runoff and the sediment load in the water efficiently. Departures from the usual pear shape are attributed to structural control by underlying and exposed bedrock formations. For example, some basins are elongated in shape when they occupy long, narrow valleys such as are often found in the Appalachian region of the eastern United States, where long, resistant ridges of sandstone and quartzite run approximately parallel with less resistant valleys underlain by shale and limestone.

Most of the runoff in the humid land areas of the world eventually flows into the oceans via a series of hydrologically connected watersheds. Thus the waters and sediment load of the Missouri and Ohio Rivers join the Mississippi River at St. Louis, Missouri, and Cairo, Illinois, respectively, and eventually flow into the Gulf of Mexico below New Orleans. Another large-scale example is that of the watersheds for the Great Lakes, furnishing the water for the St. Lawrence River, which flows eastward through Canada into the Gulf of St. Lawrence and the Atlantic Ocean. However, there are areas of the world where runoff flows into interior basins surrounded by high mountains that do not allow the stream to get to the ocean. This type of drainage system, called interior drainage, is common in semiarid and arid climates. Major examples of watersheds with interior drainage

include the Caspian Sea in Asia (3,626,000 square kilometers), the Aral Sea in Kazakhstan and Uzbekistan in Asia (1,618,750 square kilometers), Lake Eyre in Australia (1,424,500 square kilometers), and the Great Basin in Utah, Nevada, and eastern California (500,000 square kilometers).

WATERSHED DIVIDES

The divides that separate watersheds vary from sharply defined ridges in mountainous terrain to poorly defined boundaries in glaciated landscapes, regions of low relief, and areas of limited topographic expression. For example, the highest land in the Everglades (12,950 square kilometers) in Florida is only 2.1 meters above sea level, which means that natural runoff (excluding canals) flows in directions sometimes governed more by wind than by topography. Another prominent instance of a poorly defined divide occurs in southern Wyoming, where the Continental Divide in the United States, which separates the waters that flow into the Pacific Ocean from those that flow into the Gulf of Mexico, splits into two divides that surround the Great Basin Divide. This unusual situation means that anyone who drives along Interstate 80 in Wyoming, for example, will be able to cross the Continental Divide twice in an east-west direction.

Watershed divides, especially in mountainous areas, often have been used as political boundaries. Examples include the Andes between Argentina and Chile, the Pyrenees between France and Spain, and the Bitterroot Range between Idaho and Montana. Watershed divides also often serve as starting points for major cities. For example, Atlanta developed as a rail center in the nineteenth century because it was on the divide between the streams that flowed into the Gulf of Mexico (the Chattahoochee and Flint Rivers) and those that flowed into the Atlantic Ocean along the east coast of Georgia (the Ocmulgee River).

The drainage pattern or network of stream channels that develop within a watershed are related to local geologic and geomorphic factors. The most common drainage pattern that develops on horizontal and homogeneous bedrock or on crystalline rock that offers uniform resistance to erosion is called "dendritic," since it resembles the branching pattern of trees. All other types of drainage patterns reflect some form of structural control, such as the trellis pattern that is associated with the elongated watersheds in the "ridge and valley" regions in the Appalachians of the eastern United States. Rectangular patterns can develop in faulted areas where the drainage paths follow the lines of least resistance that develop along the fault lines.

Watershed size and flow can change either naturally or by anthropogenic means. Major natural examples include the deflection by continental glaciation of the upper Missouri River from Hudson Bay in eastern Canada to its present-day confluence with the Mississippi River, and the geologic subsidence and tilting that diverted the drainage of the Nyanza area in East Africa from the Zaire River (formerly the Congo), which flows into the Atlantic Ocean, to Lake Victoria, which drains into the Nile and the Mediterranean Sea. The flow through the Florida Everglades has been substantially altered by drainage activities and canal building for agricultural purposes that started in the late nineteenth century and continued into the twentieth century. Water that used to flow into the Everglades and Florida Bay from Lake Okeechobee was diverted to the canalized Caloosahatchee River, which empties into the Gulf of Mexico, and the Miami, North New River, Hillsboro, West Palm Beach, and St. Lucie Canals, which are connected with the Atlantic Ocean on the east coast of Florida. Another instance of anthropogenic intervention with watershed flow is illustrated by the diversion of water from Lake Michigan, which is part of the Great Lakes and St. Lawrence River system, to the Chicago Ship and Sanitary Canal, which is connected with the Illinois River, which flows into the Mississippi River. The purpose of the canal was to transport sewage from the Chicago metropolitan area away from Lake Michigan, which is used as a water source.

Robert M. Hordon

FURTHER READING

Albert, R. C. *Damming the Delaware.* 2d ed. University Park: Pennsylvania State University Press, 2005. An interesting history of two hundred years of water management for the Delaware River, which serves as a water source for New York City, Trenton, and Philadelphia. A good case study of the institutional factors that have resulted in a model interstate compact and the historical absence of dams on the main stem of the river.

Black, P. E. *Watershed Hydrology.* 2d ed. Boca Raton, Fla.: CRC Press, 1996. A fine introductory book that presents in an integrated fashion the various hydrologic processes that occur in a watershed. Thoroughly discusses the complex of interactions between climate, soils, vegetation, atmosphere, stream flow and channels, humans, and water-resource infrastructure. Treatment is qualitative, with only minimal uses of quantitative methodology.

DeBarry, Paul A. *Watersheds: Processes, Assessment and Management.* Upper Saddle River, N.J.: John Wiley & Sons, 2004. A comprehensive guide to watershed analysis and management that uses GIS models for assessment and effective planning for future needs; covers most of the theoretical and practical aspects of watershed geography. Describes methods for data collection, GIS data analysis, and hydrologic modeling. A unique chapter on stormwater management provides practical information for addressing runoff issues.

Dunne, E. J., K. Raja Reddy, and O.T Carton. *Nutrient in Agricultural Watersheds: A Wetlands Solution.* Wageningen: Wageningen Academic Publishers, 2005. Discusses the effects and control of nutrients in wetlands in agricultural areas, in the context of the experiences of both Europe and North America.

Fairbridge, Rhodes W., and Reginald W. Herschy, eds. *The Encyclopedia of Hydrology and Water Resources.* Boston, Mass.: Kluwer Academic, 1998. Serves as a great reference tool for anyone interested in the study of hydrology. There are sections devoted to surface water and groundwater, as well as water resources. Suitable for college-level readers. Illustrations and maps.

Fierro, Pedro, Jr., and Evan K. Nyer, eds. *The Water Encyclopedia.* 3d ed. Boca Raton, Fla.: CRC Press, 2007. A huge compendium of information about virtually all aspects of water. Includes hundreds of tables and many maps covering surface and groundwater, water use and quality, environmental problems, water resources management, and water law and treaties. An excellent reference work that contains a bewildering array of facts about water.

Grossman, Elizabeth. *Watershed: The Undamming of America.* New York: Counterpoint, 2002. Discusses the damming and removal of dams in various regions across the United States. Discusses legislature, ecology, and social impact. Written for the layperson.

Harter, Thomas and Larry Rollins, eds. *Watersheds, Groundwater and Drinking Water: A Practical Guide.* Oakland: University of California Agriculture and Natural Resources Communication Services, 2008. Provides a thorough discussion of the relationship between watersheds, groundwater, and their importance to the supply of drinking water, with regard to management of those resources and prevention of contamination.

Heathcote, Isobel W. *Integrated Watershed Management: Principles and Practice.* 2d ed. Hoboken, N.J.: John Wiley & Sons, 2009. Provides a strong overview of issues and topics measured, evaluated, and managed as a part of watershed management. Classification, watershed inventory, legislation, and social and environmental impact assessment are discussed.

Hillel, D. *Rivers of Eden.* New York: Oxford University Press, 1994. An engrossing book about water shortages in the Middle East, set against the backdrop of competing territorial claims in a highly politicized and arid environment. The major watersheds selected for study include the Tigris and Euphrates, with headwaters in Turkey and downstream areas in Iraq and Syria; the Nile, with a source region in east-central Africa; and the Jordan River in Israel, Jordan, Lebanon, and Syria. This is a well-written and well-documented study of historical watershed mismanagement and the compelling need for cooperation and water-sharing arrangements in the region.

Kaufman, Martin M., Daniel T. Rogers and Kent S. Murray. *Urban Watersheds: Geology, Contamination and Sustainable Development.* Boca Raton, Fla.: CRC Press, 2011. An extensive handbook based on ten years of environmental research on watershed contamination in heavily urbanized areas, explaining several different aspects of urban watershed contamination.

Marsh, W. M. *Landscape Planning: Environmental Applications.* 5th ed. New York: John Wiley & Sons, 2010. Covers the principles and processes in physical geography, planning, and landscape architecture as they pertain to environmental issues in landscape planning. Contains some very useful chapters on watersheds, land use, storm-water discharge and landscape change, soil erosion and stream sedimentation, and soils and development suitability.

Newsom, M. *Hydrology and the River Environment.* Oxford, England: Clarendon Press, 1994. Focuses on watersheds as the fundamental unit for water management. Although many of the examples discussed are from Great Britain, there is an inherent universality to the watershed analysis methodology. A very good set of pertinent references for each chapter is included at the end of the book.

Novotny, Vladimir. *Water Quality: Diffuse Pollution an Watershed Management.* 2d ed. Hoboken, N.J.: John Wiley & Sons, 2003. Describes many topics related to nonpoint source pollution. Discusses causes of water pollution, water quality statistics, the water cycle, erosion, and soil pollution. Provides good descriptions of management practices and mitigation. Also discusses environmental assessment and modeling.

Strahler, Alan H. *Modern Physical Geography.* 4th ed. Wiley India Pvt Limited, 2008. Provides a rigorous treatment of the topic as an undergraduate-level textbook, with some chapters devoted to the relationship between landforms and moving surface water.

Thompson, Stephen A. *Hydrology for Water Management.* Rotterdam: A. A. Balkema, 1999. This thorough account of hydrology, groundwater flow, and stream flow focuses on the management of water supplies in efforts to keep them free of pollutants and available to the largest number of people possible. Illustrations, maps, index, and bibliography.

Vigil, Kenneth M. *Clean Water.* 2d ed. Corvallis: Oregon State University Press, 2003. Written for the general public, and intended to explain issues related to water quality. Covers water chemistry, microbiology, and watershed management, among other topics. Includes a glossary, indexing, additional reading list, and online resources.

See also: Aquifers; Artificial Recharge; Dams and Flood Control; Floods; Freshwater and Groundwater Contamination Around the World; Great Lakes; Groundwater Movement; Groundwater Pollution and Remediation; Hydrologic Cycle; Mississippi River; Nile River; Precipitation; River Bed Forms; Salinity and Desalination; Saltwater Intrusion; Surface Water; Waterfalls; Water Quality; Water Table; Water Wells

WATER TABLE

The water table is the upper portion of the saturated or groundwater zone beneath the earth's surface. The depth to the water table is an important consideration in drilling wells for water supply, building and roadway construction, and septic-system and landfill-disposal design.

PRINCIPAL TERMS

- **capillary fringe:** the lowest portion of the unsaturated zone just above the water table
- **clay lens:** a subsurface layer of low-permeability clay soil, extending over a limited area, that traps groundwater and produces a secondary water table perched above the main water table
- **perched water table:** groundwater that occupies an area above the main or regional water table, as would form above a clay lens
- **pore:** a small opening in rock or between soil particles
- **saturated zone:** a subsurface zone in which all of the pore spaces are filled with water
- **unsaturated zone:** a subsurface zone in which the pore spaces are filled with both air and water

Subsurface Hydrology

The water table forms the boundary between the unsaturated and saturated zones that lie below the earth's surface. The unsaturated zone, which is also known as the zone of aeration and the vadose zone, forms the uppermost layer in the ground. The pore spaces in the subsurface materials—such as sand, silt, clay, gravel, or consolidated rock—contain both air and water in varying proportions. Water in the unsaturated zone, which includes capillary water, is contained under pressure that is lower than that of the atmosphere, whereas air and gases are generally under atmospheric pressure. Water in this zone may move up and down or sideways. Soil water in this zone can also be evaporated back into the atmosphere.

Starting at the ground surface, the unsaturated zone is divided into the belt of soil water (or root zone), the intermediate belt, and the capillary fringe. The belt of soil water is bounded on top by the land surface and on the bottom by the intermediate zone. It contains plant roots and soil water that is available for plant growth. The depth of the belt varies over the landscape, but it is generally no more than a few meters.

The intermediate belt in the unsaturated zone lies between the belt of soil water and the capillary fringe. The depth of this belt varies substantially, being much deeper in dry climates and much shallower in wet areas. The capillary fringe is the lowermost subdivision of the unsaturated zone. It is located immediately above the water table. The interstices between particles in this zone are filled with water under pressure that is lower than that of the atmosphere. The water in the capillary fringe is continuous with the water in the saturated zone below the water table, but it is held above it by surface tension. The upper boundary of the capillary fringe with the intermediate belt is somewhat indistinct, although it is sometimes arbitrarily defined as the level at which 50 percent of the pore spaces or interstices are filled with water. The vertical extent of the capillary fringe depends upon the soil texture because capillary rise is greater when the openings are smaller. Thus, the thickness in silty material may be as large as 1 meter, where the openings are very small, to as little as 1 centimeter in coarse sand or fine gravel, where the openings are much larger.

The saturated zone's pore spaces are completely filled with water or other fluids. The water table is at the top of the saturated zone and will therefore rise or fall as the saturated zone increases or decreases because of variations in precipitation or pumping. In some locations, a perched water table can exist above the regional water table. The separation is caused by a relatively impermeable layer, such as a clay lens, which impedes infiltration. The perched water table is generally shallow and of limited areal extent, although in irrigated areas it can become much larger.

Water-Table Variations

The word "table" suggests a surface that is flat and static. In the case of the water table, neither term is appropriate. Rather, the water table tends to be a subdued replica of the surface topography. It rises to higher levels under the highest portions of the landscape (hilltops and divides) and is lowest in the valleys, where it approaches the surface close to streams, lakes, or swamps. This topographic configuration is caused by water percolating through the unsaturated zone, which raises the water table, in contrast to streams, lakes, and swamps that receive base flow or seepage from groundwater in the saturated zone, which lowers the water table.

The depth to the water table from the ground surface varies enormously. It is at or close to the surface in swamps and marshes, which means that an unsaturated zone is nonexistent in those places. The depth in arid regions can be measured in tens and even hundreds of meters below the surface. Under natural conditions, the water table will rise after recharge during a period of precipitation and fall during a period of drought. The greater the amount of precipitation and resultant recharge, the larger the rise; conversely, the greater the intensity and length of the dry period, the larger the fall.

The extent of the rise and fall of the water table can be greatly magnified by anthropogenic intervention. One obvious example is the decline in the water table that is caused by groundwater extraction. Pumping for water supplies or for dewatering operations at construction sites can radically lower the water table, with the greatest amount of lowering occurring at the point from which water is removed, and decreasing with distance around that point. The resulting decline in the water table forms a cone-shaped region around the extraction point called a cone of depression, which can spread out tens and hundreds of meters from the well. In homogeneous subsurface materials, the shape of the cone of depression forms a smooth hyperbolic surface shape. If the subsurface materials are heterogeneous, which is the more common condition, the cone of depression tends to be irregular in shape and spread out over a large area. The vertical distance between the original water table (or static water level) and the new lowered water table (or pumping water level) is known as the "drawdown." The greater the rate and duration of pumping, the larger and deeper the cone of depression and the greater the drawdown. Water-bearing geologic formations called aquifers vary enormously in their permeability, a measure of the ease with which they support fluid movement. Thus, water-table fluctuations are less in aquifers that have high water transmission rates (high permeability) and much more in aquifers that have low permeability and consequently less capability for groundwater movement.

ENVIRONMENTAL ISSUES

Water-table fluctuations can present many environmental problems. For example, at the residential level, septic system disposal fields, which are typically arrays of weeping tiles, require a minimum depth to the water table of at least 1.2 meters for the effluent to be properly absorbed into the soil. If the water table is too shallow or the drainage system is overloaded, microbial decomposition of the effluent may not fully occur, which would then lead to groundwater contamination. Other problems occur with overpumping of an aquifer when the declining water table can fall below the depth of the well, resulting in a dry well. Depending upon the magnitude of the decline, either the well would have to be deepened or a new well in another location would have to be drilled. The normal hydraulic gradient generally follows the topography from high locations to lower ones, but it can be affected by pumping so that the gradient is reversed. This means that leachate from landfills or septic-system disposal fields can thus be induced to flow into a nearby well.

Overpumping, in which the pumping rate is in excess of the natural recharge from precipitation, can create a cone of depression large enough to interfere with other wells and cause them to go dry. This is a particular problem with large-diameter public wells that supply water to many users in a community. As a result, many governmental units at the local, county, or state level require pumping tests at specified rates and duration so that the decline and recovery of the water table can be measured to minimize interference with neighboring wells. These pumping tests are often seventy-two hours in duration. In areas where the groundwater yield is marginal and the water-table decline can be substantial, some municipalities even require four-hour pumping tests for domestic wells that serve only one residential dwelling unit.

One interesting illustration of the environmental impact of pumping and water-level change occurred on a large scale in Brooklyn, New York. There were many wells in Brooklyn in the early part of the twentieth century that pumped large amounts of groundwater. The resulting decline in the water table facilitated the construction of subways. When water-quality problems developed as urbanization spread in Brooklyn, the pumping stopped, and the rise of the water table started flooding the subway tracks. In order to keep the subways working, a certain amount of pumping had to be resumed even if the water was simply fed into storm sewers that drained into the ocean.

Irrigated lands often have problems with perched water tables that develop over a shallow, relatively impermeable bed such as a clay lens. The water that is applied to the irrigated soils causes the perched water table to rise toward the surface. As a result, the capillary fringe will finally reach the surface and allow groundwater to be continuously discharged to the atmosphere by evapotranspiration (evaporation plus plant transpiration). The evaporation will produce a buildup of salts in the surface soil as groundwater contains dissolved mineral matter. In addition, the rising water table can drown out plant roots near the surface.

Taken together, these two effects have created numerous problems for farmers in irrigated areas, from the days of the ancient farmers in Mesopotamia (the Tigris and Euphrates Valleys in what is now Iraq) to the vast irrigated fields in the Indus River Valley in Pakistan, the San Joaquin and Imperial Valleys in California, the Nile Delta in Egypt, and the wheat belt of Western Australia. For example, a water table that rises at an average annual rate of 0.3 meter and consequent salinization and water logging of the soil in the lower Indus River in Pakistan have caused 36,000 hectares of land to go out of production each year. The solution to this problem requires an elaborate system of drains that remove the salt-laden water from the affected area.

Overpumping in a coastal area can cause a decline in the water table, which could in turn result in saltwater or saline intrusion into a freshwater aquifer. Proximity to the sea means that saltwater can be drawn into the well and make the water unfit for human consumption. Saline intrusion problems have been well documented in Miami, Florida, which not only has large wells close to the coast but also is located above the extremely permeable Biscayne Aquifer. The solution to this problem is either to move the wells inland or to install recharge wells between the coast and the contaminated wells.

On an even larger scale, one of the major factors in the selection of Yucca Mountain in Nevada as a high-level radioactive waste disposal site was the great depth to the water table. This area is about 145 kilometers northwest of Las Vegas and has an average annual precipitation of under 200 millimeters. The deep water table and the great extent of the unsaturated zone meant that waste disposal canisters would presumably not be affected by the movement of groundwater, which could become radioactive and flow down-gradient into larger, regional groundwater flow systems. The disposal site is supposed to isolate the waste materials for 10,000 years. Whether the water table would move upward and flood the disposal site during this period of time as a consequence of climatic change is a matter of some controversy.

SIGNIFICANCE

The water table is a critical part of the subsurface portion of the hydrologic cycle. The depth of the table governs the viability of subsurface septic disposal systems and landfills, which requires specified depths to the water table in order to protect the underlying saturated zone from contamination. Hazardous and radioactive waste disposal also require placement in an unsaturated zone that is sufficiently large and distant from groundwater movement in the saturated zone. Water-table depths are an important factor in wetland determinations and in agriculture where most plants require soils that have pore spaces containing both air and water.

The water table marks the irregularly undulating top of the saturated zone. The importance of groundwater is best illustrated by the fact that it comprises an estimated 25 percent of the total volume of freshwater, as compared to just 0.3 percent in lakes and 0.03 percent in streams. The U.S. Geological Survey estimates that groundwater accounts for 38 percent of the total amount of water withdrawn for public supply purposes in the nation. Wells must go below the water table in order for groundwater to be extracted, and declining water levels resulting from overpumping or extended drought present immediate water supply problems. Ground-level subsidence in the San Joaquin Valley in California has exceeded 9 meters due to overpumping from the underlying aquifers and necessitated the establishment of recharge wells. The decline of the water table in the largest known aquifer in the United States, the High Plains Aquifer spanning the states of Nebraska, Kansas, Oklahoma, and Texas, and the potential demise of farming in this region as a result, is but another instance of the impact of water-table fluctuations.

Robert M. Hordon

FURTHER READING

Dillon, P. J., ed. *Management of Aquifer Recharge for Sustainability.* Boca Raton, Fla.: Taylor & Francis, 2002. A compilation of papers discussing groundwater management and aquifer recharging. Covers topics such as bank filtration, soil aquifer treatment, and rainwater harvesting.

Dingman, S. Lawrence. *Physical Hydrology.* 2d ed. Upper Saddle River, N.J.: Prentice Hall, 2002. Aimed at the upper-level undergraduate to graduate level for students in Earth sciences and natural resources. Requires some physics and calculus background. Discusses the water table in several chapters.

Fetter, C. W. *Applied Hydrogeology.* 4th ed. Upper Saddle River, N.J.: Prentice Hall, 2000. A standard textbook for advanced undergraduate or graduate courses containing numerous case studies, many of which involve the application of mathematics to the particular problem discussed. A lengthy text with many references and illustrations.

Healy, Richard W. *Estimating Groundwater Recharge.* New York: Cambridge University Press, 2010. Discusses many topics in groundwater management and hydrology. Contains practical information suited for working hydrologists. Discusses management, modeling, and data collection methods. The main focus is groundwater recharging.

Hornberger, George M., Jeffrey P. Raffensperger, Patricia P. Wiberg, and Keith N. Eshleman. *Elements of Physical Hydrology.* Baltimore, Md.: Johns Hopkins University Press, 1998. Designed for upper-level students in environmental or Earth sciences. Requires some familiarity with calculus and physics. The orientation is on the quantitative aspects of hydrology.

Jones, J. A. A. *Global Hydrology.* Essex, England: Addison Wesley Longman, 1997. Offers a very good introduction to the science of hydrology, with a focus on environmental issues. Although the treatment of topics is technical, no particular background in mathematics is required. Well indexed and contains many references.

Manning, John C. *Applied Principles of Hydrology.* 3d ed. Upper Saddle River, N.J.: Prentice Hall, 1997. A very readable, nonmathematical discussion of the various aspects of hydrology. Contains simple line drawings and photographs that are useful, as well as numerous case studies of problems involving water-table fluctuations.

Mays, Larry W. *Ground and Surface Water Hydrology.* Hoboken, N.J.: John Wiley & Sons, 2011. A comprehensive college-level textbook that stresses the fundamental principles of hydrologic processes relevant to groundwater and surface water by making extensive use of online resources and discussing newer topics in hydrology such as remote-sensing and GIS. Covers all principal climate types.

Moore, John E. *Field Hydrogeology.* 2d ed. Boca Raton, Fla.: CRC Press, 2012. Provides practical information on field investigation, aquifer testing, and groundwater quality testing. Discusses planning and report writing in detail. The final chapter also provides case studies from around the world. Best suited for students learning the planning and investigation of field hydrology.

Nonner, Johannes C. *Introduction to Hydrogeology.* London: Taylor & Francis Group, 2006. A university-level textbook that covers all major fields in hydrogeology, as well as the occurrence, behavior, and properties of groundwater. A well-illustrated book that makes use of numerous examples of groundwater cases from around the world.

Price, Michael. *Introducing Groundwater.* 2d ed. New York: Chapman and Hall, 1996. An excellent, very readable introduction to the study of groundwater. Aimed for the nonspecialist reader with technical terms and mathematical formulas held to a minimum. Well illustrated and indexed.

Strahler, Alan H., and Arthur N. Strahler. *Modern Physical Geography.* 4th ed. New York: John Wiley, 1992. One of the best textbooks available in physical geography. Has excellent illustrations and examples. Descriptive and nonmathematical writing. Covers the water table well in one chapter.

See also: Aquifers; Artificial Recharge; Dams and Flood Control; Drought; Floods; Freshwater and Groundwater Contamination Around the World; Great Lakes; Groundwater Movement; Groundwater Pollution and Remediation; Hydrologic Cycle; Lakes; Precipitation; Rainforests and the Atmosphere; Salinity and Desalination; Saltwater Intrusion; Seawater Composition; Surface Water; Waterfalls; Water Quality; Watersheds; Water Wells

WATER WELLS

More than one-half of the world's population depends upon groundwater for daily water supply requirements. Virtually all groundwater is obtained from wells, more specifically termed production water wells.

PRINCIPAL TERMS

- **aquifer:** a permeable geologic structure that is saturated and capable of yielding groundwater on demand
- **casing:** conventionally, a tubular material—usually a large metal, concrete, or plastic pipe—that is inserted into a raw borehole for the purpose of maintaining the integrity of the hole
- **cement grouting:** the injection of a sand-cement mix by means of pressure, resulting in an envelope of concrete lining between the outside of a casing and the undisturbed geologic material of a well borehole
- **fully confined aquifers:** those that lie sandwiched between impermeable formations and are therefore termed artesian aquifers
- **production water wells:** human-made subsurface structures designed and constructed to provide access to a water supply from an aquifer
- **pump pipe:** a tube that extends downward from the wellhead to a level below the top of the water in the well, and that serves as the conduit for water being pumped to the surface
- **rat hole:** that portion of a well that is deliberately made to extend below the base of an aquifer
- **semiconfined aquifers:** those that perform as if fully confined but receive replenishment from overlying or underlying water-bearing formations of lesser permeability than the aquifer itself
- **unconfined aquifers:** those that have no covering material, whereby the depth to water in the well is the level of the water table; also known as water-table aquifers
- **wellhead:** that portion of the casing that extends above the ground surface; its strength and stability permit the wellhead to be used as an anchor for pumping devices
- **well screen:** a tubular device containing openings that permit groundwater to flow into the well from the aquifer, commonly part of a well point; some aquifers need no screen

OVERVIEW

A water well is constructed for the sole purpose of obtaining water from an aquifer. Other types of well structures, not intended as sources of water supply, appropriately have other names, such as observation well, monitor well, and piezometer (for pressure measurement). Some aquifers are capable of yielding groundwater in only minimum quantities per day, perhaps meeting the requirements of a single household. Other aquifers are capable of supporting a cluster of production wells: for example, ten generously spaced wells each with a safe capacity of 16,000 cubic meters per day (about 15.9 million liters, or about 4.2 million U.S. gallons per day). Such a cluster, or well field, of ten wells would supply the needs of a city of some 200,000 residents.

The safe yield of water wells, however, is not solely a function of the capability of the aquifers that they tap. The suitability of well design and the quality of well construction are also critical. In the science of geohydrology, the quality of a production water well, without respect to the character of its aquifer, is known as well efficiency. Some wells have an efficiency of 100 percent, and some have an efficiency of only 40 percent. A well at 40 percent efficiency would have a safe yield two and one-half times greater if both design and construction were executed as a perfect match with the geologic character of the aquifer being tapped. That is to say, a well is 100 percent efficient when all aspects of design and construction are matched to the particular aquifer, and efficiency decreases as the extent of mismatching increases.

AQUIFER PERFORMANCE

However, perfection in well design and construction will not make a poor aquifer into a good one. The performance of an aquifer is totally dependent upon its hydrogeologic setting and its physical character. An aquifer's physical character is judged scientifically by its hydraulic conductivity, thickness, and areal dimensions. For example, a water-bearing sandstone with a consistent thickness of 50 meters throughout a county-sized area might support twice the quantity that it would if its thickness were 25 meters. Other aspects of an aquifer's physical character are also involved.

How a good production well operates in its relation to an aquifer is quite straightforward. Take as an example the case of a well that penetrates a fully confined aquifer, say, 1,000 meters deep. At the time the construction is completed and before any pumping has commenced, the well's static (non-pumping) water level is entirely determined by the natural water pressure within the aquifer. Last year's rainfall has no bearing on that confined fluid pressure. This scenario is an artesian situation. The well might actually flow without any pumping due to the pressure exerted by the aquifer structure on top of the water it contains; however, it is assumed that the water in this well stands steady at a depth of 30 meters. This assumption means that the fluid pressure in the aquifer must be sufficient to boost the water up the well to within 30 meters of ground surface. In this example, the water in the aquifer must have a confined fluid pressure of nearly 100 kilograms per square centimeter.

At the moment pumping commences, whatever the rate of withdrawal, the well enters a nonequilibrium condition, whereas, prior to pumping, the condition was at equilibrium (also called steady state). The pumping water level starts to decline, rather quickly at first and then ever more slowly. At the 1,000-meter depth, groundwater in the aquifer immediately reacts to the loss of pressure in the well and begins to migrate within the aquifer toward the well's intake area. That incoming water replaces the water that has been withdrawn to the ground surface. The groundwater migration toward the well proceeds radially inward, like spokes on a wheel. The pumping water level in the well continues to fall as long as nonequilibrium conditions prevail, perhaps for hours or even weeks. Eventually, the pumping water level stabilizes, and at that point in time hydraulic equilibrium has been reached. The moment that pumping of this hypothetical well is stopped, nonequilibrium conditions again prevail. Now, however, the situation reverses, and the well's water level rises, rapidly at first and then ever more slowly, until the well has fully recovered to its original state. Hydraulic equilibrium has then been reached again.

The scenario is very different in the case of wells that tap unconfined aquifers, such as alluvial sands

in river valleys or in deep basins. In unconfined aquifers, the loss of water level in a well upon start-up of pumping is usually at a slower pace due to the relative ease of movement of water through the saturated zone. So, too, is the rate of recovery when pumping ceases, due to the lack of excess pressure inherent in an unconfined aquifer. In unconfined aquifers, withdrawals of groundwater result in the draining of a cone-shaped portion of the aquifer itself, known as the cone of depression; that is, the water table actually declines in a cone-shaped area around the production well. It is this draining that causes slower responses because the act of dewatering requires time. Confined aquifers, in contrast, react to pumping with pressure changes only. Such aquifers remain full of water continuously.

WELL DRILLING

The initial major task in well construction is the drilling operation. The drilling plan often depends upon the area's geological configuration. For example, where there is no prior record of drilling in an area, there may be no known aquifer at any depth. In that case, it would be folly to drill a full-diameter borehole initially. A slim hole, perhaps 10 centimeters in diameter, is sufficient to make a determination of the geology and of the presence or absence of an aquifer. The lower-cost slim hole, then, can be reamed to full well diameter once an aquifer has been identified, sometimes even evaluated as to hydrologic performance. If the initial drilling reveals no aquifer, the site is wisely abandoned with manageable loss from the cost of slim-hole drilling. This case is analogous to a wildcat oil test drilled far from any existing production.

When a specific aquifer is either known or has been discovered by means of the slim-hole drilling, the diameter of the final borehole is then largely determined by the anticipated pump size, because the hole must accommodate the casing and the casing must accommodate the flow of water to be extracted. High-capacity wells, especially where the pumping water level is deep, require large-diameter pump turbines, and correspondingly large well casings. Domestic wells for household water need pumps of only minimum diameters. Such wells can be designed and constructed with casings of only 15 centimeters or less, seldom more than 7.5 centimeters in diameter, whereas wells for large industrial or public water supplies may need to have inside diameters of 30 or even 40 centimeters in order to ensure adequate water flow for high-performance pumps.

It is ordinarily impractical simply to increase the diameter of a well in the expectation of greatly increasing the maximum yield of the well. Assume, for example, a well 10 centimeters in diameter is tested and found to have a safe capacity of 2 liters per second. The water supply requirement, however, may be 4 liters per second. For that same well to have a safe capacity of 4 liters per second, solely by enlarging the diameter, the resulting well would require a diameter of about 1 meter. Therefore, it is more economical to have multiple wells of smaller diameter than to attempt to achieve the same total water supply with one huge well. The multiple-well plan is also advantageous for geohydrologic reasons, so long as the wells have adequate spacing between them so as not to interfere with each other. Optimal spacing is a calculation performed professionally by geohydrologists.

In some geologic situations, production water wells can be designed and constructed with neither casing nor well screen in the lower portion of the well. For this less costly design to be feasible, the rock left with open drill holes must be physically competent, such as limestone or granite. In all situations, however, the upper portion of the borehole requires a casing, primarily to protect the well against surface contaminants and also to provide for a stable wellhead. Surface casing requires positive sealing between the outside of the casing and the drilled borehole, as by cement grout.

In geologic situations where the borehole penetrates any soft sediment or rock lacking the strength to sustain itself with open-hole construction, a full-length casing is essential. A well screen is set in that portion of the borehole that penetrates the aquifer. Commercial well screens are fabricated in a variety of designs and different metals, typically bronze or stainless steel. Below a well screen is a short section of blank casing known as the "rat hole," which is set in the geologic material under the aquifer. The rat hole serves as a settling and collecting zone for fine-grained material that may enter the well during its lifetime.

Well screens are not filters and cannot serve as filters. Such a function would cause the well to cease its normal yield of water after a few weeks of service, due to flow-inhibiting deposits of sediments accumulating on the screen, and the well would require expensive rehabilitation at frequent intervals. Screens are for the sole purpose of giving the well physical integrity at aquifer depth, allowing water to pass readily from the aquifer into the well point while preventing other materials from doing so, and preventing weak aquifer material, such as sand, from collapsing into the well bore. The too-common practice of using casing with sawed slots or bored holes invariably results in poor well efficiency and usually dooms the well to a short life.

WELL DEVELOPMENT

The final stage of construction for most wells with screens is known as well development. The purpose of well development is to enhance the well's safe yield by increasing the permeability of the aquifer immediately outside the well. Fine-grained aquifer material is stimulated to enter and pass through the screen, thereupon to be removed from the well. This has the effect of clearing debris from the pores and interstices of the aquifer material, and effectively maximizing the pore size and, thus, the permeability of the aquifer material. The reasoning behind the maneuver is easily understood. During the time a pump is extracting water from the well, groundwater in the aquifer is moving radially inward to replace the water that is being withdrawn. As the specific quantity of groundwater moves closer and closer to the intake area of the well, the space it occupies within the aquifer becomes ever more confined. Therefore, the water's velocity must increase. (An analogy would be water flowing in a pipe of fixed diameter. Assume the pipe has a dent in it that reduces its diameter. When the water passes into the restricted place, its velocity increases until the restriction has been passed.) The removal of silt and fine sand from the aquifer just outside the well has the effect of locally increasing the permeability of the aquifer, which, in turn, helps to promote the increased flow velocity. Performance of wells can sometimes be improved 100 percent by the standard practice of applying well-development techniques, used by all good well contractors where the geologic conditions favor such treatment.

Because wells that flow from natural pressure are generally rare, most wells are useless until fitted with an appropriate pump. Where the standing water level in a well is no deeper than about 7 meters, the well can be pumped by suction for supplying small domestic needs. Suction pumps remove a portion of the prevailing atmospheric pressure within the pump pipe, thus causing the water in the pump pipe to rise to ground surface. They are sometimes referred to as shallow-well pumps, even though the depth of the well has nothing to do with the feasibility of using suction pumps. Shallow-well pumps, such as for domestic use, are typically either suction pumps that lift water by generating a pressure differential within the system, or "jet" pumps that utilize the movement of a small stream of moving water to induce the movement of a larger amount of water.

By far, most well pumps are of the type where the suction principle cannot be applied. These are crudely referred to as deep-well pumps, also a misnomer. Pumps of many varieties and ratings as to the quantities of water they can move are on the market. A few of the most common varieties need mention, including the shaft turbine, submersible, and deep-well cylinder pumps. The shaft turbine pump is commonly used in high-capacity wells for industrial and public water supplies. The energy used to run it is usually supplied by electricity or diesel fuel. A rotating stainless steel shaft extends down the pump pipe to the turbine bowls set at some carefully predetermined depth below the well's pumping water level. These pumps are capable of lifting water 100 meters or more.

Submersible pumps are in worldwide use for pumping both small domestic wells and high-capacity industrial and public water supply wells. They are always powered by electricity. The submersible pump operates essentially like a shaft turbine, except that there is no shaft. The electric motor drive is arranged in vertical orientation under the pump bowls and, therefore, submersed in the well water. All turbine pumps are sensitive to any fine sand or silt that some wells tend to produce along with the water. Turbine blades have close tolerances and suffer loss of efficiency when worn by grit. Deep-well cylinder pumps are widely used for small to modest pumping needs, often powered by wind energy, especially for livestock water supplies in remote areas. These pumps are hung deep in the well, suspended by the pump pipe. A stiff rod extends from ground surface inside the pump pipe and acts with reciprocating action. The cylinder contains a valved piston that is open on the downstroke and closed on the upstroke. Operation is virtually the same as many oil well pumps, driven by a working-head jack and an electric motor.

John W. Foster

FURTHER READING

Ahearns, T. P. "Basic Considerations of Well Design." *Water Well Journal* (April-June, 1970). A series of articles that offers a comprehensible explanation of how well design must be adapted to the prevailing geologic conditions of the well site. Covers the making of decisions in regard to well diameters, primarily controlled by the well's intended use, the owner's volumetric water requirements, and the capability of the aquifer.

ALL Consulting. *A Guide to Practical Management of Produced water from Onshore Oil and Gas Operations in the United States.* Tulsa, Okla.: Interstate Oil and Gas Compact Commission and ALL Consulting, 2006. Discusses regulations and industry trends of onshore wells. Examines water and oil wells, and covers oil and gas basins.

Brassington, Rick. *Finding Water: A Guide to the Construction and Maintenance of Private Water Supplies.* 2d ed. New York: John Wiley, 1995. A college-level text that can serve as a handbook about well construction and upkeep for the layperson. Explains the testing and planning that must be done in preparation for the construction of a private well. Illustrations, maps, index, and bibliography.

Calhoun, Donald E., III. "Water Well Design Considerations." *Water Well Journal* 33, no. 3 (1989). Provides useful suggestions about optimal sizes of well casings, the selection of casing materials, and well screens. Provides explanation for the avoidance of wells that produce silt-sand particles, which shorten the life of pumps and cause other problems for the owner. Sets forth a logical argument for elimination of an old technique used by some well contractors: the cutting of slots in casing as a substitute for the commercial well screen.

Detay, Michel. *Water Wells: Implementation, Maintenance, and Restoration.* Translated by M. N. S. Carpenter. New York: Wiley, 1997. Provides a detailed look into the fields of hydroengineering and water-resource management. Examines water supplies and reserves, as well as the management policies surrounding these resources. Illustrations, index, and bibliographical references.

Fetter, C. W. *Contaminant Hydrogeology*. Long Grove, Ill.: Waveland Publishing, 2008. Written primarily as a textbook on groundwater geology, those portions that address the nature and varieties of aquifers are comprehensible to the lay reader. Describes the nature of groundwater, which is the geologic resource tapped by all successful water wells. Water-well technology, however, is not included.

Kasenow, Michael. *Aquifer Test Data: Analysis and Evaluation*. Highlands Ranch, Colo.: Water Resources Publications, 2006. Fills a gap in water sciences by focusing on aquifer test analysis. Discusses methods of evaluation and analysis, data collection, and well field analysis. Comes with a CD-ROM with specific capacity tables and theisian tables. Provides a well-rounded overview beginning with basic testing topics and following with specific aquifer types and analyses.

_____. *Production Well Analysis: New Methods and Computer Programs in Well Hydraulics*. Highlands Ranch, Colo.: Water Resources Publications, 1996. Looks at the factors involved in well construction, including groundwater flow and measurement, aquifers, and fluid dynamics. Accompanied by a CD-ROM, as well as illustrations. Intended for the reader with some background in the subject.

Mahajan, Gautam. *Evaluation and Development of Ground Water*. New Delhi: S. B. Nangia, 2008. Focused primarily on the discovery and development of groundwater resources in India, but nevertheless presents a logical explanation of the basic principles of water well science.

Misstear, B. D. R., David Banks, and Lewis Clark. *Water Wells and Boreholes*. New York: John Wiley & Sons, 2006. Discusses various types and uses of water wells, from supply and irrigation to remediation. Discusses technology and analysis advances and provides descriptions of the types of wells and boreholes and their functions. Covers borehole design in detail, as well as borehole construction and well-water sampling and monitoring. Presents global case studies. Suitable for post-graduate students, researchers, and others.

Schon, J. H. *Physical Properties of Rocks*. Amsterdam: Elsevier, 2004. Contains information on geophysics useful to a number of professions. Discusses the physical properties of rocks, geophysics theories, and experiments. Suited for engineers, geologists, geophysicists, and well loggers.

State of California. Department of Water Resources. *Water Well Standards*. Bulletin 74-81. Sacramento: Author, 1982. Written for the water-well industry and layperson alike, providing cautionary explanations of well designs aimed at assuring the owner of freedom from surface contamination and pollution. Provides recommendations on materials suitable for use in well construction and materials that are not suitable. Generally applicable to all geographic areas, despite being published by the state of California.

See also: Aquifers; Artificial Recharge; Dams and Flood Control; Drought; Floods; Freshwater and Groundwater Contamination Around the World; Groundwater Movement; Groundwater Pollution and Remediation; Hydrologic Cycle; Precipitation; Salinity and Desalination; Saltwater Intrusion; Surface Water; Waterfalls; Water Quality; Watersheds; Water Table

WEATHER FORECASTING

Weather systems are chaotic, which limits the degree of forecasting accuracy. The study of chaos theory and chaotic systems has allowed the development of innovative techniques that give insight into weather predictability.

PRINCIPAL TERMS

- **aperiodic:** describing any phenomenon that occurs at random rather than at regularly occurring intervals, such as found in most weather cycles, rendering them virtually unpredictable
- **chaos:** an emerging scientific discipline that attempts to quantify and describe the properties of seemingly random, aperiodic events
- **nowcasting:** a weather forecast made and disseminated within an hour or less for a specific area for an approaching weather system
- **weather analogue:** an approach that uses the weather behavior of the past to predict what a current weather pattern will do in the future

DEVELOPMENT OF WEATHER FORECASTING

From the earliest days of recorded civilization, people have actively attempted to forecast the weather, and for good reason: The weather directly affects everyone. Predicting the weather has been a priority for reasons of simple comfort to protection of property and lives, and the success of agriculture. Among uneducated and superstitious people, weather forecasting has been widely associated with lunar phases, rainbows, halos, and even the behavior and appearance of animals and insects. With the advent of weather instruments such as thermometers, anemometers, hygrometers, and barometers, the science of meteorology evolved. The first recorded use of the term "weather forecast" was by Englishman Robert Fitzroy in 1860, a man with enough perception to avoid any nonscientific term such as "prophecy" or even one so bold as "prediction."

Record keeping and sharing of information across states, nations, and the world by telegraph and radio during and after World War I finally brought the science to a coherent body of knowledge. By the start of World War II, the invention of the high-altitude balloon for weather soundings (the radiosonde) enabled the tracking of upper air currents. The term "atmospheric science" began to encompass the grand, global scheme of weather forecasting. "Meteorology" technically accounts for the action in the lower atmosphere.

The earliest meaningful attempts at forecasting the weather on a scientific basis came with the advent of the barometer, a device that measures atmospheric pressure, and the realization that changes in the weather seemed to follow changes in the barometric pressure. It was also noted that weather changed with the passage of air masses, which often dramatically altered the weather from what it had been. The observation was also made that the passage of air masses was often related to the barometric pressure. The accuracy of weather prediction increased with such observations.

FORECASTING METHODS

Prediction of the weather from present conditions to two days forward is called a short-range forecast. A medium-range forecast can be stretched out to only seven days forward. Beyond seven days it is called a long-range forecast, of which thirty days forward are all that can be predicted with any statistical accuracy. A ninety-day outlook is given by the National Weather Service. Prediction method accuracy varies widely with the condition being predicted. Accurately forecasting damaging weather such as local high winds, heavy snow, dangerous thunderstorms, or tornadoes beyond twelve hours is generally not possible. Very short-range forecasting for periods of one hour or less is a relatively new technique primarily used for issuing warnings. Such immediate forecasts are called nowcasts.

Satellites offer a wide view of the planet as they orbit. The advantage of these instruments is a global view of weather patterns and their movement, which offers a wide range of immediate forecasting options when related to ground weather observations. Radar offers a view of precipitation in most forms and is useful in forecasting imminent weather patterns. Doppler radar provides a means of pinpointing tornadoes as they are forming inside thundercloud formations.

The global weather scheme is plotted by powerful computers, which collect data from all over the globe and integrate them into a planetary weather picture. From this picture, forecasters adopt mathematical models to calculate what will happen to the system over time. The weather is predicted by supercomputers using a global scheme simulating weather worldwide based on a vast grid of data points covering the globe at various resolutions. These forecasts are calculated at billions of operations per second. Yet forecasters have found that no single model or combination of models, using even the most powerful computers, gives an accurate prediction of weather schemes beyond one week. The reason for that is an intrinsic condition called chaos.

Chaos accounts for the breakdown of forecasting accuracy over time. It was first related to weather patterns by Massachusetts Institute of Technology meteorologist Edward Lorenz in 1961. By 1963, Lorenz had constructed a computerized model of the atmosphere. Lorenz discovered that regardless of the point at which the computer begins calculating the equations for predicting the weather, every data point is potentially unstable, so that very small errors are magnified over time. That is called sensitive dependence on initial conditions, or the "butterfly effect." The butterfly effect refers to the flapping of a butterfly's wings in, for example, Beijing, China, which initiates a tiny instability in the atmosphere, which is ultimately magnified through chaotic repercussions into storm systems in New York. This rather fanciful analogue of the effect of chaos in weather systems is the real problem faced in weather forecasting. The future of weather forecasting probably lies in understanding and modeling chaotic systems. Such work is under way at the National Weather Service.

APPLICATIONS OF FORECASTING METHODS

The three ranges of weather forecasting—nowcasting (one hour or less), short-range forecasting (less than two days), and long-range forecasting (up to ninety days ahead)—all use different techniques for development of the forecast. Nowcasts are usually based on ongoing observations from radar for predictions for very specific locations. For example, a tornado warning, hurricane landfall or storm surge warning, or severe thunderstorm warning may be issued for a specific city based upon actual images of the storm bearing down. The only mathematical methods applied in these cases would be tracking equations based on speed and distance.

Short-range forecasting is much more complex. Mathematical modeling equations are developed from four different types of mathematical techniques. The National Weather Service uses combinations of all these equations in its computer analyses of the weather's short-term outlook. These mathematical techniques are computations of physical parameters, computations of displacements of large weather systems, regression analysis, and statistical (time series) analyses. Computations of physical parameters are pure physical formulas: hydrodynamic, aerodynamic, thermodynamic, and classical physical laws. Examples are Sir Isaac Newton's equations for motion, rules for the conservation of mass, heat transfer equations, and the laws for gas states, all applied to dynamic (moving) weather systems. In computations of displacements of large weather systems, the rates of movement of well-defined frontal systems are calculated based on a series of equations developed for just these systems and their movements. By using a statistical analogy between past events and present conditions, a forecaster is able to relate past weather patterns to future conditions. Statistical (time series) regression analyses called model output statistics (MOS) enable the forecaster to make predictions of future weather events. These equations account for the possible variations in weather patterns over time and physical range of the weather system itself. In such forecasts, the weather is predicted to occur on a chance basis. For example, the forecast may give an area a 50 percent chance of measurable precipitation. All these parameters may be utilized in developing a single forecast.

Extended forecasting is developed by different methods from those employed in short-range forecasts. Meteorologists still use a battery of computerized tools, but the effect of chaos (instability at every point in the atmosphere) is so great beyond two days that extending the computer tools used for short-range forecasting out many days is all but useless for specific areas. Yet there are seasonal weather patterns, worldwide circulations, oceanic currents, and historical norms that account for making long-range forecasts possible. These nearly cyclic conditions are called aperiodic and enable some degree of forecasting. In the study of chaos itself, there are predictable, recognizable elements: all the nuances of aperiodicity that ultimately lead to the chaotic state. It is precisely the investigation of these elements that atmospheric scientists are now pursuing.

One of the most elementary, subjective elements of such an approach actually surfaced in the early

1950's, a decade before chaos was quantitatively linked to the weather. In such an approach, called weather analogues or weather typing, weather charts of previous seasons were categorized and cataloged. Current charts were then compared with old charts to indicate possible future trends. In the days before a full understanding of the power of even minute atmospheric instabilities, these analyses proved of no use at all and were all but abandoned in favor of powerful computerized analyses.

In using computers to make long-range forecasts, meteorologists have noted that there are times when their automated models prove correct, often even surprisingly accurate. Chaos, again, proves to be the central determinant of accuracy. Stability of the weather pattern determines the accuracy of the computerized forecast. In order to weed the good forecasts from the bad, atmospheric scientists have developed a method called the ensemble approach. In this technique, they predict the reliability of the forecast by testing the stability of the conditions: They run the same forecast analysis at least ten times using a supercomputer, altering each run very slightly to mirror tiny instabilities in the atmosphere, and then compare results. If the end result is widely variable forecasts, then the forecasting reliability for that day is low. Using such techniques, atmospheric scientists can not only predict the ultimate accuracy of their forecasts but also decide on the degree of its reliability.

SIGNIFICANCE

From the obviously detrimental effect of storms to the periodic need for rain, the weather is a phenomenon of universal relevance. Predicting the weather is a science that has developed into a study involving individuals and governments and the pooling of an immense amount of information. Some forecasting ability has resulted from ordinary and practical application, while other methods are so complex that they are understood only by a very few highly skilled meteorologists in the scientific community.

Yet without regard for human progress and understanding, the deserts of equatorial Africa have been encroaching northward at tens of kilometers per year, rendering once fertile land into useless desert; hundreds of people have died daily from famine unfolding across the vast African savannah. The frequency of hurricanes is changing along the Atlantic seaboard, threatening millions of seashore inhabitants. The sunbelt population in the United States is rapidly growing along the paths of hundreds of potentially deadly tornadoes. The world's atmospheric scientists are faced with the task of predicting the potential for the weather to directly affect the lives of millions of people. From giving imminent warnings to plotting the centimeter-by-centimeter alteration of long-term weather patterns, the significance of prediction has never been greater.

The discovery of the effect of chaos has greatly facilitated the task at hand. Many scientists have since declared the task of accurate weather forecasting to be impossible. Others continue the struggle to discern the meaning behind the science with instabilities at every point. The study of chaos itself has spread from meteorology to nearly every other discipline.

Dennis Chamberland

FURTHER READING

Ackerman, Steven, and John Knox. *Meteorology: Understanding the Atmosphere.* 3d ed. Sudbury, Mass.: Jones and Bartlett, 2012. A textbook for undergraduate students. Presents basic concepts of atmospheric phenomena and uses that information to focus on weather and climate topics.

Bader, M. J., et al., eds. *Images in Weather Forecasting: A Practical Guide for Interpreting Satellite and Radar Imagery.* New York: Cambridge University Press, 1997. This collection of essays written by leading meteorologists describes the equipment and techniques used in weather forecasting. Chapters focus on remote-sensing, radar meteorology, and satellite meteorology. Color illustrations.

Barrett, E. C. *Viewing Weather from Space.* New York: Frederick A. Praeger, 1967. Though its information is dated, this concise book provides a fine historical backdrop to the development of the weather satellite as an instrument for observing the weather from space. Also discusses the primary uses for the weather satellite as an instrument for predicting the weather. Illustrated with drawings and photographs.

Collier, Christopher G. *Applications of Weather Radar Systems: A Guide to Uses of Radar Data in Meteorology and Hydrology.* 2d ed. New York: Wiley, 1996. Offers the reader a detailed look into scientific advancements regarding the tools used in meteorology and hydrology. Chapters focus on radar meteorology, precipitation measurement, hydrometeorology, and weather forecasting.

Dolan, Ed. *The Old Farmer's Almanac Book of Weather Lore.* Dublin, N.H.: Yankee Books, 1988. No accounting of modern weather forecasting can be told without its fabulously rich heritage of centuries of folklore and history. From the very source of folk meteorology itself, *The Farmer's Almanac,* comes this definitive treatment of the subject.

Dunlop, Storm. *The Weather Identification Handbook.* Guilford, Conn.: The Lyons Press, 2003. Provides a simple and useful guide to various atmospheric objects, patterns, dynamics, and phenomena. Begins with identification of cloud formations, followed by optical phenomena such as rainbows, and various weather patterns and events. Best used as a reference for the weather enthusiast as an introduction to the study of meteorology.

Gleick, James. *Chaos: Making a New Science.* 2d ed. New York: Penguin Books, 2008. Details the emergence of a new science: the study of chaos, which began with a meteorologist attempting to write a computer program to predict the weather. This book, a national best seller, discusses the recognition and development of the study of chaos. Offers a fine treatment of weather prediction as an example of chaos and why forecasting such a chaotic system may not be impossible as once thought. Written for a general audience. Illustrated and indexed.

Hamilton, Kevin, and Wataru Ohfuchi, eds. *High Resolution Numerical Modeling of the Atmosphere and Ocean.* New York: Springer Science+Business Media, 2008. Presents a technical account of the efforts and progress in accurately modeling the climate and weather patterns of the world by computational means. Includes several papers presented by invited speakers to the first international convention focused on this endeavor.

Hodgson, Michael. *Basic Essentials: Weather Forecasting.* 3d ed. Chester, Conn.: Globe Pequot, 2007. Suited for nonmeteorologists. Describes how people are trained to make forecasts using human observations of the weather around them. Before attempting to use computer forecasts, people should have a basic understanding of the physical principles operating in the atmosphere.

Monmonier, Mark S. *Air Apparent: How Meteorologists Learned to Map, Predict, and Dramatize Weather.* Chicago: University of Chicago Press, 1999. This college-level text looks at the satellites and radar systems used to collect meteorological data, as well as the techniques used to interpret that information. Color illustrations, index, and bibliographical references.

Vasquez, Tim. *Weather Analysis and Forecasting Handbook.* Garland, Tex.: Weather Graphics Technologies, 2011. Discusses technology, techniques, and physics principles used in modern weather forecasting. Discusses thermal structure and dynamics of weather systems. Also covered are the use of models in weather forecasting and weather system visualization. Easily accessible yet still technical, useful to anyone studying weather forecasting and meteorology.

Wallace, John M., and Peter V. Hobbs. *Atmospheric Science.* 2d ed. Burlington, Mass.: Academic Press, 2006. Offers a complete study of the atmosphere. Covers the fundamental physics and chemistry topics as well as specific topics in atmospheric science such as radiative transfer, weather forecasting, and global warming. Provides significant detail and technical writing, but is still accessible to the undergraduate studying meteorology or thermodynamics.

See also: Acid Rain and Acid Deposition; Atmosphere's Evolution; Atmosphere's Global Circulation; Atmosphere's Structure and Thermodynamics; Atmospheric and Oceanic Oscillations; Barometric Pressure; Climate; Climate Modeling; Clouds; Cyclones and Anticyclones; Drought; Hurricanes; Lightning and Thunder; Long-Term Weather Patterns; Monsoons; Ozone Depletion and Ozone Holes; Recent Climate Change Research; Remote Sensing of the Atmosphere; Remote Sensing of the Oceans; Satellite Meteorology; Seasons; Severe Storms; Tornadoes; Van Allen Radiation Belts; Volcanoes: Climatic Effects; Weather Forecasting: Numerical Weather Prediction; Weather Modification; Wind

WEATHER FORECASTING: NUMERICAL WEATHER PREDICTION

Most industrialized nations use numerical weather prediction (NWP) techniques to formulate weather forecasts. NWP is based on physical laws that are incorporated into a mathematical model, with solutions determined using computer algorithms. Large amounts of data are used to initialize the numerical models and verification of short-range NWP models shows a considerable improvement over climatology. NWP models require large mainframe supercomputers to formulate each forecast.

PRINCIPAL TERMS

- **climatology:** the scientific study of climate that depends on the statistical database of weather observed over a period of twenty or more years for a specific location
- **ensemble weather forecasting:** repeated use of a single model, run many times using slightly different initial data; the results of the model runs are pooled to create a single "ensemble" weather forecast
- **forecast verification:** comparison of predicted weather to observed weather conditions to assess forecasting accuracy and reliability
- **global atmospheric model:** computational model of global weather patterns based on a spherical coordinate system representing the entire planet
- **hemispheric model:** a numerical model that extends over the whole Northern or Southern Hemisphere, or just one half of the planet
- **long-range prediction:** a weather forecast for a specific region for a period greater than one week in advance, often supplemented with climatological information
- **mesoscale model:** a weather forecast for an area of up to several hundred square kilometers in extent on a time scale of between one and twelve hours
- **nondeterminism:** chaotic, random events that cannot be predicted but that have a significant influence on the development of weather systems
- **nowcasting:** a very short-term weather forecast usually for the prediction of rapidly changing, severe weather events within a time of no more than a few hours

HISTORICAL DEVELOPMENT

The atmosphere is a very complex, chaotic natural system. Before the science of meteorology was developed, keen observers of the natural environment developed forecasting rules epitomized by such sayings as "Red sky at morning/ Sailors take warning/ Red sky at night/ Sailors delight." In the early nineteenth century, a generally acceptable systematic classification of clouds was introduced by Luke Howard, known as the father of British meteorology, and scientists began making routine daily weather observations at major cities and universities. A systematic study of the atmosphere as a chemical and physical entity began.

In 1904, Vilhelm Bjerknes brought the scientific community to understand that atmospheric motions were largely governed by the first law of thermodynamics, Newton's second law of motion, conservation of mass (the "continuity equation"), the equation of state, and conservation of water in all its forms. (These physical laws form what is now known as the "governing equations" for numerical weather prediction.) Bjerknes, writing that the fundamental governing equations constituted a determinate, nonlinear system, realized that the system had no analytic solution. He also recognized that available data to determine initial conditions were inadequate. In 1906, Bjerknes devised graphical methods to use in atmospheric physics. During the next decade, he adopted an approach to apply physics in a qualitative, as opposed to a numerical, technique to weather forecasting.

In 1916, Bjerknes began working at the Bergen Museum in Norway, a move that would be decisive in establishing meteorology as an applied science. In 1918, Bjerknes's son Jacob noticed distinctive features on weather maps that led him to publish an essay entitled "On the Structure of Moving Cyclones." This was followed by the development of the concept of "fronts" as a forecasting tool at the Bergen School in 1919. Following World War I, Norwegian and Swedish meteorologists educated at the Bergen School began using the theory of fronts operationally. Their ability to correctly predict severe weather events led other Europeans to adopt this frontal forecasting method. Enthusiasm for this empirical method blossomed and remains strong among the general public today.

Meanwhile, attempts to develop numerical weather prediction techniques languished. A method for numerically integrating the governing equations was published by L. F. Richardson in 1921. It contained several problems and errors. Following World War II, the development of mainframe computers allowed development of objective forecasting models incorporating many meteorological variables. By 1950, the first scientific results of a computer model, based on numerical integration of barotropic vorticity equations, were published. In the following decades, computer models grew increasingly sophisticated through the incorporation of larger and larger numbers of operations, iterations, and data input. Computer speeds increased dramatically, allowing use of sophisticated equations modeling atmospheric behavior. Larger models with relatively fine grids were developed.

USE OF SUPERCOMPUTERS

Modern weather forecasting attempts to model processes in the atmosphere by representing the appropriate classical laws of physics in mathematical terms. Models use calculations of assemblages of approximations of physical equations (algorithms). Large (mainframe) supercomputers generate numerical forecasts using these algorithms and an array of observations. Most models have at least fifteen vertical levels and a grid with a mesh size less than 200 kilometers. The exact formulation of any particular model depends upon the amount of data being input, how long in advance, how detailed, and which variables are being forecast.

Historically, weather observations for numerical forecasts were taken mainly at 0000 Coordinated Universal Time (UTC), or Greenwich time, and 1200 UTC using ground stations and radiosondes (weather balloons). Now these observations are supplemented by asynchronous observations from infrared and microwave detectors on satellites, radar, pilot reports, and automatic weather observation stations (including ocean buoys). These new data sources have substantially enlarged the amount of input data. However, because these data are fed into the models as they run, the distinction between input data and model predictions has become blurred. Thus, a weather map showing a numerically generated forecast (as seen on the Internet or in a television presentation) may contain information from many data sources of varying accuracy taken at various times and locations.

Data from all available observations are interpolated to fit the model grid size. Every forecast incorporates inherent errors from the observations, data interpolations, model approximations, the instabilities of the mathematics, and the limitations of the computers used. Models can be separated by their time frame into nowcasts, short-term forecasts, medium-range forecasts, long-term forecasts, and outlooks. In addition, specialized forecast models for hurricanes and other specific types of severe weather have been developed. Because of hazards associated with severe, rapidly developing weather threats, there is increasing interest in developing specialized nowcast and short-range mesoscale (local) forecast models.

Many countries staff their own meteorological offices, using satellite images and local weather observations to develop computer models uniquely suited to their needs. Countries with specific needs and adequate resources develop models to suit their own unique needs. Japan, with its high population concentrations exposed to tropical storm threats, has directed its meteorological efforts toward mesoscale forecasting. The entire country was covered by a network of weather radars by 1971, and Japan supplements its ground-based observations with geostationary weather satellites. This maximizes the Japanese ability to predict heavy rains from tropical typhoons and to issue flash flood forecasts.

In 1999, the United States National Weather Service (NWS) completed a twelve-year modernization program that included 311 automatic weather observing systems and 120 new Nexrad Doppler radars. Observed weather and forecasts were displayed on state-of-the-art computer systems at NWS forecasting offices.

In the mid-1970's, the European Centre for Medium Range Weather Forecasting (ECMWF) and the U.S. National Weather Service began utilizing high-speed supercomputers to generate and solve numerical weather models. Both of these entities have developed global atmospheric models for medium-range forecasts, producing a three- to six-day forecast. The numerical methods used in these global models involve a spectral transform method. One reason for using this method is that models frequently experience numerical problems for computations in polar latitudes. The ECMWF in 1999 was using a model with grid points spaced every 60 kilometers around the globe at thirty-one levels in the vertical. Its initial conditions used observations over the previous twenty-four hours and added in several early model runs forecasting about twenty minutes ahead to augment the observations. Wind, temperature, and humidity were then forecast at 4,154,868 points throughout the atmosphere. Although these models do very well compared with earlier, more primitive models, there is considerable room for improvement in forecasting ability, especially in the tropical latitudes. Medium-range forecast models continue to be improved periodically.

FUTURE OF NUMERICAL WEATHER PREDICTION

The greatest advancements in numerical weather prediction may arise through continued improvement in quality and quantity of weather data used as input in the models, through better methods of data interpolation, through improved algorithms of atmospheric behavior, and in the use of increasingly sophisticated supercomputers capable of more and faster iterations. Some modelers believe that departing from a latitude-longitude grid would prevent clustering of grid points near the poles, which now induces some problems in numerical computations.

Nowcasting, especially for rapidly developing severe weather conditions including severe thunderstorms, flash floods, and tornadoes, has received a great deal of attention by scientists and governments. Within the United States, it is hoped that the inclusion of the Nexrad Doppler radar observations into operational models will lead to better nowcasting.

Forecasts demonstrate both accuracy and skill. A forecast may be entirely accurate simply because of the normal weather pattern in a location, and not because of the skill of the forecaster. Conversely, a forecaster or a forecasting method demonstrates skill by accurately predicting weather that is out of the expected normal pattern for that location. Forecasts have been improving in a slow, steady fashion since the introduction of supercomputers. However, even for short-range time periods, there is still room for improvement. One method for improving any model's forecasting ability is to make ensemble forecasts by running the same model many times, each time with slightly different initial conditions, and then pooling the results statistically. This technique yields better results than any single model run, based on comparing verifications of the individual and

ensemble results for a large number of forecasts. A variation of this technique is the superensemble forecast in which forecasts from several different computer models runs or even ensemble runs are pooled. Superensemble forecasts have been found to show greater accuracy than ensemble forecasts. One way in which superensemble forecasts are thought to achieve this is in the minimization of "forecast bias" in which any one model develops a spurious trend as the increasing numbers of iterations magnify small errors.

Worldwide, better weather satellite imagery for input to more detailed hemispheric models could lead to enhanced quality of numerical weather predictions. Greater availability of weather observations for the world's oceans would also be helpful. While hemispheric models are good at forecasting at midlatitudes, less accuracy and skill are shown in tropical forecasting, as determined by model verification. Improved models incorporating more detailed initial data could provide better forecasts in the tropics.

One of the greatest challenges confronting numerical weather prediction lies in the development of reliable long-range predictive models. Long-range predictions often fail because of nondeterministic or random events. The El Niño/Southern Oscillation is an example. El Niño events are now viewed as virtually nondeterministic events; when a strong El Niño event is occurring, the output from some long-range models may be subjectively altered by meteorologists to reflect past historical events. The goal of numerical weather prediction is to provide objective forecasts using a model that verifies data more frequently than do subjective forecasts, even those formulated by highly trained meteorologists. To forecast El Niño events better, it would be advantageous to develop a predictive model that could successfully incorporate Pacific Ocean surface temperatures as initial conditions. With longer and better data records, and further study of why existing long-range predictions have failed, better models may be developed.

Dennis G. Baker and Anita Baker-Blocker

FURTHER READING

Bader, M. J., G. S. Forbes, J. R. Grant, and R. Lilley. *Images in Weather Forecasting: A Practical Guide for Interpreting Satellite and Radar Imagery.* New York: Cambridge University Press, 1997. Discusses basic techniques for interpreting midlatitude satellite images of weather systems in North America and Europe. Radar images are explained in terms of airflow and weather patterns.

Bluestein, Howard B. *Synaptic-Dynamic Meteorology in Midlatitudes.* New York: Oxford University Press, 1992. This two-volume work, designed for upper-level college students, requires a strong background in physics and calculus. For readers with this background, this is a fine reference work.

Browning, K. A., and R. J. Gurney. *Global Energy and Water Cycles.* New York: Cambridge University Press, 2007. This excellent book features reviews by Europeans and Americans on how weather forecasting models are developed and used.

Burroughs, William J. *Watching the World's Weather.* New York: Cambridge University Press, 1991. This book discusses the techniques for the collection and handling of meteorological data from radar and satellites. Data from these observations are used as initial conditions in numerical weather prediction models.

Djuric, Dusan. *Weather Analysis.* Englewood Cliffs, NJ: Prentice Hall, 1994. Written as a text for a college course in weather analysis, this illustrated text, which uses examples from real weather events, covers the basic mathematical approach to numerical weather analysis. Background knowledge of college physics and calculus is essential for understanding this work.

Hamilton, Kevin, and Wataru Ohfuchi, eds. *High Resolution Numerical Modeling of the Atmosphere and Ocean.* New York: Springer Science+Business Media, 2008. Presents a technical account of the efforts and progress in accurately modeling the climate and weather patterns of the world by computational means. Includes several papers presented by invited speakers to the first international convention focused on this endeavor.

Hodgson, Michael. *Basic Essentials: Weather Forecasting.* 3d ed. Chester, Conn.: Globe Pequot, 2007. Describes how people are trained to make forecasts using human observations of the weather around them. Before attempting to use computer forecasts, people should have a basic understanding of the physical principles operating in the atmosphere.

Katz, Richard W., and Allan H. Murphy. *Economic Value of Weather and Climate Forecasts.* New York: Cambridge University Press, 1997. Provides an overview of numerical weather prediction and methods used to verify forecasts. Offers a high-level appraisal of the relative value of objective weather forecasts.

Krishnamurti, T. N., et al. "Improved Weather and Seasonal Climate Forecasts from Multimodel Superensemble." *Science* 258 (September 3, 1999): 1548-1550. Moving to superensemble forecasting is shown to outperform all models and to have higher skills than forecasts based solely on ensemble forecasting. Argues for the establishment of a multimodel superensemble center for weather and seasonal climate forecasting.

Monmonier, Mark S. *Air Apparent: How Meteorologists Learned to Map, Predict, and Dramatize Weather.* Chicago: University of Chicago Press, 1999. Using weather maps, this book shows the growth of technology used in weather forecasting.

Santurette, Patrick, and Christo Georgiev. *Weather Analysis and Forecasting.* Burlington, Mass.: Academic Press, 2005. Discusses the use of satellite imagery to detect and analyze atmospheric moisture. Identifies factors that indicate severe weather occurrence and discusses the use of water vapor imagery to improve forecasting.

Stensrud, David J. *Parameterization Schemes: Keys to Understanding Numerical Weather Prediction Models.* New York: Cambridge University Press, 2007. Describes land surface-atmosphere, soil-vegetation-atmosphere, and water-atmosphere parameterizations. Also discusses radiation, convective schemes, turbulence, cloud cover, and orographic drag as they relate to prediction models. Useful to anyone using numerical weather prediction models.

Temmam, R. and J. Tribbia, eds. *Handbook of Numerical Analysis. Vol. XIV. Special Volume Computational Methods for the Atmosphere and the Oceans.* Oxford, England: North-Holland, 2009. Surveys numerical modeling and mathematical analysis used to study atmospheric weather patterns, particularly as they relate to the oceans and the atmosphere. Uses various mathematical methods and tools.

Vasquez, Tim. *Weather Analysis and Forecasting Handbook.* Garland, Tex.: Weather Graphics Technologies, 2011. Discusses the technology, techniques, and physics principles used in modern weather forecasting. Describes thermal structure and dynamics of weather systems. Also covers model use in weather forecasting and weather system visualization. Easily accessible yet still technical, useful to anyone studying weather forecasting and meteorology.

Zdunkowski, Wilfred, and Andreas Bott. *Thermodynamics of the Atmosphere. A Course in Theoretical Meteorology.* New York: Cambridge University Press, 2004. Aimed at graduate students and researchers in meteorology and related sciences. Focuses on the thermodynamics at work in the atmosphere. Agreement with thermodynamic principles is fundamental to the development of numerical methods of weather prediction.

See also: Atmosphere's Evolution; Atmosphere's Global Circulation; Atmospheric and Oceanic Oscillations; Climate; Clouds; Drought; Floods; Greenhouse Effect; Hurricane Katrina; Hurricanes; Lightning and Thunder; Long-Term Weather Patterns; Monsoons; Ocean-Atmosphere Interactions; Precipitation; Satellite Meteorology; Seasons; Severe Storms; Tornadoes; Van Allen Radiation Belts; Volcanoes: Climatic Effects; Weather Forecasting; Weather Modification; Wind

WEATHERING AND EROSION

The weathering process breaks down the rocks both into soluble materials and into the solid particles that form soils. These weathered products are then swept away by the various erosional agents, such as rivers and glaciers, that shape the planet's rocky surface.

PRINCIPAL TERMS

- **abrasion:** the wearing away of rock by frictional contact with solid particles moved by gravity, water, ice, or wind
- **acid rain:** rain with higher levels of acidity than normal, formed by contact of atmospheric moisture with airborne pollutants
- **chemical weathering:** the decomposition of rock by chemical rather than mechanical processes
- **erosion:** the general term for the various processes by which particles already loosened by weathering are transported from one location to another by the action of moving air or water
- **granite:** a coarse-grained, igneous rock composed primarily of the minerals quartz and feldspar
- **limestone:** a sedimentary rock composed of calcium carbonate
- **mechanical weathering:** the physical disintegration of rock into smaller particles having the same chemical composition as the parent material
- **mineral:** a naturally occurring, inorganic, crystalline material with a unique chemical composition
- **sandstone:** sedimentary rock composed of grains of sand that have become cemented together under the influences of pressure and time
- **weathering:** the general term for the group of processes that break down rocks at or near the ground surface

DESTRUCTIVE FORCES

Although the landscape rarely appears to change, constructive and destructive forces are at work on Earth, building the crust up and breaking the rocks down and carrying the resulting debris away. The destructive forces are known as weathering and erosion. "Weathering" refers to the mechanical disintegration and chemical decomposition of rocks and minerals at or near the ground surface. No movement of these materials is implied. Exposure to weather causes rocks to change their character and either crumble into soil or become transformed into even smaller particles that are readily available for removal.

"Erosion" refers to the processes by which particles already loosened by weathering are removed by the action of moving air or flowing water. This process involves two steps: First, the loose materials must be picked up, or entrained; second, the materials must be physically carried, or transported, to new locations. The major ways by which Earth materials are eroded are by means of rivers, underground water, moving ice, waves, wind, and landslides.

Weathering is a near-surface phenomenon because it involves the response of Earth materials to the elements of sunlight, rain, snow, and the like. It does not affect rocks that are buried within the crust. Only after these rocks are exposed at the surface, after a long period of uplift and removal of overlying material, does weather begin to affect them. In the changed environment, they are subject to the comparatively hostile actions of acid rain, subfreezing temperatures, and high humidity. The resulting transformations that take place in the rock are what is termed weathering.

MECHANICAL AND CHEMICAL WEATHERING

Scientists recognize two different types of weathering: mechanical and chemical. Although the two types are generally discussed separately, it is important to keep in mind that in nature they generally work hand in hand. Mechanical weathering (also known as disintegration) involves the physical breakdown of the rock into smaller and smaller grains, usually because of the application of some kind of pressure such as the expansion of water during freezing or the growth of plant roots in rock crevices. The chemical composition of the rock, however, remains unchanged. The end result of mechanical weathering is smaller pieces of rock that are identical in composition and appearance to the original larger rock mass.

Chemical weathering (also known as decomposition) involves a complex alteration in the materials that compose the original rock. These materials are chemically changed into different substances by the addition or removal of certain elements, usually through the action of water. The familiar rusting of iron is an example of chemical weathering, characterized by a total change in the composition and appearance of the original material. At first, there is a hard, silvery metal; afterward, all that remains is a soft, reddish-brown powder.

Consider the effects of mechanical weathering and chemical weathering on a cube of rock that measures 6 centimeters on a side, thus having a total surface area of 216 square centimeters. Assume that by means of mechanical weathering, the cube is broken down into 216 cubes measuring 1 centimeter on a side, having a combined total surface area of 1,296 square centimeters. Now, much more surface area is available for chemical attack. For this reason, chemical weathering proceeds much faster when a rock is first broken into smaller pieces by mechanical weathering.

In nature, mechanical weathering can proceed in a variety of ways. The best-known example involves the action of freezing water. Because water increases about 9 percent in volume as it freezes, enormously large outward-directed pressures develop within a rock when water freezes in its pore spaces and cracks. This is sufficient to force pieces of the rock apart. One example of the result of this action is the angular rock fragments found scattered about most mountain tops and sides. Soil also contains water, and horizontal lenses of ice may form within the soil when water freezes in it. These create bumps in lawns and the familiar "frost heaves" of mountain roads. When heavy trucks rumble over these heaved pavements during thaws, the pavement gives way to create potholes.

In deserts, soil water is drawn upward through the rock and evaporates at the hot upper surface, leaving its dissolved salts behind as crystals growing in the pore spaces of the rock. These growing salt crystals also exert powerful pressures within the rock, so that porous rocks, such as sandstone, undergo continuous grain-by-grain disintegration in desert climates. Mechanical weathering can also be produced when the extreme heat from a forest fire or a lightning strike causes flakes to chip off a rock or when a growing plant or tree extends its root system into cracks and splits a rock apart. Another type of rock splitting is known as exfoliation, caused by the spontaneous expansion of rock masses when they are freed from the confining pressures of overlying and surrounding

rock. This process produces large, dome bedrock knobs with an onionlike structure. Stone Mountain, Georgia, and Half Dome, in Yosemite National Park, are examples.

Chemical weathering is a more complex process than mechanical weathering because the original rock material is actually transformed into different substances. The rusting of iron has already been mentioned as an example of chemical weathering. Many common rocks and minerals contain iron. During chemical weathering, the iron in these substances combines with oxygen from the air to form various iron oxides.

Another way in which chemical weathering attacks rocks is by dissolving them. Large areas of Earth's surface are underlain by a rock type known as limestone. Limestone is readily dissolved by water containing small quantities of acid. All rainfall is weakly acidic as a result of its dissolving carbon dioxide from the air to produce dilute carbonic acid. Rains that originate in areas of high air pollution are even more acidic, a condition known as acid rain. When rainfall that contains carbonic acid comes in contact with limestone bedrock, the acid reacts with the calcium carbonate in the rock to produce calcium bicarbonate, a soluble substance that is readily carried off in solution.

A final example of chemical weathering involves the weathering of granite, a hard igneous rock composed primarily of feldspar and quartz. When granite undergoes chemical weathering, each mineral is affected differently. The feldspar is gradually transformed into a new mineral, clay, which is soft and easily molded when wet. Clay offers very little resistance to erosion. Quartz, by comparison, is highly resistant to chemical attack and is left behind when the clay is removed. Some of the quartz grains remain in the soil, but most will be carried off by rivers, becoming rounded as they tumble along. Eventually they form the sands of beaches and, in time, the sedimentary rock known as sandstone.

EROSION

The term "erosion" refers to those processes by which the loose particles formed by weathering are picked up and carried to new locations. Erosion is a highly significant geomorphological phenomenon of Earth's surface. Examples of erosion range from small gullies in a farmer's field to a catastrophic landslide in a high mountain valley. Nevertheless, the general principle involved in all types of erosion is the same: Weathered Earth materials move downslope from their place of formation to a new location, with gravity as the driving force. The materials may simply slide downhill as in a landslide, or they may be carried down the hill by an erosional agent, such as running water. Worldwide, running water in the form of streams and rivers is probably the single most important erosional agent. Locally, other erosional agents may be highly significant, including underground water flow, glaciers, waves, and wind action.

The downhill movement of weathered materials under the influence of gravity alone results in landslides if the downslope movement is rapid but in "creep" if the movement is imperceptibly slow. When large quantities of water are present in the weathered material, the downslope movement is called a mudslide. Running water can erode material from its channel banks in four different ways: Soluble material can be dissolved by weakly acidic river water, bedrock can be worn smooth as a result of abrasion by

sand and gravel carried along the streambed, unconsolidated bank and bed materials can be swept away by a strong current (resulting in bank caving), and upwardly directed turbulent eddies in the water may lift small particles from the bottom and entrain them in this fashion. Underground water erodes bedrock primarily by dissolving it, whereas glaciers act more like rivers, abrading the underlying rock by means of rock fragments frozen in the ice. Glaciers are also able to pluck rock masses from their channel walls when these rock masses have frozen to the main ice mass; the rocks are torn loose as the ice moves on.

Waves erode shorelines, wearing rock surfaces smooth by means of the sand and gravel they carry. Waves can also dislodge particles from a cliff face. Cracks quickly open in cliffs, seawalls, and breakwaters, and when water is forced into these cracks, the air in the cracks becomes highly compressed, exerting still further pressure on the rock. Wind erosion, in contrast, relies on the abrasive action of sand grains transported by the wind and on the lifting power of eddies, which are able to entrain finer-grained soil particles.

STUDY OF WEATHERING AND EROSION

Scientists have analyzed the rate at which rocks weather and have found that the important factors are rock type, mineral content, amount of moisture present, temperature conditions, topographic conditions, and amount of plant and animal activity. A rock type may be highly resistant to weathering in one climate and quite unresistant in another. Limestone, for example, which forms El Capitan, the highest peak in the desert region of southwest Texas, underlies the lowest valleys in the humid climate of the Appalachian Mountains.

Using field observations and laboratory experiments, scientists have studied the rate at which different minerals are attacked by chemical decomposition. Among the minerals formed by igneous activity, quartz is least susceptible to chemical attack, whereas olivine, a greenish-colored

A block of granite that has been hollowed out by windblown sand at Llano de Caldera, Atacama Province, Chile. (U.S. Geological Survey)

mineral rich in iron and magnesium, is one of the most susceptible. The reason is that olivine forms at high temperatures and pressures when melted rock first begins to cool and is consequently unstable at the lower temperatures and pressures that prevail at Earth's surface. Quartz, by comparison, forms late in the cooling process, when the temperatures and pressures are more similar to those encountered at Earth's surface; therefore, quartz more readily resists attack by chemical weathering. Scientists have concluded that the more the conditions under which a mineral forms are akin to those at Earth's surface, the more resistant to chemical attack the mineral will be.

Numerous observations have been made relating to the rapidity with which weathering takes place. The eruption of Mount St. Helens in Washington State on May 18, 1980, has provided a natural laboratory for such study. During the eruption, vast quantities of volcanic ash were hurled into the air and deposited to depths of several meters in the vicinity of the volcano. Scientists have carefully analyzed the changes that are taking place in the ash because of mechanical and chemical weathering and the rate at which this ash is being converted into a productive soil for the growth of vegetation. Scientists also study the rate at which tombstones and historic monuments of known age are attacked by weathering. For marble tombstones in humid climates, the amount of weathering within a single lifetime may amount to several millimeters.

The rate at which earthen materials are moved from place to place on Earth's surface by the various agents of erosion is also of interest. One way to approach this problem is to measure the quantity of sediment being carried by a river each year and then to calculate how much of a loss this amount represents for the entire area drained by the river. Data from various locations in the United States suggest that the overall rate of erosion amounts to approximately 6 centimeters per 1,000 years. Corroborating evidence comes from another source: Photographs made in scenic areas and compared with photographs made from the same vantage point one hundred years ago or more show surprisingly little erosional modification of the surface. However, once humans occupy an area intensively, erosion rates increase significantly.

SIGNIFICANCE

Weathering affects not only bedrock outcrops but also human-made structures. Unless they are

continually repaired and restored, all structures become weather-beaten and, in time, weaken and fall into ruin. Beginning in the early 1970's, people also became aware of the harmful consequences of acid rain. Concrete, limestone building blocks, and the marble used for statuary are all susceptible to the dissolving action of acid rain. In fact, many well-known statues adorning public buildings in Europe have become essentially unrecognizable because of this process.

The earthen materials produced by weathering are of great significance. The larger grains are known as regolith and, by the addition of partly decomposed organic matter, are turned into soil, the basis for agriculture. Other grains are carried by rivers into the sea to become the raw materials from which beaches are made. Residues of weathered materials are sometimes left behind, such as clay and ores of iron, aluminum, and manganese, which may form valuable mineral deposits.

Erosional processes also affect human life. Gravity's influence may bury small villages in catastrophic landslides, or it may trigger the imperceptible downslope movements, known as creep, that cause structures on hillsides to collapse. When the Alaska Pipeline was being built, construction of all kinds was hampered by problems caused by soil flow when the permafrost in the ground thawed. The erosional activity of rivers shapes the landscape, cutting gorges and supplying sediment to alluvial fans, floodplains, levees, and deltas. Sometimes the erosional activity of a river gets out of hand, causing devastating floods. Even where no stream channel is present, farmlands can be seriously damaged by soil erosion.

The erosional power of moving ice sculpts some of the world's most spectacular mountains. Along coastlines, wave erosion creates cliffs or threatens human-made structures such as lighthouses, seawalls, and breakwaters. Coastal currents may carry sand away, causing severe beach erosion. The wind contributes to erosion when it moves sand grains to create a sandstorm. This blinding cloud can sandblast the paint off a car or break a telephone pole in two. Even dust-sized material, when lifted from the ground in the form of a dust storm, can have a devastating effect. During the 1930's, an area known as the Dust Bowl developed in the Great Plains region of the United States. A prolonged drought and unwise agricultural practices resulted in severe dust storms that blew away valuable topsoil, lowering the ground level by nearly 1 meter in some places.

Donald W. Lovejoy

FURTHER READING

Birkeland, P. W. *Soils and Geomorphology.* 3d ed. New York: Oxford University Press, 1999. One of the best books on soils. Written from the perspective of a geologist. Gives many examples from around the world. Devotes more than one-half of the book to soil formation, development, and erosion. The final chapter on applications of soil formation to geology is excellent. Suitable for advanced high school and university-level readers.

Bland, Will, and David Rolls. *Weathering: An Introduction to the Scientific Principles.* New York: Arnold, 1998. An introductory college textbook that provides a clear look at weathering and erosion processes. Explores the relationships among climate, weather, and the environment. Illustrations, references, and index.

Chorley, Richard J., Stanley A. Schumm, and David E. Sugden. *Geomorphology.* New York: Methuen, 1985. A well-referenced, though older, textbook, that places emphasis on the role and function of weathering sediment transport in all environments, and closely discusses theoretical principles. Contains numerous line drawings as well as working charts and graphs.

Darby, Stephen, and David Sear. *River Restoration: Managing the Uncertainty in Restoring Physical Habitat.* Hoboken, N.J.: John Wiley & Sons, 2008. Begins with theoretical and philosophical issues relative to habitat restoration, which provides a strong foundation for decision making. Later chapters address logistics, planning, mathematical modeling, and construction stages of restoration. Finishes up with post-construction monitoring and long-term evaluations to provide a full picture of the habitat restoration process. Highly useful for anyone involved in the planning and implementing of habitat restoration.

Foresman, Timothy, and Alan H. Strahler. *Visualizing Physical Geography.* New York: John Wiley & Sons, 2012. Uses a unique approach to presenting the concepts of physical geography by heavily integrating visuals from *National Geographic* and other sources with the narrative to vividly illustrate the manner in which physical geographic processes are interconnected.

Judson, S., and Steven M. Richardson. *Earth: An Introduction to Geologic Change.* Upper Saddle River, N.J.: Prentice Hall, 1995. An introductory text that discusses the various types of weathering and the methods for studying the rates of weathering and erosion. Illustrated with photographs, diagrams, and tables that provide important data. Written at a level suitable for undergraduates.

Kourkoulis, Stavros K., ed. *Fracture and Failure of Natural Building Stones.* Dordrecht: Springer, 2006. Examines the processes involved in restoring and conserving historical stone structures. Intertwines concepts of geology, physics, and archaeology. Also takes into account mechanical properties of rocks, weathering, stress, and masonry. Discusses a number of case studies. Useful for those dedicated to protecting authentic material in buildings and structures.

Morgan, R. P. C. *Soil Erosion and Conservation.* 3d ed. Hoboken, N.J.: Wiley-Blackwell, 2005. A brief text that discusses soil erosion. Discusses erosion control methods, modeling, and erosion processes. Supplemented by many tables and figures. A concise, yet detailed resource for advanced undergraduates of geology or soil conservation.

Newson, Malcolm. *Land, Water and Development: Sustainable and Adaptive Management of Rivers.* 3d ed. London: Routledge, 2008. Presents land-water interactions. Discusses recent research, study tools and methods, and technical issues, such as soil erosion and damming. Suited for undergraduate students and professionals. Covers concepts in managing land and water resources in the developed world.

Plummer, Charles C., Diane Carlson, and Lisa Hammersley. *Physical Geology.* 13th ed. Columbus, Ohio: McGraw-Hill, 2009. An unusually readable text. Extended discussions of weathering and the various erosion processes are supplemented by excellent photographs and line drawings. Each chapter has an extended list of supplementary readings. Contains an excellent glossary. Suitable for college-level readers and interested nonspecialists.

Strahler, Alan H. *Modern Physical Geography.* 4th ed. New Delhi: Wiley India Pvt. Limited, 2008. A well-established textbook of physical geography that presents a comprehensive overview of the topic and discusses the processes of weathering and erosion as a fundamental action of many other processes.

Tarbuck, Edward J., Frederick K. Lutgens, and Dennis Tasa. *Earth: An Introduction to Physical Geology.* 10th ed. Upper Saddle River, N.J.: Prentice Hall, 2010. A popular text that offers an introduction to weathering and erosional processes. Concisely written and generously illustrated with color photographs and color line drawings. Key terms are in boldface and there is a helpful glossary. Suitable for high school readers.

See also: Alluvial Systems; Beaches and Coastal Processes; Deep-Sea Sedimentation; Deltas; Desert Pavement; Drainage Basins; Floodplains; Geochemical Cycles; Lakes; Reefs; River Bed Forms; River Flow; Sand; Sediment Transport and Deposition; Surface Ocean Currents

WEATHER MODIFICATION

Human activities can cause intentional or accidental changes in local weather situations. Many intentional weather modification experiments have focused on creating conditions to benefit agriculture.

PRINCIPAL TERMS

- **cloud seeding:** the injection of nucleating particles into clouds to enhance precipitation formation
- **dynamic mode theory:** a theory proposing that enhancement of vertical movement in clouds increases precipitation
- **fog dissipation:** removal of fog by artificial means
- **hail suppression:** a technique aimed at lessening crop damage from hailstorms by converting water droplets to snow to prevent hail formation or, alternatively, by reducing hailstone size
- **hygroscopic particulates:** minute particles that readily take up and retain moisture
- **static mode theory:** a theory assuming that natural clouds are deficient in ice nuclei, whereby clouds must be within a particular temperature range and contain a certain amount of supercooled water for cloud seeding to be successful
- **supercooled:** a liquid cooled below its normal freezing point without crystallizing or becoming solid, typically referring to water

DELIBERATE WEATHER MODIFICATION

Inadvertent weather modification, including increases or decreases in precipitation downwind from large industrial sites and the formation of fog, creates problems in some locales. Scientific attempts to deliberately modify weather activity and conditions have been pursued since World War II. The most popular techniques involve cloud seeding, the injection of cloud-nucleating particles into likely clouds to alter the physics and chemistry of condensation. Proponents of this technique claim that it may enhance precipitation amounts by 5 to 20 percent. However, some scientists believe that deliberate efforts to enhance precipitation often yield questionable results, even in favorable situations. In 1977 the United Nations passed a resolution prohibiting the use of weather modification for hostile purposes because of the threat to civilians. The United States signed the resolution but has continued defense research on operational weather modification in battlefield situations, as summarized in the U.S. Air Force position paper *Weather as a Force Multiplier: Owning the Weather in 2025.*

Studies have field-tested various methods of weather modification; results have varied widely. Weather modification has been attempted in many countries around the world, by government agencies, agricultural cooperatives, private companies, and research consortia. In agricultural areas farmers are convinced that hail suppression and precipitation augmentation have been achieved by weather modification. In some of these same locales, meteorologists have been unable to determine if weather modification has produced any change from what would have occurred without intervention. Attempts to duplicate weather modification efforts that have apparently been successful in one locale have often been met with questionable results. Meteorologists occasionally disagree among themselves as to whether a specific attempt at weather modification has succeeded. Reexamination of data from American studies undertaken in the past has led many scientists to conclude that the efficacy of cloud seeding has been overstated.

It should be clearly understood that it is impossible to change the climate of an entire region at will for a desired outcome through weather modification. It is also impossible to end a drought by seeding clouds. This is a result of long-term dynamic conditions and interactions that are essentially global in nature. Cloud seeding for agricultural purposes assumes that some enhancement of regional rainfall amounts over the course of the growing season will increase crop yields. Weather modification for hail suppression assumes that reduction in regional crop losses over the growing season is an attainable goal.

INADVERTENT WEATHER MODIFICATION

Pulp and paper mills produce huge quantities of large-and giant-diameter cloud condensation nuclei (CCN) in the effluent from their exhaust stacks. Downwind of these mills, precipitation appears to be enhanced about 30 percent above what was observed prior to construction of the mills. It is also thought that the heat and moisture emitted by these mills may play an active role in precipitation enhancement. One specific study of a kraft paper mill near Nelspruit in the eastern Transvaal region of South Africa has indicated that storms modified by the mill emissions lasted longer, grew taller, and rained harder than other nearby storms occurring on the same day. Radar measurements supported the theory that hygroscopic particulates released by this mill accelerated or amplified growth of unusually large-diameter raindrops.

An egregious example of inadvertent weather modification is the formation of ice fog over Arctic cities in Siberia, Alaska, and Canada. During winter, cities such as Irkutsk, Russia, and Fairbanks, Alaska, experience drastic reductions in visibility as particles released by combustion act as nuclei for the formation of minute ice crystals. No techniques are available to modify ice fogs.

During an investigation of the meteorological effects of urban St. Louis, Missouri, conducted during the 1970's, it was found that urban summer precipitation was enhanced by 25 percent relative to the surrounding area. Most of the increased precipitation occurred in the late afternoon and evening as a result of convective activity. The frequency of summer thunderstorms was enhanced by 45 percent, and the frequency of summer hailstorms was higher by 31 percent over the city and adjacent eastern and northeastern suburbs. During the late 1960's, studies demonstrated that widespread burning of sugar cane fields in tropical areas released large numbers of cloud condensation nuclei. Downwind, rainfall decreases of about 25 percent were noted.

CLOUD SEEDING

For millennia, people attempted to influence the weather by using prayers and incantations. Sometimes rain followed, and sometimes no rain fell for extended periods. Scientists began attempting various techniques to modify weather during World War II. In 1946 Vincent Schaefer of the General Electric Research Laboratory observed that dry ice put into a freezer with supercooled water droplets caused ice crystals to form. On November 13, 1946, Schaefer demonstrated that dry ice pellets dropped from an aircraft into stratus clouds caused liquid water droplets to change to ice crystals and fall as snow. Bernard Vonnegut, a coworker, determined that silver iodide (AgI) particles also caused

ice crystals to form. Project Cirrus involved apparently successful scientific attempts to seed clouds with ground-based AgI generators in New Mexico. These researchers then tried seeding a hurricane on October 10, 1947. The hurricane changed direction, making landfall in Georgia, resulting in a number of lawsuits against General Electric.

Early cloud-seeding experiments were empirical. AgI was dropped from aircraft, shot into clouds by rockets, or dispersed from ground-based generators. Researchers could selectively seed a pattern such as an "L" into a supercooled stratus cloud and see a visible "L" appear, thus "proving" that they could achieve results. When any rain occurred near a seeded area, it was attributed to the intervention. The apparent success of cloud seeding using AgI caused the technique to be modified and adopted in France, Canada, Argentina, Israel, and the Soviet Union. Wine-growing regions such as the south of France and Mendoza, Argentina, installed ground-based AgI generators. The former Soviet Union opted for rocket-borne AgI, which was launched in agricultural areas during thunderstorms in an effort to suppress hail.

In 1962 the U.S. Navy and Weather Bureau began an ambitious cooperative plan to modify hurricanes called Project Stormfury. Only a few hurricanes were seeded in attempts to reduce the intensity of the storms. Proponents of Stormfury suggested that seeding of Hurricane Debbie in 1969 caused a reduction of 30 percent in wind speed on one day. The following day, no seeding was done, followed by another seeding attempt. The second seeding was thought to have caused a 15 percent reduction in wind speeds. Proponents believed that 10 to 15 percent reductions in wind speeds might result in a 20 to 60 percent reduction in storm damage if similar results could be achieved by seeding other hurricanes. Stormfury was terminated in the late 1970's, with no definitive results.

During winters between 1960 and 1970, the Climax I and Climax II randomized cloud seeding studies were conducted in the Colorado Rockies. Although it was initially thought that precipitation enhancements on the order of 10 percent may have resulted, more recent examination of the results appears to indicate that cloud seeding had no statistically discernible effect on precipitation. During the Vietnam War, the U.S. military attempted to increase precipitation along the Ho Chi Minh Trail in an effort to impede enemy forces. In the United States during the 1970's, some entrepreneurs deployed ground-based AgI generators in selected agricultural regions, billing farmers for their services. Aircraft delivery of AgI became increasingly popular. By the late 1990's, a number of private companies were delivering airborne cloud seeding services in various areas worldwide.

Cloud physicists have explored why cloud seeding might be effective. The evidence suggests that seeding increases the size of droplets or ice crystals, allowing them to fall as precipitation. Two concepts have emerged: a static mode theory, which assumes that natural clouds are deficient in ice nuclei, and a dynamic mode theory, which assumes that enhancement of vertical movement in clouds increases precipitation. The static mode assumes that a "window of opportunity" exists for seeding cold continental clouds during which clouds must be within a particular temperature range and contain a certain amount of supercooled liquid water.

FOG DISSIPATION AND HAIL SUPPRESSION

During World War II, when improvements in visibility were crucial for military operations, efforts were made to dissipate fog. Fog may be dissipated by reducing the number of droplets, decreasing the radius of droplets, or both. Decreasing droplet radius by a factor of three through evaporation can provide a ninefold increase in visibility. Possible methods of fog removal include using dry ice pellets or hygroscopic materials, heating the air, and mixing the foggy air with drier air. Airports that are plagued by supercooled fog in winter, such as Denver and Salt Lake City, can dissipate the fog by dropping dry ice pellets. Dry ice causes some liquid water droplets to freeze and grow, evaporating the remaining liquid droplets and allowing the larger frozen ice crystals to fall. One way of clearing fog at military airports when there is a shallow radiation fog close to the ground is to use helicopters to provide mixing. Entrenched jet engines can also be used to heat the air over runways by directing their hot exhaust gases. This is an expensive technique that has been used operationally in France, but it is also one that poses significant risk to smaller aircraft during landings and take-offs.

Farmers and vintners worldwide fear damaging hailstorms that can devastate crops. There are three approaches to suppressing hail damage: converting all liquid water droplets to snow to prevent hail formation, seeding to promote growth of many small hailstones instead of larger damaging hail, and introducing large condensation nuclei to reduce the average hailstone size. Most weather modification proponents believe that seeding with lead iodide or AgI to cause many small hailstones to form can substantially reduce hailstone size. Because small hailstones are less damaging than large ones, this technique could potentially lessen (but not eliminate) crop losses. It has been claimed that rocket-borne lead iodide seeding in Bulgaria reduced crop losses from hail by 50 to 60 percent. Similar seeding operations in the former Soviet Union were said to have reduced crop damage by 50 to 95 percent. A randomized study in North Dakota over four summers claimed that seeding helped reduce hail severity.

Anita Baker-Blocker

FURTHER READING

Aquado, Edward, and James E. Burt. *Understanding Weather and Climate.* 5th ed. Upper Saddle River, N.J.: Prentice Hall, 2009. Discusses meteorology and climatology concepts with reference to common, everyday events. Presents conclusions from the IPCC as well as many other scientific studies on climate change. Examines weather events, structure and dynamics of atmosphere, and the past, present, and future climate on earth.

Baer, F., N. L. Canfield, and J. M. Mitchell, eds. *Climate in Human Perspective: A Tribute to Helmut E. Landsberg.* Boston: Kluwer, 1991. Several essays deal with aspects of weather modification, such as "Five Themes on Our Changing Climate," by J. Murray Mitchell, and "Climate of Cities," by Timothy R. Oke.

Congressional Research Service. *Weather Modification: Programs, Problems, Policy and Potential.* Honolulu: University Press of the Pacific, 2004. A thorough, scholarly report, originally prepared in 1978, that reviews the history, technology, activities, and various special aspects of weather modification of interest to the agricultural, scientific, commercial, and governmental fields.

Cotton, William R., and Roger A. Pielke. *Human Impacts on Weather and Climate.* 2d ed. New York: Cambridge University Press, 2007. A comprehensive overview of weather modification, written as a text for both undergraduate and graduate study in atmospheric and environmental science. Looks at weather modification with regard to both intentional and unintentional effects.

Hess, Wilmot N. *Weather and Climate Modification*. New York: Wiley, 1974. Provides a look at the "glory days" when scientists and governments enthusiastically embraced weather modification.

Hoffman, Matthew J. *Ozone Depletion and Climate Change: Constructing A Global Response*. Albany, N.Y.: State University of New York, 2005. Discusses the challenges of global policies to mitigate climate change. Examines models of climate change due to ozone depletion. Focuses on universal participation and governance of these issues.

Hopler, Paul. *Atmosphere: Weather, Climate, and Pollution*. New York: Cambridge University Press, 1994. A brief book that offers a wonderful introduction to the study of the atmosphere and its components. Chapters explain the causes and effects of global warming, ozone depletion, acid rain, and climatic change. Illustrations, color maps, and index.

Horel, John, and Jack Geisler. *Global Environmental Change: An Atmospheric Perspective*. New York: John Wiley & Sons, 1997. Major topics include global warming and stratospheric ozone depletion. Geared for beginning-level undergraduate students. Discusses the many Internet sites where graphics and information on global environmental change can be obtained.

House, Tanzy J., James B. Near, William B. Shields, Ronald J. Celentano, Ann E. Mercer, and James E. Pugh. *Weather as a Force Multiplier: Owning the Weather in 2025*. Maxwell Air Force Base, Ala.: Air University, 1996. Discusses military weather modification.

Lutgens, Frederick K., and Edward J. Tarbuck. *The Atmosphere: An Introduction to Meteorology*. 11th ed. Upper Saddle River, N.J.: Prentice Hall, 2010. A beginning college textbook. A profusely illustrated book that has twelve pages devoted to tornadoes. Contains a glossary and seven separate appendices to explain everything from metric conversions to the reading of daily weather charts.

Marshal, John, and R. Alan Plumb. *Atmosphere, Ocean and Climate Dynamics: An Introductory Text*. Burlington, Mass.: Elsevier Academic Press, 2008. An excellent introduction to atmospheres and oceans. Discusses topics such as the greenhouse effect, convection and atmospheric structure, oceanic and atmospheric circulation, and climate change. Suited for advanced undergraduates and graduate students with some background in advanced math.

Mather, Graeme K. "Coalescence Enhancement in Large Multicell Storms Caused by the Emissions from a Kraft Paper Mill." *Journal of Applied Meteorology* 91 (1991). A detailed study of the effects of kraft paper mills on precipitation.

National Research Council. *Critical Issues in Weather Modification Research*. Washington, D.C.: National Academies Press, 2003. A report prepared for the NRC by the Committee on the Status of and Future Directions in U.S. Weather Modification Research and Operations that presents a series of specialist articles addressing the title topic.

Rangno, A. L., and P. V. Hobbs. "Further Analyses of the Climax Cloud Seeding Experiments." *Journal of Applied Meteorology* 93 (1993). Discusses difficulties in assessing the effects of cloud seeding.

Smith, Jerry E. *Weather Warfare: The Military's Plan to Draft Mother Nature*. Kempton, Ill.: Adventures Unlimited Press, 2006. Covers processes that cause weather events and natural disasters, and our ability to influence these processes. Discusses cloud seeding, electromagnetic wave production, weather modification legislation, contrails, and stratospheric engineering. Written for the general population and lacking in "hard science," but presents a wide range of topics that provoke further research.

Stevens, William Kenneth. *The Change in the Weather: People, Weather, and the Science of Climate*. New York: Random House, 2001. Describes various natural and human-induced causes of changes in the climate. Includes a twenty-page bibliography and an index.

Strahler, Alan, and Arthur Strahler. *Physical Geography: Science and Systems of the Human Environment*. 3d ed. New York: John Wiley & Sons, 2005. A thorough, well-illustrated book containing considerable information about atmospheric processes and issues. Suitable for college students.

See also: Atmospheric and Oceanic Oscillations; Atmospheric Properties; Climate; Climate Change Theories; Climate Modeling; Clouds; Drought;

Hurricanes; Icebergs and Antarctica; Lightning and Thunder; Monsoons; Satellite Meteorology; Seasons; Severe Storms; Tornadoes; Van Allen Radiation Belts; Volcanoes: Climatic Effects; Weather Forecasting; Weather Forecasting: Numerical Weather Prediction; Wind

WIND

Wind is the horizontal movement of air resulting from differences in atmospheric pressure and air densities. Pressure differences may develop on a local or global scale in response to differences in the distribution of solar energy, which affect the density of air masses and, therefore, the pressure they exert relative to each other.

PRINCIPAL TERMS

- **constant pressure chart:** a chart that shows the altitude of a constant pressure, such as 500 millibars
- **convergence:** the movement of different air masses flowing toward a common point
- **divergence:** a net outflow of air in different directions from a specified region
- **geostrophic wind:** an upper-level wind that flows in a straight path in response to a balance between pressure gradient and Coriolis acceleration
- **hurricane-force wind:** a wind with a speed of 64 knots (118 kilometers per hour) or higher
- **isobar:** a line on a meteorological chart delineating points of equal pressure,
- **local winds:** winds that, over a small area, differ from the general pressure pattern owing to local thermal or orographic effects
- **pressure gradient:** the rate of change of pressure with distance at a given time
- **rawinsonde:** a radiosonde tracked by radar in order to collect wind data in addition to temperature, pressure, and humidity

FACTORS AFFECTING WIND FLOW

Wind, as defined by the meteorologist, is the horizontal movement of air. Differences in heating and internal motion in the atmosphere create differences in atmospheric pressure; when a change in pressure over distance is established, air accelerates down this pressure gradient from higher to lower pressure. The acceleration of this moving air depends on the amount of pressure change over a given distance.

Moving air associated with pressure change over a distance will either spread out over the surface (diverge) or will flow inward (converge). High-pressure areas are regions of divergence, and low-pressure areas are regions of convergence. The force associated with the air moving from high to low pressure is called the pressure gradient force. Pressure gradient force sets the wind into motion. If it were the only force affecting the wind, then winds would blow directly from high to low pressure. However, other forces affect wind direction and velocity.

A second major factor affecting wind flow is Coriolis acceleration, which results from the Earth turning on its axis. An object moving over the surface of the Earth, except at the equator, moves in a curved path when observed from the rotating Earth. In the Northern Hemisphere, there is an acceleration to the right of the path of motion; in the Southern Hemisphere, the acceleration is to the left. Thus, in the Northern Hemisphere, a wind blowing from north to south becomes a northeast wind, and a wind blowing from south to north becomes southwesterly. The reverse occurs in the Southern Hemisphere.

A third force affecting wind flow is centripetal acceleration. Air currents seldom move on a straight path for long but rather tend to develop a curved pattern as they flows parallel to curved isobars. When this type of flow pattern evolves, centripetal acceleration is directed into the center of the cell or curve, the force acting perpendicularly to the direction of flow. This acceleration is directed outward from both high- and low-pressure cells in the equally opposite sense. Therefore, airflow affected by a high pressure; centripetal acceleration is in the opposite direction as that around a low pressure. Thus air movement about a low-pressure center is cyclonic, or counterclockwise, in the Northern Hemisphere, and anticyclonic, or clockwise, about a high-pressure center. Centripetal acceleration plays a more significant and immediate role in smaller circulations such as hurricanes and tornadoes than in larger, midlatitude cyclones.

A fourth factor affecting wind velocity and direction is frictional drag, which works in a direction opposite to wind motion; therefore, friction tends to slow wind velocity. A decrease in wind velocity, however, is accompanied by a decrease in Coriolis acceleration, which causes a slight change in wind direction back toward the direction of the pressure gradient. The effect is inherent in fluid dynamics. A fluid, whether gas or liquid, flowing without restraint of any kind exhibits the property of laminar flow in which every particle of which the fluid is composed moves in unison. The presence of any kind of containing surface exerts a restraining force upon the flowing particles nearest to it as they move, thus disrupting their unity of movement. This, coupled with interactions between the particles themselves, results in the condition of turbulent flow, in which particles at different distances from the surface move at different rates. Air moving over the surface of the planet is constrained at the surface by the surface itself, while the density of the fluid decreases with altitude. Horizontally, there are no surface constraints to affect the flow of air, other than minor differences in density and pressure (the pressure gradient force). Frictional drag is thus at a maximum over land where an uneven surface consisting of trees, buildings, and hills provides barriers to the even flow of wind. Also, friction affects the flow of wind only in the first or second kilometers of the atmosphere. Wind direction and velocity in the lowest kilometer of the atmosphere are based on the sum of pressure gradient acceleration, Coriolis acceleration, centripetal acceleration, and frictional drag.

Above 1 kilometer, winds blow in response to pressure gradient, Coriolis, and centripetal acceleration. Frictional deceleration is negligible or completely absent. Consider the situation in which pressure is distributed in a linear fashion so that lines connecting points of equal pressure are straight. In this situation, pressure gradient acceleration and Coriolis acceleration are the only forces acting on the wind. Here, pressure gradient force is balanced by Coriolis acceleration so that the wind flows in a direction parallel to the isobars. Such winds are called geostrophic winds. Around circular highs and lows above the friction level, pressure gradient acceleration is balanced by both Coriolis and centrifugal acceleration. Thus, winds blow parallel to isobars in a clockwise direction around highs and in a counterclockwise direction around lows. In the Southern Hemisphere, the reverse is true. The winds thus described are called gradient winds.

MONSOON AND PRESSURE CHANGES

A seasonal wind system, called the monsoon, that changes direction from winter to summer exists over eastern Asia and the adjacent oceans, and less significantly at other locations in the world. In winter, over the large landmass of Asia, air is cooled, and a cold, dense high-pressure center forms with a clockwise circulation of winds about it. Generally, these winds flow from land to sea during winter. In summer, a thermal low forms over India, and the airflow pattern reverses, with cyclonic flow bringing air on shore from the ocean. Reinforcing the thermal low is the migration of the Intertropical Convergence Zone northward over India. Moreover, the jet stream breaks down during summer, which reinforces the monsoon flow. With this annual wind-flow reversal, the climate of Asia is greatly affected. The offshore winds in winter bring dry weather to much of eastern Asia. Conversely, the onshore winds of summer bring copious amounts of precipitation to India and adjacent areas of southeast Asia.

A granite outcrop eroded by windblown sand, Llano de Caldera, Atacama Province, Chile. (U.S. Geological Survey)

Daily changes in temperature at many places around the world result in daily pressure changes, which cause distinctive wind patterns. One such system is that of the land and sea breezes. This system develops along coastal areas and along the shorelines of large lakes and inland seas. During the day, as the land heats rapidly, the air above heats up, expands, and becomes less dense, forming a thermal low. The warm, buoyant air rises, and cooler air from the water surface flows in to replace the rising air. In this fashion, a sea breeze develops during the day and usually reaches a peak in mid-afternoon, when the daily high temperature is attained. At night, conditions are reversed. The land cools more rapidly than water. In this way, the pressure relationship between land and water is reversed day to night. At night, pressure is higher over land and lower over water, so air flows from land to water, producing a land breeze. The land breeze is usually not as well developed as is the sea breeze because the temperature contrast between land and water is not as great at night as it is during the day. Another wind system that has a day-to-night change in wind direction is that of the mountain and valley breezes. During the day, the mountain slopes warm the air, and it expands. The warm, less dense air rises and is called a valley breeze after its place of origin. At night, the slopes cool, and the air's density increases. The cool, dense air flows downslope in response to gravity and is called a mountain breeze.

LOCAL WINDS

Several local winds occur in response to topographic peculiarities and are difficult to explain on the basis of pressure patterns as they might appear on a weather map. The "chinook" in the Rockies and the "foehn" in the Alps of Europe result from a combination of topographic effects and large-scale atmospheric systems. In response to these systems, winds flow down the lee side and are heated adiabatically by compression. The warming brought by these winds is often rapid.

The "sirocco" ("khamsin" in Egypt and "sharov" in Israel) and the "haboob" are hot, dusty winds that occur on flat terrain. The sirocco precedes a low-pressure system moving across the Sahara Desert. As it crosses the Mediterranean Sea, it picks up moisture and becomes a hot, humid wind by the time it reaches the coast of Europe. The haboob is created by air spilling out of the base of a thunderstorm and attains high speeds and picks up small soil particles, creating a sand storm extending upward as high as 1 kilometer or higher.

A katabatic wind is a cold wind flowing downslope from an ice field or glacier. Wind velocities range from as little as 10 knots up to hurricane speeds. One such wind is the "bora," which originates in Russia and blows out across the Adriatic coast of Yugoslavia with speeds sometimes in excess of 100 knots. In France, a wind known as the "mistral" blows out of the French Alps and through the Rhone Valley to chill the Riviera along the Mediterranean Sea.

STUDY OF WIND

A number of instruments are used to collect data about wind direction and velocity at the surface or in the upper troposphere. The wind vane is commonly used for determining surface wind direction. Most wind vanes are simple, relatively long planar structures that will self-align to the direction of movement of the wind, such as an arrow with a tail. The arrow, or other type of vane, is attached to a vertical pole about which it can move freely and always points in the direction from which the wind is blowing.

The anemometer is an instrument used to record wind velocity. It normally consists of three hemispherical cups attached to crossbars, which are in turn attached to a vertical shaft about which it can spin freely. The cups are pushed by the wind preferentially on their open side, causing the shaft to turn, and the wind speed is recorded by a counting device at the base of the shaft. An instrument used for recording both wind direction and velocity is the aerovane. It consists of a three-bladed propeller mounted on the end of a streamlined rod, with a vertical fin at the opposite end. The propeller rotates at a rate proportional to the wind speed. The fin and aerodynamic shape keep the propeller blades facing into the wind, so wind direction is easily determined. When a recorder, often remote, is connected, a continuous record of both wind velocity and direction can be obtained.

A series of instruments also has been developed to determine wind directions and velocities at higher levels. One is the pilot balloon, a small balloon released at the surface that rises at a known rate. The balloon is tracked using a small telescope called a theodolite, and periodic measurements of the balloon's horizontal and vertical angles are taken, giving the speed and direction of the winds carrying it. The pilot balloon principle can also be applied to a radiosonde ascent. Measurements of the vertical and horizontal angles tracking the radiosonde's ascent, taken periodically along with its distance from the observing station, can supply information on wind direction and speed.

A rawinsonde can be tracked using radar, so wind speed and direction can be obtained. Radar can also be used in conjunction with rockets to collect wind data at a distance above 30 kilometers. One type of rocket ejects a parachute carrying an instrument package, which can be tracked by radar. Another type of rocket ejects metallic strips at predetermined levels that can also be tracked by radar. Doppler radar can be used to determine direction and speed of wind by making use of the Doppler effect on reflected signals. Doppler radar measures speeds of objects moving toward or away from the antenna. When a signal is sent out and reflected from a raindrop or ice crystal, the returning signal will have a higher frequency if the particle is moving toward the radar and a lower frequency if it is moving away. One drawback of Doppler radar is that velocities of objects at right angles to the unit cannot be determined, so to achieve a three-dimensional effect, two or more units must be used.

Wind directions and speeds are plotted on charts using a symbol called the wind arrow. The shaft of an arrow shows wind direction, while barbs on the end of the arrow indicate speed. A barb represents 10 knots, one-half barb 5 knots, and a flag (a triangle-shaped symbol) represents 50 knots. These symbols may be used singularly or in combination to show any wind speed. On a surface chart, the wind arrows point out from a station in the direction from which the wind is coming. In the upper air above the friction level, the wind arrow points in the direction to which the wind is moving.

Winds above the friction level are plotted on constant pressure charts. A constant pressure chart is drawn using contour lines to show the elevation above Earth's surface of a constant pressure level, such as the 500-millibar level. When pressure is particularly high in an area in relation to surrounding areas, the height of a constant-pressure surface is higher than surrounding areas, and heights of a low-pressure region are lower than surrounding regions.

The average elevation of the 500-millibar level is 5.5 kilometers but can vary from less than 5 to more than 6 kilometers.

Various constant pressure charts are used, ranging from just above the surface, such as the 850-millibar level, up to the tropopause at roughly the 200-millibar level. With the use of these constant pressure charts, meteorologists can gain a sense of the three-dimensional wind-flow profile from the surface up to the tropopause.

SIGNIFICANCE

Winds, in conjunction with temperature and humidity, can greatly affect human comfort and safety. The effects of wind influence the exchange of heat between the human body and the atmosphere. The body, particularly the surface of the skin, is continually exchanging heat with the environment. On a cold day when a wind is blowing, air molecules impact the skin, then move away, taking body heat with them. Clothing provides insulation, creating a shallow layer of warm air molecules, which form a shield that protects the skin from heat loss. The "windchill factor" relates the rate of heat loss due to wind action to the temperature having the equivalent rate of heat loss in the absence of wind.

Humankind's use of wind power may stem from the use of winds to propel sailboats or ships. Sails have been used as power sources on ships and boats for thousands of years, and were the chief source of power for water transportation until the use of steam in the latter part of the nineteenth century. The next step in the use of wind for power was through the use of windmills. The first known windmill appeared in Europe in 1105, and by the following century, thousands of windmills were in use in Europe. Then, as the burning of coal as a source of power became less expensive, it and other energy sources replaced windmills. In the early part of the twentieth century, windmills became popular as an inexpensive means of pumping water for agricultural uses on farms and ranches. Today, wind power is again being considered as a partial solution to growing energy needs. The advantages of using wind power are that windmills are nonpolluting, and they are not limited to daylight hours as are solar cells. The liabilities of using wind power are several in number: Windmills can only be used in windy areas where wind flow is steady and neither too weak nor too strong; a weak wind will not turn the blades, and a strong wind might damage the machine. Windmills detract from the aesthetics of the landscape, and their cost factor can be quite high. Finally, the amount of modern energy needs that could be satisfied by wind power is quite low, perhaps no more than 5 percent.

Ralph D. Cross

FURTHER READING

Ackerman, Steven, and John Knox. *Meteorology: Understanding the Atmosphere.* 3d ed. Sudbury, Mass.: Jones and Bartlett, 2012. A textbook for undergraduate nonmajors that uses real-world examples and atmospheric observations to present basic concepts of meteorology, then focuses on relating those concepts to atmospheric phenomena such as wind.

Ahrens, C. Donald. *Meteorology Today: An Introduction to Weather, Climate, and the Environment.* 8th ed. Belmont, Calif.: Thomson Brooks-Cole, 2007. One of the most widely used and authoritative introductory textbooks for the study of meteorology and climatology. Explains complex concepts in a clear, precise manner, supported by numerous images and diagrams. Chapters in the book specifically treat atmospheric motion and wind systems, and these serve as basic knowledge in discussion of other atmospheric events.

Christopherson, Robert W., and Mary-Louise Byrne. *Geosystems: An Introduction to Physical Geography.* Toronto: Pearson Education Canada, 2006. Discusses wind extensively in several contexts, but primarily as the immediate and inevitable result of the differential distribution of solar energy over Earth's surface, and affected by the planet's rotation. Equally considers the various effects of wind in regard to mass movement and to climatic phenomena.

Clarke, Allan J. *An Introduction to the Dynamics of El Niño and the Southern Oscillation.* Burlington, Mass.: Academic Press, 2008. Presents the physics of ENSO, including currents, temperature, winds, and waves. Discusses ENSO forecasting models. Provides good coverage of the influence ENSO has on marine life, from plankton to green turtles. Each chapter has references, and there are a number of appendices and indexing. Best suited for environmental scientists, meteorologists, and similar academics studying ENSO.

De Villiers, Marq. *Windswept: The Story of Wind and Weather.* New York: Walker Publishing Company, 2006. Written in the popular style, well suited for the layperson or as part of a high school meteorology course. References to historical windy weather events, such as Hurricane Ivan, are discussed. Covers the influence of wind on weather events, development of wind, and dynamics, along with climate patterns and global warming.

Frederick, John E. *Principles of Atmospheric Science.* Sudbury, Mass.: Jones and Bartlett Publishers, 2008. A college-level textbook written to present the foundation concepts of meteorology focusing on the atmosphere and its dynamics.

Gombosi, Tamas I. *Physics of the Space Environment.* New York: Cambridge University Press, 2004. A college-level text that explores the field of atmospheric physics to determine the makeup of the upper atmosphere and the space environment and how these forces affect the atmosphere and weather cycles. Focuses on solar winds and the magnetosphere. Intended for the advanced reader. Illustrations, index, and bibliography.

Hopkins, J. S. *The Accuracy of Wind and Wave Forecasts.* Sudbury, England: HSE, 1997. A brief pamphlet that examines and critiques the techniques and protocol associated with the science of wind and weather forecasting. Illustrations and bibliography.

Lutgens, Frederick K., Edward J. Tarbuck, and Dennis Tasa. *The Atmosphere: An Introduction to Meteorology.* 11th ed. Upper Saddle River, N. J.: Prentice Hall, 2010. An introductory college textbook. A profusely illustrated book that discusses wind phenomena at length. Contains a glossary and several separate appendices.

Saha, Kshudiram. *The Earth's Atmosphere: Its Physics and Dynamics.* Berlin: Springer-Verlag, 2008. Presents the physics and dynamics of the atmosphere in a manner that can be appreciated by anyone with an interest in understanding the mechanisms of the atmosphere.

Stevens, William Kenneth. *The Change in the Weather: People, Weather, and the Science of Climate.* New York: Random House, Inc, 2001. Describes various natural and human-induced causes of changes in the climate. Includes a twenty-page bibliography and an index.

Watts, Alan. *Instant Wind Forecasting.* Dobbs Ferry, N.Y.: Sheridan House, 2002. A succinct text that discusses the practical aspects of wind forecasting; its use in sailing, farming, flying, and even sporting events. Organized as a reference with many charts, tables, and diagrams and limited text, allowing the reader to quickly locate the desired information.

See also: Atmosphere's Global Circulation; Atmospheric and Oceanic Oscillations; Atmospheric Properties; Barometric Pressure; Climate; Clouds; Cyclones and Anticyclones; Drought; Floods; Global Energy Transfer; Hurricanes; Lightning and Thunder; Meteorological Satellites; Monsoons; Precipitation; Satellite Meteorology; Seasons; Severe Storms; Tornadoes; Tropical Weather; Van Allen Radiation Belts; Volcanoes: Climatic Effects; Weather Forecasting; Weather Forecasting: Numerical Weather Prediction; Weather Modification

WORLD OCEAN CIRCULATION EXPERIMENT

The World Ocean Circulation Experiment is an ambitious international project designed to increase knowledge about the movement of water, heat, and various substances in the sea. The data obtained are expected to be of major importance in predicting future long-term changes in climate.

PRINCIPAL TERMS

- **Coriolis effect:** the phenomenon, resulting from Earth's rotation, that causes the path of a moving object to curve away from a straight line
- **current:** the horizontal movement of ocean water at a generally uniform depth
- **downwelling:** the sinking of ocean water to a lower depth
- **Ekman layer:** the region of the sea, from the surface to about 100 meters down, in which the wind directly effects water movement
- **ocean circulation:** the worldwide movement of water in the sea
- **thermohaline circulation:** movement of ocean water caused by differences in temperature and salt concentration
- **upwelling:** the rising of ocean water from a depth toward the surface
- **wind-driven circulation:** movement of ocean water caused by frictional interaction with moving air
- **wind stress:** the frictional interaction between moving air and the surface of the ocean

MOVEMENT OF SEAWATER

The World Ocean Circulation Experiment (WOCE), which began in 1990, brought together scientists from around the globe to study the way in which water moves in all parts of the sea. The WOCE was also intended to obtain information on the movement of heat in the ocean, as well as the movement of substances such as salt and oxygen.

The movement of seawater, known as ocean circulation, consists of horizontal and vertical motion. Horizontal movements are known as currents. Vertical motions are known as upwellings and downwellings. Currents vary widely in speed, ranging from a few centimeters per second to as much as 4 meters per second. Surface currents typically move between 5 and 50 centimeters per second, with deeper currents generally moving more slowly. Vertical movement of seawater is much slower, with a typical speed of only a few meters per month.

Ocean circulation is primarily caused by two major factors. Wind-driven circulation is caused by air moving across the surface of the sea. This induces friction, known as wind stress, between the water and the air, thus applying a directional force and setting the water in motion. Thermohaline circulation is caused by differences in temperature and salt concentration. These differences cause variations in the density of seawater, leading to differences in pressure and resulting in motion. Surface currents are mostly caused by wind-driven circulation. Deeper currents and vertical movements are mostly the result of thermohaline circulation.

Several factors are involved in determining the size, shape, and speed of ocean circulation patterns. An important influence is the Coriolis effect, named for the French scientist Gustave-Gaspard de Coriolis. This effect, caused by the rotation of the planet, causes the actual path of a moving object to be curved away from the straight line path that it would otherwise follow. The Coriolis effect causes ocean currents to bend to the right in the Northern Hemisphere and to bend to the left in the Southern Hemisphere.

Friction also influences the nature of ocean circulation. Layers of water moving at different speeds produce friction where they meet, forming an intermediate zone of turbulent eddy currents as the two layers interact. This transfers energy from one layer to the other, and causes the faster layer to move more slowly and the slower layer to move more quickly. Friction also occurs between moving water and the continents, and between currents at the bottom of the sea and the ocean floor. This friction, with the attendant resulting turbulence zones, tends to slow the motion of seawater.

Important effects on ocean circulation are seen in the region of the sea known as the Ekman layer, named for the Swedish scientist Vagn Walfrid Ekman. The Ekman layer extends from the surface of the ocean to a depth of about 100 meters. In this layer, the wind has a direct effect on water movement. Wind stress, the Coriolis effect, and friction between layers of water combine to move the Ekman layer in complex ways.

Water at the surface of the ocean tends to move at an angle of about 45 degrees to the direction of the wind because of the Coriolis effect. This angle is bent to the right in the Northern Hemisphere and to the left in the Southern Hemisphere. With increasing depth, the water moves more slowly and the angle increases. At a depth where the speed of the water is about 4.3 percent of the surface speed, the water moves in the opposite direction to the wind. The overall effect is that the average movement of the water is at about 90 degrees to the wind.

This movement in the Ekman layer, combined with differences in wind stress, creates areas on the surface of the ocean where water converges or diverges. Where it converges, water sinks in downwellings. Where it diverges, water rises in upwellings. Downwellings and upwellings also occur where the wind blows parallel to the coast of a landmass. They also occur because of differences in temperature and salt concentration, both of which alter the density of the seawater. Cold water and salty water tend to sink, while warm water and less salty water tend to rise.

WORLDWIDE PATTERNS OF OCEAN CIRCULATION

The numerous factors involved in ocean circulation, combined with the irregular shapes of the continents, result in complex patterns of water movement. Although major surface currents have been known since the earliest days of ocean travel, much less is known about deeper currents. Similarly, less is also known about the Southern Hemisphere than the Northern Hemisphere. The WOCE was designed to fill these gaps in scientific knowledge.

Before the WOCE, the basic pattern of surface currents was fairly well understood. In the Northern Hemisphere, strong currents tend to move northward along the eastern coasts of the continents. These include the Gulf Stream-North Atlantic-Norway Current, along North America, and the Kuroshio-North Pacific Current, along Asia. In the Southern Hemisphere, strong currents tend to move northward along the western coasts of the continents. These include the Peru Current, along South America; the Benguela Current, along Africa; and the Western Australia Current, along Australia.

In the regions north and south of the equator, major surface currents move westward. These are the Pacific North Equatorial Current and the Pacific South Equatorial Current, between South America and Asia; the Atlantic North Equatorial Current and the Atlantic South Equatorial Current, between Africa and South America, and the Indian South Equatorial Current, between Australia and Africa.

At the equator, narrow eastward currents are found between the wider westward currents. These are the Pacific Equatorial Countercurrent, between Asia and South America; the Atlantic Equatorial Countercurrent, between South America and Africa; and the Indian Equatorial Countercurrent, between Africa and Asia. Another major surface current is the Antarctic Current, moving eastward around Antarctica.

Although less is known about deep currents, certain broad patterns of movement are now understood from WOCE data. Cold water in the northern part of the Atlantic Ocean sinks in downwellings. This deep, cold water tends to move southward along the eastern coasts of North and South America to join the deep, cold water that sinks in downwellings near Antarctica. This water then tends to flow eastward in a deep current around Antarctica. Some of this water then moves northward along the coasts of Asia and Africa, rising in upwellings as it warms. Overall, the deep ocean currents function something like a continuous conveyor belt system, moving thermal energy in ocean water and distributing it throughout the oceans. Cold water upwelling in the Indian and north Pacific Oceans circulates westward between Australia and Asia, and around the southern tip of Africa to make its way to the North Atlantic. There it sinks again to depths and enters the deep current that takes it back eastward, where it splits and rises again in the Indian and northern Pacific Ocean.

STUDYING OCEAN CIRCULATION

Scientific studies of surface currents began in the eighteenth century in order to aid navigation. Later studies concentrated on the effect of changes in ocean circulation on the weather. The need for a major effort to increase the amount of information known about the movement of seawater became clear in the 1980's. The best models of ocean circulation, based on the available data, failed to describe the conditions actually observed in the sea with complete accuracy.

A major determining factor in the establishment of the WOCE was the development of new techniques for studying ocean circulation. Temperature measurements could be made from a ship without stopping the movement of the vessel using an instrument known as a bathythermograph. Devices designed to drift in the ocean, both on the surface and at specific depths, were developed that could be tracked for months or years. Advanced methods of accurately measuring the concentration of substances present in seawater in very low concentrations were also developed. In addition, computers able to handle the enormous amount of data that the WOCE would generate were made possible through advances in electronic manufacturing methods.

Perhaps the most important new instruments available for the WOCE were satellites capable of obtaining data on ocean circulation. In 1979, the Seasat satellite mission, lasting one hundred days, demonstrated that detection of radar echoes and microwave radiation from the sea could be used to produce detailed information. After years of planning, the WOCE project was ready to begin collecting data in 1990.

Scientists from more than thirty nations participated in the many studies involved in the WOCE. In the United States, the headquarters of the WOCE is located at the Department of Oceanography at Texas Agricultural and Mechanical University. Data collection ended in 1998, but analysis of the information was expected to last until at least 2002, and many scientists expected processing of the data to last until at least 2005.

The first WOCE study began with the launching of the German research ships *Polarstern* and *Meteor* in 1990. These ships collected data in the southern part of the Atlantic Ocean between Antarctica and South Africa. Other early WOCE studies also concentrated on the Southern Hemisphere because this area had been studied in less detail prior to the WOCE than the Northern Hemisphere. Later WOCE studies moved into the Indian Ocean, the North Atlantic Ocean, and the Pacific Ocean.

Satellites used by the WOCE included the ERS series launched by the European Space Agency, the TOPEX/POSEIDON, a joint project of France and the United States, and the Japanese ADEOS. More than one thousand drifting instruments, designed to remain at specific depths far below the surface of the sea, were also used. The movement of these instruments was measured by satellites or by sonic

equipment. Tens of thousands of measurements were made at the surface of the ocean as well.

SIGNIFICANCE

The WOCE project is likely to be one of the most important sources of oceanographic data in the early twenty-first century. The official goals of the WOCE included providing a complete description of the general circulation of the ocean, creating a numerical model of ocean circulation for use in advanced computers, accounting for seasonal changes in ocean circulation, obtaining data on the exchange of substances between layers of water in the ocean, providing detailed information on the interaction between the ocean and the atmosphere, and obtaining data on the movement of heat within the ocean.

The most important application of WOCE data is in the study of the effect of ocean circulation on climate changes. This information is expected to aid scientists in predicting the effect on long-term weather patterns of various human activities, such as the increase in carbon dioxide in the atmosphere. Such data will also be useful in predicting natural changes in climate that take place over years or decades.

Several examples of the interaction between ocean conditions and changes in weather are well documented. The Sahel, a region of Africa along the southern fringe of the Sahara Desert, experienced severe droughts in the 1970's and 1980's after having experienced much wetter conditions in the 1950's. These droughts were associated with higher-than-normal surface temperatures in the South Atlantic Ocean, Indian Ocean, and southeast Pacific Ocean, and with lower-than-normal temperatures in the North Atlantic Ocean and most of the Pacific Ocean. Ocean temperature is also an important factor in the formation of tropical cyclones and other powerful storms.

Currents have a powerful effect on weather patterns. The Gulf Stream-North Atlantic-Norway Current brings relatively warm tropical water northward, moderating the climates of eastern North America, Ireland, the British Isles, and the coast of Norway. The Kuroshio-North Pacific Current does the same for Japan and western North America. These warm currents also encourage increased water evaporation, resulting in increased rainfall in these areas. The Peru Current brings cold polar water northward along the western coast of South America, decreasing water evaporation and creating deserts in Peru and Chile. The Benguela Current, running northward along the western coast of Africa, has the same effect in Namibia.

Perhaps the best-known example of the effect of changes in ocean circulation on weather is the El Niño phenomenon. This situation occurs at irregular intervals in the eastern Pacific Ocean. Increased water temperatures, typically 2 to 8 degrees Celsius higher than normal, are associated with changes in climate. Typical effects seen during an El Niño condition are droughts in Australia, northeastern Brazil, and southern Peru; excessive summer rainfall in Ecuador and northern Peru; severe winter storms in Chile; and warm winter conditions in North America.

The El Niño effect is also associated with large reductions in fish populations along the western coast of South America. During normal conditions, the water near the coast consists of a thin layer of warm, nutrient-poor water above a thick layer of cooler, nutrient-rich water. The top layer is thin enough to allow coastal upwellings to bring nutrients to the surface, supporting marine life. During El Niño conditions, the top layer of warm water is much thicker, preventing nutrients from reaching the surface. Data from the WOCE project are expected to aid in the prediction of climate changes such as El Niño, with the possibility of having a major impact on human activities.

Rose Secrest

FURTHER READING

Broecker, Wally. *The Great Ocean Conveyor.* Princeton, N.J.: Princeton University Press, 2010. Discusses ocean currents, focusing specifically on the great conveyor belt. Written by the great ocean conveyor's discoverer. Explains the conception of this theory and the resulting impact on oceanography. Written in a manner easy to follow with some background in science, yet still relevant to graduate students and scientists.

Field, J.G., Gotthilf Hempel, and C.P. Summerhayes. *Oceans 2020: Science, Trends and the Challenge of Sustainability.* Washington, D.C.: Island Press, 2002. A combined work of the Intergovernmental Oceanographic Commission, the International Council of Scientific Unions, the Scientific Committee on Oceanic Research, and the ICSU Scientific Committee on Problems of the Environment in a collection of learned essays that address the state of the oceans and issues for sustainability.

Jacques, Peter. *Globalization and the World Ocean.* Lanham, Md.: Rowman and Littlefield Publishing Group, 2006. Provides a unique analysis of how global marine and atmospheric conditions affect political conditions globally by viewing the world ocean as a single body of water composed of connected regional oceans. Aimed at researchers and students of marine sciences, and environmental and globalization studies.

Jochum, Markus, and Raghi Murtugudde, eds. *Physical Oceanography: Developments Since 1950.* New York: Springer Science + Business Media, 2006. Provide a historic overview of developments in physical oceanography in the last half of the twentieth century with senior scientists in the field authoring individual chapters. Chapter 12, by Karl Wunsch, deals exclusively with the WOCE and its aftermath.

Miller, Robert N. *Numerical Modeling of Ocean Circulation.* New York: Cambridge University Press, 2007. Designed to teach the process of numerical analysis; each chapter includes exercises to practice modeling skills. Discusses models of tropical waters, coastal waters, and shallow waters. Also covers simple and complex numerical modeling. Useful for the advanced undergraduate and graduate student. Requires a strong mathematics background.

National Research Council Ocean Studies Board. *The Ocean's Role in Global Change: Progress of Major Research Programs.* Washington, D. C.: National Academy Press, 1994. An official report sponsored by the Office of Global Programs of the National Oceanic and Atmospheric Administration that discusses the WOCE and compares it to other international projects studying the ocean.

Needler, George T. "WOCE: The World Ocean Circulation Experiment." *Oceanus* 35 (Summer, 1992): 74-77. A clear introduction to the goals of WOCE and the methods used to obtain data. Written by the first scientific director of the WOCE, who was instrumental in planning the project.

Oceanography Course Team. *Ocean Circulation.* 2d ed. Oxford: Butterworth-Heinemann, 2001. Discusses surface currents and deep water currents, with focus on the North Atlantic Gyre, Gulf Stream, and equatorial currents. Discusses the El Niño phenomenon as well as the great salinity anomaly. Provides a good introduction to oceanography.

Pedlosky, Joseph. *Ocean Circulation Theory*. Rev. ed. New York: Springer, 2010. A detailed description of modern models of ocean circulation and the effect it has on climate. An excellent resource for advanced students that demonstrates the importance of the data provided by the WOCE.

U.S. WOCE Office. *U.S. WOCE Implementation Plan: The U.S. Contribution to the World Ocean Circulation Experiment*. College Station, Tex.: Author, 1993. Discusses the goals of WOCE and the role of the United States in the project.

Vallis, Geoffrey K. *Atmospheric and Oceanic Fluid Dynamics: Fundamentals and Large-Scale Circulation*. New York: Cambridge University Press, 2006. Begins with an overview of the physics of fluid dynamics to provide foundational material on stratification, vorticity, and oceanic and atmospheric models. Part II discusses topics such as turbulence, baroclinic instabilities, and wave-mean flow interactions, while parts III and IV discuss large-scale atmospheric and oceanic circulation, respectively. Best suited for graduate students studying meteorology or oceanography.

van Aken, Hendrik Mattheus. *The Oceanic Thermohaline Circulation: An Introduction*. New York: Springer Science + Business Media, 2007. Presents a global hydrographic description of the thermohaline circulation, based on data obtained directly from the WOCE.

Wefer, Gerold, et al. *The South Atlantic: Present and Past Circulation*. New York: Springer, 1996. An example of modern scientific analysis of data obtained on ocean circulation. Deals with the region of the ocean where the earliest WOCE studies were performed.

Woods, J. D. "The World Ocean Circulation Experiment." *Nature* 314 (April 11, 1985): 501-510. An outstanding introduction to the WOCE project. Discusses the importance of ocean circulation to changes in climate, the failure of models prior to the WOCE to accurately predict ocean conditions, the goals of the WOCE, and the technology that allowed the project to take place.

See also: Carbonate Compensation Depths; Deep Ocean Currents; Gulf Stream; Hydrothermal Vents; Observational Data of the Atmosphere and Oceans; Ocean-Atmosphere Interactions; Ocean Pollution and Oil Spills; Oceans' Origin; Oceans' Structure; Ocean Tides; Ocean Waves; Recent Climate Change Research; Remote Sensing of the Oceans; Sea Level; Seamounts; Seawater Composition; Surface Ocean Currents; Tsunamis; Turbidity Currents and Submarine Fans

Y

YELLOW RIVER

The Yellow River flows through three distinct geographic regions in northern China. The river is characterized by varying features of discharge, flooding, and sediment capacity in each region. The easily eroded loess sediments in the central region make the Yellow River the muddiest river in the world. The enormous quantity of sediment deposited by the river has been a primary cause of the catastrophic floods that have destroyed property and killed millions of people in northern China throughout recorded history.

PRINCIPAL TERMS

- **aggradation:** the buildup of sediment in a river channel that causes the level of the river to rise
- **avulsion:** the process in which a river changes its course because of flooding
- **delta:** a landform developed when sediment is deposited from a stream as it enters a relatively still body of water
- **floodplain:** the area normally covered by water during flooding; in many areas, the term is used to denote the area between human-made levees
- **hyperconcentrated flood:** a flood that carries unusually large quantities of sediment
- **levee:** a natural or human-made ridge formed or constructed alongside of streams, serving to restrain water flow to the stream channel; levees are sometimes breached during large-scale flooding, leading to damage in the surrounding areas
- **loess:** wind-blown sediment that can accumulate in great thicknesses and is easily eroded if not stabilized by vegetation

GEOGRAPHY OF THE YELLOW RIVER

The Yellow River, known as the Huang He or Hwang Ho in China, is the second largest river in China. It flows 5,464 kilometers eastward from the Plateau of Tibet to its mouth at the Bohai Sea (Po Hai), a large embayment of the Yellow Sea. It has been a major site of civilization for millennia. Because of the tendency of the river to break through its levees during floods and cause death and great damage, the Yellow River is also informally known as "China's sorrow" and the "Ungovernable."

The Yellow River drains a basin of approximately 752,400 square kilometers, the third largest basin in China. The drainage basin can be divided into three distinct regions of different relief in which the river has developed different characteristics. The Yellow River begins in the Payen-k'a-la Mountains and flows for approximately 1,200 kilometers across the Tibetan Plateau highlands, where it drains an area of 124,000 square kilometers. The flow is generally due east from Ngoring Hu toward Songpan. In this upper reach of the river, in the Tibetan Plateau, its channel is incised into hard crystalline rock and in many stretches, the channel is relatively narrow. The slope of the river channel steepens to more than 2 meters per kilometer as the river leaves the plateau and passes through a number of gorges. The upper basin contributes nearly one-half of the water that flows through the river. However, because of the hard bedrock of the region, it supplies less than 10 percent of the sediment transported by the river.

As the river flows eastward out of the Tibetan Plateau and into the middle basin, it turns abruptly northwest for about 885 kilometers before turning slowly east to Lanzhou. It bends and travels northward for 885 kilometers before turning eastward for another 800 kilometers. At Lanzhou, the river turns to the north-northeast and flows directly toward Linhe, where it turns due east again to flow past Baotou. About one-fourth of the way from Baotou to Beijing, the Huang He turns again to flow for an additional 800 kilometers south toward Xi'an. Between Xi'an and Sanmenxia, the river leaves the middle basin as another turn takes the river east to Kaifeng, then northeast to the Yellow Sea at Bo Hai. At the southern end of the southward-flowing section of the great loop, the Yellow River is joined by its two largest tributaries, the Wei River and the Fen River. As the Yellow River winds it way around the great bend, the river channel traverses the great Loess Plateau of north-central China and the sandy soils of the Ordos Desert. Loess is an aeolian sediment that was deposited by winds blowing southward out of Mongolia after the last ice age. It is characteristically a poorly consolidated material that is easily eroded by wind and water. The great sediment load of the Yellow River is primarily contributed by the erosion of the loess in the middle basin. It is the immense quantity of this light-colored sediment suspended in the water that gives the river its name in both English (Yellow) and Chinese (*huang* is the Chinese term for yellow). The loess, which is up to 170 meters thick in some areas, is the thickest soil sequence in the world. The native forests that had long grown on the loess soils had been cut down even before the beginning of the Han Dynasty in the year 206. Therefore, there is relatively little vegetation to hold the soil in place, and the river easily cuts through this friable material, which has resulted in the development of deeply incised river channels.

The lower basin extends east of the Loess Plateau from the city of Zhengzhou to the river delta at Bo Hai, a distance of about 786 kilometers. The river crosses the North China Plain, a flat alluvial plain built up of sediments deposited over the last 15 million years by the Yellow and other rivers. The sediment dumped into the region during this time filled an ancient embayment of the Yellow Sea, and the Yellow River continues to build its delta seaward today. The river is contained by long human-made levees throughout this heavily populated region, and sedimentation between the levees is often excessive, occasionally leading to catastrophic flooding. The delta of the Yellow River begins approximately 70 kilometers west of Bo Hai and covers an area of over 5,440 square kilometers.

GENERAL HYDROLOGY

The average annual flow rate of the Yellow River is approximately 1,770 cubic meters per second, but it may range from up to 36,300 cubic meters per second in wet years to below 1,000 cubic meters per second in dry years. The average rainfall for the entire basin is approximately 470 millimeters per year, but varies significantly between basins and is generally concentrated between July and October, when more than 50 percent of the annual rainfall may occur. Much of the water comes out of the upper (western) basin from

the snowmelt in the higher elevations of the Tibetan Plateau, but a significant amount of water is added by tributaries in the middle basin. The average annual discharge of the river is estimated to be only 58 billion cubic meters, which is less than the Hanjiang River, a tributary of the Yangtze River. The relatively low discharge of the river is caused by the generally low precipitation rates in the river basin and by the considerable evaporation of water during its journey to the sea. In addition, a large quantity of water is withdrawn from the river for irrigation. The upper basin contributes approximately 48 percent of the water of the river, the middle basin about 37 percent, and the lower basin about 15 percent.

During the winter months, the Yellow River has historically frozen over for as many as fifteen to twenty days per year. The ice is generally broken up with explosives to allow for navigation. In 1972, the lower reaches of the river began to dry up for short periods of time. In 1995, the easternmost stretch of the river was dry for a record 122 days, about one-third of the year. Increased withdrawal of water for irrigation in the upper and middle basin has caused the loss of water in the lower basin.

SEDIMENTS

The Yellow River is the muddiest river in the world, carrying an average annual sediment load of about 1.6 billion tons. The maximum recorded sediment load was 3.9 billion tons in 1933, while the minimum load was 488 million tons in 1928. The mean annual sediment concentration is 29.6 kilograms per cubic meter of water. This is about thirty times more concentrated than the Nile River and almost three times the concentration of the Colorado River. The source of most of the sediment transported and deposited by the river is the easily eroded loess of the middle basin. It is calculated that the middle basin contributes approximately 90 percent of the sediment carried by the Yellow River. The arid nature of the middle basin, the lack of soil-stabilizing vegetation, and the friable nature of loess all contribute to extraordinary erosion rates on the Loess Plateau. It is estimated that approximately 10,000 tons of soil per square kilometer per year erodes from the plateau. Hyperconcentrated flows often result from such heavy sediment loads on the Yellow River.

The sediment is washed into the Yellow River and carried downstream to be deposited either within the river system or at the coastline. If the sediment reaches the sea at Bo Hai, it is dropped as the river enters the sea, forming a delta. The modern delta is just the latest of many that have developed over time as the Yellow River and other rivers deposited their sediment loads into a marine embayment west of the present-day Bo Hai Sea. As the deltas prograded eastward, they filled the embayment with sediment. This process of filling a marine basin has continued for the past 15 million years. More recently, the delta has continued to expand eastward at rather astonishing rates. From 1870 to 1970, the delta prograded eastward approximately 24 kilometers. Some areas experienced even higher rates of growth, with one region of the delta expanding by approximately 25 kilometers between 1949 and 1952. However, beginning in 1972, increased water consumption by the population in the middle and upper basins resulted in a drying up of the lower reaches of the Yellow River such that water and sediment did not reach the coastline for several months during the year. This phenomenon affects delta growth as it continues, and may result in erosion of the coastal sediments accompanied by encroachment of saline marine waters into the delta.

Much of the sediment eroded from the Loess Plateau is deposited in the river system itself and does not reach the coastal areas. This coarse- to fine-grained sediment is dumped into channels along the lower reach of the river, causing a buildup of the river bed. This aggradation of the bed would normally cause a change in the river channel by avulsion. The river would simply be forced out of its channel during a flood and would establish a new channel in a region of less sediment and lower elevation. This natural process of channel change causes the river to migrate back and forth across the alluvial plain that was constructed of sediments that were deposited at a previous time. It is clear from geologic studies that the Yellow River has changed its course numerous times over the last four thousand years. Over this time span, the Yellow River has entered the sea at places as much as 700 kilometers apart. The river entered the Bo Hai Sea along a northern route from about 3000 B.C.E. to 602 B.C.E., then changed its course to a more southerly channel after flooding, and entered the sea south of the Shandong Peninsula. In 70 C.E., the river again changed its course to a more northerly channel and entered the Bo Hai Sea near the location of its present mouth. Changes in the river channel also occurred inland where the Yellow River enters the lower basin. In the last two thousand years, the Yellow River has had 7 major course changes and almost 1,600 levee breaches.

The lower basin is heavily populated, and a course change can affect millions of people. As a result, the Chinese have attempted to control the river by surrounding it with human-made levees and by the construction, in 1960, of a large dam at the city of Sanmenxia. The levees, which were constructed to contain the river during major floods, have generally been successful. However, as they contain the river flood waters, they also trap the huge quantities of silt and sand carried by the waters. As a result, the river bed and surrounding floodplain between the levees continues to aggrade because of sediment deposition. As the elevation of the bed rises, it is necessary to build higher levees to contain future floods. This process has continued for hundreds of years, and now the river is actually contained within the levees at a higher elevation than the surrounding plains. In a few areas, the river level is as much as 30 meters higher than the surrounding land. This means that the river is at the highest elevation in the region and is actually the drainage divide for the area. This situation can lead to catastrophic flooding if a levee is breached.

FLOODING

The Yellow River is sometimes called "China's sorrow" because it has caused so many deaths and enormous damage when it has flooded across the North China Plain. Since the river is, in many places, much higher than the surrounding plains and since the alluvial plain is so flat, a breach in the levees causes widespread flooding. Some of the most catastrophic floods in history have occurred on the Yellow River. Chinese engineers have constructed thousands of kilometers of levees in an attempt to control the river, but these efforts have generally only delayed the flooding. There have been nearly 1,600 major and minor levee breaches recorded in the last two thousand years. Between 960 and 1048, thirty-eight major levee breaches occurred, a rate of nearly one break every other year. Better construction and maintenance of levees led a lower rate of levee breaches, but flooding continued to occur. The years of the Taiping Rebellion (1850 to 1864) were marred by a lessening of concern over the levees. As a result, breaches became more common, leading to a major river course change in 1852-1854. The Yellow

River broke through its levees near the city of Kaifeng in 1887, leading to one of the most devastating floods in history. The flood waters covered 130,000 square kilometers of the North China Plain, depositing silts and clays over the entire area. The floods inundated 21,000 hectares of cropland and deposited up to 10 meters of sediment in some areas. In all, 11 cities and 2,000 villages were flooded, and approximately 900,000 people perished. It is estimated that an additional 2 to 4 million people suffered flood-related deaths. Another major flood occurred two years later and destroyed 1,500 more villages. A devastating flood occurred in 1921 in which many villages were destroyed, particularly near the mouth of the river. In 1933, more than 1,500 villages were inundated, and more than 18,000 people died.

One of the most disastrous floods of the Yellow River was directly caused by humans when the levees were intentionally ruptured by Chinese soldiers, who were ordered to dynamite the levees in order to halt the advance of Japanese soldiers in 1938. The ensuing flood successfully stopped the Japanese advance but also destroyed eleven cities, more than four thousand villages, and many thousands of hectares of cropland. More than 1 million Chinese people died, and an additional 11 million people were left homeless. It took engineers eight years to regain control of the river and route it back into its pre-1938 channel.

Jay R. Yett

FURTHER READING

Collier, Michael. *Over the Rivers: An Aerial View of Geology.* New York: Mikaya Press, 2008. Discusses the dynamic landscape of the rivers. Explains the processes that shape the landscape and its influence on humans. Written in the popular style. Easily accessible to the general public. Filled with bits of information and extraordinary photographs. Presents multiple examples drawn from the Mississippi River.

Czaya, Eberhard. *Rivers of the World.* New York: Cambridge University Press, 1985. A general text on the world's rivers that has valuable information on the fluvial processes and a good description of the changing course of the Yellow River over the last 2,500 years.

Darby, Stephen, and David Sear. *River Restoration: Managing the Uncertainty in Restoring Physical Habitat.* Hoboken, N.J.: John Wiley & Sons, 2008. A publication that begins with theoretical and philosophical issues relative to habitat restoration, which provides a strong foundation for decision making. Later chapters address logistics, planning, mathematical modeling, and construction stages of restoration. Finishes up with post-construction monitoring and long-term evaluations to provide a full picture of the habitat restoration process. Highly useful for anyone involved in the planning and implementing of habitat restoration.

Dodgen, Randall A. *Controlling the Dragon: Confucian Engineers and the Yellow River in Late Imperial China.* Honolulu: University of Hawaii Press, 2001. Takes a historical and analytical look at attempts to control the Yellow River in earlier times.

Giordano, M., Zhongping Zhu, Ximing Cai, Shangqi Hong, Xuecheng Zhang, and Yunpeng Xue. *Water Management in the Yellow River Basin: Background, Current Critical Needs and Future Research Needs.* A comprehensive assessment of water management in agriculture that presents a summary of the geological characteristics of the Yellow River basin and discusses the historical role of the river in Chinese history as the prelude to an analysis and assessment of the water use-related issues of the area.

Hillel, Daniel. "Lash of the Dragon." *Natural History* (August, 1991): 28-37. A well-written description of the problems of soil erosion caused by the Yellow River. Also describes the extent of the effects of sedimentation and flooding.

Kusuda, Tetsuya. *The Yellow River: Water and Life.* Singapore: World Scientific Publishing Co, 2010. Examines the serious problems of water deficit and water pollution along the Yellow River, with regard to international ramifications due to increasing demands of the growing population, rising living standards, irrigation and developing industry in the Yellow River basin.

Milne, Anthony. *Floodshock.* Gloucester, England: Allan Sutton, 1986. A general reader on flooding throughout the world that contains good, readable information on the flooding of the Yellow River. Describes the 1887 Yellow River flood and the dynamiting of the levees in 1938.

Mukherji, Aditi. *Groundwater Governance in the Indo-Gangetic and Yellow River Basins: Realities and Challenges.* Leiden: CRC Press/Balkema, 2009. Discusses the socioeconomic impacts of groundwater usage on the basis that groundwater supplies some

70 percent of the water used for irrigation in the north China plains, and such use is increasing.

Wan, Chao-hui. *Hyperconcentrated Flow.* Brookfield, Vt.: A. A. Balkema, 1994. Contains a wealth of information about sediment transport in the Yellow River. Illustrations, bibliography, and index.

Wohl, Ellen. *A World of Rivers.* Chicago: University of Chicago Press, 2011. Contains chapters on the Amazon, Ob, Nile, Danube, Ganges, Mississippi, Murray-Darling, Congo, Chang Jiang, and Mackenzie rivers. Figure 1.1 contains more straight-forward and organized information than some full textbooks. Discusses natural history, anthropogenic impact, and the future environment of these ten great rivers. Organizes the bibliography by chapter.

See also: Amazon River Basin; Dams and Flood Control; Drainage Basins; Floodplains; Ganges River; Great Lakes; Lake Baikal; Lakes; Mississippi River; Nile River; Precipitation; River Bed Forms; Sand; Sediment Transport and Deposition; Surface Water

APPENDIXES

GLOSSARY

ablation: the removal of material from a glacier, ice shelf, or other mass of ice through evaporation, melting, or splitting.

abrasion: the wearing away of rock by frictional contact with solid particles moved by gravity, water, ice, or wind.

abyssal plain: the flat, sediment-covered area of the sea floor that merges with the base of the continental rise.

acid deposition: the placement of acidic materials on the ground surface through the action of precipitation.

acid rain: precipitation having elevated levels of acidity relative to pure water.

active sensor: a type of remote sensor that emits radiation at a target to study its composition and condition.

acute toxicity: the effect of a toxic agent on an organism caused by a large dose in a short time.

adiabatic: characterizing a process in which no heat is exchanged between a system and its surroundings.

aeolian deposits: material transported by wind.

aerosol: a gaseous suspension of fine liquid and solid particles.

aggradation: the buildup of sediment in a river channel that causes the level of the river to rise.

air drainage: the flow of cold, dense air downslope in response to gravity.

air mass: a mass of air in the lower atmosphere that has generally uniform properties of temperature and moisture.

air stripping: the process of passing contaminated water through an aeration chamber, causing the organic contaminants to volatilize into the gaseous waste stream.

albedo: the amount of radiation a surface reflects; higher albedo reflects more incoming radiation.

algorithm: a set of instructions used to perform a task.

alkaline: having a pH greater than 7 due to a lower concentration of hydrogen (H^+) ions than are in neutral water.

allogenic sediment: sediment that originates outside the place where it is finally deposited; sand, silt, and clay carried by a stream into a lake are examples.

alluvium: a deposit of soil and mud formed by flowing water.

alpha particle: the nucleus of a helium atom, consisting of two protons and two neutrons.

altimeter: a scientific instrument that measures the altitude of an object above a fixed level.

ammonia: a colorless and highly toxic gas with a strong odor; the odor of ammonia is frequently detected in stables or in sewage; salts of ammonia are used as fertilizer for plants.

ammonium ion: produced as a waste of such animals as fish, during decomposition of organic nitrogen wastes by bacteria, and by metabolism of some bacteria; forms after dilution of ammonia in water; acidic and toxic to humans because it interferes with respiration.

aneroid barometer: uses an aneroid capsule composed of an alloy of beryllium and copper to measure changes in external air pressure.

angle of repose: the natural angle formed between the horizontal plane and the side of a free-standing pile of sediment particles under the force of gravity in a fluid medium.

anoxic: lacking oxygen.

anthropogenic: caused by or resulting from human activities; mainly used to describe environmental pollution and pollutants.

anticyclone: a general term for a high-pressure weather system that rotates clockwise in the Northern Hemisphere and counterclockwise in the Southern Hemisphere.

antidune: an undulatory upstream-moving bed form produced in free-surface flow of water over a sand bed in a certain range of high-flow speeds and shallow-flow depths.

aperiodic: describing any phenomenon that occurs at random rather than at regularly occurring intervals, such as most weather cycles, rendering them virtually unpredictable.

aphelion: the time at which the distance between the sun and Earth is smallest; generally occurs on one of the first days of January, two weeks after the December solstice.

aquifer: a rock or sediment structure that is saturated with groundwater and is capable of delivering that water to wells and springs.

Arctic Oscillation: a long-term weather pattern in which the different air pressures in the Arctic and middle-latitude regions cause varying weather conditions.

asthenosphere: the layer of the mantle immediately beneath the lithosphere; it exists in an almost "plastic" state and therefore behaves like a very thick liquid.

atmosphere: gaseous "envelope" surrounding the planet that contains all gases produced by terrestrial sources.

atmospheric pressure: force exerted on a surface by the weight of air above that surface; measured in force per unit area.

atoll: a tropical island on which a massive coral reef, often ringlike, generally rests on a volcanic base.

ATP: adenosine triphosphate; a chemical that is the primary carrier of energy in all organisms.

aurora: a glowing light display resulting from charged particles from solar wind being pulled into Earth's atmosphere by Earth's magnetic field; most often visible near the North and South Poles.

austral: referring to an object or occurrence that is of the Southern Hemisphere.

autotroph: organism that produces complex organic molecules using materials and energy obtained through photosynthesis or chemiosynthesis.

autumnal equinox: the day that the sun passes directly over the equator in the southward direction, producing day and night of equal length and marking the beginning of autumn; in the Northern Hemisphere, the date is about September 21 and in the Southern Hemisphere, it occurs about March 21.

avulsion: a natural change in a river channel, usually caused by flooding and excess deposition of sediment.

ball lightning: a rare form of lightning appearing as luminous balls of charged air.

Baltic Sea: the body of water between Scandinavia and Eastern Europe.

bank: an elevated area of land beneath the surface of the ocean.

barchan dune: a crescent-shaped sand dune of deserts and shorelines that lies transverse to the prevailing wind direction.

barograph: a graph that records atmospheric pressure in time.

barometer: device for measuring atmospheric pressure; some are water-based, some use mercury or an aneroid cell, and some create a line graph of atmospheric pressure.

barrier islands: coastal landforms that run parallel to the mainland; formed by the action of waves and currents; these islands protect the mainland from storms and other weather events.

basalt: a typical volcanic rock of the ocean floor with a relatively low silica content.

base flow: the natural flow of groundwater into a river, which commonly maintains the minimum flow of perennial rivers during the dry season.

basin: the region drained by a river system, including all of its tributaries; or, container-like places on the ocean floor, usually elliptical, circular, or oval in shape, varying in depth and size.

basin order: an approximate measure of the size of a stream basin, based on a numbering scheme applied to river channels as they join together in their progress downstream.

bathymetric contour: a line on a map of the ocean floor that connects points of equal depth.

beach: an accumulation of loose material, such as sand or gravel, that is deposited by waves and currents at the border of a body or stream of water.

bead lightning: lightning that appears as a series of beads tied to a string.

bed configuration: the overall geometry of a sediment bed molded by sediment transport in a flowing fluid.

bed form: an individual geometrical element of a bed configuration.

bed load: sediment in motion in continuous or semi-continuous contact with the sediment bed by sliding, rolling, or hopping (saltation).

bed shear stress: the force per unit area exerted by the flowing fluid on the sediment bed, averaged over an area that is large compared to individual bed particles.

Bergeron process: precipitation formation in cold clouds whereby ice crystals grow at the expense of supercooled water droplets.

berm: an artificial ridge or wall, usually made of sand; normally used to prevent flooding but employed after the 2010 Gulf of Mexico oil spill as a barrier to keep oil from polluting beaches.

bicarbonate: a negatively charged ion that effectively neutralizes excess hydrogen ions in natural waters, reducing acidity.

bioaccumulation: the accumulation of substances, such as pesticides and metals, in an organism.

biochar: another name for charcoal, used specifically for usages of charcoal that involve positive effects such as soil improvement or carbon sequestration.

biogenic sediment: sediment that originates from living organisms.

biogeochemical cycle: cycling of chemical elements such as nitrogen, carbon, and phosphorus.

biosphere: areas on Earth that can support life.

blizzard: a winter storm characterized by cold wind having a minimum velocity of 56 kilometers per hour, large amounts of blowing snow, and low levels of visibility.

blowout preventer: a large series of safety valves installed at the wellhead of an oil rig to seal the well in case of a problem and to prevent the uncontrolled release of oil.

bluff: the edge of the remnant higher-elevated land that marks the margin of the floodplain.

boom: a floating device, usually made of either plastic or cloth, which is linked with other booms to form a flexible barrier intended to prevent oil spills from moving inland.

bore: a sudden rise in water level in a river channel manifested as an incoming wave of tidal waters.

boreal: referring to an object or occurrence that is of the Northern Hemisphere.

Bosphorus and Dardanelles Straits: straits leading to and from the Sea of Marmara; they are the only sea lanes linking the countries with shores on the Black Sea to the Mediterranean.

bottom current: a deep-sea current that flows parallel to bathymetric contours.

bottom-water mass: a body of water at the deepest part of the ocean identified by similar patterns of salinity and temperature.

brackish water: water with a salt content between that of saltwater and freshwater; it is common in arid areas on the surface, in coastal marshes, and in salt-contaminated groundwater.

braided river: a relatively shallow river with many intertwined channels; its sediment is moved primarily as riverbed material.

brash: splinters that become detached from ice floes and float in the Arctic Ocean.

calcareous algae: green algae that secrete needles or plates of aragonite as an internal skeleton; very important contributors to reef sediment.

calcareous ooze: sediment in which more than 30 percent of the particles are the remains of plants and animals composed of calcium carbonate.

calving: the breaking away of a smaller piece of ice from a larger one.

Canadian Shield: the geologic core of North America, extending over north-central Canada, that experienced glaciation during the Pleistocene epoch; characterized by an undulating surface of moderate relief and containing the oldest dated rock formations on the planet.

capacity: the total amount of sediment a river or stream can transport at a given time.

cap and trade legislation: legislation that places limits on the emission of acid-producing materials, such as sulfur dioxide, while allowing emitters of excess amounts to purchase and utilize the unused allowance of those whose emissions are below the legislated limit.

capillary force: a phenomenon in which water moves through tiny pores in rock, soil, and other materials, driven by intermolecular attraction between the water and the porous materials.

capillary fringe: the lowest portion of the unsaturated zone just above the water table.

carbonaceous chondrites: a class of meteoritic bodies found to contain large amounts of carbon in conjunction with other elements; used to date the solar system and provide chemical composition assessments of the original solar nebula.

carbon adsorption: the process of pumping contaminated water directly through carbon filters to capture contaminants by adsorptive binding to the surface of the carbon particles.

carbonate compensation depth (CCD): the depth in the oceans at which the rate of supply of calcium carbonate equals the rate of dissolution of calcium carbonate.

carbonate rocks: sedimentary rocks such as limestone, composed of calcium carbonate minerals.

carbon dioxide: CO_2, one of many minor gases that are natural components of the atmosphere; the product of the complete oxidation of carbon.

carbon fixation: a chemical process that incorporates carbon from its atmospheric state into complex organic molecules.

carbon-oxygen cycle: the process by which oxygen and carbon are cycled through Earth's environment.

carbon sequestration: long-term storage of carbon in a stable state to remove carbon from cycling in the environment.

carbon sink: a reservoir (either natural or human made) for storing or sequestering carbon.

cascade: a small waterfall or series of small falls.

casing: conventionally, a tubular material—usually a large metal, concrete, or plastic pipe—that is inserted into a raw borehole for the purpose of maintaining the integrity of the hole.

cataclastic: those formative processes of sand that relate to crushing.

catalyst: a substance that increases the rate of a chemical reaction without itself being altered in the process.

cataract: rough water or a waterfall in a river, generally obstructing navigation.

cement grouting: the injection of a sand-cement mix by means of pressure, resulting in an envelope of concrete lining between the outside of a casing and the undisturbed geologic material of a well borehole.

channel: a horizontal depression in the ground surface caused and enlarged by the concentrated flow of water.

channelization: the practice of deliberately rerouting a stream or artificially modifying its channel by straightening, deepening, widening, clearing, or lining it.

chaos: an emerging scientific discipline that attempts to quantify and describe the properties of seemingly random, aperiodic events.

chemical evolution: the synthesis of amino acids and other complex organic molecules—the precursors of living systems—by the action of atmospheric lightning and solar ultraviolet radiation on atmospheric gases.

chemical leaching: the process of extracting a substance from a solid by dissolving it in a liquid.

chemical weathering: the decomposition of rock by chemical rather than mechanical processes.

chlorofluorocarbon (CFC): a group of chemical compounds containing carbon, fluorine, and chlorine, used in air conditioners, refrigerators, fire extinguishers, spray cans, and other applications; the principal cause of ozone depletion in the stratosphere.

chronic toxicity: the effect of a toxic agent on an organism that manifests from long-term, repeated exposure to a substance.

chubasco: a type of severe storm that occurs in the Gulf of California and along the west coast of Mexico.

circulation cell: cyclic pattern of air movement within the atmosphere.

cirrus: trailing or streaky clouds at altitudes ranging from 5 to 13 kilometers that are feathery or fibrous in appearance.

clastic sediments: sediments composed of durable minerals that resist weathering.

clay: a mineral group whose particles consist of structures arranged in sandwichlike layers, usually sheets of aluminum hydroxides and silica, along with some potassium, sodium, or calcium ions.

clay lens: a subsurface layer of low-permeability clay soil, extending over a limited area, that traps groundwater and produces a secondary water table perched above the main water table.

clay minerals: a group of hydrous silicate minerals characterized by a structure of layers of thin sheets that are held together loosely.

climate: the long-term weather patterns for a region, distinct from the day-to-day weather patterns.

climate change: a change in the global climate that persists for roughly ten years or longer.

climate moderation: a change in the climate or average weather of a region that reduces the extremes of heat and cold.

climatology: the scientific study of climate that depends on the statistical database of weather observed over a period of twenty or more years for a specific location.

cloud seeding: the injection of nucleating particles into clouds to enhance precipitation formation.

cnidarian: any organism, including corals, hydras, jellyfish, and sea anemones, that belongs to the phylum Cnidaria; all cnidarians are radially symmetrical and have stinging cells known as nematocysts.

cold cloud: a visible suspension of tiny ice crystals, supercooled water droplets, or both, at temperatures below the normal freezing point of water.

cold front: an area in which a dominant stream of colder air pushes under a pocket of warmer air, causing the warm air to rise and resulting in precipitation at the leading edge of the front.

collision-coalescence process: precipitation formation in warm clouds whereby larger droplets grow through the merging of smaller droplets.

combined flow: a flow of fluid with components of both unidirectional and oscillatory flow superposed on one another to produce a more complex pattern of fluid motion.

combustion: reactions by which oxygen and organic materials become carbon dioxide and water.

competence: a concept that expresses the ability of a fluid stream to move particles of a given size.

concentration: amount of a specific substance present in a given volume of sample water; commonly used units include milligrams per liter or micrograms per liter.

condensation: the transformation of a substance from the vapor state to the liquid state; atmospheric condensation occurs when droplets of liquid form (or condense) around small particles in the atmosphere.

cone of depression: a cone-shaped depression produced in the water table by pumping from a well.

confined aquifer: an aquifer that is completely filled with water and whose upper boundary is a confining bed; it is also called an artesian aquifer.

confining bed: an impermeable layer in the geologic stratigraphy that prevents vertical water movement.

constant pressure chart: a chart that shows the altitude of a constant pressure, such as 500 millibars.

contaminant: any natural or unnatural component that is introduced into the environment in concentrations greater than those normally present.

continental drift: the gradual movement of continental landmasses across Earth's surface, driven by convection processes in the mantle.

continental margin: the area that separates the emergent continents from the deep sea floor, generally consisting of the continental shelf, continental slope, and continental rise.

continental rise: the broad and gently sloping ramp that rises from the abyssal plain to the base of the continental slope; submarine fans are found here.

continental shelf: part of a continental landmass, usually gently sloping, that extends beneath the ocean from the water's edge to the continental slope.

continental slope: the relatively steep region of the continental margin between the continental shelf and the continental rise.

convection: heat transfer by the circulating movement that occurs in fluid materials as warmer, less dense material rises above cooler, denser material.

convection cell: the cyclic path taken when warmer, less dense material in one part of a fluid or gas rises, cools, contracts, and becomes denser, then descends again to its original level.

convective overturn: the renewal of the bottom waters caused by the sinking of surface waters that have become denser, usually because of changes in temperature or salinity.

convergence: a tendency of air masses to accumulate in a region where more air is flowing in than is flowing out.

convergent plate margin: an area where two tectonic plates impinge upon each other with pressure directed toward the area of contact; typically in such regions, the lithosphere is being returned to the mantle at a subduction zone, forming volcanic "island arcs" and associated hydrothermal activity.

conveyor belt current: a large cycle of water movement that carries warm waters from the North Pacific westward across the Indian Ocean, around southern Africa, and into the Atlantic, where it warms the atmosphere, then returns to a deeper ocean level to rise and begin the process again.

coral bleaching: a pale or whitened appearance that arises from the loss of zooxanthellae, the symbiotic algae that are present in healthy reef-building corals.

coralline algae: red algae that secrete crusts or branching skeletons of high-magnesium calcite; important sediment contributors and binders on reefs.

coral polyp: the basic unit of a coral reef; a single invertebrate marine animal with a protective skeleton made up of limestone, or calcium carbonate, around a soft inner body.

coral reef: a living ecosystem in the shape of a ridge or mound, composed of colonies of coral polyps and the organisms that live in, on, and around them.

core ring or core eddy: a mass of water that is spun off of an ocean current by that current's meandering motion.

Coriolis effect: the apparent deflection of any moving body or object from its linear course, caused by Earth's rotation.

Coriolis force: an apparent force caused by the rotation of the planet, in which objects moving above Earth's surface (such as the wind) deflect to the right in the Northern Hemisphere and to the left in the Southern Hemisphere.

corona: the outermost layer of the sun, which extends into space in an irregular pattern surrounding the main body of the star.

corona discharge: a continuous electric discharge

from highly charged, pointed objects that produces the luminous greenish or bluish halo known as St. Elmo's Fire.

coronal mass ejection: a larger-than-average burst of solar wind related to deformations and reconfigurations of the sun's magnetic field.

cosmic ray: high-energy subatomic particles that are produced by phenomena in space, such as supernovae.

craton: an area of the land surface that has been stable for millions of years.

creep: the slow, gradual downslope movement of soil materials under gravitational stress.

crevasse: a break in the bank of a distributary channel causing a partial diversion of flow and sediment into an interdistributary bay.

Crimean Peninsula: a large peninsula located on the north central shore of the Black Sea; it is the most significant irregularity on the otherwise regular coastline.

cryosphere: portion of the earth's surface in which the year-round temperature remains constant enough to support permanent ice and snow.

cumulonimbus cloud: also called "thunderstorm cloud"; a very dense, tall, billowing cloud form that develops an anvil-shaped head due to high-altitude wind shear, and normally accompanied by lightning and heavy precipitation.

cumulus: clouds with vertical development rising from a seemingly flat base, often appearing as fluffy masses, at altitudes ranging from ground level to 6 kilometers above the ground; sometimes called heap clouds.

current: the horizontal movement of ocean water at a generally uniform depth.

current ripple: a small bed form, oriented predominantly transverse to the direction of flow, produced at low to moderate flow speeds in unidirectional water flows.

cyclogenesis: the series of atmospheric events that occur during the formation of a cyclone weather system.

cyclone: a general term for a low-pressure weather system that rotates counterclockwise in the Northern Hemisphere and clockwise in the Southern Hemisphere.

Danube River: probably the most famous river that enters the Black Sea; the river is a vital means for international maritime access, via the Black Sea, for several European countries.

dart leaders: surges of electrons that follow the same

intermittent ionized channel taken by the initial stepped leader of a lightning stroke.

dead zone: a local region within a body of water that does not support any living systems and so is devoid of plant and animal life.

debris flow: a flowing mass consisting of water together with a high concentration of sediment with a wide range of sizes, from fine muds to coarse gravels.

decomposition: the process by which organic matter is broken down into its most basic components by microorganisms.

deep-water wave: a wave traveling in water with a depth greater than one-half of its wave length.

deflation: the sorting out, lifting, and removal of loose, dry, silt- and clay-sized soil particles by turbulent eddy action of the wind.

deforestation: removal of forest areas or stands of trees, including for commercial and agricultural development.

delta: a deposit of sediment, often triangular, formed at a river mouth where the wave action is low and the river's current slows suddenly.

deposition: the process by which loose sediment grains fall out of water to accumulate as layers of sediment.

deranged drainage: describing a landscape whose integrated drainage network has been destroyed by irregular glacial deposition, yielding numerous shallow lake basins.

desertification: the relatively slow, natural conversion of fertile land into arid land or desert.

detection limit: the lowest concentration of a constituent that can be reliably detected.

diagenesis: all physical or chemical changes that alter a sediment's properties after deposition.

dirt cracking: a process in which clays accumulate in rock cracks, take on water, and expand to rupture the rock.

discharge: the total amount of water passing a point on a river per unit of time.

dispersant: a chemical, usually consisting of a surfactant and a solvent, that is used to break up an oil slick into smaller droplets that will then disperse into the water and be weathered more quickly.

dissolved matter: the amount of normally solid materials that are completely dissolved in water.

distributary: a river that diverges from the main river

and carries and distributes the flow of water across a delta.

distributary channel: a river that is divided into several smaller channels, thus distributing its flow and sediment load.

diurnal tide: having only one high tide and one low tide each lunar day; tides on some parts of the Gulf of Mexico are diurnal.

divergence: a tendency of air masses to spread in a region where more air is flowing out than is flowing in.

divergent margin: an area where two tectonic plates are moving away from each other; where the crust and lithosphere form by seafloor spreading.

Dobson spectrophotometer: a ground-based instrument for measuring the total column abundance of ozone at a particular geographic location.

doldrums: the equatorial zone where winds are calm and variable and there is heavy rainfall.

Doppler radar: a radar method that uses the Doppler shift to measure the speed of targets moving either toward or away from the radar.

Doppler shift: a phenomenon in which the wavelength of electromagnetic radiation (or other type of wave) is lengthened by reflection from a surface moving away from the source or shortened by reflection from a surface moving toward the source.

downburst: a convective windstorm associated with strong thunderstorm systems.

downwelling: the sinking of ocean water to a lower depth.

drainage basin: the land area that contributes water to a particular stream or river system; the edge of such a basin is a drainage divide.

drainage divide: the ridge of land that marks the boundary between adjacent watersheds.

drift: a movement similar to a current but more widespread, less distinct, slower, more shallow, and less easily delineated.

dune: a large bed form of sand, oriented predominantly transverse to the direction of flow, produced at moderate to high flow speeds.

dust devil: a rotating column of air rising above a hot ground surface, made visible by the dust it contains; dust devils are much smaller than tornadoes, having winds of less than 60 kilometers per hour, and cause little or no damage.

dynamic mode theory: a theory proposing that

enhancement of vertical movement in clouds increases precipitation.

easterly waves: localized zones of low pressure oriented parallel to Earth's rotational axis and moving from east to west across the ocean; they form an important generative component of tropical weather patterns.

eccentricity: variation in the shape of Earth's orbit around the sun, varying from circular to elliptical.

ecological backlash: the unanticipated ecological effect of what appears, at first, to be a harmless activity.

eddy: a smaller, rotating current or turbulence that forms from the movement of a primary water or wind current.

Ekman layer: the region of the sea, from the surface to about 100 meters down, in which the wind directly effects water movement.

electromagnetic radiation: radiation that includes visible light, infrared radiation (heat), radio waves, gamma rays, and X rays.

electromagnetic wave: a wave of energy consisting of oscillating electric and magnetic fields.

electromagnetism: relationship between electric energy and magnetic energy responsible for attraction between negatively and positively charged particles.

electrons: subatomic particles that have one unit of negative charge.

electron volt (eV): a unit of energy used for atomic and subatomic measurements; 1 electron volt is the kinetic energy acquired by an electron accelerated through a potential difference of 1 volt.

element: one of a number of substances composed entirely of atoms that cannot be broken into smaller particles by chemical means.

elevation head: the elevation of a given water particle above a certain point, usually mean sea level.

El Niño/La Niña: cyclical increases and decreases, respectively, in Pacific Ocean water temperature that foster shifts in weather patterns worldwide.

endemic: found in a particular locality and no other.

endogenetic: those formative processes of sand that relate to chemical and biochemical precipitation.

endogenic sediment: sediment produced within the water column of the body in which it is deposited; for example, calcite precipitated in a lake in summer.

endosymbiont: an animal-hosting autotrophic

bacterium, with both host and bacterium enjoying the benefits of symbiosis.

energy budget: an accounting of all the incoming and outgoing energy for Earth as a system.

ensemble weather forecasting: repeated use of a single model, run many times using slightly different initial data; the results of the model runs are pooled to create a single "ensemble" weather forecast.

ENSO: acronym for El Niño/Southern Oscillation, used to denote the combined atmospheric/ocean phenomenon.

entisol: a weakly developed soil layer that does not exhibit distinct horizons or stratification layers.

environmental lapse rate: the general temperature decrease within the troposphere; the rate is variable but averages approximately 6.5 degrees Celsius per kilometer.

environmental persistence: the relative length of time that oil remains in the environment with the possibility of causing negative environmental effects.

enzyme: a biologic catalyst made of proteins.

ephemeral stream: a river or stream that flows briefly in response to nearby rainfall; such streams are common in arid and semiarid regions.

epiclastic: those formative processes of sand that relate to weathering.

epidemiology: the evaluation and study of public health as it relates to the effects of environment, choice, and risk factors.

epilimnion: a warmer surface layer of water that occurs in a lake during summer stratification; during spring, warmer water rises from great depths, and it heats up through the summer season.

equator: the line of latitude on Earth that is exactly halfway between the North and South Poles.

equinox: a twice-a-year occurrence during which the tilt of Earth's axis is such that the poles are not tilted toward or away from the sun; the center of the sun is directly aligned with Earth's equator.

equipotential line: a contour line connecting points of equal hydraulic head.

erosion: the displacement of sediment from one location to another on the ground surface.

estuary: an area where the mouth of a river broadens as it approaches the sea, characterized by the mixing of freshwater and saltwater.

eustatic sea-level change: a change in sea level worldwide, observed on all coastlines on all continents.

eutrophication: process in which water bodies (rivers, ponds, lakes, and oceans) receive excess nutrients (mainly nitrogen and phosphorus) that stimulate abundant growth of algae and plants.

evaporation: the physical process occurring at the water-air interface where water changes its phase from liquid to vapor.

evapotranspiration: the combined water loss to the atmosphere from both evaporation and plant transpiration.

exosphere: the outermost layer of Earth's atmosphere.

expansion-contraction cycles: processes of wetting-drying, heating-cooling, or freezing-thawing, which affect soil particles differently according to their size.

eye: the center of a hurricane; the area of lowest surface pressure with calm, clear weather.

eye wall: just outside the eye of the hurricane; the area of the storm with peak winds and rain.

fauna: the animal population of a region.

fetch: the area or length of the sea surface over which waves are generated by wind having a constant direction and speed.

filtration: the removal of particulate matter from the water by passing it through a porous medium.

fjord: a steep-sided narrow inlet eroded into the face of seaside cliff, typical of Scandinavia but found throughout the world.

flash floods: rises in water level that occur unusually rapidly, generally because of especially intense rainfall.

flocculation: a slow process by which suspended particles are gathered together to form larger particles that can then be removed by physical means.

flood: a rising body of water that overtops its usual confines and inundates land not usually covered by water.

floodplain: a wide, flat, low-lying area, adjacent to a river, that is generally inundated by floodwaters.

flood zoning: passing laws that restrict the development and land use of flood-prone areas.

flora: the plant species of a region.

fluid dynamics: the branch of physics that deals with the movement of fluids, including gases and liquids.

flume: a laboratory open channel in which water is passed over a sediment bed to study the nature of the sediment movement.

fluorescent pigment: a coloring matter that absorbs light at a particular wavelength and emits it at a longer wavelength; these pigments, found in zoo-xanthellae, give hard corals their bright colors.

fluvial: pertaining to or resulting from the action of naturally flowing water in a streambed or watercourse.

flux: the number of particles striking a unit of surface area per unit of time.

fog dissipation: removal of fog by artificial means.

food chain: the arrangement of the organisms of an ecological community according to the order of predation in which each consumes the next, usually lower, member as a food source.

food web: the complex web of feeding relationships in nature.

forecast verification: a comparison of predicted weather to observed weather conditions, used to assess forecasting accuracy and reliability.

fossil fuels: carbon-rich, energy-storing compounds that, when burned, release greenhouse gases into the atmosphere.

free oxygen: the element oxygen by itself, not combined chemically with a different element.

freshwater: water with less than 0.2 percent dissolved salts, such as is found in most streams, rivers, and lakes

freshwater lens: the shape of the freshwater table in aquifers of coastal areas or marine islands that floats on top of a denser, underlying saltwater.

front: the boundary between two masses of air with different densities and temperatures; usually named for the mass that is advancing (for example, in a cold front, the mass that is colder is moving toward a warmer mass).

Fujita scale: a scale that rates the severity of tornadoes based on the amount of destruction they cause.

fully confined aquifers: those aquifers that lie sandwiched between impermeable formations and are therefore termed artesian aquifers.

gas hydrates: relatively stable, often crystalline, molecular combinations of water and hydrocarbon gases, especially methane, that form on the ocean floor due to the elevated pressure conditions.

general circulation models (GCMs): comprehensive, mathematical-numerical formulas in climate studies that attempt to express in equations the basic dynamics thought to govern the large-scale behavior of the atmosphere.

geoarchaeology: the technique of using ancient human habitation sites to determine the age of landforms and when changes occurred.

geochemical sinks: the processes by which elements and compounds are removed from the crust and oceans to be recycled in active chemical cycles.

geographic information system: a network of satellite-mapping technologies that can capture detailed images of the land surface.

geomagnetic storm: the effect of variations in the solar wind's interactions with Earth's atmosphere; can result in communications disruptions and auroral displays in lower-than-usual latitudes.

geomorphology: the study of the origins of landforms and the processes of landform development.

geostrophic current: a current resulting from the balance between a pressure gradient force and the Coriolis effect; the current moves horizontally and is perpendicular in direction to both the pressure gradient force and the Coriolis effect.

geostrophic wind: a wind resulting from the balance between a pressure gradient force and Coriolis force; the flow produces jet streams and is perpendicular to the pressure gradient force and the Coriolis force.

geosynchronous (geostationary): describing a satellite that orbits about Earth's equator at an altitude and speed such that it remains above the same point on the surface of the planet.

gill net: a large, meshed fishing net that allows the head of a fish to pass through, entangling its gill covers and preventing it from passing through or otherwise escaping; because of their size, gill nets often catch many marine animals in addition to the target fish.

glacial: short-term period of glaciation, generally lasting for less that 1 million years and alternating with interglacial periods.

glacial epoch: extended periods of global temperature reduction and glaciation that generally last for millions of years and contain glacial and interglacial periods.

glacial lakes: lakes formed by the melting of a glacier; an indicator used in estimating average annual temperatures.

glaciation: commonly known as an "ice age," the cyclic widespread growth and advance of ice sheets over the polar and high- to mid-latitude regions of the world.

glacier: a river of freshwater ice that is massive enough to be put into motion by gravity; usually contains ice, air, rock, and some water.

glaze: a coating of ice formed on exposed objects by the freezing of a film of supercooled water deposited by rain, drizzle, or fog.

global atmospheric model: computational model of global weather patterns based on a spherical coordinate system representing the entire planet.

global warming potential: a measure of the ability of a greenhouse gas to contribute to global warming, based on its heat-trapping efficiency and its lifetime in the atmosphere.

Gondwanaland: an ancient supercontinent that geologists theorize broke into at least two large segments; one segment became India and pushed northward to collide with the Eurasian landmass, while the other, Africa, moved westward.

graben: a down-thrown block of rock between two steeply angled normal faults.

grade: a hypothetical uniform profile of a stream seeking to achieve quasi-equilibrium; the slope of the streambed between its highest and lowest points.

granite: a coarse-grained, igneous rock composed primarily of the minerals quartz and feldspar.

graupel: ice particles between 2 and 5 millimeters in diameter that form by a process of accretion in a cloud.

gravest empirical mode: a concept in which the relationship between oceanic subsurface density and surface elevation is examined.

great conveyor belt: a system of ocean circulation in which heat is carried to warm certain parts of the earth; also called great ocean conveyor belt.

greenhouse effect: a natural process by which water vapor, carbon dioxide, and other gases in the atmosphere absorb heat and reradiate it back to Earth.

greenhouse gas: a gas in Earth's atmosphere that can absorb and emit infrared radiation.

ground state metal: a metal in its elemental form with an oxidation state of zero.

groundwater: the water contained in soil and rock pores or fractures below the water table.

groundwater recharge: the water that infiltrates from the ground surface downward through soil and rock pores to the water table, causing its level to rise.

growing degree-day index: a measurement system that uses thermal principles to estimate the approximate date when crops will be ready for harvest.

guyot: a drowned volcanic island with a flat top caused by wave erosion or coral growth.

gyre or gyral: the very large, semiclosed surface circulation patterns of ocean currents in each of the major ocean basins.

hail suppression: a technique aimed at lessening crop damage from hailstorms by converting water droplets to snow to prevent hail formation or, alternatively, by reducing hailstone size.

half-life: the time it takes for any initial quantity of a radioactive isotope to decay to one-half of that initial amount.

halocline: a zone within a body of water, characterized by a rapid rate of change in salinity.

heat budget: the balance between the incoming solar radiation and the outgoing terrestrial reradiation.

heliosphere: the portion of space affected by the presence of the sun or another star.

hermatypic: of or relating to corals with stony skeletons that are formed from limestone and that grow in colonies to form coral reefs.

heterosphere: a zone of the atmosphere at an altitude of 80 kilometers, including the ionosphere, made up of rarefied layers of oxygen atoms and nitrogen molecules.

heterotroph: an organism that cannot absorb atmospheric carbon for growth; it must consume organic carbon in the bodies of other organisms to fuel growth and the development of complex organic molecules.

high-pressure area: region in which the atmospheric pressure is greater than the areas around it; represented by H on weather maps.

histosol: soil composed primarily of organic material.

homeostasis: property of a system that causes it to maintain a certain internal state, such as temperature.

homosphere: a major zone of the atmosphere below the heterosphere whose chemical makeup is consistent with the proportions of nitrogen, oxygen, argon, carbon dioxide, and trace gases at sea level; includes the troposphere, stratosphere, and mesosphere.

horse latitudes: the belts of latitude approximately 30 degrees north and 30 degrees south of the equator, where winds are very light and the weather is hot and dry.

hot spot: a column or plume of molten rock that rises from deep within the mantle and can cause volcanic eruptions if it penetrates the lithosphere.

hurricane: a severe tropical cyclone, typically between 500 and 600 kilometers in diameter, with winds in excess of 65 knots (74 miles or 120 kilometers) per hour.

hurricane-force wind: a wind with a speed of 64 knots (118 kilometers per hour) or higher.

hyaloclastite: the rock type that results when lava is chilled rapidly and explosively beneath the sea at shallow depths, resulting in a fragmented, glassy texture.

hydraulic geometry: a set of equations that relate river width, depth, and velocity to discharge.

hydraulic head: the sum of the elevation head and the pressure head at any given point in the subsurface.

hydrocarbon: any of a large group of organic compounds containing various combinations of carbon and hydrogen atoms; a common substance in petroleum products, including crude oil and natural gas.

hydrograph: a plot recording the variation of stream discharge over time.

hydrological: relating to the systematic flow of water in accordance with physical laws.

hydrologic cycle: the circulation of water as a liquid and vapor from the oceans to the atmosphere and back to the oceans.

hydrology: the branch of science dealing with water and its movement in the environment.

hydrosphere: the areas of Earth that are covered by water, including the oceans, seas, lakes, and rivers.

hydrostatic pressure: the pressure at any given point in a body of water at rest from the weight of the overlying water column.

hydrothermal vent: an undersea location where superheated liquid and gases are released because of volcanic activity.

hygroscopic particulates: minute particles that readily take up and retain moisture.

hyperconcentrated flood: a flood that carries unusually large quantities of sediment.

iceberg: a large mass of ice that has broken from an ice shelf or a glacier; floats in a body of water.

ice core: a cylinder-shaped piece of ice that is collected by drilling into a glacier; can be used to analyze climatic history.

ice core record: ice sheet samples used for chemical analysis of temperature, atmospheric and volcanic activity, and precipitation.

ice floes: large formations of ice, usually 2.5 to 3.5 meters thick, that float in the waters of the Arctic Ocean.

ice sheet: a broad, flat glacial mass with relatively gentle relief; ice sheets once covered extensive portions of North America.

ice shelf: a large, flat sheet of ice formed from a glacier or an ice sheet; floats in a body of water.

ice storm: a storm characterized by freezing rain, with the formation of glaze on objects below.

ice stream: a rapidly moving current of ice flowing from an ice sheet and moving more quickly than the ice that surrounds it; carries ice from the ice sheet.

igloo: a temporary structure made from blocks of dense snow.

inceptisol: relatively recent soil deposits that exhibit the first signs of horizon differentiation.

infiltration: the movement of water into and through the soil.

infrared radiation: electromagnetic radiation with wavelengths longer than visible light but shorter than radio waves; the type of electromagnetic radiation perceived as heat.

interception: the process by which precipitation is captured on the surfaces of vegetation before it reaches the land surface.

interdistributary bay: a shallow, triangular bay between two distributary channels; over time, the bay becomes filled with sediment and colonized with marsh plants or trees.

interglacials: periods of reduced glacial coverage that alternate with glacials within a global glacial epoch.

interior drainage: watersheds in arid areas where the runoff does not flow into the oceans.

Intertropical Convergence Zones (ITCZ): low-pressure areas where southern and northern trade winds meet.

Inuit: the native dwellers of the northern polar regions, whose name means "the People"; often referred to incorrectly as Eskimos, a word from a more southerly native language.

inversion: an unusual atmospheric condition in which temperature increases with altitude.

ion exchange: the reversible switching of ions between water being treated and an ion exchange resin by which undesirable ions in the water are exchanged with acceptable ions on the resin.

ionosphere: portions of the upper atmosphere consisting of part of the mesosphere, thermosphere, and exosphere; characterized by gas ionization through exposure to solar radiation.

irradiance: the power of electromagnetic radiation over a given unit of area, usually in watts per square meter; used to measure the influx of energy through an area.

irrigation: the relocation and application of water by means of ditches or pumping as an aid to crop production.

isobar: on a map, a line connecting two or more points that share the same atmospheric pressure, either at a particular time or, on average, in a particular period.

isostasy: equilibrium between the lithosphere and the liquid layer of rock in the inner layers of the strata.

isostatic rebound: a tendency of continental surfaces to rise after being depressed by continental glaciers, without faulting.

isotopes: atoms of an element containing the identical number of protons but different numbers of neutrons in their nuclei.

Java Trench: one of the deepest areas of the Indian Ocean, located off the southern coasts of Java in Indonesia; it is a form of geological canyon created by the upward thrust of mountain ridges from the ocean floor.

jökulhlaup: a flood produced by the release of water sequestered by a glacier, most often due to the failure of some type of glacial dam or to subglacial volcanic activity.

Kerch Straits: the strategic narrows that join the Black Sea to the Sea of Azov, located northeast of the Crimean Peninsula and sharing a similar ecology.

knickpoint (or nickpoint): an abrupt change in the stream profile, generally caused by a resistant rock layer that retards the rate of erosion.

knot: a unit of nautical distance equivalent to 1.86 kilometers or 1.15 miles.

Kuroshio: the current, also known as the Japan Current, where cold continental air flows over warm ocean currents moving toward the poles.

lagoon: a long, narrow body of saltwater that is separated from the ocean by a bank of sand.

lake basin: an enclosed depression on the land surface in which surface waters collect; basins are created primarily by glacial activity and tectonic movement.

La Niña: a meteorological condition in which the waters of the eastern, tropical Pacific Ocean are cooled by a lack of radiation from the atmosphere.

latent heat: the energy absorbed or released during a change of physical state.

lava: magma that has erupted from a volcano.

LD$_{50}$: median lethal dose (LD) to 50 percent of subjects in a toxicity study.

leachate: contaminated fluid produced by the passage of water through decaying garbage in a landfill.

levee: a dike-like structure, usually made of compacted earth and reinforced with other materials, that is designed to constrain a stream flow to its natural channel.

lidar: type of remote sensor that operates similarly to radar but uses lasers instead of radio waves.

ligand: an atom, ion, or molecule that combines with a central metal atom or ion, without being chemically bonded to it, to form a stable molecular complex.

limestone: a common sedimentary rock containing the mineral calcite that originated from fossil shells of marine plants and animals or by precipitation directly from seawater.

lithosphere: the outer solid layer of Earth consisting of the crust and part of the upper mantle.

littoral: adjacent to or related to a sea.

local base level: that elevation below which a stream of equilibrium will not degrade.

local sea-level change: a change in sea level only in one area of the world, usually by land rising or sinking in that specific area.

local winds: winds that, over a small area, differ from the general pressure pattern owing to local thermal or orographic effects.

loess: wind-blown sediment that can accumulate in great thicknesses and is easily eroded if not stabilized by vegetation.

longitudinal bar: a midchannel accumulation of sand and gravel with its long axis oriented roughly parallel to the river flow.

longitudinal dune: a long sand dune parallel to the prevailing wind.

long-range prediction: a weather forecast for a specific region for a period greater than one week in advance, often supplemented with climatological information.

longshore current: a slow-moving current between a beach and the breakers, moving parallel to the beach; the current direction is determined by the wave refraction pattern.

longshore drift: the movement of sediment parallel to the beach by a longshore current.

loop current: an ocean current that transports warm

water from the Caribbean Sea into the Gulf of Mexico.

losing stream: a stream that is located above the elevation of the water table and that loses water to the ground via infiltration through the stream bed; the opposite of a gaining stream.

lower atmosphere: region of the atmosphere comprising the troposphere and the tropopause, reaching an altitude as high as 19 kilometers (12 miles).

low-pressure area: region where the atmospheric pressure is lower than that in surrounding areas.

Madden-Julian oscillation: intraseasonal tropical wave that travels around the globe, causing monsoons and other high-water storms and also suppresses them.

magma: molten rock generated by melting in the mantle.

magnetic field: magnetic lines of force that are projected from a planet's interior and out into space.

magnetosphere: outer layer of the atmosphere constituted by the interaction between Earth's magnetic field and charged particles released by the sun.

mantle plume: a rising current of extra-hot magma in the mantle.

maximum contaminant levels (MCLs): enforceable standards for drinking water established by government regulatory agencies, such as the U.S. Environmental Protection Agency under the Safe Drinking Water Act

meander: a large sinuous curve or bend in a stream of equilibrium on a floodplain.

meandering river: a river confined essentially to a single channel that transports much of its sediment load as fine-grained material in suspension.

mean sea level: the average height of the sea surface over a multiyear time span, taking into account storms, tides, and seasons.

mechanical toxicity: the process by which most organisms are affected or killed by spilled oil, as ingesting or being coated by oil may lead to death by suffocation or exposure.

mechanical weathering: the physical disintegration of rock into smaller particles having the same chemical composition as the parent material.

Mediterranean climate: a pattern of weather conditions characterized by a long, hot, dry summer and a short, cool, wet winter.

mercury barometer: glass tube of a minimum of 84 centimeters (33 inches), closed at one end, with a mercury-filled pool at the base; the weight of the mercury creates a vacuum at the top of tube; mercury adjusts its level to the weight of the mercury in the higher column.

mesoscale model: a weather forecast for an area of up to several hundred square kilometers in extent on a time scale of between one and twelve hours.

mesosphere: the extremely rarefied atmospheric layer at altitudes from 50 to 80 kilometers above the surface, characterized by rapid decreases in temperature.

meteorology: the study of changes in temperature, air pressure, moisture, and wind direction in the troposphere; the interdisciplinary scientific study of the atmosphere.

middle atmosphere: region of the atmosphere comprising the mesosphere, mesopause, stratosphere, and stratopause.

mid-latitude cyclone: a synoptic-scale cyclone found in the mid-latitudes (between 30 and 60 degrees north and south of the equator).

midocean ridge: a region of the sea floor where new oceanic crust is created by seafloor spreading.

millimole: a universal relative quantity equal to one-thousandth of a mole.

mineral: a naturally occurring, inorganic, crystalline material with a unique chemical composition.

mineraloid: a solid substance with a constant chemical composition but without a well-ordered crystal structure.

mitigation: with respect to greenhouse gases, strategies to prevent emissions from passing current baseline levels.

mixed tide: having the characteristics of diurnal and semidiurnal tidal oscillations; these tides are found on the Pacific coast of the United States.

mixing zone: the area of contact between a freshwater lens and the underlying saltwater.

mole: the quantity, in grams, of any pure material numerically equivalent to the atomic or molecular weight of that material.

monsoon: a seasonal air current system; in the Northern Hemisphere's winter, dry winds flow from the continents to the ocean, whereas in summer, moist winds flow from the ocean to the continents and cause heavy rains.

mousse: a gelatinous oil-water emulsion resembling chocolate pudding that is created when crude oil is spilled in churning seawater.

national primary drinking water standards: the list of MCLs and MCLGs for organic and inorganic constituents; the list also includes various standards for asbestos fibers, turbidity, bacteria, viruses, and radioactive emitting constituents, established using less common concentration units.

natural levee: a low ridge deposited on the flanks of a river during a flood stage.

neap tide: a tide with the minimum range, or when the level of the high tide is at its lowest.

near-infrared radiation: the shortest-wavelength segment of infrared radiation, which has a longer wavelength than visible light; some solar radiation is in the near-infrared frequency range.

near-polar orbit: an orbit of Earth that lies in a plane that passes close to both the North and South Poles.

negative emission: a process that removes carbon dioxide from the atmosphere; technologies include biochar and bioenergy with carbon capture and storage.

net radiative heating: the driving force for atmospheric thermodynamics, essentially the difference between heat entering the atmosphere due to solar heating and heat leaving the atmosphere as infrared radiation.

neutralization: the adjustment of the concentration of hydrogen ions in solution in order to achieve neutral pH.

neutrinos: massless (or nearly massless) particles given off in certain types of nuclear reactions.

nipping: process in which ice pushes forcibly against the edge of a ship.

nitrate: the ion of nitric acid; an essential nutrient for plants.

nitric acid (biology): an acid formed in rain from nitric oxide gases in the air.

nitric oxide gases: gases formed by a combination of nitrogen and oxygen, particularly nitrogen dioxide and nitric oxide.

nitrite: the ion of nitrous acid; source for some microorganisms; extremely hazardous to humans, especially babies.

nitrogen: a key chemical element on Earth; a colorless and odorless component of air.

noble gas: any of the elements helium, neon, argon, krypton, xenon, and radon; they are often called inert gases because they are normally chemically inert.

nodule: a lump of mineral rock typically found on the ocean floor.

nondeterminism: chaotic, random events that cannot be predicted but that have a significant influence on the development of weather systems.

nonpoint source: a large, diffuse source of contamination.

nor'easter: massive, rotating Atlantic coastal storm that produces large amounts of precipitation and strong winds.

Northern Ocean: the Arctic portion of Earth's oceanic system.

Norwegian Sea: the body of water north of the North Sea.

nowcasting: a very short-term weather forecast usually for the prediction of rapidly changing, severe weather events within a time of no more than a few hours.

nuclear fusion: atomic nuclei join together to form a heavier nucleus; in the sun and other main-sequence stars, hydrogen is fused to form helium.

obliquity: long-term variations in the tilt of Earth relative to the sun; varies through a cycle of 42,000 years.

ocean circulation: the worldwide movement of water in the sea.

ocean current: horizontal movement of seawater induced by the wind and affected by rotation of the planet, nearby landmasses, and the temperature and salinity of the water.

off-gassing: the spontaneous emission of entrained or entrapped gases from within natural and artificial sources.

one-hundred-year-flood: a hypothetical flood whose severity is such that it would occur on an average of only once in a period of one hundred years; equates to a 1 percent probability each year.

ophiolite: a section of oceanic crust and upper mantle that has been thrust out of the ocean floor and up onto the continental crust.

optics: the branch of physics that deals with the properties and characteristics of light.

orography: study of mountains that incorporates assessment of how they influence and are affected by weather and other variables.

oscillation: variation of some physical property or condition between two opposing states, much like the rising and falling of a wave between its maximum and minimum heights.

oscillation ripple: a small to large bed form, oriented predominantly transverse to the direction of flow, produced at low to moderate flow speeds in oscillatory water flows.

oscillatory flow: a flow of fluid with a regular back-and-forth pattern of motion.

oscillatory wave: a wind-generated wave in which each water particle describes a circular motion; such waves develop far from shore, where the water is deep.

osmosis: a natural process whereby the solvent, usually water, in a weak solution migrates across a semipermeable membrane into a similar solution of higher concentration, with the end result being the equalization of the solution concentrations.

outgassing: the process by which volatile materials trapped within rock formations are released into the atmosphere and the environment.

outlet works: gates or conduits in a dam that are generally kept open so as to discharge the normal stream flow.

overland flow: the flow of water over the land surface caused by direct precipitation.

oxbow lake: a lake formed from an abandoned meander bend when a river cuts through the meander at its narrowest point during a flood.

oxides of nitrogen: several gases that are formed when molecular nitrogen is heated with air during combustion, primarily NO and NO_2.

oxides of sulfur: gases formed when fuels containing sulfur are burned, primarily SO_2.

ozone: a form of oxygen containing three joined oxygen atoms; responsible for blocking much of the solar radiation that hits Earth's atmosphere.

ozone layer: a region in the lower stratosphere, centered about 25 kilometers above the ground surface, which contains the highest concentration of ozone found in the atmosphere.

pack ice: large, mobile masses of frozen, floating seawater that are not attached to a landform; also known as sea ice.

paleoclimatology: study of climate conditions in Earth's ancient and prehistoric past.

paleocurrent: the geologic system at the time of deposition.

paleodepth: an estimate of the water depth at which ancient seafloor sediments were originally deposited.

Palmer Drought Index: a widely adopted quantitative measure of drought severity that was developed by W. C. Palmer in 1965.

Pangaea: the supercontinent that geologists hypothesize existed about 280 million years ago, when all the landmasses of the world were one.

parameterization: process of setting parameters for a measurement or other analysis system.

passive sensor: type of remote sensor that detects naturally emitted energy, such as reflected sunlight, from target sources.

pedosphere: the soil.

pelagic: meaning "of the deep sea"; refers to sediments that are fine-grained and are deposited very slowly at great distances from continents.

perched water table: groundwater that occupies an area above the main or regional water table, as would form above a clay lens.

perennial stream: a stream that has water flowing in it throughout the year.

perihelion: the point in a planet's orbit at which it is closest to the sun.

permeability: the ability of rock, soil, or sediment to transmit a fluid.

petrochemical: a chemical substance obtained from or derived from natural gas or petroleum.

petroleum: a natural mixture of hydrocarbon compounds produced by conversion of organic matter under conditions of high heat and pressure in the absence of oxygen.

pH: a measure of the hydrogen ion concentration, which determines the acidity of a solution; the lower the pH, the greater the concentration of hydrogen ions and the more acidic the solution.

photochemical oxidants: pollutants formed in air by primary pollutants undergoing a complex series of reactions driven by light energy.

photochemical reaction: a type of chemical reaction that can occur in polluted air driven by the interaction of sunlight with various pollutant gases.

photodissociation: the condition in which light energy absorbed by a molecule is sufficient to dissociate the bonds between atoms in the molecule, typically caused by light in the ultraviolet range.

photon: the smallest energy packet of light for a given frequency; X rays and gamma rays are examples of high-energy photons.

photosynthesis: the process by which plants convert

carbon dioxide and water into sugar and oxygen.

phytoplankton: tiny plants that make up the lowest part of the food chain.

picocurie (pci): a unit of radioactivity corresponding to one-trillionth of that from 1 gram of radium (0.037 disintegration per second or 2.22 disintegrations per minute).

pillow lavas: lavas that have been rapidly cooled by water as they erupt and consequently develop crusted, rounded, or pillow-shaped structures.

pingo: a large, stable ice intrusion of the Arctic tundra terrain, appearing as a large, dome-shaped, earth-covered mound with cracks visible at the top, the core being solid ice.

plane bed: a bed configuration without rugged bed forms produced in both unidirectional and oscillatory flows at high flow speeds.

planetary winds: the large, relatively constant prevailing wind systems that result from Earth's absorption of solar energy and that are affected by Earth's rotation.

plankton: forms of microscopic life that drift or float in water.

plasma: state of matter similar to a gas in which a portion of the molecules have become ionized, giving rise to matter built from free ions and electrons.

Pleistocene epoch: the most recent ice age period, during which Earth experienced cycles of continental glaciation.

point bar: an accumulation of sand and gravel that develops on the inside of a meander bend.

point source: a single, defined source of contamination.

polar low: a severe, mesocyclonic winter storm that occurs in higher ocean latitudes.

polar stratospheric clouds: clouds of ice crystals formed at extremely low temperatures in the polar stratosphere.

polar vortex: a closed atmospheric circulation pattern around the South Pole that exists during the winter and early spring; atmospheric mixing between the polar vortex and regions outside the vortex is slow.

pollution: the presence of environmental components that are not naturally present; reaches contaminant levels at objectionable concentrations.

pore: a small opening in rock or between soil particles.

porosity: the ratio of the volume of void space in a given geologic material to the total volume of that material.

positron: the antiparticle to the electron.

potable water: freshwater that can be used for domestic consumption.

potential evapotranspiration: the water needed for growing plants, accounting for water loss by evaporation and transpiration.

prebiotic: relating to the period of time before the appearance of life on Earth.

precession: variation in the angle of Earth's rotational tilt relative to an astronomical point of reference; shifts through a cycle of 26,000 years.

precipitate: to form a solid phase of material from dissolved components, thus separating them from the solution.

precipitation (weather): any form of liquid water or ice that falls from the atmosphere to the ground.

pressure gradient: a difference in pressure that causes fluids (both liquids and gases) to move from regions of high pressure to regions of low pressure.

pressure gradient force: a wind-producing force caused by a difference in pressure between two different locations.

pressure head: the height of a column of water that can be supported by the hydrostatic pressure at any given point in the subsurface.

primary crystalline rock: the original or first solidified molten rock on Earth.

primordial solar nebula: an interstellar cloud of gases and dust that condensed by the action of gravitational forces to form the bodies of the solar system about 5 billion years ago.

prodelta: a sedimentary layer composed of silt and clay deposited under water; it is the foundation on which a delta is deposited.

production water wells: human-made subsurface structures designed and constructed to provide access to a water supply from an aquifer.

productivity: the rate at which plankton reproduce in surface waters, which in turn controls the rate of precipitation of calcareous or siliceous shells or tests by these organisms.

protons: positively charged subatomic particles; the antimatter counterpart of electrons.

provenance: all the factors relating to the production of sand.

proxies: traces of ancient environments that reveal details, such as climatic data, about those environments.

pulse Doppler: type of radar system that emits waves of electromagnetic energy at an atmospheric target; provides a detailed profile of motion, precipitation, and other conditions and objects.

pump pipe: a tube that extends downward from the wellhead to a level below the top of the water in the well, and that serves as the conduit for water being pumped to the surface.

pycnocline: a zone within a body of water characterized by a rapid rate of change in density.

pyroclastic: those formative processes of sand that relate to volcanic action.

pyroxene: a rock-forming mineral commonly found in igneous rocks such as basalt or gabbro.

radiation: the transfer of energy emitted from one body through a transparent medium to another body, as occurs when light and heat energy from the sun reach Earth.

radiational cooling: the cooling of Earth's surface and the layer of air immediately above it by a process of radiation and conduction.

radiative equilibrium: a state in which Earth's incoming radiation and outgoing radiation are equal; results in a generally stable climate as there is no net gain or loss of energy from the planet's system.

radiative forcing: a measurement of how much the greenhouse gas in a given area will impact the solar radiation.

radioactivity: the spontaneous emission from unstable atomic nuclei of high-energy, sub-nuclear particles and electromagnetic radiation; radioactive emissions typically include helium nuclei (alpha particles), electrons (beta particles), and electromagnetic waves (gamma and X rays).

radiometer: an instrument that quantitatively measures reflected or emitted electromagnetic radiation within a particular wavelength interval.

rain gauge: an instrument for measuring rainfall, usually consisting of a cylindrical container open to the sky.

range: the difference between the high-tide water level and the low-tide water level.

rapids: a turbulent flow in a stream caused by obstructions and constrictions of the channel or by resistant rock layers.

rat hole: that portion of a well that is deliberately made to extend below the base of an aquifer.

rating curve: a plot of river discharge in relation to elevation of the water surface; permits estimation of discharge from the water elevation.

rawinsonde: a radiosonde tracked by radar in order to collect wind data in addition to temperature, pressure, and humidity.

recharge well: a well designed to pump surface water underground in order to recharge the groundwater; sometimes called an injection well.

recurrence interval: the average time interval in years between occurrences of a flood of a given magnitude in a measured series of floods.

red clays: fine-grained, carbonate-free sediments that accumulate at depths below the carbonate compensation depth in all ocean basins; their red color is caused by the presence of oxidized fine-grained iron particles.

regression: the retreat of the sea from the land, allowing land erosion processes to occur on material previously below the sea surface.

relief: the difference in elevation between the highest and lowest points of land in a particular region.

remediation: the removal of pollution or contaminants from environmental systems.

remote-sensing satellites: satellites that carry instruments to monitor and collect climate data while orbiting Earth.

resilience: in ecological terms, the ability of an ecosystem as a whole to recover from natural or anthropogenic disturbances and stresses and to continue to thrive and reproduce; the opposite of resilience is vulnerability.

respiration: physiological process that allows organisms to exchange carbon dioxide produced by biochemical processes within the organism's body for atmospheric oxygen.

return stroke: the luminous lightning stroke that propagates upward from the ground surface toward the base of a cloud as electrons surge downward and a positive current flows to the cloud.

reverse osmosis: in practice, the forced passage of seawater through a semipermeable membrane against the natural osmotic pressure in order to obtain pure water.

riffles: a smaller version of rapids; a turbulent flow between calm pools, found in nearly all streams for hydraulic reasons.

rift: a crack or split in the crust, typically in a continental mass.

riparian: transitional zones between terrestrial and aquatic systems that exhibit characteristics of both

639

systems.

rugose corals: a Paleozoic coral group also known as "tetracorals," sometimes colonial, but more often solitary and horn-shaped.

runoff: the portion of precipitation that flows across the land and eventually gathers in surface streams.

Saffir/Simpson hurricane scale: a hurricane category scale that classifies storms according to their winds and effects and their storm surge; categories range from 1 (least severe) to 5 (most severe).

Sahel: the semiarid southern fringe of the Sahara in West Africa that extends from Mauritania on the Atlantic coast to Chad in the interior.

saline lake: a lake with elevated levels of dissolved solids, primarily resulting from evaporative concentration of salts; saline lakes lack an outlet to the sea.

salinity: a measure of the concentration of dissolved salts in water.

saltation: a mode of sediment transport in a moving fluid, in which sediment particles moved forward in discrete increments rather than continuously, often as one particle bumps into another and drives it forward.

saltwater: water with a salt content of 3.5 percent, such as is found in normal ocean water.

saltwater wedge: a wedge-shaped intrusion of seawater from the ocean into the bottom of a river; the thin end of the wedge points upstream.

salt weathering: the granular disintegration or fragmentation of rock material affected by saline solutions or by salt-crystal growth.

sandstone: sedimentary rock composed of grains of sand that have become cemented together under the influences of pressure and time.

saturated zone: a subsurface zone in which all of the pore spaces are filled with water.

scatterometer: active radar that emits high-frequency microwave pulses at a target.

scleractinian corals: modern corals or "hexacorals," different from their more ancient counterparts in details of the skeleton and the presence of a symbiosis with unicellular algae in most shallow-water species.

sediment: matter that settles to the bottom of a body of water; may be sand, silt, or pieces of broken-up rock.

sediment discharge: the rate of transport of sediment past a planar section normal to the flow direction, expressed as volume, mass, or weight per unit time; also called sediment transport rate.

sediment discharge formula: a formula or equation designed to predict the sediment discharge that would be observed for a given combination of flow conditions and sediment characteristics.

sedimentary rock: rock that has broken from igneous, metamorphic, or other sedimentary rocks to form new deposits.

seiche: the rocking motion of lake level from one end of the lake to the other following high winds and low barometric pressure; frequently, a seiche will follow a storm event.

seismic activity: movements occurring within the crust that often cause various other geological phenomena to occur.

semiconfined aquifers: those that perform as if fully confined but receive replenishment from overlying or underlying water-bearing formations of lesser permeability than the aquifer itself.

semidiurnal: having two high tides and two low tides each lunar day.

seston: a general term that encompasses all types of suspended lake sediment, including minerals, mineraloids, plankton, and organic detritus.

siliceous ooze: fine-grained sediment in which more than 30 percent of the particles are organic remains of plants and animals composed of silica.

silviculture: the practice of controlling the establishment, growth, health, and quality of forests.

skimmer: a specialized oil-spill response vessel that picks up floating oil with an absorbent conveyor belt; skimmers are most effective during calm seas.

slash-and-burn agriculture: a paradigm of subsistence agriculture commonly practiced in the developing world.

slip face: the downwind or steep leeward front of a sand dune that continually stabilizes itself to the angle of repose of sand grains.

smokers: undersea vents on active rift areas that emit large amounts of superheated water and dissolved minerals from within the crust.

sodium chloride: the main chemical compound found as dissolved material in seawater.

soil moisture: the water contained in the unsaturated zone above the water table.

solar cycle: an approximately eleven-year-long cycle of varying solar activity; solar cycles are tracked based on the visibility of sunspots.

solar flux: the total energy entering Earth's atmosphere from the sun.

solar irradiance: energy from the sun's rays that reach Earth; measured in units of power over time (typically watts per second).

solar radiation: transfer of energy from the sun to Earth's surface, where it is absorbed and stored.

solar ultraviolet radiation: biologically lethal solar radiation in the spectral interval between approximately 0.1 and 0.3 micron (1 micron = 0.0001 centimeter).

solar wind: charged particles emanating from the sun that extend to the end of the heliosphere.

solstice: a twice-a-year occurrence during which the sun appears at its highest point in the sky (once a year as seen from the North Pole and once a year as seen from the South Pole).

Somali Current: a seasonally reversing current that moves between the eastern coasts of Africa and the Arabian Peninsula.

Southern Ocean: the Antarctic portion of Earth's oceanic system.

Southern Oscillation: the reversal of atmospheric pressures that occurs between opposite sides of the tropical Pacific Ocean.

spatial resolution: the extent to which a sensor is able to differentiate between closely spaced features.

specific heat: the amount of heat (energy) it takes to raise the temperature of the unit mass of a given substance by a given amount, usually one degree; functionally, a substance's capacity to store heat.

spillway: generally, a broad reinforced channel near the top of a dam, designed to allow rising waters to escape the reservoir without overtopping the dam.

spodosol: an acidic soil characterized by subsurface accumulations of humus complexed with aluminum and iron.

spring tide: a tide with the maximum range, occurring when lunar and solar tides reinforce each other a few days after the full and new moons.

squall line: any line of vigorous thunderstorms created by a cold downdraft that spreads out ahead of a fast-moving cold front.

SST: commonly used abbreviation for sea surface temperature, or the temperature of water measured within the top few meters of the surface; a critical factor affecting ocean ecosystems, including coral reefs.

star dune: a starfish-shaped dune with a central peak from which three or more arms radiate.

static mode theory: a theory assuming that natural clouds are deficient in ice nuclei, whereby clouds must be within a particular temperature range and contain a certain amount of supercooled water for cloud seeding to be successful.

stepped leader: an initial discharge of electrons that proceeds in a series of steps from the base of a thundercloud toward the ground.

storm surge: an offshore rise in water associated with a low-pressure weather system.

strait: a narrow waterway connecting two larger bodies of water.

stratigraphy: the internal fabric and structures, the external geometry, and the nature of the basal contact of sand bodies.

stratosphere: uppermost region of the atmosphere able to support life; extends from 10 to 50 kilometers (6 to 31 miles) above Earth's surface.

stratus: sheet or layer clouds, at altitudes ranging from 2 to 6 kilometers above the ground (altostratus, or middle) or from 0 to 2 kilometers above the ground (stratocumulus, or low).

stream: a body of flowing water that delivers surplus water from the land to the sea; this term covers all such moving water, including creeks and rivers.

stream of equilibrium: a stream that is carrying its maximum load of sediment; it will not erode its channel any deeper but instead will establish a floodplain.

stromatolites: layered columnar or flattened structures in sedimentary rocks, produced by the binding of sediment by blue-green algal (cyanobacterial) mats.

stromatoporoids: spongelike organisms that produced layered, mound-shaped, calcareous skeletons and were important reef builders during the Paleozoic era.

submarine canyon: a submerged, V-shaped canyon cut into the continental shelf and continental slope, through which turbidity currents funnel into the deeper parts of the oceans.

subsidence: in meteorology, the slow descent of air that becomes increasingly dry in the process, usually due to an area of high pressure.

subsistence agriculture: the practice of growing to meet the needs of a self-sufficient farmer rather than the market.

sulfur dioxide: a gas whose molecules consist of one sulfur atom and two oxygen atoms, formed by the combustion of sulfur in the presence of oxygen.

sulfuric acid: an acid formed as the primary

component of acid rain by reaction of sulfur dioxide gas with liquid water in the atmosphere.

summer solstice: the day when the sun is directly over the Tropic of Cancer in the Northern Hemisphere; in the Southern Hemisphere, it is the day when the sun is directly over the Tropic of Capricorn.

sunspot: a cooler area on the sun's surface that appears darker than the surrounding area; a zone of decreased temperature resulting from the complex shape of the sun's magnetic field.

sun-synchronous orbit: for an Earth satellite, a near-polar orbit at an altitude such that the satellite always passes over any given point on Earth at the same local time.

supercell thunderstorm: severe type of storm characterized by strong updrafts that produce torrential rain, hail, and tornadoes.

supercooled: a liquid cooled below its normal freezing point without crystallizing or becoming solid, typically referring to water.

supersaturation: a state in which the air's relative humidity exceeds 100 percent, the condition necessary for vapor to begin transformation to a liquid state.

surface water: relatively warm seawater between the ocean surface and that depth marked by a rapid reduction in temperature.

surfactant: a substance that reduces the surface tension of a liquid in which it is dissolved.

suspended load: sediment in motion above the sediment bed, supported by the vertical motions of turbulent eddies.

suspended solids: the solid particles that can be found dispersed in the water column.

swell: ocean waves that have traveled out of their wind-generating area.

synoptic scale: a scale used to describe high- and low-pressure atmospheric systems that have a horizontal span of 1,000 kilometers (621 miles) or more.

synthetic aperture radar (SAR): a space-borne radar imaging system that uses the motion of the spacecraft in orbit to simulate a very long antenna

tabulate "corals": colonial organisms with calcareous skeletons that were important Paleozoic reef builders; considered to be more closely related to sponges than to corals.

tarball: a dense, sticky blob of weathered oil that can travel great distances and is difficult to break down.

tectonic: relating to differential motions and deformation of the earth's crust, usually associated with faulting and folding of rock layers.

tectonic plates: large segments of the earth's crust, affected by the movement of magma in the underlying mantle layer.

tectonics (tectonic activity): vertical or horizontal movements in the earth's crust, displacing rocks, landforms, and stream gradients.

temperature inversion: a condition in which a region of warmer occupies a position above its normal location, causing air temperature to increase with increasing elevation from the ground surface.

test: an internal skeleton or shell precipitated by a one-celled planktonic plant or animal.

Tethys Sea: the much larger geological predecessor of both the Black Sea and the Caspian Sea to its east; named after the Titan and wife of the Greek god of the great outer sea, Oceanus.

thermal budget: the balance of incoming and outgoing radiative energy on Earth.

thermal fracture: the formation of a fracture or crack in a rock as a result of temperature changes.

thermal infrared radiation: the longest-wavelength segment of infrared radiation, which has a longer wavelength than visible light; Earth emits radiation in the thermal infrared frequency range.

thermocline: the depth interval at which the temperature of ocean water changes abruptly, separating warm surface water from cold, deep water.

thermohaline circulation: a mode of oceanic circulation that is driven by the sinking of denser water and its replacement at the surface with less dense water.

thermosphere: the outer region of the atmosphere between 80 and 800 kilometers (50 to 497 miles) from the surface where temperature increases with increasing altitude because of bombardment by solar radiation.

threshold of movement: the conditions for which a flow is just strong enough to move the sediment particles at the surface of a given sediment bed.

throughflow: the subsurface movement of surplus water through the soil to a stream.

tidal range: the difference in height between high tide and low tide at a given point.

tide: the periodic, predictable rising and falling of the sea surface as a result of Earth's rotation and the gravitational attractions of the moon and sun.

topography: the relief features or surface

configuration of a certain area.

tornado: a violent rotating column of air that forms and extends downward from a cumulonimbus cloud and has the appearance of a funnel, rope, or column that touches the ground.

total column abundance of ozone: the total number of molecules of ozone above a 1-centimeter-square area of Earth's surface.

Total Ozone Mapping Spectrometer (TOMS): a space-based instrument for measuring the total column abundance of ozone globally.

toxicity: a measure of the dose required to produce a negative health effect.

trade winds: winds at the level of the ocean surface that blow from the east to the west in the tropical Pacific.

transgression: the advance of the sea over the land, allowing marine sediments to be deposited on what had previously been dry land.

transpiration: the process by which plants give off water vapor through their leaves.

transverse bar: a flat-topped body of sand or gravel oriented transverse to the river flow.

tree-ring data: data gathered from tree rings that reflect climate data from the past; thicker rings indicate the presence of light and nutrients that allow more growth.

trench: a long, narrow, depressed area in the ocean floor.

tributary: a stream or river that flows into another stream that becomes the main stream; a tributary may be a significant river in its own right, but it loses its identity when it merges with the main river.

tropical climate: a climate characterized by high annual temperature.

tropical cyclone: tropical storm marked by clear rotation around a central, warm column of air and wind speeds above 119 kilometers (74 miles) per hour.

tropical depression: cyclonic thunderstorms with wind speeds from 36 to 64 kilometers per hour.

tropical storm: a thunderstorm with cyclonic winds circulating at speeds of 64 to 118 kilometers per hour.

tropical zone: area between the Tropic of Cancer and the Tropic of Capricorn that falls directly under the sun during a part of the year.

Tropic of Cancer: a line of latitude 23.5 degrees north of the equator; the most northerly latitude on Earth at which the noon sun passes directly overhead.

Tropic of Capricorn: a line of latitude 23.5 degrees south of the equator; the most southerly latitude on Earth at which the noon sun passes directly overhead.

tropopause: the transition zone at the top of the troposphere between the troposphere and the stratosphere.

troposphere: the lowest level of Earth's atmosphere lying between 0 and 10 kilometers (0 and 6 miles) above sea level within which weather patterns develop.

trough: a long and relatively narrow area of low barometric pressure.

tsunami: a series of long, high sea waves caused by seismic activity or other disturbances.

tsunami warning: the second phase of a tsunami alert; it is issued after the generation of a tsunami has been confirmed.

tsunami watch: the first phase of a tsunami alert; it is issued after a large earthquake has occurred on the sea floor.

T Tauri stars: a class of stars that exhibit rapid and erratic changes in brightness.

turbidity current: a mass of water and sediment that flows downhill along the bottom of a body of water because it is denser than the surrounding water; common on continental slopes.

turbulent flow: the swirling flow that is typical of rivers, as opposed to smooth, laminar flow.

ultraviolet light: electromagnetic radiation having a frequency of in the range of 1,015 to 1,017 Hz.

ultraviolet solar radiation: electromagnetic radiation having wavelengths between 4 and 400 nanometers.

unconfined aquifers: aquifers that have no covering material, whereby the depth to water in the well is the level of the water table; also known as water-table aquifers.

unidirectional flow: a flow of fluid oriented everywhere and at all times in the same direction.

unsaturated zone: the area of the soil or rock between the land surface and the water table, in which voids between the soil and rock particles contain both air and moisture; also called the vadose zone.

unstable air: a condition that occurs when the air above rising air is unusually cool so that the rising air becomes relatively warmer and accelerates upward.

upconing: the upward flexure of the mixing zone toward the ground surface produced by excessive groundwater withdrawal by wells, analogous to an inverted cone of depression.

upwelling: an oceanic phenomenon in which warm surface waters are pushed away from the coast and are replaced by cold waters that carry more nutrients up from depth.

vadose zone: the region of soil between the surface and the water table in which void spaces contain both air and water.

variability: with respect to climate, refers to small-scale changes, such as those in a few years.

várzea: the part of the rainforest that is flooded for up to six months per year.

velocity head: the height to which the kinetic energy of fluid motion is capable of lifting that fluid.

ventifact: any stone or pebble that is shaped, worn, faceted, cut, or polished by the abrasive action of wind-blown sand, generally under desert conditions.

vernal equinox: the day that the sun passes directly over the equator in the northward direction, producing day and night of equal length and marking the beginning of spring; in the Northern Hemisphere, the date is about March 21, and in the Southern Hemisphere, it is about September 21.

volatile outgassing: the release of the gases and liquids, such as argon, water vapor, carbon dioxide, and nitrogen sulfur, trapped within Earth's interior during its formation.

volatiles: chemical elements and compounds that become gaseous at fairly low temperatures.

volcanic aerosols: volcanic ash released into the atmosphere that can affect the amount of solar radiation reaching Earth through components such as sulfur dioxide.

vortex: a mass of air, water, or other fluid that spins about a central axis, capable of reaching high velocities.

warm cloud: a visible suspension of tiny water droplets at temperatures above freezing.

warm front: area in which a dominant warm current of air rises over a pocket of cold air to cause condensation and precipitation at the trailing edge of the front.

water-based barometer: also known as a storm glass or Goethe barometer; a device with a glass container and a sealed body half full of water; also has a spout that fills with more or less water depending upon atmospheric conditions and their forces.

water cycle: the process by which water moves through the environment.

water equilibration: a condition in a lake or other body of water in which the water lost by evaporation is equal to the water added by rainfall or runoff.

water of hydration: water that is bound to the crystal structure of minerals without being part of their actual molecular structure.

water resources: all the surface water and groundwater that can be effectively harvested by humans for domestic, industrial, or agricultural uses.

watershed: the region draining into a river, lake, stream, or other body of water.

waterspout: a tornado that exists over water; less violent and smaller waterspouts form in fair weather just as dust devils do over dry land.

water spreading: an artificial recharge technique in which floodwaters are diverted from the stream channel and spread in a thin sheet over a flat land surface, allowing the water to infiltrate the ground.

water supply: the amount of water that is actually delivered to various consumer groups.

water table: the upper surface of groundwater in an aquifer, with a direct connection overhead to the atmosphere such that the water pressure is equal to atmospheric pressure.

water-treatment plant: a facility where water is treated by physical and chemical processes until its quality is improved to that of potable water.

wave base: the depth to which water particles of an oscillatory wave have an orbital motion; generally the wave base is equal to one-half the distance between successive waves.

wave energy: the capacity of a wave to erode and deposit; as wave energy increases, erosion increases.

wave height: the vertical distance between a wave crest and the adjacent wave trough.

wave length: the horizontal distance between two successive wave crests or wave troughs.

wave orbit: the path followed by a water particle affected by wave motion; in deep water, the orbit is nearly circular.

wave period: the time (usually measured in seconds) required for two adjacent wave crests to pass a point.

wave refraction: the process by which a wave crest is bent as it moves toward shore.

weather analogue: an approach that uses the weather

behavior of the past to predict what a current weather pattern will do in the future.

weathering: breakdown of rocks, minerals, and other earth material in contact with the atmosphere, biosphere, or hydrosphere.

wellbore: a hole drilled into the earth to look for or extract a natural resource, such as oil, water, or gas.

wellhead: a general term for the equipment installed at the surface of a wellbore; designed to provide a pressure seal for the oil or other substance being extracted.

well screen: a tubular device containing openings that permit groundwater to flow into the well from the aquifer, commonly part of a well point; some aquifers need no screen.

wetlands: areas along a coast where the water table is near or above the ground surface for at least part of the year; wetlands are characterized by wet soils, water-tolerant plants, and high biological production.

wind-driven circulation: movement of ocean water caused by frictional interaction with moving air.

wind stress: the frictional interaction between moving air and the surface of the ocean.

winter solstice: the diametric opposite of the summer solstice, occurring in the Northern Hemisphere when the sun passes directly over the Tropic of Capricorn, and in the Southern Hemisphere when it passes over the Tropic of Cancer.

zone of saturation: a subsurface zone in which all void spaces are filled with water.

zooplankton: tiny animals that feed on phytoplankton.

zooxanthellae: single-celled organisms that inhabit the living cells of hard corals and provide them with energy in the form of oxygen and nutrients; a type of tiny algae.

BIBLIOGRAPHY

Abdelly, Chedly, et al. *Biosaline Agriculture and High Salinity Tolerance.* Boston: Birkhauser Basel, 2008.

Abraham, Wolf-Rainer. "Megacities as Sources for Pathogenic Bacteria in Rivers and Their Fate Downstream." *International Journal of Microbiology* (2011).

Abrahamson, Dean Edwin, ed. *The Challenge of Global Warming.* Washington, D.C.: Island Press, 1989.

Abuzinada, Abdulaziz H., et al., eds. *Protecting the Gulf's Marine Ecosystems from Pollution.* Basel, Switzerland: Birkhäuser Verlag, 2008.

Ackerman, Steven A., and John A. Knox. "Extratropical Cyclones and Anticyclones." In *Meteorology: Understanding the Atmosphere.* Sudbury, Mass.: Jones and Bartlett, 2012.

Adams, J. M. *Vegetation-Climate Interaction: How Vegetation Makes the Global Environment.* New York: Springer, 2007.

Adams, W. M., and N. Nakashizuka. "A Working Vocabulary for Tsunami Study." *Tsunami Hazards* 3 (1985): 45-51.

Adar, Korwa G., and Nicasius A. Check. *Cooperative Diplomacy, Regional Stability and National Interests: The Nile River and Riparian States.* Pretoria: Africa Institute of South Africa, 2011.

Adib-Moghaddam, Arshin. *The International Politics of the Persian Gulf: A Cultural Genealogy.* New York: Routledge, 2006.

Aghedo, A. M., et al. "The Impact of Orbital Sampling, Monthly Averaging, and Vertical Resolution on Climate Chemistry Model Evaluation with Satellite Observations." *Atmospheric Chemistry and Physics* 11, no. 13 (2011): 6493-6514.

Ahearns, T. P. "Basic Considerations of Well Design." *Water Well Journal* (April-June, 1970).

Ahmed, S., R. Jayakumar, and Abdin Saleh. *Groundwater Dynamics in Hard Rock Aquifers: Sustainable Management and Optimal Monitoring Network Design.* Dordrecht: Springer, 2008.

Ahr, Wayne M. *Geology of Carbonate Reservoirs.* Hoboken, N.J.: John Wiley & Sons, 2008.

Ahrens, C. Donald. "Air Masses, Fronts, and Middle-Latitude Cyclones." In *Essentials of Meteorology: An Invitation to the Atmosphere.* Belmont, Calif.: Brooks/Cole, 2011.

_____. *Essentials of Meteorology: An Invitation to the Atmosphere.* 6th ed. Belmont, Calif.: Brooks/Cole, 2011.

_____. *Meteorology Today: An Introduction to Weather, Climate and the Environment.* 8th ed. Belmont, Calif.: Thomson Brooks-Cole, 2007.

_____. *Meteorology Today: An Introduction to Weather, Climate and the Environment.* 9th ed. Belmont, Calif.: Brooks/Cole Cengage Learning, 2009.

Ahrens, C. Donald, and Perry J. Samson. *Extreme Weather and Climate.* Independence, KY. Brooks Cole, 2010.

Alaska Wilderness League. *Preventing the Next Valdez Ten Years After Exxon's Spill New Disasters Threaten Alaska's Environment.* Washington, D.C.: Alaska Wilderness League, 1999.

Al-Atawy, Mohamed-Hatem. *Nilopolitics: A Hydrological Regime.* Cairo: American University in Cairo Press, 1996.

Al-Azab, M., W. El-Shorbagy, and S. Al-Ghais, eds. *Oil Pollution and Its Environmental Impact in the Arabian Gulf Region.* San Diego: Elsevier, 2005.

Alberotanza, Luigi. "Active and Passive Remote Sensors as a New Technology for Coastal and Lagoon Monitoring." *Aquatic Conservation* 11, no. 4 (2001): 267-272.

Albert, R. C. *Damming the Delaware.* 2d ed. University Park: Pennsylvania State University Press, 2005.

Aldrete, Gregory S. *Floods of the Tiber in Ancient Rome.* Baltimore: Johns Hopkins University Press, 2006.

Alexander, David. *The Sun.* Santa Barbara, Calif.: Greenwood Press, 2009.

ALL Consulting. *A Guide to Practical Management of Produced Water from Onshore Oil and Gas Operations in the United States.* Tulsa, Okla.: Interstate Oil and Gas Compact Commission and ALL Consulting, 2006.

Allen, Gerald R., and D. Ross Robertson. *Fishes of the Tropical Eastern Pacific.* Honolulu, Hawaii: University of Hawaii Press, 1994.

Allen, J. R. L. *Principles of Physical Sedimentology.* Caldwell, N.J.: Blackburn Press, 2001.

Allen, Philip A. *Earth Surface Processes.* Oxford, England: Blackwell Science, 1997.

Allen, Robert J., and Charles S. Zender. "Forcing of the Arctic Oscillation by Eurasian Snow Cover." *Journal of Climate* 24, no. 24 (2011): 6528-6539.

Alley, Richard B. *Earth: The Operators' Manual.* New York: Norton, 2011.

Ambraseys, N. N., C. P. Melville, and R. D. Adams. *The Seismicity of Egypt, Arabia and the Red Sea: A Historical Review.* Cambridge, England: Cambridge University Press, 2005.

American Meteorological Society. "Policy Statement of the American Meteorological Society of Global Climate Change." *Bulletin of the American Meteorological Society* 72 (1991): 57-59.

American Museum of Natural History. *Ocean.* New York: Dorling Kindersley Limited, 2006.

Amineh, Mehdi Parvizi. *Towards the Control of Oil Resources in the Caspian Region.* New York: St. Martin's Press, 1999.

Amirahmadi, Hooshang, ed. *The Caspian Region at a Crossroad: Challenges of a New Frontier of Energy and Development.* New York: St. Martin's Press, 2000.

Anderson, R. N. *Marine Geology: A Planet Earth Perspective.* New York: John Wiley & Sons, 1986.

Annin, Peter. *The Great Lakes Water Wars.* Washington, D.C.: Island Press, 2006.

Anthes, Richard A. *Meteorology.* 7th ed. Upper Saddle River, N.J.: Prentice Hall, 1997.

Appelo, C. A. J., and Dieke Postma. *Geochemistry, Groundwater and Pollution.* 2d ed. Boca Raton, Fla.: CRC Press, 2005.

Aquado, Edward, and James E. Burt. *Understanding Weather and Climate.* 5th ed. Upper Saddle River, N.J.: Prentice Hall, 2009.

Archer, David. *Global Warming: Understanding the Forecast.* Malden, Mass.: Blackwell, 2007.

Asano, Takashi, ed. *Artificial Recharge of Groundwater.* Boston, Mass.: Butterworth, 1985.

ASCE Hurricane Katrina External Review Panel. *The New Orleans Hurricane Protection System: What Went Wrong and Why.* Reston, Va.: American Society of Civil Engineers, 2007.

Attenborough, David. *The Living Planet.* Boston: Little, Brown, 1984.

Awulachew, Seleshe Bekele. *The Nile River Basin: Water, Agriculture, Governance and Livelihoods.* London: Taylor & Francis, 2012.

Badash, Lawrence. *A Nuclear Winter's Tale: Science and Politics in the 1980s.* Boston: Massachusetts Institute of Technology, 2009.

Bader, M. J., et al., eds. *Images in Weather Forecasting: A Practical Guide for Interpreting Satellite and Radar Imagery.* New York: Cambridge University Press, 1995.

Bader, M. J., G. S. Forbes, J. R. Grant, and R. Lilley. *Images in Weather Forecasting: A Practical Guide for Interpreting Satellite and Radar Imagery.* New York: Cambridge University Press, 1997.

Baer, F., N. L. Canfield, and J. M. Mitchell, eds. *Climate in Human Perspective: A Tribute to Helmut E. Landsberg.* Boston: Kluwer, 1991.

Bai, Xuezhi, et al. "Severe Ice Conditions in the Bohai Sea, China, and Mild Ice Conditions in the Great Lakes During the 2009/10 Winter: Links to El Niño and a Strong Negative Arctic Oscillation." *Journal of Applied Meteorology and Climatology* 50, no. 9 (2011): 1922-1935.

Baker, D. J. "Models of Oceanic Circulation." *Scientific American* 222 (January, 1970): 114.

Baker, Victor R., ed. *Catastrophic Flooding: The Origin of the Channeled Scabland.* Stroudsburg, Pa.: Dowden, Hutchinson & Ross, 1981.

Baker, Victor R., R. C. Kochel, and P. C. Patton, eds. *Flood Geomorphology.* New York: John Wiley & Sons, 1988.

Balbi, Amedeo. *The Music of the Big Bang: The Cosmic Microwave Background and the New Cosmology.* Berlin: Springer-Verlag, 2010.

Ballard, Robert D., and Malcolm McConnell. *Explorations: My Quest for Adventure and Discovery Under the Sea.* New York: Hyperion, 1995.

Balogna, Julie, and Christopher K. Passante. *The Complete Idiot's Guide to Extreme Weather.* New York: Alpha Books, 2006.

Bamzai, A. S., and J. Shukla. "Relations Between Eurasian Snow Cover, Snow Depth, and the Indian Summer Monsoon: An Observational Study." *Journal of Climate* 12 (1999): 3117-3132.

Bandy, A. R., ed. *The Chemistry of the Atmosphere: Oxidants and Oxidation in the Earth's Atmosphere.* Cambridge, England: Royal Society of Chemistry, 1995.

Banerjee, Subhankar. *Arctic National Wildlife Refuge: Seasons of Life and Land.* Seattle: Mountaineers Books, 2003.

Bardintzeff, Jacques-Marie, and Alexander R. McBirney. *Volcanology.* 2d ed. Burlington, Mass.: Jones & Bartlett Publishers, 2000.

Barrett, E. C. *Viewing Weather from Space.* New York:

Frederick A. Praeger, 1967.

Barrett, E. C., and L. F. Curtis. *Introduction to Environmental Remote Sensing.* 3d ed. New York: John Wiley & Sons, 1992.

Barry, James Dale. *Ball Lightning and Bead Lightning: Extreme Forms of Atmospheric Electricity.* New York: Plenum Press, 1980.

Barry, Roger C., and Richard J. Chorley. *Atmosphere, Weather, and Climate.* 8th ed. New York: Routledge, 2003.

_____. *Atmosphere, Weather, and Climate.* 9th ed. London: Routledge, 2010.

Barter, James. *Rivers of the World; The Ganges.* Farmington Hills, Mich.: Lucent Books, 2002.

Bartolini, Claudio, Richard T. Buffler, and Abelardo Cantu-Chapa. *The Western Gulf of Mexico Basin: Tectonics, Sedimentary Basins and Petroleum Systems.* Tulsa, Okla.: American Association of Petroleum Geologists, 2001.

Bascom, Willard. *Waves and Beaches: The Dynamics of the Ocean Surface.* Rev. ed. New York: Anchor Books, 1980.

Bashkin, V. N., and Robert W. Howarth. *Modern Biogeochemistry.* New York: Kluwer Academic, 2002.

Bast, Joseph L., Peter J. Hill, and Richard C. Rue. *Eco-Sanity: A Common Sense Guide to Environmentalism.* Lanham, Md.: Madison Books, 1994.

Battarbee, R. W., and H. A. Binney. *Natural Climate Variability and Global Warming: A Holocene Perspective.* Malden, Mass.: Blackwell, 2008.

Batu, Vedat. *Applied Flow and Solute Transport Modeling in Aquifers.* Boca Raton, Fla.: CRC Press, 2006.

_____. *Aquifer Hydraulics: A Comprehensive Guide to Hydrogeology Data Analysis.* New York: Wiley, 1998.

Bear, Jacob, et al., eds. *Seawater Intrusion in Coastal Aquifers: Concepts, Methods, and Practices.* Norwell, Mass.: Kluwer Academic Publishers, 2011.

Beatty, J. Kelly, Carolyn Collins Petersen, and Andrew Chaikin, eds. *The New Solar System.* 4th ed. Cambridge, Mass.: Sky Publishing, 1999.

Beehler, Bruce M. P. *Lost Worlds: Adventures in the Tropical Rainforest.* New Haven, Conn.: Yale University Press, 2008.

Beisel, Richard H., Jr. *America's Top 100 Western Waterfalls.* Parker, Colo.: Outskirts Press , 2008.

Benn, Douglas I., and David J. A. Evans. *Glaciers and Glaciation.* 2d ed. London: Hodder Education Publishers, 2010.

Bennett, Matthew M., and Neil F. Glasser. *Glacial Geology: Ice Sheets and Landforms.* Hoboken, N.J.: John Wiley and Sons, 2009.

Benson, Keith Rodney, and Philip F. Rhebock. *Oceanographic History: The Pacific and Beyond.* Seattle, Wash.: University of Washington Press, 2002.

Berger, Wolfgang H. "Sedimentation of Deep-Sea Carbonate: Maps and Models of Variations and Fluctuations." *Journal of Foraminiferal Research* 8 (October, 1978): 286-302.

Berger, Wolfgang H., and E. L. Winterer. "Plate Stratigraphy and the Fluctuating Carbonate Line." In *Pelagic Sediments: On Land and Under the Sea,* edited by Kenneth J. Hsü and Hugh C. Jenkyns. Oxford, England: Blackwell Scientific, 1974.

Bernard, Eddie N., and Allan R. Robinson. *The Sea, Volume 15: Tsunamis.* Cambridge, Mass.: Harvard University Press, 2009.

Berner, Elizabeth K., and Robert A. Berner. *The Global Water Cycle: Geochemistry and Environment.* Englewood Cliffs, N.J.: Prentice-Hall, 1986.

Berner, Robert A. *The Phanerozoic Carbon Cycle: CO_2 and O_2.* New York: Oxford University Press, 2004.

Bernstein, Lenny, et al. *Climate Change 2007: Synthesis Report.* Geneva: IPCC, 2008.

Bertness, Mark D. *Atlantic Shorelines: Natural History and Ecology.* Princeton, N.J.: Princeton University Press, 2006.

Berton, Pierre. *Niagara: A History of the Falls.* New York: Kodansha International, 1997.

Betz, H. D., U. Schumann, and P. Laroche, eds. *Lightning: Principles, Instruments, and Applications.* New York: Springer, 2009.

Bigg, Grant R. *The Oceans and Climate.* 2d ed. Cambridge, England: Cambridge University Press, 2003.

Billington, David P., and Donald Conrad Jackson. *Big Dams of the New Deal Era: A Confluence of Engineering and Politics.* Norman: University of Oklahoma Press, 2006.

Birch, Eugenie L., and Susan M. Wachter. *Rebuilding Urban Places After Disaster: Lessons from Hurricane Katrina.* Philadelphia: University of Pennsylvania Press, 2006.

Bird, Eric C. *Beach Management.* New York: John Wiley, 1996.

_____. *Coastline Changes: A Global Review.* New

York: John Wiley & Sons, 1985.

Birkeland, P. W. *Soils and Geomorphology.* 3d ed. New York: Oxford University Press, 1999.

Bischof, Jens. *Ice Drift, Ocean Circulation and Climate Change.* Chichester: Praxis Publishing, 2000.

Black, Brian, and Gary J. Weisel. *Global Warming.* Santa Barbara, Calif.: Greenwood Press, 2010.

Black, J. A. *Oceans and Coasts.* Dubuque, Iowa: Wm. C. Brown, 1986.

Black, P. E. *Watershed Hydrology.* 2d ed. Boca Raton, Fla.: CRC Press, 1996.

Bland, Will, and David Rolls. *Weathering: An Introduction to the Scientific Principles.* New York: Arnold, 1998.

Blatt, Harvey, Robert J. Tracy, and Brent Owens. *Petrology: Igneous, Sedimentary, and Metamorphic.* New York: W. H. Freeman, 2005.

Bloom, Arthur L. *Geomorphology: A Systematic Analysis of Late Cenozoic Landforms.* 3d ed. Upper Saddle River, N.J.: Prentice-Hall, 1998.

Bluestein, Howard B. *Synaptic-Dynamic Meteorology in Midlatitudes.* New York: Oxford University Press, 1992.

_____. *Tornado Alley: Monster Storms of the Great Plains.* New York: Oxford University Press, 1999.

_____. *Tornado Alley: Monster Storms of the Great Plains.* New York: Oxford University Press, 2006.

Bogdanov, Uri. *Mysteries of the Deep: From the Depths of Lake Baikal to the Ocean Floor.* Moscow: Progress Publishers, 1989.

Bolch, Ben W., and Harold Lyons. *Apocalypse Not: Science Economics and Environmentalism.* Washington, D.C.: Cato Institute, 1993.

Bolius, David. *Paleoclimate Reconstructions Based on Ice Cores: Results from the Andes and the Alps.* Berlin: SVH-Verlag, 2010.

Bolsenga, S. J., and C. E. Herdendorf. *Lake Erie and Lake St. Clair Handbook.* Detroit, Mich.: Wayne State University Press, 1993.

Bone, Neil. *Aurora: Observing and Recording Nature's Spectacular Light Show.* New York: Springer, 2007.

_____. *The Aurora: Sun-Earth Interactions.* 2d ed. New York: Wiley, 1996.

Bonotto, Daniel Marcus, and Ene Gloria da Silveira. *The Amazon Goldruch and Environmental Mercury Contamination.* Hauppauge, N.Y.: Nova Science Publishers, 2009.

Bowker, Michael, and Valerie Holcomb. *Layperson's Guide to Flood Management.* Sacramento, Calif.: The

Foundation, 1995.

Boyle, Godfrey, ed. *Renewable Energy.* 2d ed. New York: Oxford University Press, 2004.

Bradley, Raymond S. *Paleoclimatology: Reconstructing Climates of the Quaternary.* San Diego, Calif.: Academic Press, 1999.

Brancazio, Peter J., ed. *The Origin and Evolution of Atmospheres and Oceans.* New York: John Wiley & Sons, 1964.

Brassington, Rick. *Finding Water: A Guide to the Construction and Maintenance of Private Water Supplies.* 2d ed. New York: John Wiley, 1995.

Brauer, Jurgen. *War and Nature: The Environmental Consequences of War in a Globalized World.* Lanham, Md.: AltaMira/Rowman and Littlefield, 2009.

Breckle, Siegmar-W., Walter Wucherer, Liliya A. Dimeyeva, and Nathalia P. Ogar. *Aralkum; A Man-Made Desert: The Desiccated Floor of the Aral Sea (Central Asia).* Berlin: Springer-Verlag, 2012.

Brimblecombe, Peter. *Air Composition and Chemistry.* 2d ed. New York: Cambridge University Press, 1996.

Brimblecombe, Peter, et al., eds. *Acid Rain – Deposition to Recovery.* Dordrecht: Springer, 2010.

Brinkley, Douglas. *The Great Deluge: Hurricane Katrina, New Orleans, and the Mississippi Gulf Coast.* New York: Morrow, 2006.

Broad, William J. *The Universe Below: Discovering the Secrets of the Deep Sea.* New York: Simon and Schuster, 1997.

Broecker, Wally. *The Great Ocean Conveyor.* Princeton, N.J.: Princeton University Press, 2010.

Brookins, Douglas G. *The Indoor Radon Problem.* New York: Columbia University Press, 1990.

Brooks, H. E., C. A. Doswell III, and M. P. Kay. "Climatological Estimates of Local Daily Tornado Probability for the United States." *Weather Forecasting* 18 (2003): 626-640.

Brooks, Kenneth N. *Hydrology and the Management of Watersheds.* Ames: Iowa State University Press, 1997.

Browning, K. A., and R. J. Gurney. *Global Energy and Water Cycles.* New York: Cambridge University Press, 2007.

Brunet, M.-F., M. Wilmsen, and J. W. Granath, eds. *South Caspian to Central Iran Basins.* Special Publication 312. London: Geological Society of London, 2009.

Brusca, Richard C., ed. *The Gulf of California: Biodiversity and Conservation.* Tucson, Ariz.: University of

Arizona Press, 2010.

Bryant, Duncan Alan. *Electron Acceleration in the Aurora and Beyond.* Philadelphia: Institute of Physics, 1999.

Bryant, Edward A. *Natural Hazards.* 2d ed. Cambridge, England: Cambridge University Press, 2005.

Bryson, Reid A., and Thomas J. Murray. *Climates of Hunger.* Madison: University of Wisconsin Press, 1977.

Bull, William B. *Tectonic Geomorphology of Mountains: A New Approach to Paleoseismology.* Malden, Mass.: Wiley-Blackwell, 2007.

Burch, David. *The Barometer Handbook: A Modern Look at Barometers and Applications of Barometric Pressure.* Seattle: Starpath, 2009.

Burroughs, William J. *Climate Change: A Multidisciplinary Approach.* 2d ed. New York: Cambridge University Press, 2007.

_____. *Watching the World's Weather.* New York, NY: Cambridge University Press, 1991.

Burt, Christopher C. *Extreme Weather: A Guide and Record Book.* New York: Norton, 2007.

Buster, Noreen A., and Charles W. Holmes. *Gulf of Mexico Origin, Waters and Biota.* College Station, Tex.: Texas A & M University Press, 2011.

Bychkov, Vladimir L., Gennady V. Golubkov, and Anatoly I. Nikitin, eds. *The Atmosphere and Ionosphere. Dynamics, Processes and Monitoring.* New York: Springer Verlag, 2010.

Byers, Michael. *Who Owns the Arctic? Understanding Sovereignty Disputes in the North.* Vancouver: Douglas & McIntyre Publishers, 2009.

Byrne, John, and Steven M. Hoffman, eds. *Governing the Atom: The Politics of Risk.* New Brunswick, N.J.: Transaction, 1996.

Cagin, Seth, and Philip Dray. *Between Earth and Sky: How CFCs Changed Our World and Endangered the Ozone Layer.* New York: Pantheon Books, 1993.

Calhoun, Donald E., III. "Water Well Design Considerations." *Water Well Journal* 33, no. 3 (1989).

Cameron, Silver Donald. *The Living Beach.* Toronto: Macmillan Canada, 1998.

Campbell, Bruce A. *Radar Remote Sensing of Planetary Surfaces.* New York: Cambridge University Press, 2002.

Campbell, I. M. *Energy and the Atmosphere: A Physical-Chemical Approach.* New York: John Wiley & Sons, 1986.

Campbell, James B., and Randolph H. Wynne. *Introduction to Remote Sensing.* 5th ed. New York:

Guilford Press, 2011.

Canter, L. W., R. C. Knox, and D. M. Fairchild. *Ground Water Quality Protection.* Chelsea, Mich.: Lewis, 1987.

Cantón-Garbín, Manuel. "Satellites Oceans Observation in Relation to Global Change." In *Earth Observation of Global Change: The Role of Satellite Remote Sensing in Monitoring the Global Environment,* edited by Emilio Chuvieco. New York: Springer, 2008.

Cap, Ferdinand. *Tsunamis and Hurricanes: A Mathematical Approach.* New York: SpringerWien, 2006.

Case, Ted J., Martin L. Cody, and Exequiel Ezcurra. *A New Island Biogeography of the Sea of Cortés.* New York: Oxford University Press, 2002.

Chadwick, Wallace L., ed. *Environmental Effects of Large Dams.* New York: American Society of Civil Engineers, 1978.

Chamberlain, Joseph W. *Theory of Planetary Atmospheres: An Introduction to Their Physics and Chemistry.* 2d ed. San Diego, Calif.: Academic Press, 1987.

Chan, Johnny C. L., and Jeffrey D. Kepert, eds. *Global Perspectives on Tropical Cyclones: From Science to Mitigation.* London: World Scientific, 2010.

Chang, Chih-Pei. *East Asian Monsoon.* Hackensack, N.J.: World Scientific Publishing, 2004.

Chang, Chih-Pei, and Mong-Ming Lu. "Intraseasonal Predictability of Siberian High and East Asian Winter Monsoon and Its Interdecadal Variability." *Journal of Climate* 25, no. 5 (2012): 1773-1778.

Chang, Chih-Pei, Yihui Ding, and Ngar-Cheung Lau. *The Global Monsoon System: Research and Forecast.* Hackensack, N.J.: World Scientific Publishing, 2011.

Chang, Raymond, and Jason Overby. *General Chemistry: The Essential Concepts.* 6th ed. Columbus, Ohio: McGraw-Hill, 2010.

Changnon, Stanley A., ed. *The Great Flood of 1993: Causes, Impacts, and Responses.* Boulder, Colo.: Westview Press, 1996.

Chapra, Steven C. *Surface Water-Quality Modeling.* Waveland Press, 2008.

Charabe, Yassine, and Salim al-Hatrushi. *Indian Ocean Tropical Cyclones and Climate Change.* Dordrecht: Springer, 2010.

Charlier, R. H., and C. W. Finkl. *Ocean Energy: Tide and Tidal Power.* Berlin: Springer-Verlag, 2009.

Charlton, Ro. *Fundamentals of Fluvial Geomorphology.* Abingdon: Routledge, 2007.

Chassignet, Eric P. and Jacques Verron, eds. *Ocean Weather Forecasting: An Integrated View of Oceanography*. Dordrecht: Springer, 2006.

Cheng, Alexander H. D., and Driss Oazar, eds. *Coastal Aquifer Management: Monitoring, Modeling, and Case Studies*. Boca Raton, Fla.: CRC Press, 2004.

Chernousenko, Vladimir M. *Chernobyl: Insight from the Inside*. Berlin: Springer-Verlag, 1991.

Chester, Roy. *Furnace of Creation, Cradle of Destruction*. New York: AMACOM Books, 2008.

Chester, R., and Stefano Guerzoni, eds. *Impact of Desert Dust Across the Mediterranean*. Norwell, Mass.: Kluwer Academic Publishers, 1996.

Cheung, Chan Chik. *Synoptic Patterns Associated with Wet and Dry Northerly Cold Surges of the Northeast Monsoon*. Hong Kong: Royal Observatory, 1997.

Chorley, Richard J., Stanley A. Schumm, and David E. Sugden. *Geomorphology*. New York: Methuen & Co., 1985.

Christopherson, Robert W., and Mary-Louie Byrne. *Geosystems: An Introduction to Physical Geography*. Toronto, ON: Pearson Education Canada Inc., 2006.

Churchill, Winston. *The River War*. New York: Longmans, Green, 1899.

Clague, John, Chris Yorath, and Richard Franklin. *At Risk: Earthquakes and Tsunamis on the West Coast*. Vancouver: Tricouni Press. 2006.

Clarke, Allan J. *An Introduction to the Dynamics of El Niño and the Southern Oscillation*. London: Academic Press/Elsevier, 2008.

Clerbaux, Cathy, Solene Turquety, and Pierre Coheur. "Infrared Remote Sensing of Atmospheric Composition and Air Quality: Toward Operational Applications." *Comptes Rendus Geoscience* 342, nos. 4/5 (2010): 349-356.

Clift, Peter D., and R. Alan Plumb. *The Asian Monsoon*. New York: Cambridge University Press, 2008.

Clift, P. D., R. Tada, and H. Zheng. *Monsoon Evolution and Tectonics: Climate Linkage in East Asia*. Bath, England: Geological Society, 2010.

Climate, Drought, and Desertification. Geneva, Switzerland: World Meteorological Organization, 1997.

Coe, Angela L., ed. *The Sedimentary Record of Sea-Level Change*. New York: Cambridge University Press, 2003.

Cole, Leonard A. *The Element of Risk: The Politics of Radon*. Washington, D.C.: AAAS Press, 1993.

Coleman, J. M. *Deltas: Process of Deposition and Models for Exploration*. Boston: International Human Resources Development Corporation, 1982.

Coleman, Robert G. *Geologic Evolution of the Red Sea*. New York: Oxford University Press, 1993.

Collier, Christopher G. *Applications of Weather Radar Systems: A Guide to Uses of Radar Data in Meteorology and Hydrology*. 2d ed. New York: Wiley, 1996.

Collier, Michael. *Over the Rivers: An Aerial View of Geology*. New York: Mikaya Press, Inc., 2008.

Colling, Angela. *Ocean Circulation*. 2d ed. Oxford: Butterworth-Heinemann, 2001.

Collins, B., and T. Dunne. *Fluvial Geomorphology and River-Gravel Mining: A Guide for Planners*. Sacramento, Calif.: California Department of Conservation, 1990.

Collins, Elizabeth. *The Living Ocean*. New York: Chelsea House, 1994.

Collins, Robert O. *The Nile*. Harrisonburg, Va.: R. R. Donnelley & Sons, 2002.

Collinson, J. D., Nigel Mountney, and D. B. Thompson. *Sedimentary Structures*. 3d ed. Edinburgh: Dunedin Academic Press, Ltd., 2006.

Comerio, Mary C. *Disaster Hits Home: New Policy for Urban Housing Recovery*. Berkeley, Calif.: University of California Press, 1998.

Committee on the Safety of Existing Dams, Water Science and Technology Board, Commission on Engineering and Technical Systems, and the National Research Council. *Safety of Existing Dams: Evaluation and Improvement*. Washington, D.C.: National Academy Press, 1983.

Congressional Research Service. *Weather Modification: Programs, Problems, Policy and Potential*. Honolulu: University Press of the Pacific, 2004.

Cooke, Ronald U. "Stone Pavements in Deserts." *Annals of the Association of American Geographers* 60 (1970): 560-577.

Cooke, Ronald U., Andrew Warren, and Andrew Goudie. *Desert Geomorphology*. London: UCL Press, 1993.

Cooper, Bill, and Laurel Cooper. *Back Door to Byzantium: To the Black Sea by the Great Rivers of Europe*. London: Adlard Coles Nautical, 1997.

Cooper, H. H., F. A. Kohout, H. R. Henry, and R. E. Glover. *Sea Water in Coastal Aquifers*. Washington, D.C.: Government Printing Office, 1964.

Corrigan, Patricia, and Geoffrey H. Nash. *Waterfalls*. New York: Chelsea House, 2007.

Cotton, William R., and Roger A. Pielke. *Human Impacts on Weather and Climate.* 2d ed. New York: Cambridge University Press, 2007.

Cowie, Jonathan. *Climate Change: Biological and Human Aspects.* New York: Cambridge University Press, 2007.

Crabbe, M. James C., Emma L. L. Walker, and David B. Stephenson. "The Impact of Weather and Climate Extremes on Coral Growth." In *Climate Extremes and Society,* edited by Henry F. Diaz and Richard J. Murnane. New York: Cambridge University Press, 2011.

Croissant, Cynthia. *Azerbaijan, Oil, and Geopolitics.* Commack, N.Y.: Nova Science, 1998.

Cronin, Thomas M. *Principles of Paleoclimatology.* New York: Columbia University Press, 1999.

Crosby, Alfred W. *Children of the Sun: A History of Humanity's Unappeasable Appetite for Energy.* New York: Norton, 2006.

Crow, Ben. *Sharing the Ganges: The Politics and Technology of River Development.* Thousand Oaks, Calif.: Sage, 1995.

Cruz, Joan. *Ocean Wave Energy: Current Status and Future Perspectives.* Berlin: Springer-Verlag, 2010.

Cullen, Robert. "The Rise and Fall of the Caspian Sea." *National Geographic* 195 (May, 1999): 2-35.

Curley, Robert. *New Thinking About Pollution.* New York: Britannica Educational Publishing, 2011.

Curry, Judith A., and Peter J. Webster. "Climate Science and the Uncertainty Monster." *Bulletin of the American Meteorological Society* 92, no. 12 (2011): 1667-1682.

_____. *Thermodynamics of Atmospheres and Oceans.* San Diego, Calif.: Academic Press, 1999.

Czaya, Eberhard. *Rivers of the World.* New York: Cambridge University Press, 1985.

D'Aleo, Joseph S., and Pamela G. Grube. *The Oryx Resource Guide to El Niño and La Niña.* Westport, Conn.: Greenwood Press, 2002.

Damon, Thomas D. *Introduction to Space.* 4th ed. Malabar, Fla.: Krieger Publishing Company, 2011.

D'Angelo, Salvatore, Thomas G. Richardson, Richard P. Arber, et al., eds. *Using Reclaimed Water to Augment Potable Water Resources.* 2d ed. Denver, Colo.: American Water Works Association, 2008.

Darby, Stephen, and David Sear. *River Restoration: Managing the Uncertainty in Restoring Physical Habitat.* Hoboken, N.J.: John Wiley & Sons, 2008.

Darrow, K. K. "Cosmic Radiation: Discoveries Reported in *The Physical Review.*" In *The Physical Review: The First 100 Years.* New York: American Institute of Physics, 1999.

Darwin, Charles. *The Structure and Distribution of Coral Reefs.* 1851. Berkeley, Calif.: University of California Press, 1962.

Dassenakis, Manos, et al. "Remote Sensing in Coastal Water Monitoring: Applications in the Eastern Mediterranean Sea (IUPAC Technical Report)." *Pure and Applied Chemistry* 84, no. 2 (2012): 335-375.

Davidson, Keay. "What's Wrong with the Weather? El Niño Strikes Again." *Earth* (June, 1995): 24-33.

Davidson, Osha Gray. *The Enchanted Braid: Coming to Terms with Nature on the Coral Reef.* New York: Wiley, 1998.

Davies, P., ed. *The New Physics.* New York: Cambridge University Press, 1990.

Davis, R. A., Jr. *Depositional Systems: A Genetic Approach to Sedimentary Geology.* 2d ed. Englewood Cliffs, N.J.: Prentice-Hall, 1992.

_____. *The Ocean.* San Francisco: W. H. Freeman, 1972.

_____. *Oceanography: An Introduction to the Marine Environment.* 2d ed. Dubuque, Iowa: W. C. Brown Publishers, 1991.

_____. *Sea-Level Change in the Gulf of Mexico.* Nansha: Everbest Printing Company, 2011.

Davis, Richard, Jr., and Duncan Fitzgerald. *Beaches and Coasts.* John Wiley & Sons, 2009.

Davis, Wade. *One River: Explorations and Discoveries in the Amazon Rain Forest.* New York: Simon & Schuster, 1996.

Dawson, Alastair G. *Ice Age Earth: Late Quaternary Geology and Climate.* New York: Routledge, 1996.

Day, John A., and Vincent J. Schaefer. *Peterson First Guides: Clouds and Weather.* New York: Houghton Mifflin, 1991.

Dean, Robert G., and Robert A. Dalrymple. *Coastal Processes with Engineering Applications.* Cambridge, England: Cambridge University Press, 2002.

De Angelis, Hernan, and Pedro Skvarca. "Glacier Surge After Ice Shelf Collapse." *Science* 299 (2003): 1560-1562.

DeBarry, Paul A. *Watersheds: Processes, Assessment and Management.* Upper Saddle River, N.J.: John Wiley & Sons, 2004.

de Boer, Jella Zeilinga, and Donald Theodore Sanders. *Volcanoes in Human History: The*

Far-Reaching Effects of Major Eruptions. Princeton, N.J.: Princeton University Press, 2002.

Decker, Robert W., and Barbara Decker. *Volcanoes.* 4th ed. New York: Freeman, 2005.

Dennis, Jerry. *The Living Great Lakes.* New York: Thomas Dunne Books, 2003.

Desbois, Michel, and Françoise Désalmand, eds. *Global Precipitations and Climate Change.* New York: Springer-Verlag, 1994.

Detay, Michel. *Water Wells: Implementation, Maintenance, and Restoration.* Translated by M. N. S. Carpenter. New York: Wiley, 1997.

De Villiers, Marc. *Windswept: The Story of Wind and Weather.* New York: Walker, 2006.

Di Duca, Marc. *Lake Baikal: Siberia's Great Lake.* Chalfont St. Peter, England: Bradt Travel Guides, 2010.

Diaz, Henry F., and Vera Markgraf, eds. *El Niño: Historical and Paleoclimatic Aspects of the Southern Oscillation.* Cambridge, England: Cambridge University Press, 1992.

Dickson, R. R., Jens Meincke, and Peter Rhines, eds. *Arctic-Subarctic Ocean Fluxes: Defining the Role of the Northern Seas in Climate.* Dordrecht: Springer, 2008.

Diermendjian, Diran. *"Nuclear Winter": A Brief Review and Comments on Some Recent Literature.* Santa Monica, Calif.: RAND Corporation, 1988.

Dillon, P. J., ed. *Management of Aquifer Recharge for Sustainability.* Boca Raton, Fla.: Taylor & Francis, 2002.

Dingman, S. L. *Physical Hydrology.* 2d ed. Long Grove, Ill.: Waveland Press, Inc. 2008.

Dixon, Lloyd S., Nancy Y. Moore, and Ellen M. Pint. *Drought Management Policies and Economic Effects in Urban Areas of California, 1987-92.* Santa Monica, Calif.: RAND, 1996.

Djuric, Dusan. *Weather Analysis.* Englewood Cliffs, NJ: Prentice-Hall, 1994.

Dodds, Walter K., and Matt R. Wiles. *Freshwater Ecology: Concepts and Environmental Applications of Limnology.* 2d ed. Burlington, Mass.: Academic Press, 2010.

Dodgen, Randall A. *Controlling the Dragon: Confucian Engineers and the Yellow River in Late Imperial China.* Honolulu: University of Hawaii Press, 2001.

Dodson, John. *Changing Climates, Earth Systems, and Society.* New York: Springer, 2010.

Dolan, Ed. *The Old Farmer's Almanac Book of Weather Lore.* Dublin, N.H.: Yankee Books, 1988.

Dormin, Lev I. *Cosmic Rays in the Earth's Atmosphere and Underground.* Dordrecht: Kluwer Academic Publishers, 2004.

Douglas, Michael W., Robert A. Maddox, Kenneth W. Howard, and Sergio Reyes. "The Mexican Monsoon." *Journal of Climate* 6 (August, 1993): 1665-1677.

Douglas, R. J. W. *Geology and Economic Minerals of Canada.* Report Number I. Ottawa: Geological Survey of Canada, 1970.

Dow, Kirstin, and Thomas E. Downing. *The Atlas of Climate Change: Mapping the World's Greatest Challenge.* Berkeley: University of California Press, 2006.

Dubinsky, Zvy, and Noga Stambler, eds. *Coral Reefs: An Ecosystem in Transition.* Dordrecht: Springer, 2011.

Dudley, W. C., and M. Lee. *Tsunami!* 2d ed. Honolulu: University of Hawaii Press, 1998.

Dumont, Henri, Tamara A. Shiganova, and Ulrich Niermann, eds. *Aquatic Invasions in the Black, Caspian, and Mediterranean Seas.* Boston: Kluwer Academic Publishers, 2004.

Dunlop, Storm. *The Weather Identification Handbook.* Guilford, Conn.: Lyons Press, 2003.

Dunne, E. J., K. Raja Reddy, and O.T Carton. *Nutrient in Agricultural Watersheds: A Wetlands Solution.* Wageningen: Wageningen Academic Publishers, 2005.

Durrer, Ruth. *The Cosmic Microwave Background.* New York: Cambridge University Press, 2008.

Easterbrook, Don. *Evidence Based Climate Science: Data Opposing CO_2 Emissions as the Primary Source of Global Warming.* Burlington, Mass.: Elsevier, 2011.

_____. *Surface Processes and Landforms.* 2d ed. Upper Saddle River, N.J.: Prentice Hall, 1999.

Eddy, John A. *The Sun, the Earth, and Near-Earth Space: A Guide to the Sun-Earth System.* Washington, D.C.: National Aeronautics and Space Administration, 2009.

Edwards, Alasdair J., and Stephen M. Head. *Red Sea.* New York: Oxford University Press, 1987.

Edwards, John. *Plate Tectonics and Continental Drift.* North Mankato, Minn.: Smart Apple Media, 2006.

Ehrlich, Paul R., et al. *The Cold and the Dark: The World After Nuclear War.* New York: W. W. Norton, 1984.

_____. "Long-Term Biological Consequences of the Nuclear War." *Science* 222 (1983): 1293-1300.

Ehteshami, Anoushiravan, and Emma C. Murphy. *The International Politics of the Red Sea.* London:

Taylor & Francis, 2011.

Ellis, William S. "The Aral: A Soviet Sea Lies Dying." *National Geographic* (February, 1990): 70-93.

Elsner, James B., and Thomas H. Jagger. *Hurricanes and Climate Change.* New York: Springer, 2009.

Emanuel, Kerry. *Divine Winds: The History and Science of Hurricanes.* New York: Oxford University Press, 2005.

Emelyanov, Emelyan M. *The Barrier Zones in the Ocean.* Berlin: Springer-Verlag, 2005.

Emerson, Steven, and John Hedges. *Chemical Oceanography and Marine Carbon Cycle.* New York: Cambridge University Press, 2008.

Emiliani, Cesare. *Planet Earth: Cosmology, Geology, and the Evolution of Life and Environment.* Cambridge, England: Cambridge University Press, 1992.

Environmental and Water Resources Institute. *Standard Guidelines for Artificial Recharge of Ground Water.* Reston, Va.: American Society of Civil Engineers, 2001.

Erickson, Jon. *Violent Storms.* Blue Ridge Summit, Pa.: TAB Books, 1990.

Etheridge, Laura S., ed. *Persian Gulf States: Kuwait, Qatar, Bahrain, Oman and the United Arab Emirates.* New York: Britannica Educational Publishing, 2011.

Etkin, Dagmar Schmidt. *Financial Costs of Oil Spills in the United States.* Arlington, Mass.: Cutter Information, 1998.

_____. *Marine Spills Worldwide.* Arlington, Mass.: Cutter Information, 1999.

Fagan, Brian M., ed. *The Complete Ice Age: How Climate Change Shapes the World.* New York: Thames & Hudson, 2009.

Fahy, Frank. *Air: The Excellent Canopy.* Chichester, England: Horwood, 2009.

Fairbridge, Rhodes W., ed. *The Encyclopedia of Oceanography.* New York: Reinhold, 1966.

Fairbridge, Rhodes W., and Reginald W. Herschy, eds. *The Encyclopedia of Hydrology and Water Resources.* Boston: Kluwer Academic, 1998.

Falck-Ytter, Harald. *Aurora: The Northern Lights in Mythology, History, and Science.* Hudson, N.Y.: Bell Pond Books, 1999.

Fall, J. A., et al. *Long-Term Consequences of the* Exxon Valdez *Oil Spill for Coastal Communities of South-Central Alaska.* Technical Report 163. Anchorage, Alaska: Alaska Department of Fish and Game, Division of Subsistence, 2001.

Fanchi, John R. *Energy: Technology and Directions for the Future.* Burlington, Mass.: Elsevier Academic Press, 2004.

Fanchi, John R., and Christopher J. Fanchi. *Energy in the 21st Century.* 2d ed. Hackensack, N.J.: World Scientific Publishing Co., 2011.

Fang, Hsai-Yang. *Introduction to Environmental Geotechnology.* New York: CRC Press, 1997.

Faranda, Francesco, Letterio Guglielmo, and Giancarlo Spezie. *Mediterranean Ecosystems: Structures and Processes.* Milan: Springer-Verlag Italia, 2001.

Fein, Jay S., and Pamela L. Stephens, eds. *Monsoons.* New York: Wiley, 1987.

Felder, Darryl L., and David K. Camp. *Gulf of Mexico Origin, Waters, and Biota.* Amherst, Tex.: Texas A&M University Press, 2009.

Fetter, C. W. *Applied Hydrogeology.* 4th ed. Upper Saddle River, N.J.: Prentice Hall, 2000.

_____. *Contaminant Hydrogeology.* Long Grove, Ill.: Waveland Publishing, 2008.

Feudale, Laura, and Jagadish Shukla. "Influence of Sea Surface Temperature on the European Heat Wave of 2003 Summer. Part I: An Observational Study." *Climate Dynamics* 36, nos. 9/10 (2011): 1691-1703.

Few, Arthur A. "Thunder." *Scientific American* 233 (July, 1975): 80-90.

Field, J. G., Gotthilf Hempel, and C. P. Summerhayes. *Oceans 2020: Science, Trends and the Challenge of Sustainability.* Washington, D.C.: Island Press, 2002.

Fierro, Pedro, Jr., and Evan K. Nyer, eds. *The Water Encyclopedia.* 3d ed. Boca Raton, Fla.: CRC Press, 2007.

Fingas, Mervin F, ed. *Oil Spill Science and Technology.* Burlington, Mass.: Elsevier, 2011.

Finkl, Charles W., ed. *Coastal Hazards: Prediction, Susceptibility, and Mitigation.* Charlottesville, Va.: Coastal Education and Research Foundation, 1994.

Firor, John. *The Changing Atmosphere: A Global Challenge.* New Haven, Conn.: Yale University Press, 1990.

Fisher, David E. *Fire and Ice: The Greenhouse Effect, Ozone Depletion, and Nuclear Winter.* New York: Harper & Row, 1990.

Fisher, R. J. *If Rain Doesn't Come: An Anthropological Study of Drought and Human Ecology in Western Rajasthan.* New Delhi: Manohar, 1997.

Fisher, Richard V., Grant Heiken, and Jeffrey B. Hulen. *Volcanoes: Crucibles of Change.* Princeton,

N.J.: Princeton University Press, 1997.

Fishman, Jack, and Robert Kalish. *The Weather Revolution.* New York: Plenum Press, 1994.

Fitzpatrick, Patrick J. *Contemporary World Issues: Hurricanes.* 2d ed. Santa Barbara, Calif.: ABC-CLIO, 2006.

Flemming, Nicholas Coit, Council for British Archaeology, and English Heritage. *Submarine Prehistoric Archaeology of the North Sea: Research Priorities and Collaboration with Industry.* York: Council for British Archaeology, 2004.

Foresman, Timothy, and Alan H. Strahler. *Visualizing Physical Geography.* New York: John Wiley & Sons, 2012.

Formin, L. I. *Cosmic Rays in the Earth's Atmosphere and Underground.* Dordrecht: Kluwer Academic Publishers, 2004.

Forrester, Glenn C. *Niagara Falls and the Glacier.* Hicksville, N.Y.: Exposition Press, 1976.

Foster, J. W. *The Mississippi Valley: Its Physical Geography.* Chicago: S. C. Griggs, 1869.

Frakes, L. A. *Climates Throughout Geologic Time.* New York: Elsevier, 1980.

Francis, Peter, and Clive Oppenheimer. *Volcanoes.* 2d ed. New York: Oxford University Press, 2004.

Fraser, Lauchlan H., and Paul A. Keddy. *The World's Largest Wetlands: Ecology and Conservation.* Cambridge, England: Cambridge University Press, 2005.

Frederick, John E. *Principles of Atmospheric Science.* Sudbury, Mass.: Jones and Bartlett, 2008.

Frederiksen, Harald D. *Drought Planning and Water Resources Implications in Water Resources Management.* Washington, D.C.: World Bank, 1992.

Freitag, Bob, et al. *Floodplain Management: A New Approach for a New Era.* Washington, D.C.: Island Press, 2009.

French, Hugh, and Olav Slaymaker. *Changing Cold Environments: A Canadian Perspective.* Oxford: Wiley-Blackwell, 2012.

Freuchen, Peter. *Peter Freuchen's Book of the Seven Seas.* Guilford, Conn.: The Lyons Press, 2003.

Freudenburg, William R., et al. *Catastrophe in the Making: The Engineering of Katrina and the Disasters of Tomorrow.* Washington, D.C.: Island Press/ Shearwater Books, 2009.

Friedman, John. *Out of the Blue: A History of Lightning: Science, Superstition and Amazing Stories of Survival.* New York: Delta/Random House, 2009.

Frolov, Ivan E. *The Arctic Basin: Results from the Russian Drifting Stations.* Chichester: Praxis Publishing, 2005.

Gaffney, Vincent, Kenneth Thomson, and Simon Fitch, eds. *Mapping Doggerland: The Mesolithic Landscapes of the Southern North Sea.* Oxford: Archaeopress, 2007.

Gaisser, Thomas K. *Cosmic Rays and Particle Physics.* New York: Cambridge University Press, 1990.

Gardner, Jim. *Multibeam Mapping in the Outer Continental Shelf Region of the Northwestern Gulf of Mexico.* Washington, D.C.: U.S. Department. of the Interior, Minerals Management Service, Gulf of Mexico OCS Region, 2003.

Garrison, Tom S. *Essentials of Oceanography.* 6th ed. Belmont, Calif.: Brooks/Cole Cengage Learning, 2012.

_____. *Oceanography: An Invitation to Marine Science.* Belmont, Calif.: Brooks/Cole, Cengage Learning, 2010.

Garstang, Michael, and David R. Fitzjarrald. *Observations of Surface to Atmosphere Interactions in the Tropics.* New York: Oxford University Press, 1999.

Gates, Alexander E., and Linda C. S. Gundersen, eds. *Geologic Controls on Radon.* Boulder, Colo.: Geological Society of America, 1992.

Gates, David M. *Climate Change and Its Biological Consequences.* Sunderland, Mass.: Sinauer Associates, 1993.

Ghosh, Some Nath. *Flood Control and Drainage Engineering.* 3d ed. Boca Raton, FL: Taylor & Francis, 2006.

Giacomelli, Giorgio, Maurizio Spurio, and Jamal Eddine Derkaoui. NATO Scientific Affairs Division. *Cosmic Radiations: From Astronomy to Particle Physics.* Dordrecht: Kluwer Academic Publishers, 2001.

Gibilisco, Stan. *Meteorology Demystified.* New York: McGraw-Hill, 2006.

_____. *Violent Weather, Hurricanes, Tornadoes, and Storms.* Blue Ridge Summit, Pa.: TAB Books, 1984.

Gilbert, Janine, Dan L. Danielopol, Jack A. Stanford, et al., eds. *Groundwater Ecology.* San Diego, Calif.: Academic Press, 1994.

Giordano, M., Zhongping Zhu, Ximing Cai, Shangqi Hong, Xuecheng Zhang, and Yunpeng Xue. *Water Management in the Yellow River Basin: Background, Current Critical Needs and Future Research Needs.*

Glavin, Terry. *The Last Great Sea.* Vancouver: Greystone Books, 2000.

Gleick, James. *Chaos: Making a New Science.* 2d ed.

New York: Penguin Books, 2008.

Glennie, Kw. *Petroleum Geology of the North Sea: Basic Concepts and Recent Advances.* 4th ed. New York: John Wiley & Sons, 2009.

Glennon, Robert. *Unquenchable. America's Water Crisis and What to Do About It.* Washington, D.C.: Island Press, 2009.

Godish, Thad. *Indoor Air Pollution Control.* Chelsea, Mich.: Lewis, 1989.

Golde, R. H., ed. *Lightning.* London: Academic Press, 1977.

Gombosi, Tamas I. *Physics of the Space Environment.* New York: Cambridge University Press, 2004.

Goni, G. J., and Paola Malanotte-Rizzoli. *Interhemispheric Water Exchange in the Atlantic Ocean.* Amsterdam: Elsevier B.V., 2003.

Gore, Albert, and Melcher Media. *An Inconvenient Truth: The Planetary Emergency of Global Warming and What We Can Do About It.* New York: Rodale, 2006.

Gore, Robert H. *The Gulf of Mexico: A Treasury of Resources in the American Mediterranean.* Sarasota, Fla.: Pineapple Press, 1992.

Goreau, Thomas F., et al. "Corals and Coral Reefs." *Scientific American* 241 (August, 1979): 16, 124-136.

Gorelick, Steven M., et al., eds. *Groundwater Contamination: Optimal Capture and Contamination.* Boca Raton, Fla.: Lewis, 1993.

Gornitz, Vivien. *Encyclopedia of Paleoclimatology and Ancient Environments.* New York: Springer, 2009.

Goulding, Michael, Ronaldo Barthem, and Efrem Ferreira. *The Smithsonian Atlas of the Amazon.* The Smithsonian, 2003.

Grady, Wayne. *The Great Lakes: The Natural History of a Changing Region.* Vancouver: Greystone Books, 2007.

Graedel, T. E., and Paul J. Crutzen. *Atmospheric Change: An Earth System Perspective.* New York: W. H. Freeman, 1993.

Graf, William L. *The Colorado River: Instability and Basin Management.* Washington, D.C.: Association of American Geographers, 1985.

Graham, Bob, et al. *Deep Water: The Gulf Oil Disaster and the Future of Offshore Drilling.* National Commission on the BP Deepwater Horizon Oil Spill and Offshore Drilling, 2011.

Graham, Linda E., and Lee W. Wilcox. *Algae.* Upper Saddle River, N.J.: Prentice Hall, 2000.

Graham, N. E., and W. B. White. "The El Niño Cycle: A Natural Oscillator of the Pacific Ocean Atmosphere System." *Science* 240 (June 3, 1988): 1293-1302.

Grasshoff, Klaus, Klaus Kremling, and Manfred Ehrhardt, eds. *Methods of Seawater Analysis.* 3d ed. New York: Wiley-VCH, 1999.

Gray, Theodore. *The Elements: A Visual Exploration of Every Known Atom in the Universe.* New York: Black Dog & Leventhal Publishers, 2009.

Grazulis, Thomas P. *The Tornado: Nature's Ultimate Windstorm.* Norman: University of Oklahoma Press, 2003.

Greene, Owen. *Nuclear Winter: The Evidence and the Risks.* Cambridge, England: Polity Press, 1985.

Gregory, K. J., and D. E. Walling. *Paleohydrology and Environmental Change.* New York: John Wiley, 1998.

Gregory, R. L., ed. *Tidal Power and Estuary Management.* Dorchester, England: Henry Ling, 1978.

Grimsditch, Gabriel D., and Rodney V. Salm. *Coral Reef Resilience and Resistance to Bleaching.* Gland, Switzerland: International Union for Conservation of Nature, 2006.

Gross, M. Grant. *Oceanography: A View of the Earth.* 7th ed. Englewood Cliffs, N.J.: Prentice-Hall, 1996.

Grossman, Elizabeth. *Watershed: The Undamming of America.* New York: Counterpoint, 2002.

Grotjahn, R. *Global Atmospheric Circulations: Observations and Theories.* Oxford, England: Oxford University Press, 1993.

Grotzinger, John, Thomas S. Jordan, and Frank Press. *Understanding Earth.* 5th ed. New York: W. H. Freeman, 2006.

Guadalupi, Gianni. *The Discovery of the Nile.* New York: Stewart, Tabori, and Chang, 1997.

_____. *The Nile: History, Adventure, and Discovery.* Vercelli: White Star, 2008.

Guidoboni, Emanuela, and John E. Ebel. *Earthquakes and Tsunamis in the Past: A Guide to Techniques in Historical Seismology.* New York: Cambridge University Press, 2009.

Gunde-Cimerman, Nina, Aharon Oren, and Ana Plemenita. *Adaptation to Life at High Salt Concentrations in Archaea, Bacteria, and Eukarya.* New York: Springer, 2011.

Gurney, R. J., J. L. Foster, and C. L. Parkinson, eds. *Atlas of Satellite Observations Related to Global Change.* Cambridge, England: Cambridge University Press, 1993.

Gurvich, Evgeny G. *Metalliferous Sediments of the World Ocean.* Berlin: Springer-Verlag, 2010.

Guymon, Gary L. *Unsaturated Zone Hydrology.* Upper Saddle River, N.J.: Prentice-Hall, 1994.

Guzzi, Rodolfo, ed. *Exploring the Atmosphere by Remote Sensing Techniques.* New York: Springer, 2010.

Haerens, Margaret. *Global Viewpoints: Air Pollution* Farmington Hills, Mich.: Greenhaven Press, 2011.

Håkanson, Lars, and M. Jansson. *Principles of Lake Sedimentology.* Caldwell, N.J.: Blackburn Press, 2002.

Hall, M. J. *Crisis on the Coast.* Portland, Ore.: USCG Marine Safety Office, 1999.

Hallegatte, Stephane, Fanny Henriet, and Jan Corfee-Morlot. "The Economics of Climate Change Impacts and Policy Benefits at City Scale: A Conceptual Framework." *Climatic Change* 104, no. 1 (2011): 51-87.

Hamblin, Kenneth W., and Eric H. Christiansen. *Earth's Dynamic Systems.* 10th ed. Upper Saddle River, N.J.: Prentice Hall, 2003.

Hambrey, Michael J., and Jurg Alean. *Glaciers.* 2d ed. New York: Cambridge University Press, 2004.

Hamilton, Kevin, and Wataru Ohfuchi, eds. *High Resolution Numerical Modeling of the Atmosphere and Ocean.* New York: Springer Science+Business Media, 2008.

Harris, Peter T., and Elaine K. Baker, eds. *Seafloor Geomorphology as Benthic Habitat.* New York: Elsevier, 2011.

Harrison, Roy M. *Principles of Environmental Chemistry.* Cambridge, England: Royal Society of Chemistry, 2007.

Harter, Thomas, and Larry Rollins, eds. *Watersheds, Groundwater and Drinking Water: A Practical Guide.* Oakland: University of California Agriculture and Natural Resources Communication Services, 2008.

Harvey, Adrian M., Anne E. Mather, and Martin R. Stokes. *Alluvial Fans: Geomorphology, Sedimentology, Dynamics.* Geological Society Special Publication 251. London: Geological Society Publishing House, 2005.

Harvie, Christopher. *Fool's Gold: The Story of North Sea Oil.* London: Hamish Hamilton, 1994.

Harwell, Mark. *Nuclear Winter: The Human and Environmental Consequences of Nuclear War.* New York: Springer-Verlag, 1984.

Haslett, Simon K. *Coastal Systems.* 2d ed. Abingdon: Routledge, 2009.

Hatfield, Jerry L., et al., eds. *Impacts of El Niño and Climate Variability on Agriculture.* ASA Special Publication Number 63. Madison, Wisc.: American Society of Agronomy, 2001.

Hawley, T. M. *Against the Fires of Hell: The Environmental Disaster of the Gulf War.* New York: Harcourt, Brace and Jovanovich, 1992.

Hay, William A. "Paleoceanography: A Review for the GSA Centennial." *Geological Society of America Bulletin* 100 (December, 1988): 1934-1956.

Haykin, Simon S., and Sadasivan Puthusserypady. *Chaotic Dynamics of Sea Clutter.* New York: John Wiley, 1999.

Healy, Richard W., and Bridget R. Scanlon. *Estimating Groundwater Recharge.* New York: Cambridge University Press, 2010.

Heathcote, Isobel W. *Integrated Watershed Management: Principles and Practice.* 2d ed. Hoboken, N.J.: John Wiley & Sons, 2009.

Hecht, Susanna B., and Alexander Cockburn. *The Fate of the Forest: Developers, Destroyers and Defenders of the Amazon.* Chicago: University of Chicago Press, 2010.

Hekinian, R. *Petrology of the Ocean Floor.* New York: Elsevier, 1982.

Hem, J. D. *Study and Interpretation of the Chemical Characteristics of Natural Water.* 3d ed. United States Geological Survey Water-Supply Paper 2254. Washington, D.C.: U.S. Government Printing Office, 1992.

Henderson, Bonnie. *Strand: An Odyssey of Pacific Ocean Debris.* Corvallis, Oreg.: Oregon State University Press, 2008.

Henderson-Sellers, A. *The Origin and Evolution of Planetary Atmospheres.* Bristol, England: Adam Hilger, 1983.

Henderson-Sellers, Ann, and Kendal McGuffie. *The Future of the World's Climate.* Boston: Elsevier, 2012.

Henes, Donna. *Celestially Auspicious Occasions: Seasons, Cycles, and Celebrations.* New York: Berkley, 1996.

Henry, Georges. *Geophysics for Sedimentary Basins.* Translated by Derrick Painter. Paris: Editions Technip, 1997.

Henry, J. G., and G. W. Heinke. *Environmental Science and Engineering.* 2d ed. Upper Saddle River, N.J.:

Prentice Hall, 1996.

Hess, Wilmot N. *Weather and Climate Modification.* New York: Wiley, 1974.

Hester, R. E., and R. M. Harrison. *Chemistry in the Marine Environment.* Cambridge, England: Royal Society of Chemistry, 2000.

Hidore, John, John E. Oliver, Mary Snow, and Richard Snow. *Climatology.* 3d ed. Columbus, Ohio: Merrill, 1984.

Hilgenkamp, Kathryn. *Environmental Health: Ecological Perspectives.* Sudbury, Mass.: Jones and Bartlett Publishers, 2005.

Hill, Janice. *Weather from Above.* Washington, D.C.: Smithsonian Institution Press, 1991.

Hill, Marquita K., *Understanding Environmental Pollution.* Cambridge, England: Cambridge University Press, 2010.

Hillel, D. "Lash of the Dragon." *Natural History* (August, 1991): 28-37
_____. *Rivers of Eden.* New York: Oxford University Press, 1994.

Hirschmann, Kristine. *Extreme Places: The Deepest Lake.* San Diego: KidHaven Press, 2002.

Hobbs, Peter V. *Introduction to Atmospheric Chemistry.* Cambridge, England: Cambridge University Press, 2000.

Hodges, Kip. "Climate and the Evolution of Mountains." *Scientific American* 295 (2006): 72-79.

Hodgson, Michael. *Basic Essentials: Weather Forecasting.* 3d ed. Chester, Conn.: Globe Pequot, 2007.

Hoff, Raymond, et al. "Applications of the Three-Dimensional Air Quality System to Western US Air Quality: IDEA, Smog Blog, Smog Stories, AirQuest, and the Remote Sensing Information Gateway." *Journal of the Air and Waste Management Association* 59, no. 8 (2009): 980-989.

Hoffmann, Matthew J. *Ozone Depletion and Climate Change: Constructing a Global Response.* Albany: State University of New York Press, 2005.

Hogarth, Peter J. *The Biology of Mangroves and Seagrasses.* 2d ed. New York: Oxford University Press, 2007.

Holland, H. D. *The Chemical Evolution of the Atmosphere and Oceans.* Princeton, N.J.: Princeton University Press, 1984.

Hollick, Julian Crandall. *Ganga: A Journey Down the Ganges River.* Washington, D.C.: Island Press, 2008.

Hollister, C. D., A. Nowell, and P. A. Jumar. "The Dynamic Abyss." *Scientific American* 250 (March, 1984): 42.

Holman, J. Alan. *In Quest of Great Lakes Ice Age Vertebrates.* East Lansing: Michigan State University Press, 2001.

Holmes-Siedle, A. G., and L. Adams. *Handbook of Radiation Effects.* 2d ed. London: Oxford University Press, 2002.

Holthujsen, Leo H. *Waves in Oceanic and Coastal Waters.* New York: Cambridge University Press.

Holton, James R. *An Introduction to Dynamic Meteorology.* 4th ed. Burlington, Mass.: Academic Press, 2004.

Hood, Peter J., ed. *Earth Science Symposium on Hudson Bay.* National Advisory Committee on Research Geological Survey of Canada Paper 68-53 (1968).

Hopkins, J. S. *The Accuracy of Wind and Wave Forecasts.* Sudbury, England: HSE, 1997.

Hopler, Paul. *Atmosphere: Weather, Climate, and Pollution.* New York: Cambridge University Press, 1994.

Hopley, David. *Encyclopedia of Modern Coral Reefs: Structure, Form and Process.* Dordrecht: Springer, 2011.

Horel, John, and Jack Geisler. *Global Environmental Change: An Atmospheric Perspective.* New York: John Wiley & Sons, 1997.

Hornberger, George M., Jeffrey P. Raffensperger, Patricia P. Wiberg, and Keith N. Eshleman. *Elements of Physical Hydrology.* Baltimore, Md.: Johns Hopkins University Press, 1998.

Houghton, John. *Global Warming: The Complete Briefing.* 4th ed. Cambridge, England: Cambridge University Press, 2009.

House, Tanzy J., James B. Near, William B. Shields, Ronald J. Celentano, Ann E. Mercer, and James E. Pugh. *Weather as a Force Multiplier: Owning the Weather in 2025.* Maxwell Air Force Base, Ala.: Air University, 1996.

Houseknecht, David W., and Edward D. Pittman, eds. *Origin, Diagenesis, and Petrophysics of Clay Minerals in Sandstones.* Tulsa, Okla.: Society for Sedimentary Geology, 1992.

Houston, Roy S. *Natural History Guide to the Northwestern Gulf of California and the Adjacent Desert.* Bloomington, Ind.: Xlibris Corporation, 2006.

Hovland, Martin. *Deep-Water Coral Reefs: Unique Biodiversity Hot-Spots.* Chichester, England: Praxis, 2008.

Howell, P. P., and J. A. Allan, eds. *The Nile: Sharing a Scarce Resource.* Cambridge, England: Cambridge University Press, 1994.

Hsu, Kenneth J. *Physics of Sedimentology.* 2d ed. New York: Springer, 2010.

Huang, P. M., and Iskandar Karam, eds. *Soils and Groundwater Pollution and Remediation: Asia, Africa, and Oceania.* Boca Baton, Fla.: Lewis, 2000.

Humphreys, Jay. *Seasons of the Sea.* Sarasota, Fla.: Pineapple Press, 2001.

Humphris, Susan E., et al., eds. *Seafloor Hydrothermal Systems.* Washington, D.C.: American Geophysical Union, 1995.

Huneke, H., and T. Mulder. *Deep-Sea Sediments.* Amsterdam: Elsevier, 2011.

Hunt, Constance Elizabeth. *Thirsty Planet: Strategies for Sustainable Water Management.* New York: St. Martin's Press, 2004.

Hunter, Nick. *Offshore Oil Drilling.* Chicago: Heinemann Library, 2012.

Hupp, Betty, and Marilyn Malone. *The Edge of the Sea of Cortez.* Operculum, 2008.

Husain, Tahir. *Kuwaiti Oil Fires: Regional Environmental Perspectives.* New York: Elsevier Science, 1995.

Hutchings, P. A., Michael Kingsford, and Ove Hoegh-Guldberg, eds. *The Great Barrier Reef: Biology, Environment, and Management.* New York: Springer, 2008.

Ilyina, Tatjana. *The Fate of Persistent Organic Pollutants in the North Sea: Multiple Years Model Simulations of γ-HCH, α-HCH and PCB 153.* Berlin: Springer-Verlag, 2007.

Imberger, Jeorg, ed. *Physical Processes in Lakes and Oceans.* Washington, D.C.: American Geophysical Union, 1998.

Imeson, Anton. *Desertification, Land Degradation and Sustainability.* Hoboken, N.J.: Wiley, 2012.

Ingebritsen, S. E., Ward E. Sanford, and C. E. Neuzil. *Groundwater in Geologic Processes.* 2d ed. New York: Cambridge University Press, 2006.

Ingmanson, Dale E., and William J. Wallace. *Oceanography: An Introduction.* 5th ed. Belmont, Calif.: Wadsworth, 1995.

Intergovernmental Panel on Climate Change. *Climate Change 2001: IPCC Third Assessment Report.* Geneva: IPCC Secretariat, 2001.

_____. "Northern Hemisphere Temperatures During the Past Millennium: Inferences, Uncertainties, and Limitations." *Geophysical Research Letters* 26, no. 6 (1999): 759-762.

_____. Working Group I. *Climate Change 2007: The Physical Science Basis.* New York: Cambridge University Press, 2007.

_____. Working Group II. *Climate Change 2007: Impacts, Adaptation, and Vulnerability.* New York: Cambridge University Press, 2007.

_____. Working Group III. *Climate Change 2007: Mitigation of Climate Change.* New York: Cambridge University Press, 2007.

Ittekko, Venugopalan, et al., eds. *Particle Flux in the Ocean.* New York: John Wiley and Sons, 1996.

Izrael, Urii Antonievich. *Radioactive Fallout After Nuclear Explosions and Accidents.* Oxford: Elsevier Science, 2002.

Jacobson, Michael C., et al. *Earth System Science: From Biogeochemical Cycles to Global Change.* San Diego, Calif.: Academic Press, 2006.

Jacques, Peter. *Globalization and the World Ocean.* Lanham, Md.: Rowman and Littlefield Publishing Group Inc., 2006.

James, Ian N. *Introduction to Circulating Atmospheres.* Cambridge, England: Cambridge University Press, 1994.

Janssen, Sarah, ed. *The World Almanac and Book of Facts, 2011.* Mahwah, N.J.: World Almanac Books, 2011.

Jeftic, L., et al., eds. *Climatic Change and the Mediterranean: Environmental and Societal Impacts of Climatic Change and Sea-Level Rise in the Mediterranean Region.* New York: E. Arnold, 1992.

Jeleff, Sophie, ed. *Oceans.* Strasburg: Council of Europe, 1999.

Jenkins, Jerry C., et al. *Acid Rain in the Adirondacks: An Environmental History.* Ithaca, N.Y.: Cornell University Press, 2007.

Jochum, Markus, and Raghi Murtugudde, eds. *Physical Oceanography: Developments Since 1950.* New York: Springer Science + Business Media Inc., 2006.

Johnson, Markes E., and Jorge Ledesma-Vazquez. *Atlas of Coastal Ecosystems of the Western Gulf of California: Tracking Limestone Deposits on the Margin of a Young Sea.* Tucson, Ariz.: University of Arizona Press, 2009.

Johnson, Robert G. *Secrets of the Ice Ages: The Role of the Mediterranean Sea in Climate Change.* Minnetonka, Minn.: Glenjay Publishing, 2002.

Jones, J. A. A. *Global Hydrology: Processes, Resources, and Environmental Management.* Essex, England: Longman, 1997.

Joseph, Antony. *Tsunamis: Detection, Monitoring and Early Warning Technologies.* Burlington, Mass.: Academic Press/Elsevier, 2011.

Joseph, P. *Deep Water Sedimentation in the Alpine Basin of SE France.* Special Publication 221. London:

Geological Society of London, 2004.

Joughin, Ian, and Richard B. Alley. "Stability of the West Antarctic Ice Sheet in a Warming World." *Nature Geoscience* 4 (2011): 506-513.

Judson, S., and Steven M. Richardson. *Earth: An Introduction to Geologic Change*. Upper Saddle River, N.J.: Prentice Hall, 1995.

Juhasz, Antonia. *Black Tide: The Devastating Impact of the Gulf Oil Spill*. Hoboken, N.J.: John Wiley, 2011.

Jury, Mark R. "An Intercomparison of Observational, Reanalysis, Satellite, and Coupled Model Data on Mean Rainfall in the Caribbean." *Journal of Hydrometeorology* 10, no. 2 (2009): 413-420.

Kagan, Boris A. *Ocean-Atmosphere Interaction and Climate Modeling*. Cambridge, England: Cambridge University Press, 2006.

Kalin Arroyo, Mary T., Paul H. Zedler, and Marilyn D. Fox, eds. *Ecology and Biogeography of Mediterranean Ecosystems in Chile, California, and Australia*. Vol. 108. New York: Springer-Verlag, 1995.

Kämpf, J., and M. Sadrinasab. "The Circulation of the Persian Gulf: A Numerical Study." *Ocean Science Discussions* 2 (2005): 129-164.

Kandel, Robert. "Understanding and Measuring Earth's Energy Budget: From Fourier, Humboldt, and Tyndall to CERES and Beyond." *Surveys in Geophysics* (January, 2012): 1-12.

_____. *Water from Heaven: The Story of Water from the Big Bang to the Rise of Civilization and Beyond*. New York: Columbia University Press, 2003.

Kaplan, Eugene H. *A Field Guide to Coral Reefs of the Caribbean and Florida, Including Bermuda and the Bahamas*. Boston: Houghton Mifflin, 1988.

Karl, David M., ed. *The Microbiology of Deep-Sea Hydrothermal Vents*. Boca Raton, Fla.: CRC Press, 1995.

Kasenow, Michael. *Aquifer Test Data: Analysis and Evaluation*. Highlands Ranch, Colo.: Water Resources Publications, 2006.

_____. *Production Well Analysis: New Methods and Computer Programs in Well Hydraulics*. Highlands Ranch, Colo.: Water Resources Publications, 1996.

Kashiwaya, Kenji. *Long Continental Records from Lake Baikal*. Tokyo: Springer-Verlag Tokyo, 2003.

Katz, Richard W., and Allan H. Murphy. *Economic Value of Weather and Climate Forecasts*. New York: Cambridge University Press, 1997.

Kaufman, Martin M., Daniel T. Rogers and Kent S. Murray. *Urban Watersheds: Geology, Contamination and Sustainable Development*. Boca Raton, Fla.: CRC Press, 2011.

Kaufman, Wallace, and Orrin Pilkey. *The Beaches Are Moving: The Drowning of America's Shoreline*. Durham, N.C.: Duke University Press, 1983.

Kaye, Catheryn Berger, and Philippe Cousteau. *Going Blue*. Minneapolis, Minn.: Free Spirit Publishing, 2009.

Keating, Barbara H., Patricia Fryer, Rodney Batiza, and George W. Boehlert, eds. *Seamounts, Islands, and Atolls*. 2d ed. Washington, D.C.: American Geophysical Union, 1988.

Keim, Barry D., and Robert A. Muller. *Hurricanes of the Gulf of Mexico*. Baton Rouge, La.: Louisiana State University Press, 2009.

Kelkar, R. R. *Satellite Meteorology*. Hyderabad: BS Publications, 2007.

Kelley, Joseph T., Orrin H. Pilkey, and J. A. G. Cooper. *America's Most Vulnerable Coastal Communities*. Boulder, Colo.: Geological Society of America, 2009.

Kennedy, A., J. M. Straka, and E. N. Rasmussen. "A Statistical Study of the Association of DRCs with Supercells and Tornadoes." *Weather Forecasting* 22 (2007): 1191-1199.

Kennet, James P. *Marine Geology*. Englewood Cliffs, N.J.: Prentice-Hall, 1982.

Kennish, Michael J. *Practical Handbook of Marine Science*. 3d ed. Boca Raton, Fla.: CRC Press, 2001.

Kiehl, J. T., and V. Ramanathan. *Frontiers of Climate Modeling*. New York: Cambridge University Press, 2006.

Kiehl, J. T., and Kevin E. Trenberth. "Earth's Annual Global Mean Energy Budget." *Bulletin of the American Meteorological Society* 78 (February, 1997): 197-208.

King, Charles. *The Black Sea: A History*. Oxford: Oxford University Press, 2005.

King, Cuchaine A. M. *Introduction to Marine Geology and Geomorphology*. London: Edward Arnold, 1974.

Kirby, Richard R. *Ocean Drifters: A Secret World Beneath the Waves*. Winchester, England: Studio Cactus, 2010.

Klaassen, G. *Acid Rain and Environmental Degradation: The Economics of Emission Trading*. Brookfield, Vt.: Edward Elgar, 1996.

Klingeman, Peter C., et al., eds. *Gravel-Bed Rivers in the Environment*. Highlands Ranch, Colo.: Water

Resources Publications, 1995.

Knight, Gregory, Ivan Raev, and Marieta Staneva, eds. *Drought in Bulgaria*. Hants, England: Ashgate Publishing Limited, 2004.

Knighton, David. *Fluvial Forms and Processes: A New Perspective*. 2d ed. London: Edward Arnold, 1998.

Knox, Pamela Naber. "A Current Catastrophe: El Niño." *Earth* (September, 1992): 31-37.

Knudson, Tom. "An Overview of the Destruction of the Sea of Cortez." *Sacramento Bee* (December, 1995): 10-13.

Ko, A., and D. B. Guy. "Brackish and Seawater Desalting." In *Reverse Osmosis Technology: Application for High-Purity-Water Production*. New York: Marcel Dekker, 1988.

Kokhanovsky, Alexander A., ed. *Light Scattering and Remote Sensing of Atmosphere and Surface*. Vol. 6 in *Light Scattering Reviews*. New York: Springer, 2011.

Kolumban, Hutter, Yongqi Wang, and Irina P. Chubarenko. *Physics of Lakes: Foundation of the Mathematical and Physical Background*. Dordrecht: Springer, 2011.

Komar, Paul D. *Beach Process and Sedimentation*. Upper Saddle River, N.J.: Prentice Hall, 1998.

Kondratyev, K. Y., V. F. Krapivin, and Costas A. Varotsos. *Global Carbon Cycle and Climate Change*. New York: Springer, 2003.

Koppel, Tom. *Ebb and Flow: Tides and Life on Our Once and Future Planet*. Ontario: Dundern Press, 2007.

Koptyug, Valentin A., ed. *Sustainable Development of the Lake Baikal Region: A Model Territory for the World*. New York: Springer, 1996.

Kostianoy, Andrey G. *The Aral Sea Environment*. Berlin: Springer-Verlag, 2010.

Kostianoy, Andrey G., and A. Kosarev. *The Black Sea Environment*. Dordrecht: Springer, 2007.

_____. *The Caspian Sea Environment*. Berlin: Springer-Verlag, 2005.

Kotir, Julius H. "Climate Change and Variability in Sub-Saharan Africa: A Review of Current and Future Trends and Impacts on Agriculture and Food Security." *Environment, Development, and Sustainability* 13, no. 3 (2011): 587-605.

Kotlyakov, V. M. "The Aral Sea Basin: A Critical Environmental Zone." *Environment* 23 (1): (January, 1991).

Kotlyakov, V., M. Uppenbrink, and V. Metreveli, eds. *Conservation of Biological Diversity as a Prerequisite for Sustainable Development in the Black Sea Region*. Dordrecht: Kluwer, 1998.

Kourkoulis, Stavros K., ed. *Fracture and Failure of*

Natural Building Stones. Dordrecht: Springer, 2006.

Kovar, Karel, et al., eds. *Hydrology, Water Resources, and Ecology in Headwaters*. Wallingford, England: International Association of Hydrological Sciences, 1998.

Kowahata, Hodaka, and Yoshio Awaya. *Global Climate Change and Response of the Carbon Cycle in the Equatorial Pacific and Indian Oceans and Adjacent Landmasses*. Amsterdam: Elsevier, 2006.

Kozhova, Olga Mikhaeilovna, and L. R. Izmestseva, eds. *Lake Baikal: Evolution and Biodiversity*. Leiden: Backhuys, 1998.

Krešić, Neven. *Groundwater Resources: Sustainability, Management, and Restoration*. New York: McGraw-Hill, 2009.

Krishnamurti, T. N., et al. "Improved Weather and Seasonal Climate Forecasts from Multimodel Superensemble." *Science* 258 (September 3, 1999): 1548-1550.

Kshudiram, Saha. *Tropical Circulation Systems and Monsoons*. New York: Springer, 2010.

Kuhn, Gerald G. "The Impact of Volcanic Eruptions on Worldwide Weather." *Twenty-first Century Science and Technology* (Winter, 1997-1998): 48-58.

Kukushkin, A. B., and V. A. Rantsev-Kartinov. "Evidence for Skeletal Structures in Tornado and the Probable Role of Nanodusty Plasma in Severe Weather Phenomena." *31st EPS Conference on Plasma Physics: Europhysics Conference Abstracts* 28G: O5.08.

Kusuda, Tetsuya. *The Yellow River: Water and Life*. Singapore: World Scientific Publishing Co., 2010.

LaBlanc, R. J., ed. *Modern Deltas*. Tulsa, Okla.: American Association of Petroleum Geologists, 1976.

Lade, Poul V., and Jerry A. Yamamuro. "Evaluation of Static Liquefaction Potential of Silty Sand Slopes." *Canadian Geotechnical Journal* 48 (2011): 247-264.

Laity, Julie J. *Deserts and Desert Environments*. Hoboken, N.J.: John Wiley & Sons, 2008.

Lambert, David, and the Diagram Group. *Field Guide to Geology*. 2d ed. New York: Facts on File, 2007.

Lane, Carter N. *Acid Rain: Overview and Abstracts*. Hauppauge, N.Y.: Nova Science Publishers, 2003.

Lang, Kenneth. *Sun, Earth and Sky*. 2d ed. New York: Springer, 2006.

Larssen, Thorjørn, et al. "Acid Rain in China." *Environmental Science & Technology* 40 (2006): 418-425.

Lau, William K. M., and Duane E. Waliser. *Intraseasonal*

Variability in the Atmosphere-Ocean Climate System. 2d ed. New York: Springer-Verlag, 2012.

Lawton, Jerry. *Waterfalls: The Niagara Escarpment.* Richmond Hill, Ontario: Boston Mills Press, 2000.

Leatherman, Stephen P. *Barrier Island Handbook.* 3d ed. College Park, Md.: Laboratory for Coastal Reasearch, University of Maryland, 1988.

Leeder, Mike R. *Sedimentology and Sedimentary Basins: From Turbulence to Tectonics.* 2d ed. Hoboken, N.J.: John Wiley & Sons, 2011.

Lehner, Peter, and Bob Deans. *In Deep Water: The Anatomy of a Disaster, the Fate of the Gulf, and How to End Our Oil Addiction.* New York: OR Books, 2010.

Lemke, Peter, and Hans-Werner Jacobi. *Arctic Climate Change: The Acsys Decade and Beyond.* New York: Springer Science+Business Media, 2012.

Lencek, Lena, and Gideon Boskar. *The Beach: The History of Paradise on Earth.* New York: Viking, 1998.

Leopold, Luna B. *A View of the River.* Cambridge, Mass.: Harvard University Press, 2006.

_____. *Water: A Primer.* San Francisco: W. H. Freeman, 1974.

_____. *Water, Rivers, and Creeks.* Sausalito, Calif.: University Science Books, 2009.

Lerman, A. "Geochemical Cycles." In *The Oxford Companion to the Earth.* Edited by Paul Hancock and Brian J. Skinner. New York: Oxford University Press, 2000.

Lerman, Abraham, Dieter M. Imboden, and Joel R. Gat, eds. *Physics and Chemistry of Lakes.* New York: Springer-Verlag, 1995.

Lesser, Michael P. "Coral Bleaching: Causes and Mechanisms." In *Coral Reefs: An Ecosystem in Transition,* edited by Zvy Dubinsky and Noga Stambler. New York: Springer, 2011.

_____. "Coral Reef Bleaching and Global Climate Change: Can Corals Survive the Next Century?" *PNAS* 104, no. 13 (2007): 5259-5260.

Le Sueur, Meridel. *North Star Country.* 2d ed. Minneapolis: University of Minnesota Press, 1998.

Letcher, Trevor, and Daniel Vallero, eds. *Waste: A Handbook for Management.* Burlington, Mass.: Academic Press/Elsevier, 2011.

Lévêque, C. *Ecology from Ecosystem to Biosphere.* Enfield, N.H.: Science, 2003.

Levine, Joel S., ed. *The Photochemistry of Atmospheres: Earth, the Other Planets, and Comets.* Orlando, Fla.: Academic Press, 1985.

Levinton, Jeffery S., and John R. Waldman. *The Hudson River Estuary.* New York: Cambridge University Press, 2006.

Lewis, John S., and Ronald G. Prinn. *Planets and Their Atmospheres: Origin and Evolution.* New York: Academic Press, 1983.

Lighthill, James, and Robert Pearce, eds. *Monsoon Dynamics.* New York: Cambridge University Press, 2009.

Likens, Gene E., R. F. Wright, J. F. Galloway, and T. F. Butler. "Acid Rain." *Scientific American* 241 (October, 1979): 43-51.

Lillesand, Thomas M., Ralph W. Kiefer, and Jonathan Chipman. *Remote Sensing and Image Interpretation.* 6th ed. Hoboken, N.J.: John Wiley & Sons, 2008.

Lionello, P. *The Climate of the Mediterranean Region: From the Past to the Future.* London: Elsevier, 2012.

Liu, William, and Masaki Fujimoto, eds. *The Dynamic Magnetosphere.* New York: Springer, 2011.

Longshore, David. *Encyclopedia of Hurricanes, Typhoons, and Cyclones.* New York: Facts on File, 2008.

Lubin, Dan, and Robert Massom. *Polar Remote Sensing: Atmosphere and Oceans.* Chichester, England: Praxis Publishing, 2006.

Lutgens, Frederick K., Edward J. Tarbuck, and Dennis Tasa. *The Atmosphere: An Introduction to Meteorology.* 11th ed. Upper Saddle River, N.J.: Prentice Hall, 2009.

_____. *Essentials of Geology.* 11th ed. Upper Saddle River, N.J.: Prentice Hall, 2011.

Mabbutt, J. A. *Desert Landforms.* Cambridge, Mass.: MIT Press, 1977.

MacDonald, Ian R., and Charles Fisher. "Life Without Light." *National Geographic* 190 (October, 1996).

MacDougall, Doug. *Frozen Earth: The Once and Future Story of Ice Ages.* Berkeley, Calif.: University of California Press, 2006.

MacGorman, Donald R., and W. David Rust. *The Electrical Nature of Storms.* New York: Oxford University Press, 1998.

Machtinger, Erika T. *Riparian Systems.* Washington, D.C.: Natural Resources Conservation Service, 2007.

MacLeish, William H. *The Gulf Stream.* Boston: Houghton Mifflin, 1989.

Madigan, Michael T., et al. *Brock Biology of Microorganisms.* 13th ed. Boston: Benjamin Cummings, 2012.

Magill, Frank N., and Russell R. Tobias, eds. *USA in*

Space. Pasadena, Calif.: Salem Press, 1996.

Magnuson, John J., Timothy K. Kratz, and Barbara J. Benson. *Long-Term Dynamics of Lakes in the Landscape: Long-Term Ecological Research on North Temperate Lakes.* Oxford: Oxford University Press, 2006.

Mahajan, Gautam. *Evaluation and Development of Ground Water.* New Delhi: S. B. Nangia, 2008.

Mainguet, Monique. *Aridity: Drought and Human Development.* Berlin: Springer-Verlag, 2010.

Majumdar, Shyamal K., et al., eds. *The Oceans: Physical-Chemical Dynamics and Human Impact.* Easton, Pa.: Pennsylvania Academy of Science, 1994.

Malakoff, David. "Death by Suffocation in the Gulf of Mexico." *Science* 5374 (July 10, 1998): 190-192.

Malhi, Y., and O. Phillips. *Tropical Forests and Global Atmospheric Change.* New York: Oxford University Press, 2005.

Mann, Charles C. *1491: New Revelations of the Americas Before Columbus.* New York: Knopf, 2005.

Mann, Michael E., Raymond S. Bradley, and Malcolm K. Hughes. "Global-Scale Temperature Patterns and Climate Forcing over the Past Six Centuries." *Nature* 392 (1998): 779-787.

Manning, John C. *Applied Principles of Hydrology.* 3d ed. Upper Saddle River, N.J.: Prentice Hall, 1997.

Markov, Sergei A., Michael J. Bazin, and David O. Hall. "Potential of Using Cyanobacteria in Photobioreactors for Hydrogen Production." In *Advances in Biochemical Engineering/Biotechnology,* edited by A. Fiechter. Vol. 52. New York: Springer, 1995.

Marsh, W. M. *Landscape Planning: Environmental Applications.* 5th ed. New York: John Wiley & Sons, 2010.

Marshal, John, and R. Alan Plumb. *Atmosphere, Ocean and Climate Dynamics: An Introductory Text.* Burlington, Mass.: Elsevier Academic Press, 2008.

Marti, Joan, and Gerald Ernst. *Volcanoes and the Environment.* New York: Cambridge University Press, 2005.

Martin, John Wilson. *Precipitation Hardening.* 2d ed. Boston: Butterworth-Heinemann, 1998.

Martin, Seelye. *An Introduction to Ocean Remote Sensing.* New York: Cambridge University Press, 2004.

Marvin, Charles Thomas. *The Region of the Eternal Fire: An Account of a Journey to the Petroleum Region of the Caspian in 1883.* London: W. H. Allen, 1891. Elibron Classics, Adamand Media Corporation, 2005.

Marzano, Frank S., and Guido Visconti, eds. *Remote*

Sensing of Atmosphere and Ocean from Space: Models, Instruments, and Techniques. New York: Springer, 2011.

Maslin, Mark. *Global Warming: Causes, Effects and the Future.* St. Paul, Minn.: MBI Publishing Company, 2007.

Mason, Betsy. "Season of Fire." *Discover* 24 (2003): 32-39.

Masselink, G., and M. G. Hughes. *Introduction to Coastal Processes and Geomorphology.* London: Hodder Arnold Publication, 2003.

Mather, Graeme K. "Coalescence Enhancement in Large Multicell Storms Caused by the Emissions from a Kraft Paper Mill." *Journal of Applied Meteorology* 91 (1991).

Mather, John R. *Groundwater Contaminants and Their Migrations.* London: Geological Society, 1998.

Mathur, Anuradha, and Dilip da Cunha. *Mississippi Floods: Designing a Shifting Landscape.* Boston: Yale University Press, 2001.

Matthiessen, Peter. *Baikal: Sacred Sea of Siberia.* San Francisco: Sierra Club Books, 1995.

Mavrodiev, Strachimir Chterev. *Applied Ecology of the Black Sea.* Commack, N.Y.: Nova Science, 1999.

Mays, Larry W. *Ground and Surface Water Hydrology.* Hoboken, N.J.: John Wiley & Sons, 2011.

_____. *Water Resources Engineering.* Hoboken, N.J.: John Wiley & Sons, 2011.

McCarthy, James, et al., eds. *Climate Change 2001: Impacts, Adaptation, and Vulnerability.* New York: Cambridge University Press, 2001.

McCarthy, Kevin T., Thomas Pichler, and Roy E. Price. "Geochemistry of Champagne Hot Springs Shallow Hydrothermal Vent Field and Associated Sediments, Dominica, Lesser Antilles." *Chemical Geology* 224 (2005): 55-68.

McClain, Michael E., Reynaldo L. Victoria, and Jeffrey Edward Richey. *The Biogeochemistry of the Amazon Basin.* New York: Oxford University Press, 2001.

McCormick, John. *Acid Earth: The Politics of Acid Pollution.* 3d ed. London: Earthscan, 1997.

McCully, James Greig. *Beyond the Moon: A Conversational, Common Sense Guide to Understanding the Tides.* Hackensack, N.J.: World Scientific Publishing, 2006.

McCurry, Steve. *Monsoon.* New York: Thames and Hudson, 1988.

McElhinny, M. W., ed. *The Earth: Its Origin, Structure, and Evolution.* New York: Academic Press, 1979.

McFadden, Lucy-Ann Adams, Paul Robert Weissman,

EARTH'S WEATHER, WATER, AND ATMOSPHERE

and T. V. Johnson. *Encyclopedia of the Solar System.* San Diego, Calif.: Academic Press, 2007.

McGinnies, William G., B. J. Goldman, and P. Paylore, eds. *Deserts of the World.* Tucson: University of Arizona Press, 1968.

McGinnis, Tim. "Seafloor Drilling." In *Drilling in Extreme Environments: Penetration and Sampling on Earth and Other Planets*, edited by Yoseph Bar-Cohen and Kris Zacny. Hoboken, N.J.: Wiley, 2009.

McGonigal, David. *Antarctica: Secrets of the Southern Continent.* London: Francis Lincoln, 2009.

McGranahan, Gordon, and Frank Murray, eds. *Air Pollution and Health in Rapidly Developing Countries* London: Earthscan Publications, 2003.

McKinney, Frank. *The Northern Adriatic Ecosystem: Deep Time in a Shallow Sea.* New York: Columbia University Press, 2007.

McKinney, Michael L., Robert M. Schoch, and Logan Yonavjak. *Environmental Science: Systems and Solutions.* 4th ed. Sudbury, Mass.: Jones and Bartlett Publishers, 2007.

McKinnon, Michael. *Arabia: Sand, Sea, Sky.* BBC/Parkwest, 1992.

McLellan, H. J. *Elements of Physical Oceanography.* Elmsford, N.Y.: Pergamon Press, 1977.

Melanotte-Rizzoli, P., ed. *Modern Approaches to Data Assimilation in Ocean Modeling.* New York: Elsevier Science, 1996.

Melchoir, Paul. *The Tides of the Planet Earth.* Elmsford, N.Y.: Pergamon Press, 1978.

Melesse, Assefa M. *Nile River Basin: Hydrology, Climate and Water Use.* Dordrecht: Springer, 2011.

Menard, H. W. *Islands.* New York: W. H. Freeman, 1986.

Menzel, W. Paul. *Applications with Meteorological Satellites.* Geneva: World Meteorological Organization, 2001.

Merritt, Michael L. *Assessment of Saltwater Intrusion in Southern Coastal Broward County, Florida.* Tallahassee, Fla.: U.S. Department of the Interior, Geological Survey, 1997.

Metcalf & Eddy, Inc. *Wastewater Engineering: Treatment and Reuse.* 4th ed. New York: McGraw-Hill, 2003.

Micale, Giorgio, Andrea Cipollina, and Lucio Rizutti, eds. *Seawater Desalination: Conventional and Renewable Energy Processes.* Berlin: Springer-Verlag, 2009.

Micallef, Anton, and Allan Williams. *Beach Management: Principles and Practice,* London: Earthscan, 2009.

Michaels, Patrick J., and Robert C. Balling. *Climate of Extremes: Global Warming Science They Don't Want You to Know.* Washington, D.C.: Cato Institute, 2009.

Middleton, Gerard V., ed. *Encyclopedia of Sediments and Sedimentary Rocks.* Dordrecht: Springer, 2003.

Middleton, Gerard V., and John B. Southard. *Mechanics in the Earth and Enviromental Sciences.* New York: Cambridge University Press, 1994.

Middleton, Nick. *Deserts: A Very Short Introduction.* Oxford: Oxford University Press, 2009. Intended for general readership. Delivers an introductory overview of desert environments around the world.

Middleton, W. E. K. *The History of the Barometer.* Baltimore: Johns Hopkins University Press, 1964.

Miller, Robert N. *Numerical Modeling of Ocean Circulation.* New York: Cambridge University Press, 2007.

Miller, Tom, and Elmar Baxter. *The Baja Book.* 16th ed. Santa Ana, Calif.: Baja Trail Publications, 1992.

Mills, Eric L. *The Fluid Envelope of Our Planet: How the Study of Ocean Currents Became a Science.* Toronto: Toronto University Press Inc., 2009.

Mills, K. H., S. M. Chalanchuk, and D. J. Allan. "Recovery of Fish Populations in Lake 223 from Experimental Acidification." *Canadian Journal of Fisheries and Aquatic Sciences* 57 (2000): 192-204.

Milne, Anthony. *Floodshock.* Gloucester, England: Allan Sutton, 1986.

Minoura, Koji. *Lake Baikal: A Mirror in Time and Space for Understanding Global Change Processes.* Amsterdam: Elsevier, 2000.

Mirza, M. Monirul Qader. *The Ganges Water Diversion: Environmental Effects and Implications.* Norwell, Mass.: Kluwer Academic Publishers, 2010.

Mirza, M. Monirul Qader, Ahsan Uddin Ahmed, and Qazi Kholiquzamman Ahmad. *Interlinking of Rivers in India: Issues and Concerns.* Boca Raton, Fla.: CRC Press, 2008.

Misstear, B. D. R., David Banks, and Lewis Clark. *Water Wells and Boreholes.* New York: John Wiley & Sons, 2006.

Mityagina, M. I., O. Y. Larova, and S. S. Karimova. "Multi-sensor Survey of Seasonal Variability in Coastal Eddy and Internal Wave Signatures in the North-Eastern Black Sea." *International Journal of Remote Sensing* 31, nos. 17/18 (2010): 4779-4990.

Mogil, H. Michael. *Extreme Weather: Understanding the Science of Hurricanes, Tornadoes, Floods, Heat Waves, Snow Storms, Global Warming, and Other Atmospheric Disturbances.* New York: Black Dog & Leventhal, 2007.

Mohnen, Volker A. "The Challenge of Acid Rain."

Scientific American 259 (August, 1988): 30-38.

Mojetta, Angelo. *The Red Sea: Underwater Paradise.* New York: Sterling/White Star, 2005.

Monmonier, Mark S. *Air Apparent: How Meteorologists Learned to Map, Predict, and Dramatize Weather.* Chicago: University of Chicago Press, 1999.

Monroe, James S., Reed Wicander, and Richard Hazlett. *Physical Geology: Exploring the Earth.* 6th ed. Belmont, Calif.: Thomson Higher Education, 2007.

Montgomery, C. W. *Environmental Geology.* 9th ed. Columbus, Ohio: McGraw-Hill, 2010.

_____. *Physical Geology.* 3d ed. Dubuque, Iowa: Wm. C. Brown, 1993.

Montgomery, Sy. *Seasons of the Wild: A Year of Nature's Magic and Mysteries.* Buffalo, N.Y.: Firefly, 1995.

Mooney, Chris. *Storm World: Hurricanes, Politics and the Battle Over Global Warming.* Orlando, Fla.: Harcourt Inc., 2007.

Moore, John E. *Field Hydrogeology.* 2d ed. Boca Raton, Fla.: CRC Press, 2012.

Moran, Emilio. *Developing the Amazon.* Bloomington: Indiana University Press, 1981.

Moran, Joseph M. *Weather Studies: Introduction to Atmospheric Science.* Washington D.C.: American Meteorological Association, 2009.

Moran, Joseph M., and Michael D. Morgan. *Meteorology: The Atmosphere and the Science of Weather.* 5th ed. Upper Saddle River, N.J.: Prentice Hall, 1996.

Morgan, J. P. "Deltas: A Resume." *Journal of Geologic Education* 18 (1970): 107-117.

Morgan, Michael D., Joseph M. Moran, and James H. Wiersma. "The Vanishing Aral Sea: Can It Be Saved?" *Environmental Science: Managing Biological and Physical Resources.* Dubuque, Iowa: Wm. C. Brown, 1993.

Morgan, R. P. C. *Soil Erosion and Conservation.* 3d ed. Hoboken, N.J.: Wiley-Blackwell, 2005.

Morozov, Eugene G., Alexander N. Demidov, Roman Y. Tarakanov, and Walter Zenk. *Abyssal Channels in the Atlantic Ocean: Water Structure and Flows.* Dordrecht: Springer, 2010.

Mozdzynski, George, ed. *Use of High Performance Computing in Meteorology.* Singapore: World Scientific, 2007.

Mukherji, Aditi. *Groundwater Governance in the Indo-Gangetic and Yellow River Basins: Realities and Challenges.* Leiden: CRC Press/Balkema, 2009.

Mukhopadhyay, Ranadhir, Anil K. Ghosh, and Sridhar D. Iyer. *The Indian Ocean Nodule Field: Geology and Resource Potential.* Volume 10 of the *Handbook of Exploration and Environmental Geochemistry.* Edited by M. Hale. Amsterdam: Elsevier, 2012.

Murphy, Jessica A. *Sand Dunes: Conservation, Types and Desertification.* New York: Nova Science Publishers, 2011.

Murray, John, and Alphonse J. Renard. *Deep Sea Deposits.* Edinburgh: Neill, 1891.

Murthy, R., P. V. Wolfendale, and A. W. Wolfendale. *Gamma-Ray Astronomy.* 2d ed. New York: Cambridge University Press, 1993.

Myles, Douglas. *The Great Waves.* New York: McGraw-Hill, 1985.

Nairn, Alan E. M., Francis G. Stehli, and Seiya Uyeda, eds. *The Ocean Basins and Margins. Vol. 7A: The Pacific Ocean.* New York: Plenum Press, 1985.

Nance, John J. *What Goes Up: The Global Assault on Our Atmosphere.* New York: William Morrow, 1991.

Nash, J. Madeleine. *El Niño: Unlocking the Secrets of the Master Weather-Maker.* New York: Warner Books, 2002.

National Assessment Synthesis Team, ed. *Climate Change Impacts on the United States: Foundation Report.* New York: Cambridge University Press, 2001.

National Research Council Ocean Studies Board. *The Atmospheric Sciences: Entering the Twenty-First Century.* Washington, D.C.: National Academy Press, 2010.

_____. *Critical Issues in Weather Modification Research.* Washington, D.C.: National Academies Press, 2003.

_____. *Desalination: A National Perspective.* Washington, D.C.: National Academies Press, 2008.

_____. *Drawing Louisiana's New Map: Addressing Land Loss in Coastal Louisiana.* Washington, D.C.: National Academies Press, 2006.

_____. *Mississippi River Water Quality and the Clean Water Act: Progress, Challenges and Opportunities.* Washington, D.C.: The National Academies Press, 2008.

_____. *The Ocean's Role in Global Change: Progress of Major Research Programs.* Washington, D. C.: National Academy Press, 1994.

Nebel, Bernard J., and Richard T. Wright. *Environmental Science: Towards a Sustainable Future.* Englewood Cliffs, N.J.: Prentice Hall, 2008.

Needler, George T. "WOCE: The World Ocean Circulation Experiment." *Oceanus* 35 (Summer, 1992): 74-77.

Neelin, David J. *Climate Change and Climate Modeling.*

New York: Cambridge University Press, 2011.

Neprochnov, Y. P., et al., eds. *Intraplate Deformation in the Central Indian Ocean Basin.* Bangalore, India: Geological Society of India, 1998.

Nett, Mary T., Martin A. Locke, and Dean A. Pennington. *Water Quality Assessments in the Mississippi Delta: Regional Solutions, National Scope.* Washington, D.C.: American Chemical Society, 2004.

Newell, Norman D. "The Evolution of Reefs." *Scientific American* 226 (June, 1972): 12, 54-65.

Newsom, M. *Hydrology and the River Environment.* Oxford, England: Clarendon Press, 1994.

Newson, Malcolm. *Land, Water and Development: Sustainable and Adaptive Management of Rivers.* 3d ed. London: Routledge, 2008.

Nicholson, Sharon E. *Dryland Climatology.* New York: Cambridge University Press, 2011.

Niedoroda, Alan W. "Shelf Processes." In *Encyclopedia of Coastal Science.* Edited by M. Schwartz. Dordrecht: Springer, 2005.

Nielson, Kurt Ambo. *Fractured Aquifers; Formation Evaluation by Well Testing.* Vancouver: Trafford Publishing, 2007.

Nihoul, Jacques C. J., Peter O. Zavialov, and Philip P. Micklin, NATO Scientific Affairs Division. *Dying and Dead Seas: Climatic versus Anthropic Causes.* Dordrecht: Kluwer Academic Publishing, 2004.

Nonner, Johannes C. *Introduction to Hydrogeology.* London: Taylor & Francis Group, 2006.

Novotny, Vladimir. *Water Quality: Diffuse Pollution and Watershed Management.* 2d ed. Hoboken, N.J.: John Wiley & Sons, 2003.

Nuclear Winter and National Security: Implications for Future Policy. Maxwell Air Force Base, Ala.: Air University Press, 1986.

Nunn, Patrick D. *Climate, Environment and Society in the Pacific During the Last Millenium.* Amsterdam: Elsevier, 2007.

Nyer, Evan K. *Groundwater and Soil Remediation: Practical Methods and Strategies.* Chelsea, Mich.: Ann Arbor Press, 1998.

Oceanography Course Team. *Ocean Circulation.* 2d ed. Oxford: Butterworth-Heinemann, 2001.

Ogawa, Yujiro, Ryo Anma, and Yildirim Dilek. *Accretionary Prisms and Convergent Margin Tectonics in the Northwest Pacific Basin.* New York: Springer Science+Business Media, 2011.

O'Hare, Margaret P., et al. *Artificial Recharge of Ground Water.* Chelsea, Mich.: Lewis, 1986.

O'Laughlin, Karen Fay, and James F. Lander. *Caribbean Tsunamis: A 500-Year History from 1498-1998.* Dordrecht: Kluwer Academic Publishers, 2003.

Oldfield, Sara. *Rainforest.* Cambridge, Mass.: MIT Press, 2002.

Oliver, John E., ed. *The Encyclopedia of Climatology.* Dordrecht: Springer, 2004.

Open University Oceanography Course Team. *Ocean Circulation.* 2d ed. Oxford, England: Butterworth Heinemann, 2001.

Oppenheimer, Clive. *Eruptions That Shook the World.* New York: Cambridge University Press, 2011.

Organization for Economic Cooperation and Development. *Space Technologies and Climate Change: Implications for Water Management, Marine Resources, and Maritime Transport.* Paris: Author, 2008.

Orsi, Jared. *Hazardous Metropolis: Flooding and Urban Ecology in Los Angeles.* Berkeley: University of California Press, 2004.

Oshima, Harry T. *Strategic Processes in Monsoon Asia's Economic Development.* Baltimore: Johns Hopkins University Press, 1993.

Ostmann, Robert. *Acid Rain: A Plague upon the Waters.* Minneapolis, Minn.: Dillon Press, 1982.

Oti, Michael N., and George Postma, eds. *Geology of Deltas.* Brookfield, Vt.: A. A. Balkema, 1995.

Ozsoy, Emin, and Alexander Mikaelyan, eds. *Sensitivity to Change: Black Sea, Baltic Sea, and North Sea.* Boston: Kluwer Academic Publishers, 1997.

Palmer, Tim. *Endangered Rivers and the Conservation Movement.* Lanham, Md.: Rowan and Littlefield Publishers, 2004.

Parker, Larry, and Wayne A. Morrissey. *Stratospheric Ozone Depletion.* Hauppauge, N.Y.: Nova Science Publishers, 2003.

Parker, Sybil P., ed. *Meteorology Source Book.* New York: McGraw-Hill, 1988.

Parnell, John, ed. *Geofluids: Origin, Migration, and Evolution of Fluids in Sedimentary Basins.* London: Geological Society, 1994.

Parson, L. M., C. L. Walker, and D. R. Dixon, eds. *Hydrothermal Vents and Processes.* London: Geological Society, 1995.

Parsons, A. J., and Athol D. Abrahams. *Geomorphology of Desert Environments.* Springer Science+Business Media B.V., 2009.

Partridge, R. B. *3K: The Cosmic Microwave Background Radiation.* New York: Cambridge University Press, 2007.

Paschmann, Götz, Stein Haaland, and Rudolf Treumann, eds. *Auroral Plasma Physics*. Dordrecht: Kluwer Academic Publishers, 2003.

Pauwels, H., M. Pettenati, and C. Greffie. "The Combined Effect of Abandoned Mines and Agriculture on Groundwater Chemistry." *Journal of Contaminant Hydrology* 115 (2010): 64-78.

Pavlopoulos, Kosmas, and Niki Evelpidou. *Mapping Geomorphological Environments*. New York: Springer, 2009.

Pearce, Fred. "Poisoned Waters." *New Scientist 2000* (October 21, 1995): 29-33.

Pearson, Michael Naylor. *The Indian Ocean*. New York: Routledge, 2003.

Pedlosky, Joseph. *Ocean Circulation Theory*. Rev. ed. New York: Springer, 2010.

Pelling, Mark. *Adaptation to Climate Change: From Resilience to Transformation*. New York: Routledge, 2010.

Penny, Malcolm. *Seas and Oceans: The Polar Seas*. Austin, Tex.: Raintree Steck-Vaughn, 1997.

Perry, J., and E. Vanderklein. *Water Quality: Management of a Natural Resource*. Cambridge, Mass.: Blackwell Science, 1996.

Peterson, J. F. "Using Miniature Landforms in Teaching Geomorphology." *Journal of Geography* 85 (November/December, 1986): 256-258.

Pethick, John. *An Introduction to Coastal Geomorphology*. Baltimore, Md.: Edward Arnold, 1984.

Pettijohn, F. J., Paul Edwin Potter, and Raymond Siever. *Sand and Sandstone*. 2d ed. New York: Springer-Verlag, 1987.

Phalen, Robert N. *Air Pollution Science*. Burlington, Mass.: Jones and Bartlett, 2011.

Pham, Tien Duc, David Gerard Simmons, and Ray Spurr. "Climate Change-Induced Economic Impacts on Tourism Destinations: The Case of Australia." *Journal of Sustainable Tourism* 18, no. 3 (2010): 449-473.

Philander, S. George. *El Niño, La Niña, and the Southern Oscillation*. San Diego, Calif.: Academic Press, 1990.

Philippi, Nancy S. *Floodplain Management: Ecology and Economic Perspectives*. San Diego, Calif.: Academic Press, 1996.

Pickard, G. L., and W. J. Emery. *Descriptive Physical Oceanography: An Introduction*. 5th ed. Oxford, England: Pergamon Press, 1995.

Pielke, R. A., Jr., and R. A. Pielke, Sr. *Hurricanes: Their Nature and Impacts on Society*. New York: John Wiley & Sons, 1997.

Pielou, Evelyn Chrystalla. *Fresh Water*. Chicago: University of Chicago Press, 1998.

_____. *A Naturalist's Guide to the Arctic*. Chicago: University of Chicago Press, 1994.

Pienitz, Reinhard, Marianne S. V. Douglas, and John P. Smol. *Long-Term Environmental Change in Arctic and Antarctic Lakes*. Dordrecht: Springer, 2004.

Pierrehumbert, Raymond T. *Principles of Planetary Climate*. New York: Cambridge University Press, 2011.

Pilkey, Orrin H., and Rob Young. *The Rising Sea*. Washington, D.C.: Island Press, 2009.

Pinet, Paul R. *Invitation to Oceanography*. 5th ed. Sudbury, Mass.: Jones and Bartlett Publishers, 2009.

Pitcher, T. J. *Seamounts: Ecology, Fisheries and Conservation*. Oxford: Blackwell Publishing, 2007.

Plummer, Charles C., Diane Carlson, and Lisa Hammersley. *Physical Geology*. 13th ed. Columbus, Ohio: McGraw-Hill, 2009.

Pluschke, Peter. *Indoor Air Pollution*. Berlin: Springer-Verlag, 2004.

Pollard, Michael. *The Ganges*. London: Evans Brothers Publishing, 2003.

Ponnamperuma, C., ed. *Cosmochemistry and the Origins of Life*. Dordrecht: Reidel, 1982.

Porteous, A. *Saline Water Distillation Processes*. London: Longman, 1975.

Postel, Sandra. *Pillar of Sand*. New York: W. W. Norton, 1999.

Pretor-Pinney, Gavin. *The Cloud Collector's Handbook*. San Francisco, Calif.: Chronicle Books, 2011.

_____ *The Cloudspotter's Guide: The Science, History and Culture of Clouds*. New York: Berkeley Publishing Group, 2006.

Price, Michael. *Introducing Groundwater*. 2d ed. New York: Chapman and Hall, 1996.

Pringle, Laurence. *Rivers and Lakes*. New York: Time-Life Books, 1985.

Prothero, Donald R. *Catastrophes!: Earthquakes, Tsunamis, Tornadoes, and Other Earth-Shattering Disasters*. Baltimore: Johns Hopkins University Press, 2011.

Prothero, Donald R., and Fred Schwab. *Sedimentary Geology: An Introduction to Sedimentary Rocks and Stratigraphy*. New York: W. H. Freeman, 2003.

Pruppacher, Hans R., and James D. Klett, eds. *Microphysics of Clouds and Precipitation*. 2d ed. New York: Springer, 2010.

Pye, Kenneth, and Haim Tsoar. *Aeolian Dust and Dust Deposits*. London: Academic Press, 1987.

_____. *Aeolian Sand and Sand Dunes*. Berlin:

Springer-Verlag, 2009.

Qu, John J., Robert E. Murphy, Wei Gao, Vincent V. Salomonson, and Menas Kofatos, eds. *Earth Science Satellite Remote Sensing. Science and Instruments*. Vol. 1. Beijing: Tsinghua University Press, 2006.

Rackley, Stephen A. *Carbon Capture and Storage*. Burlington, Mass.: Butterworth-Heinemann/Elsevier, 2010.

"Radiometric Normalization of Sensor Scan Angle Effects in Optical Remote Sensing Imagery." *International Journal of Remote Sensing* 28, no. 19 (2007): 4453-4469.

Rakov, Vladimir A., and Martin A. Uman. *Lightning: Physics and Effects*. New York: Cambridge University Press, 2007.

Ramage, Colin S. "El Niño." *Scientific American* (June, 1986): 76-83.

Randall, David A. *Atmosphere, Clouds, and Climate*. Princeton, N.J.: Princeton University Press, 2012.

Randolph, John. *Environmental Land Use Planning and Management*. Washington, D.C.: Island Press, 2004.

Rangno, A. L., and P. V. Hobbs. "Further Analyses of the Climax Cloud Seeding Experiments." *Journal of Applied Meteorology* 93 (1993).

Rao, P. V., ed. *The Indian Ocean: An Annotated Bibliography*. Delhi: Kalinga, 1998.

Raphael, C. N., and E. Jaworski. "The St. Clair River Delta: A Unique Lake Delta." *The Geographical Bulletin* 21 (April, 1982): 7-28.

Rapp, Donald. *Ice Ages and Interglacials: Measurements, Interpretations, and Models*. New York: Springer, 2009.

Ratnayaka, Don D., Malcolm J. Brandt, and K. Michael Johnson. *Twort's Water Supply*. 6th ed. Burlington, Mass.: Butterworth-Heinemann, 2009.

Ravindra, Rasik, et al. "Antarctica." In *Encyclopedia of Snow, Ice, and Glaciers*, edited by Vijay P. Singh, Pratap Singh, and Umesh K. Haritashya. New York: Springer, 2011.

Reading, H. G., ed. *Sedimentary Environments: Processes, Facies, and Stratigraphy*. 3d ed. Cambridge, Mass.: Blackwell Science, 1996.

Redfern, Ron. *Origins: the Evolution of Continents, Oceans and Life*. Norman, Okla.: University of Oklahoma Press, 2001.

Reece, Jane B., et al. *Campbell Biology*. 9th ed. Boston: Benjamin Cummings, 2011.

Rees, W. G. *Physical Principles of Remote Sensing*. 2d ed.

New York: Cambridge University Press, 2001.

Reineck, H. E., and I. B. Singh. *Depositional Sedimentary Environments*. 2d ed. Berlin: Springer-Verlag, 1992.

Repetto, Robert, and Robert Easton. "Climate Change and Damage from Extreme Weather Events." *Environment* 52, no. 2 (2010): 22-33.

Richards, Keith. *Rivers, Form, and Process in Alluvial Channels*. Caldwell, N.J.: Blackburn Press, 2004.

Rigo, M., et al. "A Rise in the Carbonate Compensation Depth of Western Tethys in the Carnian (Late Triassic): Deep-Water Evidence for the Carnian Pluvial Event." *Palaeogeography, Palaeoclimatology, Palaeoecology* 246 (2007):188-205.

Riley, John L. *Flora of the Hudson Bay Lowland and Its Postglacial Origins*. Ottawa: National Research Council (Canada) Research Press, 2003.

Rizutti, Lucio, Hisham Mohamed Ettouney, and Andrea Cipollina, eds. *Solar Desalination for the 21st Century: A Review of Modern Technologies and Researches on Desalination Coupled to Renewable Energies*. Dordrecht: Springer, 2007.

Roan, Susan. *Ozone Crisis: The Fifteen-Year Evolution of a Sudden Global Emergency*. New York: John Wiley & Sons, 1989.

Robinson, Andrew. *Earth Shock: Hurricanes, Volcanoes, Earthquakes, Tornadoes, and Other Forces of Nature*. London: Thames and Hudson, 1993.

Robinson, Ian S. *Discovering the Ocean from Space: The Unique Applications of Satellite Oceanography*. New York: Springer, 2010.

Robock, A., et al. "Climatic Consequences of Regional Nuclear Conflict." *Atmospheric Chemistry and Physics* 7 (2007): 2003-2012.

Rodionov, Sergei N. *Global and Regional Climate Interaction: The Caspian Sea Experience*. Dordrecht: Kluwer, 1994.

Rodriguez-Iturbe, Ignacio, and Andrea Rinaldo. *Fractal River Basins: Chance and Self-organization*. Cambridge, England: Cambridge University Press, 2001.

Rogers, R. R., and M. K. Yau. *A Short Course in Cloud Physics*. 3d ed. Woburn, Mass.: Butterworth-Heinemann, 1989.

Rohwer, Forest, Merry Youle, and Derek Vosten. *Coral Reefs in the Microbial Seas*. Plaid Press, 2010.

Rona, P. A., and S. D. Scott. "A Special Issue on Sea-Floor Hydrothermal Mineralizations: New Perspectives." *Economic Geology* 88, no. 8 (1993): 1933-2249.

Rose, John, ed. *Acid Rain: Current Situation and Remedies*. Langhorne, Pa.: Gordon and Breach Science Publishers, 1994.

Rosenberg, Eugene, and Yossi Loya, eds. *Coral Health and Disease*. New York: Springer, 2004.

Rosenfeld, Jeffery. *Eye of the Storm: Inside the World's Deadliest Hurricanes, Tornadoes and Blizzards*. Cambridge, Mass.: Basic Books, 2003.

Ross, David A. *Introduction to Oceanography*. 5th ed. New York: HarperCollins College Publishers, 1995.

Rowland, F. Sherwood. "Stratospheric Ozone Depletion." *Annual Review of Physical Chemistry* 42 (1991): 731.

Ruddiman, William F. *Earth's Climate: Past and Future*. 2d ed. New York: W. H. Freeman, 2007.

Ruddiman, W. F., and H. E. Wright. *North America and Adjacent Oceans During the Last Deglaciation*. Boulder, Colo.: Geological Society of America, 1987.

Rundel, Phillip W., F. M. Jaksic, and G. Montenegro, eds. *Landscape Disturbance and Biodiversity in Mediterranean-Type Ecosystems*. New York: Springer-Verlag, 2010.

Ryann, Amy L., and Nathan J. Perkins. *The Black Sea: Dynamics, Ecology and Conservation*. Hauppauge, N.Y.: Nova Science Publishers, 2011.

Sadiq, Muhammad, and John C. McCain. *Gulf War Aftermath: An Environmental Tragedy*. Dordrecht: Kluwer Academic Publishers, 1993.

Saether, Ola M., and Patrice de Caritat, eds. *Geochemical Processes, Weathering, and Groundwater Recharge in Catchments*. Rotterdam: A. A. Balkema, 1997.

Sagan, Carl. "Nuclear Winter and Climatic Catastrophe: Some Policy Implications." *Foreign Affairs* 62 (Winter, 1983): 257-292.

Sagan, Carl, and Richard Turco. *A Path Where No Man Thought: Nuclear Winter and the End of the Arms Race*. New York: Random House, 1990.

Saha, Kshudiram. *The Earth's Atmosphere: Its Physics and Dynamics*. Berlin: Springer-Verlag, 2008.

Salby, Murray L. *Physics of the Atmosphere and Climate*. New York: Cambridge University Press, 2011.

Saliot, Alaine. *The Mediterranean Sea*. Berlin: Springer-Verlag, 2005.

Samaras, Tim, Stefan Bechtel, and Greg Forbes. *Tornado Hunter: Getting Inside the Most Violent Storms on Earth*. Washington, D.C.: National Geographic Society, 2009.

Santurette, Patrick, and Christo Georgiev. *Weather Analysis and Forecasting*. Burlington, Mass.: Academic Press, 2005.

Sarachik, Edward S., and Mark A Cane. *The El Niño-Southern Oscillation Phenomenon*. New York: Cambridge University Press, 2010.

Satake, Kenji, ed. *Tsunamis: Case Studies and Recent Developments*. Dordrecht: Springer, 2005.

Savenije, Hubert H.G. *Salinity and Tides in Alluvial Estuaries*. San Diego: Elsevier, 2005.

Savino, John, and Marie Jones. *Supervolcano*. Franklin Lakes, N.J.: New Page Books, 2007.

Schaefer, Vincent J., and John A. Day. *A Field Guide to the Atmosphere*. Boston: Houghton Mifflin, 1998.

Schaetzl, Randall J., and Sharon Anderson. *Soils: Genesis and Geomorphology*. Cambridge, England: Cambridge University Press, 2005.

Schmidt, Paul E. *River Deltas: Types, Structures and Ecology*. New York: Nova Science Publishers, 2011.

Schmitt, Raymond W. *The Ocean Freshwater Cycle*. College Station, Tex.: A&M University, 1994.

Schmoll, Oliver. *Protecting Groundwater for Health: Managing the Quality of Drinking Water Sources*. London: IWA Publishing, 2006.

Schneider, Bonnie. *Extreme Weather: A Guide to Surviving Flash Floods, Tornadoes, Hurricanes, Heat Waves, Snowstorms, Tsunamis and Other Natural Disasters*. Palgrave Macmillan, 2012.

Schneider, David. "On the Level: Central Asia's Inland Seas Curiously Rise and Fall." *Scientific American* (July, 1995): 14.

Schneider, Stephen Henry, and Michael D. Mastrandrea. *Encyclopedia of Climate & Weather*. 2d ed. New York: Oxford University Press, 2011.

Schneider, Stephen H., and Terry L. Root. *Wildlife Responses to Climate Change: North American Case Studies*. Washington, D.C.: Island Press, 2002.

Schneider, Tapio, and Adam H. Sobel, eds. *The Global Circulation of the Atmosphere*. Princeton, N.J.: Princeton University Press, 2007.

Schon, J. H. *Physical Properties of Rocks*. Amsterdam: Elsevier, 2004.

Schreiber, B. C., S. Lugli, and M. Babel, eds. *Evaporites through Space and Time*. Special Publication 285. London: Geological Society of London, 2007.

Schulz, Horst D., and Matthias Zabel. *Marine Geochemistry*. 2d ed. Berlin: Springer-Verlag, 2006.

Schumm, Stanley A. *Active Tectonics and Alluvial Rivers*.

New York: Cambridge University Press, 2002.

Schwartz, M. *Encyclopedia of Coastal Science*. Dordrecht: Springer, 2005.

Scott, Ralph C. *Physical Geography*. New York: John Wiley & Sons, 1988.

"Scour Power: Big Storms Shift Coastal Erosion into Overdrive." *Science News* 178, no. 5 (2010): 14.

Segar, Douglas. *An Introduction to Ocean Sciences*. 2d ed. New York: W. W. Norton, 2007.

Seibold, Eugen, and Wolfgang H. Berger. *The Sea Floor: An Introduction to Marine Geology*. 3d ed. New York: Springer-Verlag, 2010.

Seidel, Klaus, and Jaroslav Martinec. *Remote Sensing in Snow Hydrology: Runoff Modelling, Effect of Climate Change*. New York: Springer, 2010.

Sene, Kevin. *Flood Warning, Forecasting and Emergency Response*. Dordrecht: Springer Science+Business Media, 2008.

Sergeev, Mark. *The Wonders and Problems of Lake Baikal*. Translated by Sergei Sumin. Moscow: Novosti Press Agency, 1989.

Serreze, Mark C., and Roger Graham Barry. *The Arctic Climate System*. New York: Cambridge University Press, 2005.

Severin, Tim. *The China Voyage: Across the Pacific by Bamboo Raft*. Reading, Mass.: Addison-Wesley, 1994.

Shafer, L. H., and M. S. Mintz. "Electrodialysis." In *Principles of Desalination*. 2d ed. New York: Academic Press, 1980.

Shaffer, James L., and John T. Tigges. *The Mississippi River: Father of Waters*. Charleston, S.C.: Arcadia Publishing, 2000.

Shanmugam, G. *Deep-water Processes and Facies Models: Implications for Sandstone Petroleum Reservoirs*. Amsterdam: Elsevier, 2006.

Shaw, Glenn E. *Clouds and Climatic Change*. Sausalito, Calif.: University Science Books, 1996.

Sheets, Bob, and Jack Williams. *Hurricane Watch: Forecasting the Deadliest Storms on Earth*. New York: Vintage Books, 2001.

Shell, E. R. "Weather Versus Chemicals." *The Atlantic* 259 (May, 1987): 27-31.

Shennan, Ian, and Julian E. Andrews, eds. *Holocene Land-Ocean Interaction and Environmental Change Around the North Sea*. Special Publication No. 166. London: Geological Society of London, 2000.

Sheppard, Charles R. C., Simon K. Davy, and Graham M. Pilling. *The Biology of Coral Reefs*. New York:

Oxford University Press, 2009.

Shukla, Ashok Chandra, and A. Vandana. *Ganga: A Water Marvel*. New Delhi: Ashish, 1995.

Siebert, Lee, Tom Simkin, and Paul Kimberly. *Volcanoes of the World*. 3d ed. Berkeley: University of California Press, 2010.

Siedler, Gerold, John Church, and John Gould. *Ocean Circulation and Climate: Observing and Modelling the Global Ocean*. London: Academic Press, 2001.

Sikora, Todd D., et al. "A Synthetic Aperture Radar-Based Climatology of Open-Cell Convection Over the Northeast Pacific Ocean." *Journal of Applied Meteorology and Climatology* 50, no. 3 (2011): 594-603.

Silberberg, R., C. H. Tsao, and J. R. Letaw. "Composition, Propagation, and Reacceleration of Cosmic Rays." In M. M. Shapiro et al., eds., *Particle Astrophysics and Cosmology*. Boston: Kluwer Academic Publishers, 1993.

Simon, Franz-Georg, T. Meggyes, and Chris McDonald. *Advanced Groundwater Remediation: Active and Passive Technologies*. London: Thomas Telford Publishing, 2002.

Sincero, A. P., and G. A. Sincero. *Environmental Engineering: A Design Approach*. Upper Saddle River, N.J.: Prentice-Hall, 1996.

Singh, Vijay P. *Dam Breach Modeling Technology*. Boston: Kluwer Academic Publishers, 2010.

_____, ed. *Hydrology of Disasters*. Boston: Kluwer Academic Publishers, 2010.

Sinha, P. C., ed. *Sea Level Rise*. New Delhi: Anmol Publications, 1998.

Sliter, William V., Allan W. H. Be, and Wolfgang H. Berger, eds. *Dissolution of Deep-Sea Carbonates*. Washington, D.C.: Cushman Foundation for Foraminiferal Research, 1975.

Smith, F. G. "Measuring Ocean Currents." *Sea Frontiers* 18 (May, 1972): 166.

Smith, Jerry E. *Weather Warfare: The Military's Plan to Draft Mother Nature*. Kempton, Ill.: Adventures Unlimited Press, 2006.

Smith, Norman J. *A History of Dams*. London: P. Davies, 1971.

_____. *North Sea Oil and Gas, British Industry and the Offshore Supplies Office*. Vol. 7. Edited by John Cubitt. Boston: Elsevier, 2011.

_____. *The Sea of Lost Opportunity: North Sea Oil and Gas, British Industry and the Offshore Supplies Office*. Oxford: Elsevier, 2011.

Smith, Roland. *The Sea Otter Rescue: The Aftermath of an Oil Spill.* New York: Puffin Books, 1999.

Smithson, Peter, Kenneth Addison, and Kenneth Atkinson. "Energy and Earth." In *Fundamentals of the Physical Environment.* 3d ed. New York: Routledge, 2002.

_____. "Energy Flows and Nutrient Cycles in Ecosystems." In *Fundamentals of the Physical Environment.* 3d ed. New York: Routledge, 2002.

_____. "Heat and Energy in the Atmosphere." In *Fundamentals of the Physical Environment.* 3d ed. New York: Routledge, 2002.

Snead, Roman E. *World Atlas of Geomorphic Features.* Huntington, N.Y.: Robert E. Krieger, 1980.

Snow, J. T., and S. B. Harley. "Basic Meteorological Observations for Schools: Rainfall." *Bulletin of the American Meteorological Society* 69 (1988): 497-507.

Soloviev, Alexander, and Roger Lukas. *The Near-Surface Layer of the Ocean: Structure, Dynamics and Applications.* Dordrecht: Springer, 2006.

SOMER. *Regional Report of the State of the Marine Environment.* Safat, Kuwait: Regional Organization for the Protection of the Marine Environment, 2003.

Somerville, Richard C. J. *The Forgiving Air: Understanding Environmental Change.* 2d ed. Boston: American Meteorological Society, 2008.

Sorokin, I. O. U. *The Black Sea: Ecology and Oceanography.* Kerkwerve: Backhuys Publishing, 2002.

Sosson, M, et al., eds. S*edimentary Basin Tectonics from the Black Sea and Caucasus to the Arabian Platform.* Special Publication 340. London: Geological Society of London, 2010.

Soucek, Svatopluk. *The Persian Gulf: Its Past and Present.* Costa Mesa, Calif.: Mazda Publishers, 2008.

Spalding, Mark D., Edmund P. Green, and Corinna Ravilious. *World Atlas of Coral Reefs.* Berkeley, Calif.: University of California Press, 2001.

Sparks, R. S. *Volcanic Plumes.* New York: Wiley, 1997.

Spaulding, Nancy E., and Samuel N. Namowitz. *Earth Science.* Boston: Houghton Mifflin Harcourt, 2004.

Sponsel, Leslie E., Thomas N. Headland, and Robert C. Bailey. *Tropical Deforestation: The Human Dimension.* New York: Columbia University Press, 1996.

Sportisse, Bruno. *Fundamentals in Air Pollution: From Processes to Modelling.* New York: Springer, 2009.

Spring, Barbara. *The Dynamic Great Lakes.* Baltimore: Independence Books, 2001.

Stacey, Frank D., and Paul M. Davis. *Physics of the Earth.* 4th ed. New York: Cambridge University

Press, 2008.

Stanley, Steven M. *Earth System History.* New York: W. H. Freeman, 2004.

State of California. Department of Water Resources. *Water Well Standards.* Bulletin 74-81. Sacramento: Author, 1982.

Steele, John H., Steve A. Thorpe, and Karl K. Turekian, eds. *Marine Chemistry and Geochemistry.* New York: Academic Press, 2010.

Steenvoorden, J. H. A. M., and Theodore A. Endreny, eds. *Wastewater Re-use and Groundwater Quality.* Wallingford, England: International Union of Geodesy and Geophysics, 2004.

Steere, Richard C., ed. *Buoy Technology: An Aspect of Observational Data Acquisition on Oceanography and Meteorology.* Berkeley: University of California Press, 1967.

Stein, Ruediger. *Arctic Ocean Sediments: Processes, Proxies and Paleoenvironment.* Amsterdam: Elsevier, 2008.

Stein, Ruediger, and Robie W. Macdonald. *The Organic Carbon Cycle in the Arctic Ocean.* Berlin: Springer, 2004.

Steinacker, Reinhold, Dieter Mayer. and Andrea Steiner. "Data Quality Control Based on Self-Consistency." *Monthly Weather Review* 139, no. 12 (2011): 3974-3991.

Steinbeck, John. *The Log from the Sea of Cortez.* New York: Penguin Books, 1995.

Stensrud, David J. *Parameterization Schemes: Keys to Understanding Numerical Weather Prediction Models.* New York: Cambridge University Press, 2007.

Stevens, William Kenneth. *The Change in the Weather: People, Weather, and the Science of Climate.* New York: Random House, 2001.

Stevenson, F. J., and M. A. Cole. *Cycles of Soil: Carbon, Nitrogen, Phosphorus, Sulfur, Micronutrients.* New York: John Wiley & Sons, 1999.

Stevenson, R. E., and F. H. Talbot, eds. *Oceans.* New York: Time-Life, 1993.

Stille, Darlene R. *The Greenhouse Effect: Warming the Planet.* Minneapolis: Compass Point Books, 2006.

Stoddart, D. R. "Ecology and Morphology of Recent Coral Reefs." *Biological Reviews* 44 (1969): 433-498.

Stolarski, Richard S. "The Antarctic Ozone Hole." *Scientific American* 258 (January, 1988): 30-36.

Stolberg, F., United Nations Environment Program. *Caspian Sea.* New York: United Nations, 2006.

Stone, Richard. "Coming to Grips with the Aral Sea's Grim Legacy." *Science* 284 (April 2, 1999): 30-33.

Stowe, Keith. *Exploring Ocean Science.* 2d ed. New York: John Wiley & Sons, 1996.

Strahler, Alan H. *Modern Physical Geography.* 4th ed. New Delhi: Wiley India, 2008.

Strahler, Alan H., and Arthur N. Strahler. *Environmental Geoscience: Interaction Between Natural Systems and Man.* Santa Barbara, Calif.: Hamilton, 1973.

_____. *Introducing Physical Geography.* 5th ed. New York: John Wiley & Sons, 2010.

_____. *Modern Physical Geography.* 4th ed. New York: John Wiley, 1992.

_____. *Physical Geography: Science and Systems of the Human Environment.* 3d ed. New York: John Wiley & Sons, 2005.

Straka, Jerry M. *Cloud and Precipitation Microphysics: Principles and Parameterizations.* New York: Cambridge University Press, 2009.

Strangeways, Ian. *Precipitation: Theory, Measurement and Distribution.* New York: Cambridge University Press, 2007.

Stumm, Werner, ed. *Chemical Processes at the Particle-Water Interface.* New York: John Wiley & Sons, 1987.

Sutton, Gerard K., and Joseph A. Cassalli, eds. *Catastrophe in Japan: The Earthquake and Tsunami of 2011.* Hauppauge, N.Y.: Nova Science Publishers, 2011.

Sverdrup, Keith A., Alyn C. Duxbury, and Alison B. Duxbury. *An Introduction to the World's Oceans.* 8th ed. Boston, Mass.: McGraw-Hill, 2004.

Swart, Peter K., Gregor Eberli, and Judith A. McKenzie, eds. *Perspectives in Carbonate Geology.* Hoboken, N.J.: Wiley-Blackwell, 2009.

Symons, Leslie. *The Soviet Union: A Systematic Geography.* New York: Routledge, 1990.

Tainter, Joseph A., and Tadeusz W. Patzek. *Drilling Down: The Gulf Oil Debacle and Our Energy Dilemma.* New York: Copernicus Books, 2011.

Takada, Jun. *Nuclear Hazards in the World.* New York: Springer, 2010.

Talley, Lynne D., et al. *Descriptive Physical Oceanography: An Introduction.* 6th ed. San Diego: Academic Press, 2011.

TAO Project Office of NOAA/Pacific Marine Environmental Laboratory. *Upper Ocean Heat Content and ENSO.* Seattle: National Oceanic and Atmospheric Administration (NOAA) Web site (http://www.pmel.noaa.gov/tao).

Tarbuck, Edward J., and Frederick K. Lutgens. *Earth: An Introduction to Physical Geology.* 10th ed. Upper Saddle River, NJ: Prentice Hall, 2010.

Taylor, Brian, and James Natland, eds. *Active Margins and Marginal Basins of the Western Pacific.* Washington, D.C.: American Geophysical Union, 1995.

Taylor, Leighton R. *The Red Sea.* Woodbridge, Conn.: Blackbirch, 1998.

Tebbutt, T. H. Y. *Principles of Water Quality Control.* 5th ed. Woburn, Mass.: Butterworth-Heinemann, 1998.

Temmam, R. and J. Tribbia, eds. *Handbook of Numerical Analysis Vol. XIV. Special Volume Computational Methods for the Atmosphere and the Oceans* Oxford, England: North-Holland, 2009.

Teramoto, Toshihiko. *Deep Ocean Circulation: Physical and Chemical Aspects.* New York: Elsevier, 1993.

Thomas, David N., and Gerhard Dieckmann, eds. *Sea Ice.* Ames, Iowa: Blackwell, 2010.

Thomas, David S. G. *Arid Zone Geomorphology: Process, Form and Change in Drylands.* 3d ed. Chichester: Wiley-Blackwell, 2011.

Thompson, Russell D. *Atmospheric Processes and Systems.* London: Routledge, 1998.

Thompson, Stephen A. *Hydrology for Water Management.* Rotterdam: A. A. Balkema, 1999.

Thorsen, G. W. "Overview of Earthquake-Induced Water Waves in Washington and Oregon." *Washington Geologic Newsletter* 16 (October, 1988).

Thurman, H. V., and Alan P. Trujillo. *Introductory Oceanography.* 10th ed. Upper Saddle River, N.J.: Prentice-Hall, 2003.

Tiwary, Abhishek, and Jeremy Colls. *Air Pollution: Measurement, Modelling and Mitigation.* New York: Routledge, 2010.

Todd, D. K. *Groundwater Hydrology.* 3d ed. New York: John Wiley & Sons, 2004.

Toon, Brian, Alan Robock, and Rich Turco. "Environmental Consequences of Nuclear War." *Physics Today* 61 (Dec. 2008): 37-42.

Trefil, James. *Meditations at Sunset: A Scientist Looks at the Sky.* New York: Charles Scribner's Sons, 1988.

Tregenza, L. A., and Joseph John Hobbs. *The Red Sea Mountains of Egypt and Egyptian Years.* Cairo: American University in Cairo Press, 2004.

Trenberth, K. E *Climate System Modeling.* New York: Cambridge University Press, 2005.

_____. "An Imperative for Climate Change Planning: Tracking Earth's Global Energy." *Current Opinion in Environmental Sustainability* 1 (2009): 19-27.

Trenberth, K. E., and John T. Fasullo. "Tracking Earth's Energy." *Science* 328 (April, 2010): 316-317.

Trujillo, Alan P., and Harold V. Thurman. *Essentials of Oceanography*. New York: Prentice-Hall, 2010.

Tsuchiya, Yoshito, and Nobuo Shuto, eds. *Tsunami: Progress in Prediction, Disaster Prevention, and Warning*. Boston: Kluwer Academic Publishers, 2010.

Tucker, Maurice E. *Sedimentary Rocks in the Field*. 4th ed. New York: John Wiley & Sons, 2011.

Tufty, Barbara. *1001 Questions Answered About Hurricanes, Tornadoes, and Other Natural Air Disasters*. New York: Dover, 1987.

Turco, Richard P., et al. "The Climatic Effects of Nuclear War." *Scientific American* 251, no. 2 (August, 1984): 33-43.

_____. "Nuclear Winter: Global Consequences of Multiple Nuclear Explosions." *Science* 222 (1983): 1283-1292.

Turekian, K. K., and H. D. Holland, eds. *Treatise on Geochemistry*. San Diego, Calif.: Elsevier, 2004.

Ulanski, Stan L. *The Gulf Stream: Tiny Plankton, Giant Bluefin, and the Amazing Story of the Powerful River in the Atlantic*. Chapel Hill: University of North Carolina Press, 2008.

Uman, Martin A. *The Lightning Discharge*. Mineola, N.Y.: Dover Publications, 2001.

U.S. Congress. House. *Effects of Drought on Agribusiness and Rural Economy*. 100th Congress, 2d session, 1988.

U.S. Department of the Interior, Minerals Management Service (USDI MMS). *Alaska Outer Continental Shelf Beaufort Sea Planning Area Oil and Gas Lease Sales 186, 195, and 202, Final Environmental Impact Statement*. Anchorage: OCS EIS/EA, MMS, 2003.

_____. *Environmental Survey of Potential Sand Resource Sites Offshore Delaware and Maryland*. Herndon, Va.: Office of International Activities and Marine Minerals, 2000.

_____. *Programmatic Environmental Assessment: Arctic Ocean Outer Continental Shelf Seismic Surveys*. U.S. Department of the Interior Minerals Management Service, Alaska OCS Region, 2006.

Usdowski, Eberhard, and Martin Dietzel. *Atlas and Data of Solid-Solution Equilibria of Marine Evaporites*. New York: Springer, 1998.

U.S. Environmental Protection Agency. *The Great Lakes: An Environmental Atlas and Resource Book*. Chicago: Great Lakes Program Office, 1995.

_____. *Protecting Water Quality from Agricultural Runoff: Clean Water Is Everybody's Business*. Washington, D.C: Author, 2003.

U.S. Geological Survey. Office of Water. *The Quality of Our Nation's Water: Nutrients and Pesticides*. Creston, Va.: USGS Information Services, 1999.

U.S. WOCE Office. *U.S. WOCE Implementation Plan: The U.S. Contribution to the World Ocean Circulation Experiment*. College Station, Tex.: U.S. WOCE Office, 1993.

Vacher, Leonard, and Terrence M. Quinn. *Geology and Hydrogeology of Carbonate Islands*. New York: Elsevier, 2004.

Vallero, Daniel A. *Environmental Biotechnology: A Biosystems Approach*. Amsterdam: Academic, 2010.

_____. *Fundamentals of Air Pollution*. 4th ed. Burlington, Mass.: Academic Press, 2008.

Vallis, Geoffrey K. *Atmospheric and Oceanic Fluid Dynamics: Fundamentals and Large-scale Circulation*. New York: Cambridge University Press, 2006.

Van Aken, Hendrik Mattheus. *The Oceanic Thermohaline Circulation: An Introduction*. New York: Springer Science + Business Media Inc., 2007.

Van Allen, James A. *Origin of Magnetospheric Physics*. Iowa City: University of Iowa Press, 2004.

_____. "Radiation Belts Around the Earth." *Scientific American* 200, no. 3 (March, 1959).

Van Beynen, Philip E. *Karst Management*. New York: Springer, 2011.

Van der Voo, Rob. *Paleomagnetism of the Atlantic, Tethys and Iapetus Oceans*. New York: Cambridge University Press, 2004.

Van Dover, Cindy Lee. *The Ecology of Deep-Sea Hydrothermal Vents*. Princeton, N.J.: Princeton University Press, 2000.

Van Ness, H. C. *Understanding Thermodynamics*. Mineola, N.Y.: Dover Publications, 1983.

Vanoni, V. A., ed. *Sedimentation Engineering*. 2d ed. New York: American Society of Civil Engineers, 2006.

Van Oppen, Madeleine J. H., and J. M. Lough, eds. *Coral Bleaching: Patterns, Processes, Causes, and Consequences*. New York: Springer, 2009.

Vasquez, Tim. *Weather Analysis and Forecasting Handbook*. Garland, Tex.: Weather Graphics Technologies, 2011.

Vassallo, L. F., et al. "Paleogene Magmatism and Associated Skarn-Hydrothermal Mineralization in The Central Part of Mexico." *Boletin de la Sociedad Geológica Mexicana*.

Vaughn, Jacqueline. *Environmental Politics: Domestic and Global Dimensions*. 6th ed. New York: Wadsworth, Cengage Learning, 2011.

Ver Berkmoes, Ryan, Thomas Huhti, and Mark Lightbody. *Great Lakes*. Melbourne: Lonely Planet Publishing, 2000.

Vesilind, Priit J. "Monsoons." *National Geographic* 166 (December, 1984): 712-747.

Viessman, W., Jr., and M. J. Hammer. *Water Supply and Pollution Control*. 8th ed. Upper Saddle River, N.J.: Prentice Hall, 2008.

Vigil, Kenneth M. *Clean Water*. 2d ed. Corvallis: Oregon State University Press, 2003.

Voituriez, Bruno. *The Gulf Stream*. New York: UNESCO, 2006.

Voronin, P., and C. Black. "Earth's Atmosphere as a Result of Coevolution of Geo- and Biospheres." *Russian Journal of Plant Physiology* 54 (2007): 132-136.

Walker, H. J. "Coastal Morphology." *Soil Science* 119 (January, 1975).

Walker, R. G., ed. *Facies Models: Response to Sea Level Change*. 2d ed. Tulsa, Okla.: Society of Economic Paleontologists and Mineralogists, 1994.

Walker, Sally M. *Frozen Secrets: Antarctica Revealed*. Minneapolis: Carolrhoda Books, 2010.

Walker, Sharon, and David McMahon. *Biochemistry Demystified*. New York: McGraw-Hill, 2008.

Wallace, John M., and Peter V. Hobbs. *Atmospheric Science: An Introductory Survey*. 2d ed. Burlington, Mass.: Academic Press, 2006.

Wan, Chao-hui. *Hyperconcentrated Flow*. Brookfield, Vt.: A. A. Balkema, 1994.

Wang, Bin. *The Asian Monsoon*. Chichester: Praxis Publishing, 2006.

Ward, Peter D. *Under a Green Sky: Global Warming, the Mass Extinctions of the Past, and What They Can Tell Us About Our Future*. New York: Harper Perennial, 2008.

Warren, E. A., and P. C. Smalley. *North Sea Formation Waters Atlas*. London: Geological Society, 1994.

Warren, John K. *Evaporites: Sediment, Resources and Hydrocarbons*. Berlin: Springer-Verlag, 2006.

Warrick, Joby. "Death in the Gulf of Mexico." *National Wildlife* 37 (June/July, 1999): 48-52.

Washington, Warren M., and Claire L. Parkinson. *An Introduction to Three Dimensional Climate Modeling*. 2d ed. South Orange, N.J.: University Science Books, 2005.

Waterlow, Julia. *The Atlantic Ocean*. Austin, Tex.: Raintree Steck-Vaughn, 1997.

Watts, Alan. *Instant Wind Forecasting*. Dobbs Ferry, N.Y.: Sheridan House Inc., 2002.

Weber, Lyne, and Jim Weber. *Nature Watch Austin*. Austin: Texas A&M University Press, 2011.

Weber, Michael, Richard T. Townsend, and Rose Bierce. *Environmental Quality in the Gulf of Mexico: A Citizen's Guide*. 2d ed. Washington, D.C.: Center for Marine Coordination. 1992.

Webster, P. J., et al. "Monsoons: Processes, Predictability, and the Prospects for Prediction." *Journal of Geophysical Research* 103 (June 29, 1998): 14,451-14,510.

Wefer, Gerold, et al. *The South Atlantic: Present and Past Circulation*. New York: Springer, 1996.

Wegener, Alfred. *The Origin of Continents and Oceans*. Mineola, N.Y.: Dover Publications, 1966.

Weiner, Jonathan. *Planet Earth*. Toronto: Bantam Books, 1986.

Welland, Michael. *Sand: A Journey Through Science and the Imagination*. New York: Oxford University Press, 2010.

_____.*Sand: The Never-Ending Story*. Berkeley: University of California Press, 2011.

Wells, Neil C. *The Atmosphere and Ocean: A Physical Introduction*. 3d ed. New York: John Wiley & Sons, 2012.

Wentzel, Donat G. *The Restless Sun*. Washington, D.C.: Smithsonian Institution Press, 1989.

Wetzel, R. G., ed. *Limnology*. 3d ed. San Diego: Elsevier Science, 2001.

White, David. *The Physiology and Biochemistry of Prokaryotes*. New York: Oxford University Press, 2011.

Wiggert, Jerry D. *Indian Ocean Biogeochemical Processes and Ecological Variability*. Danvers, Mass.: American Geophysical Union, 2009.

Wilhelm, Helmut, Walter Zuern, Hans-Georg Wenzel, et al., eds. *Tidal Phenomena*. Berlin: Springer, 1997.

Wilhite, Donald A., ed. *Drought and Water Crises: Science, Technology, and Management Issues*. Boca Raton, Fla.: CRC Press, 2005.

Wilhite, Donald A., and William E. Easterling, with Deborah A. Wood, eds. *Planning for Drought: Toward a Reduction of Societal Vulnerability*. Boulder, Colo.: Westview Press, 1987.

Williams, Earle R. "The Electrification of Thunderstorms." *Scientific American* 259 (November, 1988): 88-99.

Williams, Jack, *The "USA Today" Weather Book.* 2d ed. New York: Random House, 1997.

Williams, James Thaxter. *The History of Weather.* Commack, N.Y.: Nova Science Publishers, 1998.

Williams, Richard G., and Michael J. Follows. *Ocean Dynamics and the Carbon Cycle: Principles and Mechanisms.* New York: Cambridge University Press, 2011.

Wilson, Elizabeth J., and David Gerard. *Carbon Capture and Sequestration: Integrating Technology, Monitoring, and Regulation.* Ames, Iowa: Blackwell, 2007.

Winchester, Simon. *Krakatoa: The Day the World Exploded, August 27, 1883.* New York: Harper-Collins Publishers, 2003.

Wohl, Ellen. *A World of Rivers.* Chicago: University of Chicago Press, 2011.

Wolanski, Eric. *Oceanographic Processes of Coral Reefs: Physical and Biological Links in the Great Barrier Reef.* Boca Raton, Fla.: CRC Press, 2001.

Wood, Rachel. *Reef Evolution.* New York: Oxford University Press, 1999.

Woods, J. D. "The World Ocean Circulation Experiment." *Nature* 314 (April 11, 1985): 501-510.

Woods Hole Oceanographic Institution (WHOI) Web site (http://www.whoi.edu/index.html).

Woodward, Jamie. *The Physical Geography of the Mediterranean.* Oxford: Oxford University Press, 2009.

Workman, James G. *Heart of Dryness: How the Last Bushmen Can Help Us Endure the Coming Age of Permanent Drought.* New York: Walker Publishing Company, 2009.

World Health Organization. *WHO Handbook on Indoor Radon: A Public Health Perspective.* Geneva, SWI: WHO Press, 2009.

Wurtz, Mauritzio. *Mediterranean Pelagic Habitat: Oceanic and Biological Processes: An Overview.* Malaga: International Union for Conservation of Nature, 2010.

Wylie, Francis E. *Tides and the Pull of the Moon.* Brattleboro, Vt.: Stephen Greene Press, 1979.

Wyman, Richard L., ed. *Global Climate Change and Life on Earth.* New York: Chapman and Hall, 1991.

Yalin, M. S. *River Mechanics.* New York: Pergamon Press, 1992.

Yanko-Hombach, Valentina, et al., eds. *The Black Sea Flood Question: Changes in Coastline, Climate, and Human Settlement.* Dordrecht: Springer, 2007.

Young, Ian R. *Wind Generated Ocean Waves.* New York: Elsevier, 1999.

Yuen, David A., Shigenori Maruyama, Shun-ichiro Karato, and Brian F. Windley, eds. *Superplumes: Beyond Plates Tectonics.* Dordrecht: Springer, 2007.

Yung, Yuk Ling, and William B. DeMore. *Photochemistry of Planetary Atmospheres.* New York: Oxford University Press, 1999.

Zahran, M. A. *Climate-Vegetation: Afro-Asian Mediterranean and Red Sea Coastal Lands.* New York: Springer, 2010.

Zaitsev, Y. P., and B. G. Alexandrov, eds. *Black Sea Biological Diversity: Ukraine.* Black Seas Environmental Series 7. New York: United Nations, 1998.

Zavialov, Peter O. *Physical Oceanography of the Dying Aral Sea.* Chichester: Praxis Publishing, 2005.

Zdunkowski, Wilfred, and Andreas Bott. *Thermodynamics of the Atmosphere: A Course in Theoretical Meteorology.* New York: Cambridge University Press, 2004.

Zeilik, Michael, and Elske V. P. Smith. *Introductory Astronomy and Astrophysics.* 4th ed. Independence, Ky.: Brooks\Cole Cengage Learning, 1998.

Zhong, B., S. Liang, and B. Holben. "Validating a New Algorithm for Estimating Aerosol Optical Depths Over Land from MODIS Imagery." *International Journal of Remote Sensing* 28, no. 18 (2007): 4207-4214.

Ziegler, Karen, Peter Turner, and Stephen R. Daines, eds. *Petroleum Geology of the Southern North Sea: Future Potential.* London: Geological Society, 1997.

Zielinski, Gregory A. "A Classification Scheme for Winter Storms in the Eastern and Central United States with an Emphasis on Nor'easters." *Bulletin of the American Meteorological Society* 83, no. 1 (2002).

Zonn, Igor S., et al. *The Caspian Sea Encyclopedia.* New York: Springer-Verlag, 2010.

ATMOSPHERIC PRESSURE: ABOVE AND BELOW SEA LEVEL

The table below provides atmospheric pressure values in both pounds per square inch (psi) and atmospheres (atm). Pressure values are listed for varying altitudes above sea level and depths below sea level. These data are represented in the following graphs: Atmospheric Pressure (psi) and Atmospheric Pressure (atm).

Altitude (meters)	Atmospheric Pressure	
	psi	atm
30,510	0.16	0.01
27,459	0.25	0.02
24,408	0.41	0.03
21,357	0.64	0.04
18,306	1.05	0.07
16,781	1.33	0.09
15,255	1.69	0.11
13,730	2.15	0.15
12,204	2.73	0.19
10,679	3.47	0.24
9,153	4.37	0.30
7,628	5.46	0.37
6,102	6.76	0.46
4,577	8.29	0.56
3,050	10.10	0.69
2,746	10.50	0.71
2,441	10.91	0.74
2,136	11.34	0.77
1,831	11.78	0.80

| Altitude | Atmospheric Pressure | |
(meters)	psi	atm
1,526	12.23	0.83
1,373	12.46	0.85
1,220	12.69	0.86
1,068	12.93	0.88
915	13.17	0.90
763	13.41	0.91
610	13.66	0.93
458	13.91	0.95
305	14.16	0.96
153	14.43	0.98
0*	14.70	1.00
-153	224.91	15.30
-305	448.35	30.50
-458	673.26	45.80
-610	896.70	61.00
-763	1,121.61	76.30
-915	1,345.05	91.50
-1,068	1,569.96	106.80
-1,220	1,793.40	122.00
-1,373	2,018.31	137.30
-1,526	2,243.22	152.60
-2,100	3,087.00	210.00

* Below sea level values are absolute pressure in depth of saltwater

Altitude (meters)	Atmospheric Pressure	
	psi	atm
-3,000	4,410.00	300.00
-3,800	5,586.00	380.00
-5,000	7,350.00	500.00
-11,000	16,170.00	1,100.00

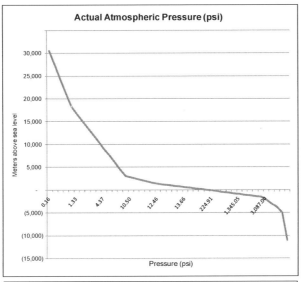

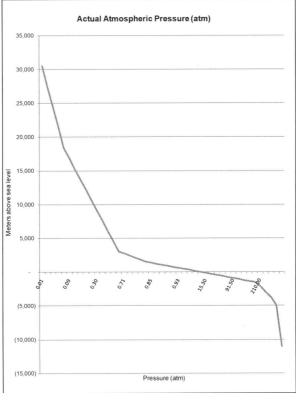

Sources:

Values were adapted from information provided on the Web sites below. Pressure axis is in logarithmic scale.

National Oceanic and Atmospheric Administration (NOAA) http://www.noaa.gov/

National Aeronautics and Space Administration (NASA) http://www.nasa.gov/centers/glenn/home/index.html

MAJOR OIL SPILLS IN MODERN HISTORY

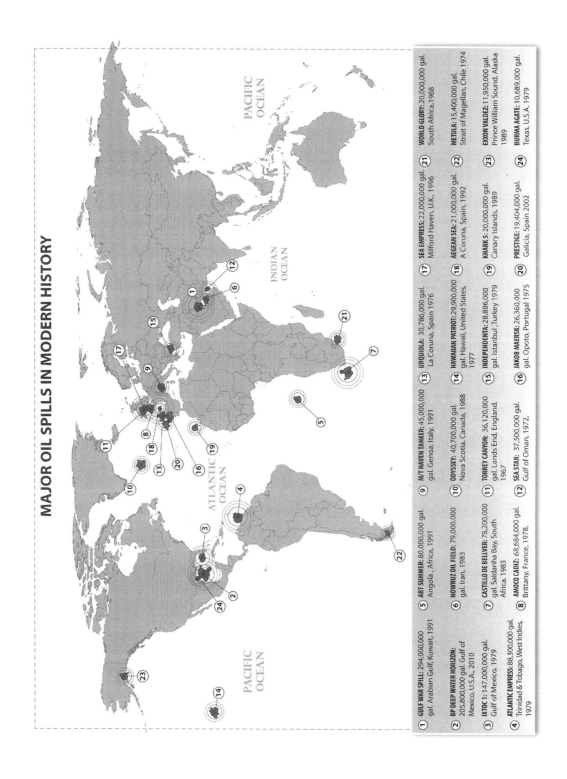

1. **GULF WAR SPILL:** 294,000,000 gal. Arabian Gulf, Kuwait, 1991
2. **BP DEEP WATER HORIZON:** 205,800,000 gal. Gulf of Mexico, U.S.A, 2010
3. **IXTOC 1:** 147,000,000 gal. Gulf of Mexico, 1979
4. **ATLANTIC EMPRESS:** 88,300,000 gal. Trinidad & Tobago, West Indies, 1979
5. **ABT SUMMER:** 80,000,000 gal. Angola, Africa, 1991
6. **NOWRUZ OIL FIELD:** 79,000,000 gal. Iran, 1983
7. **CASTILLO DE BELLVER:** 78,200,000 gal. Saldanha Bay, South Africa, 1983
8. **AMOCO CADIZ:** 68,684,000 gal. Brittany, France, 1978,
9. **M/T HAVEN TANKER:** 45,000,000 gal. Genoa, Italy, 1991
10. **ODYSSEY:** 40,700,000 gal. Nova Scotia, Canada, 1988
11. **TORREY CANYON:** 36,120,000 gal. Lands End, England, 1967
12. **SEA STAR:** 37,500,000 gal. Gulf of Oman, 1972,
13. **URQUIOLA:** 30,786,000 gal. La Coruna, Spain 1976
14. **HAWAIIAN PATRIOT:** 29,900,000 gal. Hawaii, United States, 1977
15. **INDEPENDENTA:** 28,886,000 gal. Istanbul ,Turkey 1979
16. **JAKOB MAERSK:** 26,360,000 gal. Opoto, Portugal 1975
17. **SEA EMPRESS:** 22,000,000 gal. Milford Haven, U.K, 1996
18. **AEGEAN SEA:** 21,000,000 gal. A Coruna, Spain, 1992
19. **KHARK 5:** 20,000,000 gal. Canary Islands, 1989
20. **PRESTIGE:** 19,404,000 gal. Galicia, Spain 2002
21. **WORLD GLORY:** 20,000,000 gal. South Africa,1968
22. **METULA:** 15,400,000 gal. Strait of Magellan, Chile 1974
23. **EXXON VALDEZ:** 11,950,000 gal. Prince William Sound, Alaska 1989
24. **BURMA AGATE:** 10,689,000 gal. Texas, U.S.A. 1979

BODIES OF WATER

Body of water	Volume (cubic kilometers)	Surface Area (square kilometers)	Average Depth (meters)	Maximum Depth (meters)	Salinity (parts per thousand)	Average Surface Temperature (°C)	Surface Temperature Range (°C)
Oceans							
Arctic	18,750,000	15,558,000	1,205.00	5,567.00	35.0	0.50	0.0–1.0
Atlantic	310,410,900	85,133,000	3,646.00	8,486.00	37.0	13.50	0.0–27.0
Indian	264,000,000	70,560,000	3,741.00	7,906.00	34.8	25.00	22.0–28.0
Pacific	660,000,000	161,760,000	4,080.00	10,803.00	33.5	6.50	-2.0–15.0
Southern	71,800,000	21,960,000	3,270.00	7,075.00	35.0	4.00	-2.0–10.0
Seas							
Baltic	20,900	406,000	51.00	392.00	12.5	5.50	-5.3–16.3
Bering	3,750,000	2,291,900	1,547.00	4,773.00	33.0	4.15	-1.7–8.0
Black	547,000	436,400	1,253.00	2,212.00	18.0	12.50	0.0–25.0
Caribbean	9,573,000	2,753,000	2,647.00	7,686.00	35.0	26.50	25.5–28.0
Caspian	78,200	394,299	170.00	946.00	1.0–13.5	5.50	0.0–11.0
Coral	**	4,791,000	2,394.00	9,140.00	34.5–35.5	26.00	19.0–28.0
Dead	147,000	810,000	120.00	330.00	33.0	27.50	15.0–40.0
Mediterranean	3,750,000	2,965,800	1,429.00	4,632.00	38.5	20.00	12.0–28.0
North	94,000	575,200	94.00	660.00	35.0	11.50	6.0–17.0
Red	233,000	438,000	491.00	2,211.00	40.0	28.40	26.2–30.5
South China	3,850,000	2,319,000	1,652.00	5,016.00	33.5	28.50	24.0–31.0
Tasman	**	2,300,000	3,000.00	5,200.00	35.0	**	**
Weddell	**	2,796,000	**	4,500.00	35.0	1.00	**

**— Data unavailable.
Var— Varies signifcantly based on geography.

Body of water	Volume (cubic kilometers)	Surface Area (square kilometers)	Average Depth (meters)	Maximum Depth (meters)	Salinity (parts per thousand)	Average Surface Temperature (°C)	Surface Temperature Range (°C)
Gulfs							
California	56,300	99,420	810.00	2,590.00	35.8	23.00	16.0–30.0
Mexico	2,434,000	1,813,000	1,615.00	3,875.00	38.0	**	**
Persian	6,250	251,000	25.00	90.00	35.0	24.00	16.0–32.0
Bays							
Baffin	**	689,000	861.00	2,100.00	31.7	-0.90	-1.8–0.0
Bengal	**	2,173,000	2,600.00	4,694.00	33.5	28.00	25.0–30.0
Biscay	**	223,000	1,744.00	4,735.00	35.0	**	**
Chesapeake	**	11,601	14.00	53.00	20.0	14.90	0.0–29.0
Fundy	**	9,300	30.00	215.00	35.0	6.00	0.0–12.0
Hudson	**	1,232,000	101.00	270.00	35.0	-12.60	-5.0–8.0
Port Phillip	26	1,930	8.00	24.00	**	16.00	10.0–22.0
San Francisco	65	4,144	15.00	30.00	10.0–30.0	10.50	7.0–14.0
Rivers							
Amazon	14,000,000	4,023,360	50.00	130.00	**	26.11	26.1
Colorado	**	631,960	12.19	25.91	**	Var	Var
Mississippi	600,000,000	2,896,819	3.66	60.96	**	Var	Var
Missouri	**	1,369,861	37.64	231.00	**	Var	Var
Nile	84,000,000	3,349,000.00	9.50	1,500.00	**	**	**
Yangtze	**	1,808,500	6.15	10.50	30.0	7.00	-2.0–16.0

** — Data unavailable.
Var — Varies signifcantly based on geography.

Body of water	Volume (cubic kilometers)	Surface Area (square kilometers)	Average Depth (meters)	Maximum Depth (meters)	Salinity (parts per thousand)	Average Surface Temperature (°C)	Surface Temperature Range (°C)
Lakes							
Baikal	23,600	31,500	730.00	1,637.00	**	14.50	9.0–20.0
Chad	72	1,540	1.50	8.00	**	21.40	**
Erie	484	25,821	19.00	64.00	**	13.34	0.0–26.7
Eyre	30	9,691	3.10	5.70	7.0–40.0 (seasonal)	22.50	13.0–33.0
Great Salt	19	3,750	4.27	10.00	11.0–28.0 (regional)	**	**
Huron	3,540	59,600	59.00	229.00	**	**	**
Malawi	7,775	29,500	264.00	706.00	**	24.00	**
Michigan	4,920	57,800	85.00	282.00	**	**	**
Ontario	1,640	18,960	86.00	244.00	**	**	**
Superior	12,100	82,170	147.00	406.00	**	3.89	-3.5–15.0
Tanganyika	19,000	32,600	570.00	1,435.60	**	26.00	24.0–28.0
Victoria	2,760	68,870	40.00	80.00	**	**	**

** — Data unavailable.
Var — Varies signifcantly based on geography.

Sources
Encyclopedia Britannica http://www.britannica.com
Food and Agriculture Organization of the United Nations http://www.fao.org/docrep/W4347E/w4347e0k.htm
Global Water Partnership, Water, Climate and Development Programme for Africa http://www.gwp.org/en/WACDEP/
Great Lakes Information Network http://www.great-lakes.net/
National Oceanic and Atmospheric Administration, National Geophysical Data Center http://ngdc.noaa.gov/
Office of Naval Research http://www.onr.navy.mil/
U.S. Environmental Protection Agency http://www.epa.gov/
U.S. Geological Survey http://www.usgs.gov/
World Lake Database, International Lake Environment Committee Foundation http://wldb.ilec.or.jp/
World Lakes http://www.worldlakes.org/
WWF Global http://wwf.panda.org/

SEVERE WEATHER

The tables below provide data on severe weather events from modern history, including tornadoes, cyclones, hurricanes, and other significant storms. Tornado severity is categorized using the Fujita-Pearson scale (F0-F5) when applicable. Inc. indicates that the severity data are incomplete. Names of the cyclones, hurricanes, and other storms are provided and severity is categorized using the Saffir-Simpson hurricane scale (Category 1-Category 5) when applicable. The storms are organized chronologically, and all storms comparable using the impact information, including the number of deaths and/or wreckage.

TORNADOES

Year	Location	Severity	Impact
1912	Regina, Saskatchewan	Inc.	28 deaths; $1.2 million in property damage (1912 USD); 2,500 left homeless
1925	Missouri, Illinois, and Indiana (Tri-State)	F5	695 deaths; 219-mile-long path of destruction; the main part of a series of smaller tornadoes that day that killed almost 750 people in Kansas, Alabama, Tennessee, Kentucky, and Indiana; 2,027 injured
1932	Alabama Super Outbreak	F4	268 deaths; 1,874 injured; 98 homes destroyed; 2,000 left homeless
1936	Tupelo, Mississippi	F5	216 deaths; 700 left injured
1936	Gainesville, Georgia	F4	203 deaths; 1,600 injured
1947	Texas, Kansas, and Oklahoma	F5	181 deaths; 970 injured
1964	Magura-narail, Khulna Division, Bangladesh	Inc.	500+ deaths
1965	Indiana, Michigan, and Ohio	F4	265 deaths; $30 million in damage as eleven tornadoes moved through twenty counties (1965 USD)
1969	Dhaka, Bangladesh	Inc.	660 deaths; 4,000 injured; a second tornado from the same storm system brought the total death toll to 883
1970	Bulahdelah, New South Wales, Australia	F4-F5	Over 1 million trees destroyed; a 13-mile-long path of destruction
1973	Manikganj, Singair, and Nawabganj, Bangladesh	Inc.	681 confirmed deaths, but death toll could be as high as 1,000
1973	Brisbane, Australia	F3	1,400 buildings damaged

Tornadoes (*continued*)

Year	Location	Severity	Impact
1974	Alabama, Georgia, Kentucky, Illinois, Indiana, Mississippi, Michigan, North Carolina, Tennessee, Virginia, and West Virginia (Xenia Tornado Outbreak)	F4-F5 (148 tornadoes, 30 severe)	330 dead; 5,484 injured; 2,500-mile-long path of destruction
1984	Ivanovo-Yaroslavl, Russia	F4-F5	400+ deaths with 3 tornadoes; 213 injured
1984	Carolinas Tornado Outbreak	F2-F4	22 tornadoes; 57 deaths; $200 million in property damage (1984 USD)
1985	Pennsylvania-Ohio Outbreak	F3-F5	41 tornadoes (including one F5); 76 deaths; $450 million in property damage across two states (1985 USD)
1987	Edmonton, Alberta	F4	27 deaths; 200 injured
1989	Daulatpur to Saturia, Bangladesh	F5	1,300 deaths; 50-mile-long path of destruction; 80,000 people left homeless
1996	Madarganj to Mirzapur, Bangladesh	Inc.	700 deaths; 30,000 homes destroyed
1998	West Bengal-Orissa, India	Inc.	175+ deaths; 2,000 injured; 10,000 left homeless
2011	Joplin, Missouri	EF5	157 deaths; 1,000 injured

Cyclones and Hurricanes

Year	Location	Name	Severity	Impact
1502	Hispaniola and Puerto Rico	Columbus's First Hurricane	unknown	500 deaths; 25 ships sank
1667	North Carolina, Virginia, and Maryland	Dreadful Hurricane of 1667	unknown	10,000 houses destroyed, along with tobacco and corn crops

CYCLONES AND HURRICANES (*continued*)

Year	Location	Name	Severity	Impact
1737	Bengal, India	Hooghly River Cyclone	unknown	300,000–350,000 deaths; 20,000 sea vessels destroyed
1780	Caribbean islands of Barbados, St. Vincent, Grenada, Martinique, St. Eustatius, Puerto Rico, and Grand Turk Island	Great Hurricane of 1780	Category 4	27,500 deaths
1876	Bengal, India	Bengal Cyclone of 1876	unknown	200,000 deaths; intense flooding
1881	Haiphong, Vietnam	Haiphong Typhoon	unknown	300,000 deaths
1882	Bombay (Mumbai), India	1882 Bombay Cyclone	unknown	100,000 deaths
1893	U.S. Southeast, South Carolina, and Georgia	Seas Islands Hurricane	Category 3	2,000 deaths; 30,000 left homeless
1899	San Ciriaco, Puerto Rico, North Carolina, and South Carolina	San Ciriaco Hurricane	Category 3	3,433 deaths in Puerto Rico, 50 in the Carolinas
1900	Galveston, Texas	Great Galveston Hurricane	Category 4	8,000 deaths; 3,600 buildings destroyed; $516 million in damage (2009 USD)
1900	The Great Galveston Hurricane	Galveston, Texas	Category 4	8,000 deaths; 3,600 buildings destroyed; $516 million in damage (2009 USD)
1919	Florida Keys Hurricane	Corpus Christi, Texas	Category 4	750 deaths; $22 million in damage (1919 USD)

CYCLONES AND HURRICANES (*continued*)

Year	Location	Name	Severity	Impact
1928	Caribbean Islands and Florida	Okeechobee Hurricane	Category 5	2,500 deaths; $50 million in damage (1928 USD) in Puerto Rico
1937	Hong Kong, China	Great Hong Kong Typhoon	Category 4	11,000 deaths; 240-kilometer-per-hour winds; 9.1-meter tidal wave
1959	Japan	Typhoon Vera	Category 5	5,000+ deaths; 255-kilometer-per-hour winds; $1.67 billion in damage (2007 USD); 1.6 million left homeless
1970	Bangladesh	Great Bhola Cyclone	Category 3	300,000–500,000 deaths; over $490 million in damage (2009 USD); 85 percent of homes in the area destroyed
1970	Australia	Cyclone Ada	Category 4	14 deaths; $390 million in property damage (1970 USD)
1980	Gulf of Mexico	Hurricane Allen	Category 5	290 deaths; $1.5 billion in damage (1980 USD)
1989	Charleston, South Carolina	Hurricane Hugo	Category 5	50 deaths; $17.5 billion in damage (2010 USD)
1991	Bangladesh	Bangladesh Cyclone 02B	Category 5	140,000 deaths; 270-kilometer-per-hour winds; 6-meter-high storm surge
1991	Philippines	Typhoon Thelma	Category 5	6,000 deaths; 217-kilometer-per-hour winds; $19 million in damage; 50,000 left homeless; caused dam failures, landslides, and flash flooding
1992	South Florida	Hurricane Andrew	Category 5	65 deaths; $26.5 billion in damage (1992 USD); 266-kilometer-per-hour winds
1998	Honduras and Nicaragua	Hurricane Mitch	Category 5	11,000 deaths; 285-kilometer-per-hour winds; $5 billion in damage (1998 USD)
2004	Florida	Hurricane Charley	Category 4	15 deaths; $16.3 billion in damage (2004 USD)

CYCLONES AND HURRICANES (*continued*)

Year	Location	Name	Severity	Impact
2005	Florida-Louisiana (two landfalls) and Mississippi	Hurricane Katrina	Category 5	1,353 deaths; major destruction due to levee breaks; $60 billion in damage (2006 USD)
2008	Burma (Myannmar)	Cyclone Nargis	Category 4	135,000 deaths; over $10 billion in damages (2008 USD)
2008	U.S. Gulf Coast	Hurricane Ike	Category 2	195 deaths; storm surge equivalent to that of a category 5 hurricane; $24.9 billion in damage (2008 USD)
2011	Australia	Cyclone Yasi	Category 5	285-kilometer-per-hour winds; $3.6 billion in property damage (2011 USD); destroyed sugar cane and banana crops as well as trees

OTHER STORMS

Year	Location	Name	Type	Impact
1953	Britain and the Netherlands	Europe Storm Surge	Strong ocean storm/high tide	1,800+ deaths; 3-meter storm surge
1993	U.S. Atlantic Seaboard	March 1993 Superstorm	Nor'easter	243 deaths; $2 billion in damage (1993 USD); record snowfalls

SOURCES

Discovery *World's Worst Tornadoes* http://www.discoveryuk.com/web/storm-chasers/about/worlds-worst-tornadoes/

NOAA National Climatic Data Center http://www.ncdc.noaa.gov/ sou

PBS *Savage Planet* http://www.pbs.org/wnet/savageplanet/

The Tornado Project http://www.tornadoproject.com/

The Weather Channel http://www.weather.com/

SUBJECT INDEX

Note: Page numbers in **bold** indicate main discussion.

tsunami warning, 539, 541–542

tsunami watch, 539

tsunami wave train, 539–540

T Tauri stars, 51, 52–53

tundra, 264

turbidity currents: deep ocean currents, 146; deep-sea sedimentation, 151, 152, 153; sand, 472, 473–474

turbidity currents and submarine fans, **545–548**

turbulent flow: river flow, 456; turbidity currents and submarine fans, 545, 546; wind, 605

Turco, Richard B., 358

Turkey, 91, 92

Turkmenistan, 108, 109

Tuscaloosa, Alabama, tornado (2011), 508

Tyndall, John, 226

typhoons: satellite meteorology, 481; severe and anomalous weather in recent decades, 509; severe storms, 514; tropical weather, 537

Tyrrhenian Sea, 328, 329

U

Ucayali River, 18

Ukraine, 91, 92

ultrafiltration for desalination, 464

ultraviolet light, 62, 65–66, 67

ultraviolet solar radiation: atmosphere's evolution, 51, 52, 53, 54; ozone depletion and ozone holes, 397, 398, 400, 401

umiaks, 35, 36

unconfined aquifers: aquifer, 24; aquifers, 22, 24; water wells, 579, 580

unidirectional flow of rivers, 451, 452

United Nations Environmental Program: IPCC, 304; ozone depletion and ozone holes, 401

United Nations Framework Convention on Climate Change, 295

unlikely, defined, 28

unsaturated zone: artificial recharge, 40, 41, 42, 43; drainage basins, 166; water table, 575–576, 577

unstable air, and tornadoes, 529, 530, 532

upconing, 467, 468, 470

upward displacement of desert pavement, 162–163

upwelling: atmospheric and oceanic oscillations, 70, 71; deep ocean currents, 146, 149; deep-sea sedimentation, 151, 152; World Ocean Circulation Experiment, 610, 611, 613

Ural River, 108

Uranium Mill Tailings Act (1978), 422

Uranus, 52

urban heat island effect, 218

Urubamba River, 18

U.S. Army Corps of Engineers: dams and flood control, 143; floodplains, 189; tsunamis, 542

U.S. Environmental Protection Agency: freshwater and groundwater contamination around the world, 201; groundwater pollution and remediation, 237; radon gas, 423; water quality, 567–568

U.S. Forest Service, 431

U.S. Geological Survey: surface water, 523; water quality, 566, 568

U.S. National Weather Service: hydrologic cycle, 280; long-term weather patterns, 326; satellite meteorology, 480; tornadoes, 532; tropical weather, 537; tsunamis, 542; weather forecasting, 584; weather forecasting: numerical weather prediction, 589

U.S. Public Health Service, 566

U.S. Safe Drinking Water Act (1974), 568

Utah: Bonneville Salt Flats, 462; Great Salt Lake, 166, 462

V

vadose zone: aquifers, 22; artificial recharge, 40; groundwater movement, 230

Van Allen radiation belts, **549–554**

Varanasi, India, 204

Vardar River, 328

variability in climate, 304

varves: Great Lakes, 223–224; lakes, 317

várzea, 18, 19

velocity head, 230, 231

Venezuela, 562

Venice, Italy, 159

ventifacts, 161, 164

Venus: atmosphere's evolution, 51, 53–54; atmosphere's structure and thermodynamics, 67; greenhouse effect, 226; oceans' origin, 379

Verhoogen, John, 378

vernal equinox, 493, 494, 496

very likely, defined, 28

very unlikely, undefined, 28

Vibro shiloi, 96

Vicksburg, Mississippi, 143

Victoria Falls, Africa, 562, 563

virga (precipitation), 415

virtually certain, defined, 28

volatile outgassing, 51–52, 53, 54

volatiles, and oceans' origin, 376, 377

volcanic aerosols/ash: atmosphere's structure and thermodynamics, 63; IPCC, 304; lakes, 315